W9-CXY-729

"A major work about

     World War II . . . so authentic it
sounds like a tape recording playing back all the fears,
hopes, and emotions of men under fire . . . and if it is read
carefully by the men who have the responsibility of war at
their fingertips, they might learn a thing or two."

—Trenton Times-Advertiser

"Here is a book that has the sound, smell and sights of
World War II as it was fought . . . a great job of reporting the emotional experience of being an ordinary, foot-
slogging infantryman . . . Atwell's dialogue is as sharp as
the report of an M-1. It's soldier's talk, unvarnished, real,
true."

—Denver Post

PRIVATE was originally published at $5.00
by Simon and Schuster, Inc.

ABOUT THE AUTHOR

Lester Atwell was born in 1908 in Brooklyn, where he still makes his home. Educated at Brooklyn Prep, Fordham, and the Art Students League, he began writing in 1937, and his articles and short stories have appeared in practically all the major national magazines. He went into the Army in June 1943 and served until November 1945. His original intention in taking notes was simply to keep some record for himself so that he would remember where he had been in the World War II campaigns and what had happened there. Only much later did he realize that he was writing a book—this book.

PRIVATE
LESTER ATWELL

POPULAR LIBRARY · NEW YORK

© 1958 by Lester Atwell
Library of Congress Catalog Card Number: 58-6278

Published by arrangement with Simon and Schuster, Inc.
Simon and Schuster edition published in May, 1958
First printing: January, 1958

DEDICATION:

TO HAROLD MATSON

CONTENTS

In writing this account of the months I spent in Europe during World War II, I have tried to recall incidents as accurately as possible. However, I have scrupulously changed all unit designations as well as the names and origins of the men who served with me.

L. A.

1944 December

Toward three-thirty that afternoon we got off the trucks, hoisted the duffel bags up onto our shoulders and started to trudge in a bent-over procession along a muddy, curving road approaching a group of widely scattered suburban houses in an outlying district of Metz. The houses were sizable, of gray stone or pale-colored plaster, set down in victory gardens and truck farms that now were sodden and wintry-brown. Beyond them, the abrupt edge of the city could be seen, deserted, with empty black windows and smashed-in roof lines. A short block to our left, rising high above everything, high as the Palisades, there was a long, wooded, almost perpendicular cliff.

Word sprang up suddenly, passing from man to man as we hunched along: "Houses! Hey, we're goin' into houses! Hey, this is a good deal!"

We turned down the short side street and halted. Our company appeared to be alone in the vicinity. While waiting for something to develop, I set the clean, freshly oiled butt of my rifle down on the damp, pebbly earth, doing it lightly, unwillingly. Clouds streamed across the wet sky. With the mountain ridge so near, we seemed to be pygmies, a formation of them standing outside tiny partly ruined houses, with the wide, lumpy brown fields raying out. Though it was early December, it was not cold, and the autumnal smell of wet plowed earth rose up.

Sergeant Danowski returned from a consultation and led our squad around the corner, along the road at the base of the cliff, through the doorway of a walled courtyard and down one step. A path had been cleared through, but the place bristled with furniture, rubbish, beams, a wire bird cage, and cartons of—what? Everything there was wet and grayish.

The kitchen was large and old-fashioned, with a coal stove, sink, table and chairs, and two tufted Empire sofas without arms. There was a long window, all its small panes broken, and quantities of K-ration cans on the sill. I was surprised that I was not more surprised. The place had been bombed; its owners were gone. What of it?

We dropped our equipment and began at once to investigate. It was a small villa, belonging evidently to a family of some means. The drawing room, on the second floor, was high-ceilinged, with French windows opening onto little balconies. A wide mirror in a heavy gilt frame, set between the two front windows, gave our startled reflections as we rushed into the room. Wet orangy-red silk draperies hung from the windows; all the glass panes lay broken on the floor. The furniture was gone save for a large armoire of satinwood, bulging of front, with a splintered, sagging door. There was a music stand and a wet Aubusson rug on the parquet floor. It was the only important room in the house, but you could imagine spring evenings there when the windows would be open; you could see a girl in a white dress idling, wondering what to do. And maybe later someone would play the violin . . .

The bedrooms had dark red or brown wallpaper, heavy high Victorian beds, chamber pots, marble-topped night tables and washstands. The beds were unmade, the red mattresses soaked with rain. Leaves had blown in and were piled in the corners of the rooms. Holy pictures were lying amid shattered glass on the floor. Upstairs there were smaller bedrooms, a narrow hall, and a vast jagged shell hole in the roof showing the distant gray sky above.

We came downstairs, through the somber shuttered dining room, and, under Sergeant Danowski's orders, started to

8

clean the kitchen and arrange a blackout against the coming night. Two of the men who had been previously stationed in the house returned to gather up their equipment: their division was pulling back for a rest—to Rheims, they thought, or maybe even to Paris. Seasoned warriors where we were green, they swaggered about and rolled their packs laconically. "Sixty-four days in the f---in' line, that's a record!" said one to the other for our benefit, but gradually it developed that they had seen little if any combat. The greatest part of their sixty-four days had been spent standing guard here on the hills above Metz outside some German fortresses that had refused to surrender when the city itself gave up. One of the departing warriors even admitted that it had been easy. "There's nothin' to it. You guys'll be doin' the same thing. Just waitin' around for them to give up."

A truck called for the two men. At the parting moment they gave us some leftover K rations, and to Private Howard Hepp, who had been open in his admiration of them, they gave a rubber poncho, the first we had seen. They ran out the door, hopped up into the truck and were driven away, the last men of their division. We had been left in charge of the vicinity. Every now and then an artillery shell or two, sometimes a slight barrage, whistled through the deepening twilight and exploded somewhere with a dull roar, causing nervous cackles of laughter in the room.

Someone asked, "Hey, d'you guys believe what those two guys said? That we're just going to starve out some forts?"

"Boy, if we do," came the reply, "I hope them forts take it nice an' easy. I wouldn't mind sittin' right here till the whole war ends."

According to the most favored and persistent rumor, we had been brought overseas to become part of the Army of Occupation. The fall of Germany was expected in a few weeks—certainly by Christmas. In another rumor, not quite so well liked, we were all to be made Military Police and set guarding roads and bridges. The least popular rumor of all had us trailing behind combat divisions to mop up bypassed pockets of resistance. Though ours was an Infantry division, few in it wanted anything to do with combat.

"Why, sure they're going to use us; I been saying that all along," said a more authoritative voice in the kitchen. It was Ahlhauser, a serious, older man, who was speaking. "And I don't mind telling you it's going to be a slaughter. Bunch of

9

untrained men and officers. But what do they care? They sit back of the lines . . . They wouldn't hesitate a minute to send us right into combat tomorrow."

"Do you honestly think that?" I asked.

He drew me apart into a corner of the room and began to talk in an undertone, almost as if we were conspirators. He told me he was positive we were to be used as front-line combat troops, and he was deeply worried by the nature and inexperience of the men who would be leading us.

"You take Captain Hillier, or Lieutenant Ellis, or Giossi— it's criminal to have them over men! You *couldn't* respect them! And most of the noncoms we have—my God, they're a pitiful lot. Pitiful!" He looked around; his voice dropped even lower. "And Sergeant Danowski... All right, he's my friend; we're tentmates and all that, and I don't want to say anything against him personally, but he . . . Someone's always got to prod him! He doesn't see the angles! His mind's 'way off on something else."

Another artillery barrage whistled over the house and exploded.

"But what can anyone do about it now? Isn't it pretty late in the day to—?"

"No!" he said urgently. "No! This is coming down to a case of every man for himself, and I tell you what *I'm* going to do. Out of self-preservation! Instead of helping Danowski all the time, I'm going to start assuming some responsibility around here myself. I'm going to grab it and use it to pull myself up to where *I'll* be making the decisions; my life won't always be in their hands. And I'd advise you to do the same thing. Anyone with any intelligence. I understand in combat there's all sorts of ways. You can get a battlefield commission—"

We were interrupted. It was time to eat. Lining up in single file with our mess kits, we went out onto the road, and, maintaining a five-yard interval so that if a shell came in we might not all be hit, we went a short distance down for our food and carried it back into the kitchen to eat. There were three lighted candles on the table set in puddles of melted wax. Part way through the meal my tentmate, Dave Rossofsky, fell into a long daze, picking his nose.

"Hey, Rossofsky," said Husey, one of the other young boys, "d'you mind not picking your nose? I mean, Jeez! At the table!"

"Oh!" said Dave, coming to equably. "No, I'm sorry. I know it's a very bad habit I have. Correct me whenever I do it, will you, Huse?"

Husey glared and was nettled. Never friendly with Dave, who was unaware of the fact, he had become his bitter enemy at our Thanksgiving dinner in England when Dave carelessly overturned a full mess kit of turkey, potatoes, gravy and canned fruit salad on Husey's brand-new, sharply creased uniform. Dave had not been able to understand Husey's wild flare-up of temper.

"So vuss is he screaming for?" Dave asked me in an aside. "It's only a uniform." Turning back to Husey, he said, "Listen, I'll give you my other set of ODs if that's what you want."

"*Yours*, for crissake!" Husey was trim, slim-waisted, and took great pains with his appearance. Dave was heavy, and yet his rumpled uniforms always seemed to belong to a still heavier man.

Dave Rossofsky came from Detroit and was nineteen years old. He was a large, clumsy youth, short-necked and mildly bull-like in appearance, with a black crew cut, a pallor, bushy eyebrows and dark-brown bloodshot eyes set in smudgy brown shadows. His teeth were crooked and on the dingy side. During the summer when he first landed in Fort Jackson from a basic-training camp, his bulk won him the position as Browning Automatic Rifleman on our squad. The Browning Automatic Rifle, known as the B.A.R., had great fire power but it was much larger than the Garand rifle and much heavier to carry around. It was mounted on annoying bipods, it was difficult to clean, and no one, at least in training, wanted to be burdened with it.

"I don't know why they gave the damned thing to me," Dave said with a laugh one night in the barracks. He had a slight impediment in his speech, almost a lisp. "I never even fired one. And ith's not that I'm strong. You can see: this is just baby fat I still have." It was true. He had his shirt off and he appeared as yet to have no muscles, nor did it seem likely he'd develop any in the very near future.

There was a great passive laziness about him, coupled with a thorough lack of interest in Army life, that made him the butt of unending corrections, shouts and curses. He was unusually careless and lost his equipment continually. In the apple orchard we had just left, he lost his wool-knit cap and

11

adopted in its place an overseas cap with the flaps pulled down to his shaggy eyebrows and the steel helmet jammed on top of that.

He had tapering fingers with extra-long, dirty, grayish nails. Oriental hands he called them, studying them with impersonal dislike; he claimed they had next to no strength in them. He loved long knives. "The knife is the most civilized of weapons," he said, weighing the one he carried sticking out of his legging. He had just finished high school and was undecided whether to become a doctor or an actor.

"You mean character parts?" I asked.

"Yes. I could do slow old men," he replied.

Despite the outward appearance of sloppiness, despite that habit of prolonged and dreamy nose-picking, he had a fastidiousness of spirit and a discrimination that was lacking in many of the others, all of whom found him lazy and useless.

From time to time I asked him how he was progressing with the awkward, heavy Browning Automatic Rifle. "Well, I'm learning a *little*," he'd say. He had been given a manual on the weapon, and had dipped into it occasionally but without the enthusiasm expected by the Army. Recently, during our one month's stay in England, Sergeant Danowski had issued to him—mistakenly, it proved—a small pigskin box of spare parts, many of which Dave lost at once: in opening the box, it fell out of his Oriental hands, and tiny springs, wheels and pins rolled away under the bunk and down through the cracks in the floor. There came with the box a little jeweler's eyeglass that exercised an endless fascination for Dave. With that in his eye, and the rifle in pieces about him, he stared mesmerized for ten or fifteen minutes at a time at the small print on a pack of Camels, or at the lines in his hand. I used the glass once to look down the bore of the B.A.R. and saw craterlike pits, whorls, scratches and gobs of oily rust.

"It looks awfully dirty, Dave."

"B.A.R.s are always dirty," he informed me complacently. Whether this was true or not I didn't know, but it was always true of ours, for in addition to being a regular rifleman, I was Dave's assistant on the B.A.R.

Why I had been so selected was a mystery, because I had not trained with the company for more than three or four days in all, and I had no idea how to fire the B.A.R. Early

12

the previous summer I had been sent into the Infantry from Antiaircraft, where I had worked as an illustrator and photo-retoucher on training strips; and after learning how to fire the M1 rifle the Infantry way, I was assigned to the battalion art shop to make visual training aids. The appointment as assistant Browning Automatic Rifleman had come shortly before we left the United States, and I thought it a mere courtesy title, one given so that the Table of Organization might balance, but in this evidently I was wrong.

"I'm not kiddin'," Sergeant Danowski once said during the few informal indoor classes on the B.A.R. that we had in England. "If we git in combat and Rossofsky is hit, you pick up the B.A.R. That's your job; that's what assistant *means*. You pick it up, and the idea is get it up there fast wherever we're going, y'understand?"

At the moment that this had come up, Sergeant Danowski was trying to extricate some small moving part that Dave had got into the rifle backward, that showed no disposition to come out.

Private Howard Hepp, the nervous member of the squad, disturbed by our lack of knowledge, said, "Sergeant Danowski, if we git in any tight spot, you'll fire the B.A.R. yourself, won't you? I mean t' say, you won't let these two guys—"

"Yeah," said Sergeant Danowski sadly, "I'll fire the son of a bitch."

Sergeant Stanley Danowski was a college student, about twenty-three years old, broad and heavy-set, with a head that came slightly forward. He neither drank nor smoked, and had soft blunt features, coloring as clear as a country girl's, and mild spaniel-like brown eyes the whites of which were bluish, like a baby's. It was said he could find his way by instinct anywhere in the dark. Withdrawn, slow-moving, often morose, worried about his young wife, who was expecting a child, he reminded me of a trained bear in that he never appeared to like what he was doing. The other two squad leaders of our platoon, Sergeants Brauer and Janovic, were quicker to seize an advantage for themselves and indirectly for their men.

Watching Sergeant Danowski's struggle to remove the obstinate moving part, Dave Rossofsky said, "What *I* think—I think this B.A.R. has a malfunction." That was the Army's special word, and Dave used it freely.

"If it has a malfunction," Sergeant Danowski shouted,

"then, goddam it, you gave it to it!"

Dave laughed. "You know, it's funny but I can never get sore at you, Sergeant Danowski. You're just like my big brother when he yells at me back home. You don't believe me? *Honest!*"

"Here. Let me get out of here," Sergeant Danowski said, handing back the jammed rifle. "Let me get out of here before I go *nuts!*"

When we finished eating, we washed the mess kits at the sink, the table was cleared, the red-printed V-mail forms came out, and the eternal letter writing began. As usual someone was trying to borrow a sheet of ruled paper to slip under the V-mail form as a guide to straight penmanship. The fire was warm, the blackouts secure; the room became quiet with the whispering of pens. Every now and then it was a surprise to me that I was finding the moment comfortable. Eight or nine oddly assorted men, crowded with their belongings into the kitchen of a bombed-out house . . . I looked up from my letter, glancing from one to the other.

Sergeant Danowski.

Dave Rossofsky.

Louden, the ammunition bearer of our three-man B.A.R. team, a dark, insignificant, sullen, tough little Hoboken kid, dirty, with a soft adolescent mustache, with a reform-school background. Any ordinary kindness or attempts at friendliness on the part of the others made him suspicious; he waited always for the hidden stick to crack down on him.

The tall, hungry-lean Virgil Smathers of Tennessee, former short-order cook and used-car dealer, with flat tan hair, a sallow face and spread nostrils that seemed to be scenting trouble.

The hot-tempered Husey sat next. Of a good family, dark, hawk-nosed, nineteen, he was from Flint, Michigan, where for a year he had worked in the men's clothing department of a large store. Aggressive and selfish at times, he was writing to one of the most beautiful girls I've seen photographed. In the barracks at Fort Jackson, Sergeant Brauer used to pause often before her picture and say, "*Chee*zus! *Beau*tiful! *Vot* soft features!"

Private Howard Hepp, of somewhere in Illinois, was Husey's friend and tentmate. An intense nervousness made him talk, curse, almost stutter his words out incessantly. He tried to hide the fact that he loved being on his own, in the Army, away from the supervision of a conventional family, in whose eyes he was doubtless a very nice, obedient boy. He, like Dave Rossofsky and little Louden, was also nineteen years old. He had a round, rubbery, pimply face with GI glasses, a tireless rubbery body, and he threw himself, cursing but wholehearted, into any work. He talked cars, motors, guns, and basic training at Camp Rucker unendingly.

Clyde Merkel . . . Perhaps twenty-seven. Slow, unhygienic, plunged in some lasting despondency, uncomplaining—silent, really—he reminded me, for what reasons I couldn't say, of a dark, smelly country store. Yet there was something comfortable about him and goodhearted. In the hurly-burly of climbing on a crowded truck, he always looked quickly about for other members of the squad to give them a hand up. His dour uncomplicated face and the way his sticky dark-red hair swept across his forehead made him look like a daguerreotype of someone who had fought in the Civil War.

Then Lambert, thirty-five, from Portland, Oregon, a quiet, self-reliant man with short regular features, blue eyes and thick straight gray hair; of Italian ancestry, a builder. "I do —oh, construction work," he said in one of the few times he spoke about himself. He was married and had a nine-year-old daughter. His name had originally been Lamberto "or something like that."

George Ahlhauser, the man who was so sure we were going to be used as front-line troops, had come from Antiaircraft with Lambert a month or so before we left the United States; I believe both had been declared overage for combat at the time their original outfit was shipping out. Ahlhauser was about thirty-four, tall, handsomely built, dignified in bearing, with a grave, fine-featured Germanic face, light hair, blue eyes and a light mustache. He had been a policeman in a small Midwestern town.

"With a job like mine," he told me on the way overseas, "I didn't have to get into this; I volunteered." It was a story that was evidently often on his mind. He and a much younger brother had been left orphans. "My whole life went into bringing that kid up. I think he was just about the finest boy' in the world. Smart in school, wonderful athlete—a natural athlete. People used to think I was crazy for putting in so much time on him. I never ran around much. Then I met this girl. Well, after a while, she started talking about getting married, but I wasn't sure; I was never certain she had the kid's best interests at heart. It was natural, I guess, but she resented him, underneath. I mean she knew he came first with me. It went on like that for quite a few years and then finally we did get married. Well, the next thing you know, the kid gets to be seventeen, the war comes along and he wants to join up with the Marines. I wouldn't hear of it. But he keeps after me and after me; then he starts working through the wife, and the both of them—Jesus, I could kill myself now—I let them talk me into it. I signed the papers and let him go. He shipped out to the Pacific and was killed the first day, making a landing. When I got the War Department notice, I nearly went out of my head.

"Then, you see, I start thinking *I* should do something, you know, like to make up to him for . . . Well, I wanted to get into it. The wife didn't want me to, but I told her, I said as long as you were so goddam willing to let the kid go—" Even in telling it he became angry with her. "Oh, hell, I don't know. Anyway, I couldn't stand it any longer at home, so one day I went out and volunteered. I thought I could make some kind of a worth-while contribution, but as soon as I got in and saw how they used you—like cattle—I was disgusted from that time on."

I looked over at him now in the candlelight, his profile bent above a letter to his wife. He took the pipe out of his mouth, thought seriously, wrote another sentence, thought again.

Beside him at the kitchen table, Gramling, the assistant squad leader, cleaned the gold nib of his pen, trying it against his thumbnail. He had been a student at the University of Minnesota; nineteen years old, palely freckled, with pale, stubby red hair, GI glasses, long noticeable gums and yellowish teeth. In the barracks at Fort Jackson on a Saturday afternoon when the platoon in fatigues black with sweat raced pell-mell up the stairs yelling, "Cha-a-arge! Cha-a-arge!" Gramling came into his own. Rifles were flung into the rack. Footlockers slammed. Fatigues were ripped off and the first naked men raced down to the showers.

"Hey, who's going to town? Who's got five bucks to lend me? . . . All right, three bucks?" Gramling had the three dollars. "Who's got a clean belt to lend me?" "Who's got an extra pro-kit?" "Who's got a Blitz cloth?" Gramling, beef-red and glazed with sweat, racing helpfully around in wrinkled shorts and a wet, yellowish undershirt, had all the things to lend. "Rifle inspection, boys! Rifle inspection before you get a pass." "Aw, for crissake! . . . Hey, I'm late! Who'll clean my rifle?" "Who's got the other rod?" "Who's got any clean patches?" Gramling had. Gramling would clean the rifle. "Hey, Gramling, how's about lending me fifty cents?" "Hey, listen, I got a date there, boy. How about lending me a shirt? I ain't got any clean." "Who the f---'s got a tie? Gramling, you're not goin' to town. Give us your tie."

A half hour of racing excitement, further borrowing, cleaning of rifles, shining of shoes, standing on footlockers, shoving legs into freshly pressed, starched suntan pants, and off they raced to line up for passes at the company office. Gramling, still in shorts, GI shoes and the sweaty undershirt, fell back on his bunk, broke, his clean uniforms gone, but he was strangely happy.

"Why didn't you go to town?" I asked. I had just come into the company and could not have a pass.

"I was going to, but by the time I get all my guys ready I'm always too tired."

In the midst of all the letter writing, Lieutenant MacKenzie came through to look at our billet and to explain the situation officially. Metz itself had given up some time ago, but the forts surrounding it on the mountaintops still held out. A division had been in the town preceding ours by about six weeks; they had kept guard on the fortresses, waiting for them to surrender. We, in replacing them, had the same mission. "We're just goin' to sit here an' starve 'em out." The lieutenant, as always, was lively, high-spirited and smiling, enjoying himself and liking the men. "So fix your places as comfortable as you can, men. We're goin' to be here for a long time. This is a good deal!" His Georgia accent was marked. "Be back an' see y'all again." He went out.

"Boy, he's good!" "He's swell, isn't he?" "A damn good egg!" "The best goddam officer—"

In the morning, after breakfast, we set about in earnest making the place habitable. The sink, at first reported out of order, was, on the removal of a sock from the drain, found to be working perfectly. I went out into the wet courtyard and saw Sergeant Danowski standing there, lost in thought. His broad face lifted against the damp sky had a look of tremendous loneliness. Becoming conscious of me, he said, "All this s——'s got to be cleared out of here," but he spoke without conviction or interest—rather, in sadness—and he went inside.

At the end of the morning I opened one of the kitchen doors and found that it led to a small low room with a dirt floor. I was startled to see a live goat standing in it, and called to the others. They came in and stared. The goat moved off a few paces, then turned and stared at *us*. Smathers came in with his hunting knife, brushing everyone aside. "Goat's da-a-amn good eatin', don't you know that?" I turned to get out of the place but not before I saw him go over, kneel on one knee, put one arm around the goat's neck. I didn't see the rest, but he quickly slit the goat's throat and let the blood run out on the dirt. Then he skinned it, cut off the lower legs, cut out "the guts," and sawed off the head. That whole mess was left lying on the dirt floor.

"Faahn eatin'," he said later. "Got to know how to cook 'em, though." He had been a cook in the officers' mess and had been broken down to private for getting drunk and going AWOL. "Three grades of meat on a goat. Firs' grade's jes as tender as a baby. I'm gonna cook it slo-ow. Gonna have us a feast tonight, boys, an' don't no one go tellin' a thing about it."

In the cellar he had come upon some "Snops" and had kept out one bottle for himself, but the rest was put away for the dinner party.

At noon we heard that Sergeant Brauer, acting as interpreter, had climbed up the mountain and read off over a loud-speaker an order to the German commandant of the fortress, telling him to surrender. The commandant had roared back over his loud-speaker that he flatly refused: he had so many barrels of water and so many rounds of ammunition; he would stay until the last of it was expended, and then he would see about surrendering. "Vot the hell," Sergeant Brauer said with a shrug when he came in to see our billet. "For those guys war is a business. I tell him, 'Give up,' and he tells me, 'Go to hell.' So we both know where we stand. Everything is all right." No hard feelings, I gathered.

Looking over at Sergeant Brauer, I remembered coming back to the barracks one hot August afternoon from watch-

18

ing the training film *Know Your Enemy*. It had shown the German people, innocent to the eye, waltzing in their beer gardens; suddenly the waltz stopped and a cathedral was blown to bits. Every German civilian was a spy and a sniper.

"You believe that?" Sergeant Brauer had asked when I walked into the latrine with some of the others. A towel wrapped around his waist, he turned from the scratched metal mirror, holding his straight razor, a neat, competent-looking man with the appearance and air of a professional soldier. He was thirty years old and had thinning slicked-back light hair, sunburned skin, blue eyes and a little mustache.

"Well, I don't know," I said. "I believe some of it, but I think propaganda's always a little overdone."

The others disagreed with me, but Sergeant Brauer said hotly in his Teutonic accent, "I have seen that film many times and it is a lot of s---! I have one brother in the German Navy and two in the German Army. You think they are like that? That they wanted war? They are chust like us! Like you and me. People are the same all over, everywhere."

At the time I was a newcomer, and I was vaguely alarmed, wondering if he shouldn't be reported to someone. The others, who knew him better, paid no attention. I found out later he was a Czechoslovakian, and the best sergeant in the company. It must, however, have been a strange experience for him when he was up on the cliff shouting to the German commandant to surrender, for the thought surely crossed his mind that one of his brothers might have been inside the enemy fortress listening unknowingly to the sound of his voice.

After lunch, I went out with Dave Rossofsky and Husey and one or two others for a walk through the city itself. It was the first badly smashed one we had seen. There were no civilians at all. Here and there an MP stood in the road, directing the traffic of jeeps and trucks that sped past. Again, I was conscious of no great surprise seeing rows of buildings jagged and wide-open as the backs of dolls' houses, roofs smashed to hanging skeletons, wires and cables all over the streets, glass and deep eruptions in the road, heaped up bricks, broken cement and staring windows everywhere.

"There's a dud! Don't go near it!"

"Where?"

"There!"

19

It would not have struck my notice, but there it was, a large fat shell lying near a corner building. It had been roped off with white tape. Now and then you'd see a soldier or two in an empty building, searching for loot. We had been told not to go out of our area, but since no one had explained what that was, we continued. The MPs didn't stop us, and we walked down what must have been a street behind the main shopping district: gray stone town houses, flat-faced and rather narrow.

"Should we go in?"

"Yeah, come on."

Hesitantly we stepped inside a basement hall.

"Watch out for booby traps. Don't touch anything." We had been well warned about the Germans leaving booby traps behind.

The first thing I saw, on a stone window sill, was an elaborate gilt crucifix under a glass bell-jar. Still hesitant, we went up the staircase and, like Radio City sight-seers, moved slowly through the bombed, desolate rooms, seeing wide beds with wet red mattresses, fallen plaster, holes in the ceiling and the sky showing above, seeing wrenched-out window frames, furniture soaked with rain and wet plaster lying on it like a jigsaw puzzle. The stillness I found oppressive. Here and there a sagging curtain would stir. You'd get a glimpse of a dead-looking city back yard.

"Come on."

Like sleepwalkers, we moved through the rooms. Chinese bowls on a mantel. Framed photographs still on the walls: whiskered faces looking at you soberly. Victorian sofas upholstered in red velvet. A family Bible covered with fallen plaster on a marble-topped table. A fringed silk chandelier with a big hole through it. A marquetry table with all the inlay sprung.

We came down the staircase and, once outside, fell into conversation again. Every now and then we'd go into another house, to move silent through the strange rooms that looked as though human beings would never return to them. There were things of value, but on our part there was no desire to take them or even to touch them. By and large the furnishings were heavy, late Victorian, belonging, one would think, to sober people leading stolid provincial lives. All at once I became depressed; and I had seen enough.

We returned through the ghostly streets, pausing to stare

at a hole where a house that had received a direct hit had caved in from roof to cellar. We felt freer, starting back for the country houses. Other companies of our battalion, nearer the town, were established in quite handsome houses. You'd see the men working in pairs, struggling, carrying mattresses, stoves and easy chairs into their houses. Here on the road, a group was working over a motorcycle.

To get down to our own street, we cut through a field that had been turned into a victory garden. Our feet sank into the moist earth and I saw carrots underfoot, cabbages a little farther on, then a field of potatoes. Fresh vegetables, if we stayed long enough.

When we got back to the house, Virgil Smathers was cooking the goat. I told him about seeing the vegetables, and, suddenly enthusiastic, he asked me to go back and get some. "You know, Atwell, the little-bitty tender ones." I took a large washpan and with Dave Rossofsky, who was completely uninterested, went back to the truck farm. The little carrots, the onions and potatoes came easily from the ground. The early-winter afternoon was beginning to grow chill; the sky had become melancholy. There was the sound of intermittent shelling. No, I did not want to be here, pulling up vegetables in a strange country—but if we could stay here a few more weeks till the war ended . . . I started back with the heavy pan. The men farther down the road had the motorcycle going. An inexperienced rider went flying by on it, bucking. The others stood laughing.

Smathers had become more wavering and mellow under the influence of his bottle. He took the vegetables, washed them, scraped them, cut them into small pieces and arranged them in the three pans of goat meat. The rest of the boys were straightening the kitchen again and setting the table. A crepe-paper cloth had been found, and a row of candles of assorted sizes had been placed down the center. "No mess kits tonight, guys; we're going to eat out of *dishes!*" Nescafé, sugar, and fruit bars from the breakfast rations had been pooled. Crystal glasses and Japanese demitasse cups suddenly appeared on the table.

By now Smathers' smile was an ear-to-ear affair and his tongue kept licking about at his lips. He remained at the stove, wavering, basting frequently and almost falling in on top of the goat meat. Frequent nips and the heat of the stove caused perspiration to stream down his face. More and more often, he claimed, he needed a drink to keep him going.

Just as we were about to sit down at the table, bad news came: our squad had to pull guard that night and had to begin at once. The announcement came in the midst of the same sort of happy excitement that precedes a big Thanksgiving dinner. Faces fell. Since I was a comparative outsider and had trained with them only a few days, I offered to take the starting shift, and I left them with the two guests of honor, Lieutenant MacKenzie and Sergeant Brauer, having their first drink with all the candles lighted.

I put on my glasses and helmet, took my rifle and went down the dark passage. I opened the heavy front door and saw that rain was falling. Behind me I could hear the noise of the celebration. I stood in the shadow of the doorway and rested my rifle on the step. Farther up the street, on the opposite side, another guard from C Company stood at the entrance of a little shed. We had been warned to stay in the shadows and to remain alert, for German patrols were constantly prowling out of the fortress at night, coming down the mountainside and along the road, trying to estimate the number of Americans and to take back prisoners.

Over the steep looming cliff, the rainy sky had a purplish-red flare. I could see my breath smoking and fancied at first I could hear someone approaching by stealth, or a stone rattling down the cliff. How endless those solitary hours always were!

Here came someone now. I was aware of the guard up the street stiffening, slowly bringing up his rifle. I felt mine. Yes. Unlocked. But whoever was coming made no effort at concealment. Feet splashed in the puddles. The guard across the way growled the password: "William." The approaching figure, ludicrously small, in a large raincoat, gave a whining, annoyed reply—not the countersign, "Mary"—and then began to beg: "Don't shoot! For crissake, it's *me*! It's Shorty!" Shorty Witherspoon. "You know—Shorty! Goddam this—" Splash, splash. "Anyone know where the f--- Lieutenant MacKenzie is?"

"Yes," I said, breaking into laughter. "In here."

"Where? Where the hell are you?" He was coughing, talking with a heavy cold. He had been made Company Messenger a short while before and he did not like being out alone at night. He seldom kept the messages straight, was generally lost, could never remember the passwords, and, in terror

22

of being shot by his own men or the Germans, made his way around calling loudly in advance, "Don't shoot! It's me! It's Shorty!" He was an illiterate little Texan, neat and spruce as a jockey, and not quite all right in the head. "Well, look out," he said, brushing past me. "I gotta see Lieutenant MacKenzie. Got some kind of a message for him."

He went in and perhaps delivered the correct message. A day or two later he developed pneumonia, was sent to the hospital, and we never saw him again.

Farther up the road, some German soldiers did come down the cliff that night. They succeeded in slipping through the triple cordon of guards in that sector and presented themselves for surrender to the flabbergasted officers and clerks at the Regimental Command Post.

At the end of my guard shift, Merkel came out to relieve me and I went back to the kitchen. Dinner was about over. Smathers was to have saved dinner for me but he was drunk and had forgotten. Lambert, ordinarily quiet, was on his feet, unsteady, attempting to make an after-dinner speech. The candles were guttering a little. I sat down and ate some potatoes and carrots.

Opposite me, Lieutenant MacKenzie said, "You missed a very good party, Atwell." He thought I was unfriendly and had missed it intentionally. "I like these little coffee cups very much," he remarked, picking one up. "I'd like to send something like that home."

"I don't think these are particularly good," I said thoughtlessly, and after a hesitation he agreed, but as if I had corrected him.

Feeling a little high, ruddy and laughing in the candlelight, he was saying to the others a few minutes later, "No, but what I was tryin' to say is, in my family someone's ohlways distinguished himself in war. They've been military men for generations an' generations. We go ohll the way back to Mary, Queen of Scots—least that's what I'm told; that's when the family began—an' ever since then, in every war, we've had someone who's been outstandin'. Either in the Army or the Navy. That's why I have something to live up to. An' I really look forward to it! I think it'll be a lot of fun!"

I said, "Well the only one ever to distinguish himself in my family was a colonel in the Grand Army of the Republic.

He was wounded during the Civil War—I always heard, throwing his leg over a horse to escape, so you can see what I have to live up to."

Lieutenant MacKenzie laughed but thought I was making fun of him. A few minutes later he reached under his chair for his helmet and stood up to leave with Sergeant Brauer, who said, "I haf been telling the boys, Atwell, if ever we get near my father's place in Czechoslovakia, I want you to come and see it. Dere is a big farm we got—the most beautiful place—and, under the trees in the orchard, long tables to sit at, and lots of beer or wine. Lots of it. They bring it out in big pitchers. My father would be glad to see all of you." They thanked us for the party and went out.

I continued to eat while the noise in the room grew deafening, with everyone talking and laughing simultaneously. Without warning, Smathers and Lambert started a fight and rose up, pushing back their chairs. There was the loud smash of blows. Everyone jumped up and tried to separate them. The two contestants strained at their captors, cursing, then Smathers broke away, threw a punch at Lambert and the whole crowd fell against the table, upsetting the candles and glasses. Smathers, ruffled, shaking himself, walked off a few paces, then started back and, going suddenly wild, began to hurl and smash the dinner plates, throwing chairs out of his way; a moment later he was crying and begging Lambert to shake hands with him. Lambert refused and almost precipitated another fight.

"Ah, go ahead and make up," the others were saying. "What the hell's the matter with you two guys? Spoiling everything."

Smathers stood bawling and wiped the blood away from his nose. It was startling to see Lambert too in tears, his face contorted. Both kept stumbling, knocking into the table, sending plates and glasses to the floor.

Before they could be talked into shaking hands—an act that caused Smathers to burst into tears again—Lieutenant MacKenzie was back, smiling and high-spirited, to say that we were to get to sleep at once: we were going out on a mission just before dawn to the fortress of Jeanne d'Arc.

"Light packs. Light packs, everyone. This is your first taste of combat. Everyone be ready to fall out by 0400. Danowski, have them ready." Smiling, jaunty, he went out.

Immediately the feast was forgotten. "What? Where we

goin'?" "What time'd he say?" "Hey, Sarge, what are we going to do?" "Hey, what'd he say? What'd he say?"

"All I know," cried Sergeant Danowski in annoyance, "is that we're going on a *mission!* You can hear, can't you? What's the matter with you?"

Some started hastily to clean their weapons, one eye on the flickering candlelight. Hepp's words came out with machine-gun rapidity and insistence. Dave Rossofsky and I began to spread out our blankets on the floor. Two blankets down, then the sleeping bags, then two blankets over them. Some of the candles had gone out. Sergeant Danowski was about to snuff out the remaining two, but Hepp begged him to wait just a little longer; he was reassembling his rifle.

Surprisingly, I fell asleep almost at once. It seemed no time until we were awakened and, by the light of one candle, were reaching out for leggings, field jackets, helmets, dressing quickly, shivering in the cold, smoking cigarettes nervously. Everyone hurried; we scarcely spoke. It was as though we were engaged in a race. Quick. Outside to the latrine. I had forgotten and still carried my cigarette. Bright sparks blew off it in the wind. That's just to let you know up there that I'm coming. Yes, still raining. Back inside, unrolling the raincoat and putting it on. Clamping the heavy cartridge belt on top of it. Water in the canteen? Yes.

At the last minute Dave Rossofsky turned out not to have a raincoat. It had been stolen. Hepp, in the sudden camaraderie, generously offered his prized poncho. "Take damned good care of that," he said sharply. Dave, in his inept way, tried to put it on. "Here! Christ!" Hepp was officious. "Don't you even know how to put it on?" He settled the cape on Dave's shoulders and buttoned it at the neck. The cape, though, interfered with carrying the B.A.R., and Dave had to switch it around so that the opening left one shoulder free. His gloves, too, were lost, and in place of them he pulled on a pair of khaki socks, giving his hands a wrinkled, helpless look. Everything seemed an effort; he appeared too trussed up, too hampered, too clumsy. Before starting, he was tired out with the preparations and was on the point of giving up. I helped him into the unconventional rope suspenders he had made to hold up the heavy B.A.R. ammunition belt. He sighed windily and let his head sag under the weight of the steel helmet.

Lieutenant MacKenzie came in breezily. "All right, men.

25

Here's the dope." Everyone pressed in unnecessarily close. "The plans have all been changed an' instead of sittin' around here an' starvin' out the forts, General Purvis an' Colonel Mauck have decided on an attack straight on." Stunned, I looked to see what he thought, but he was smiling. "The whole battalion's ready an' the Artillery's drawn up, ready to give 'em everything they have. We're all to open up at the same time. Everyone's to make as much noise as possible. Just scare the *hell* out of them!" It sounded crazy. None of his enthusiasm was transmitted to me. He glanced about. "We'll have to leave some men behind to take care of our things here. Let me see . . . Smathers, you stay; you're not feelin' well. An' Louden, you stay. The rest—be ready to fall out in a few minutes. Right on the road outside."

"We're in for it," I said to Dave.

"Vuss kemmen teen?" He shrugged helplessly.

"Kemmen laben, but men lust nicht."

And he answered, "Men lust nicht."

Shortly after, we were called outside. This is it, I thought, grabbing my rifle, going through the door and across the little court, but no picture formed. Aside from a slight nervousness, there was no feeling. It will be like those two battalion problems at Fort Jackson where you don't know what's going on and you fire when someone tells you to; and though nothing seems to happen as far as the eye can see, later you hear of some astoundingly successful result. That's what it's going to be like. I hope.

The rain fell on us. "All right, men. No noise. Line up in a column of ducks." A brief consultation took place out of hearing. "Tenshun!" The order was given in a low voice, tensely. "Lef'—face! Forward—march!" Tramp, tramp, tramp: feet on the muddy road. "Remember, men, no noise. Route step. Be as quiet as you can. Step it up there, Sergeant. There's quite a climb, and we've got to be up there in time."

A short distance down the road we went through a back garden and started to climb the mountainside. For a while there was a path going up steeply. I looked back at one point and was surprised to see the rooftop of a house just below me, seemingly at my ankles. We continued to climb. I had been nervous about my night-blindness and thought I'd fall into holes, but we were close together, in single file, almost at one another's heels. Soon breaths began to strain. You grabbed onto saplings and pulled your way up, hand over hand, your feet slithering and slipping in the wet leaves. Another tree, its exposed roots almost level with your eyes. You reached up for a good grasp, hoisting yourself up. We were bearing slightly to the right. There; someone had fallen with a *Flump!* It was Dave Rossofsky. Then someone else slipped, fell backward with a cry, grasping wildly for the saplings. "Hey, *shh!* What the hell's the matter with you?"

"I fell, for crissake!"

"*Shh!*"

"Shh, my ass. What d'ya expect me to do?"

Fifteen minutes later we were still straining, pulling at the trees as we ascended. Some men had fallen behind, out of their positions. Panting, I looked in back of me for Dave and saw him lose his footing again, slither back, fall to his knees and let the B.A.R. go into the mud. "This goddam f---ing cape!" He tore at it. I waited for him and at first couldn't make out what he was doing. With his beloved knife he was sawing Hepp's poncho off. Suddenly cutting through, the arm with the knife came free and shot over his head. The cape fell from him in sections and he left it there. He began to climb, the last man on the line, using the B.A.R. as a staff, plunging it into the mud and then pulling himself up by it, cursing and slipping. I very nearly laughed aloud.

"Damned cape was *choking* me!" He sounded surprised. "I'll get it when we come down," he added complacently.

"What makes you think we're *coming* down?" I asked. We laughed and went on struggling upward from tree to tree.

At last, the top. I looked up and saw heads peering down at us. Hands reached down and drew us up onto a level plateau. But it was not the top; it was merely a grassy shelf. The cliff rose still higher, though you could see the top dimly against the paler sky. The rain was stopping. I was surprised that the whole battalion wasn't around, and before we began the next climb our platoon was split into thirds. To two of the squads, Lieutenant MacKenzie had given their orders, and in silence they set off to the left. The rest of us, the third squad, toiled on, grasping and clawing, lifting ourselves up the face of the cliff. There were no more than eight of us, including Sergeant Danowski and Lieutenant MacKenzie. We finally crawled over the top.

"Now," the lieutenant whispered, "gather close, men. From now on, not a sound. We're right at the fortress." I looked but I couldn't see it. "We're to set up an observation

27

post an' it's unfortunate that where we're goin' has never been reconnoitered. American scouts have never been able to go that far." Oh, fine! I thought. Fine! Nice work! "Remember, no noise. Keep low. An' on no account fire your weapons—unless, of course, we're ambushed and attacked. We're here to find out." Find out what? I was just about to ask, when he whispered, "One last word: Watch out for land mines."

"How?" I asked. We were in a sort of football huddle, and he looked astonished. "How do you watch out for them? I've never seen one." This, I realized, was no time to be going into that—but then, what better time than the present?

"That's right, you haven't had any of this. Well, you'll—you'll see a round—a perfectly round dark mark in the road. Watch out for that." But I can't see the road, I thought of pointing out; I can't see as far as my feet. "You'll see them in the daylight," he added, clairvoyant. "Round black marks." And till then? I wanted to inquire. Between now and daylight? But I let him off. "All right now, stay low. Get into your positions."

My position, I discovered, was toward the end of the line, next to the last man, Merkel. Dave was just ahead, having trouble with the bipods of the B.A.R. The men in front, I could not help thinking, would be inclined to set off the mines first. For the sake of swiftness, we had come out of the fringe of bushes and trees and were hurrying along the middle of the dirt road, bent over. And we were, at least to my ears, anything but silent. You could hear footsteps, the jingle of equipment, whispers: "Hey, what the hell—?" "Shh, you goddam fool!" "Hey, shut up, you two guys. Come on!" The Americans, I thought. A strange and wonderful people: until the last crack of doom they go on resisting orders and being individuals. It was impossible not to imagine eyes watching our progress. And weren't we going dangerously fast? What if we were advancing into a trap? This wasn't anything as I had imagined actual combat, this lonely little string of men. When I thought of it at all, I saw a battlefield and rows of men advancing shoulder to shoulder, cannons firing, the first ranks being mowed down. I realized I had been thinking of scenes from *The Birth of a Nation*.

Suddenly we stopped. A whisper: "Git down!" What was this? Ahead, Sergeant Danowski and some of the others had crawled together and were whispering. Lieutenant MacKenzie wriggled back. We all crawled close.

"Listen, men. We've come to a crossroads here. I'm going forward with Danowski. When I give the signal, you come forward one at a time. An' for crissake, *keep low!* If we trip off any flares, remember, freeze. Don't move."

"Like playing Statues," I said.

"Yes, like—" He laughed. "An' as soon as the flare dies down, run like hell."

Like lizards, we separated again; Lieutenant MacKenzie and Sergeant Danowski went forward. I heard one make a sudden dash across the road; a moment later the other scurried over. I crawled up next to Dave and we lay shoulder to shoulder. I started to whisper something to him and instead felt myself shaken with laughter. Then he started to say something to me, and he too began to laugh. "So damned silly" was all I could say. Merkel inched his way up to see what was going on, or what we were saying. We lay there for perhaps two minutes, waiting. What silence! And didn't it seem to be growing a little lighter? Then Sergeant Danowski crawled back, whispering, "Where's Atwell?"

A mission alone . . .

"He's not here," I said.

"Listen, Atwell, what's 'Gefahr, Aufpassen' mean?"

"*What?*"

"What's 'Gefahr, Auf*pass*en' mean?"

"How in God's name would I know?"

He stared. "Aren't you the German interpreter for the battalion?"

"No!" I seemed continually to surprise him. "I don't know *any* German!"

"Oh, Jesus Christ." Silence. He put his head down in his arms and seemed to give up, disgusted with all of us.

Lieutenant MacKenzie came crawling back. He whispered, "Do you know what it is, Atwell? Do you think it means mines? Or is the word 'minen—'?"

"Yes, I'm sure it's mines," I said, beginning to laugh. "Let's get out of here."

"No, we'll have to try it. Get ready, men, to follow us across."

Lieutenant MacKenzie crawled away and raced across the road; Sergeant Danowski and one or two others had followed. I moved up in line and was getting ready to sprint for it when something popped like a Fourth-of-July fire-

29

works and an intense pale-pink radiance bloomed over us. "*Flare!*" someone cried. I was shocked and blinded but I remained half up, half down, shaking. Somewhere behind the first flare another went off. I was startled by the sharpness of the shadow I cast upon the road. Then: Bru-u-u-*up!* Bup, bup, bup, bup, bup! Bru-u-uu-up, bup, bup, bup, bup, bup! A German machine gun stuttering. *God!* Where would you fire? What would you aim at? Where the hell was the firing coming *from?*

"Back! Back!" someone was shouting. "Run! Run! Get the f--- out of here!" Figures loomed up in the dying flarelight, pounding past. And suddenly I too was galvanized into action, running as fast, as silently as I could, trying to keep my head, thinking we might have to stand and open fire. "Down!" someone shouted. "Down out of here! Down the hill!"

"What happened?" I gasped.

"Don't know." "Flare!" "They opened up on us—" "Burp gun!" "Get down!"

We started to slide, fall and slither down the cliff. Trees rushed up at you, and you grabbed them, swung down Tarzan-like, bending the branches with your weight, grabbing the next tree below. That tree's roots would, in a moment, be higher than your head. Gramling had fallen and was sliding as fast as if a sled had been placed under him. It was growing light.

Shaken, scratched, plastered with mud, we landed in a breathless heap on the narrow plateau.

"Who won?" I asked.

Lieutenant MacKenzie burst out laughing. "Oh, Atwell, Atwell . . ." He shook his head. "We just messed up on our initial taste of combat."

The big attack had opened up. The *whoosh* and crash of artillery shells and the lighter crack of rifles could be heard. I expected that we would have to join in, but we continued down the remainder of the cliff in the growing whiteness of the morning light. Suddenly the orange tiled roofs of the houses could be seen. You thought: If I fell, I'd land 'way below there on that roof. But we came down gradually, gained the little footpath, stepped down into someone's back garden and walked out onto the road where yesterday the boys had been riding the motorcycle.

30

Our cooks were there, setting up the three ash barrels of boiling water for washing mess kits. They were grinning sleepily in their khaki undershirts, their long sleeves rolled up. "How'd yiz make out?" they asked. I don't think anyone answered. In double file again, we went along to our court-yard. Before it we were halted, given left face, and told to fall out: somehow a surprisingly formal little finish to the escapade.

"I'm done in," I said in the kitchen. "I'm going to sleep for a month." I lit a cigarette, took off the muddy gas mask and pack, unhooked the heavy belt and sat in a straight chair. The young boys were hurrying to get their mess kits out.

I tagged along with them down the road and we got our breakfast: an unknown hot cereal and powdered milk all frothing with tiny bubbles, two K-ration crackers with a paste of peanut butter and marmalade, and a canteen cup of coffee. We came back to the kitchen, hurrying along the road, watchful that the coffee didn't spill, that the catch that held the handle up didn't collapse.

The kitchen was a discouraging sight with the remains of last night's dinner on the table, the sink piled high with pots and pans, broken dishes and glasses and pieces of goat meat lying about. A rapid-fire review of our "mission" began, with almost everyone talking at once. I had no clear idea of what had happened beyond the fact that Lieutenant MacKenzie, raising his hand to signal someone on, had touched a wire that set off the flares. At the moment I didn't care one way or the other. I turned to Dave, who was equally uninter-ested. "I hope," I said, "that we don't have to clean this place up before we go to sleep," and before he could reply, Lieu-tenant MacKenzie was in with the news that in one hour we were to be ready with light pack and raincoat—"You'll be given rations"—to go up the cliff again. There were cries. "Wait. Wait, men. It's just—it's just to go on guard there. Watching the fort. That's all. You'll be gone twenty-four hours."

"How about blankets?" I asked.

"Oh, yes, blankets. One to each man. Ready in an hour. Have them ready, Danowski."

So that now instead of resting, one had to finish breakfast in a rush, run back down the road to wash the mess kit, re-turn, wash sketchily at the dirty sink in cold water, brush

31

one's teeth . . . As the day grew lighter, how tired one became! Sergeant Danowski was back, passing out the boxes of K rations—one breakfast, one lunch, one dinner apiece. There was no handy way of carrying the boxes, and one or two you slipped inside your shirt. "We ought to clean this mess up a little," Sergeant Danowski said, but no one seemed to hear him. Another trip down the road to fill the canteen from the lister bag. The rifles were mud-spattered. Some men cleaned theirs hastily; I brushed mine without taking it apart. Dave and I were laughing at the condition of the B.A.R. which he had used as an alpenstock, when Hepp came over looking for his poncho. Upon hearing what had happened to it, he flew into a fury, then settled into a state of despondency.

By daylight the climb up the side of the cliff did not seem as long or as dangerous, and there was no need to be silent. With the element of excitement gone, it was merely tiring. Not knowing what to expect in daylight on reaching the top, I was surprised to find ourselves being led along a trench that had been used during the First World War: a long straight trench with, every here and there, semicircular indentations where two men stood, their chins about level with the ground. We relieved the platoon that had spent the night there, and were stationed two men in each of the indentations. *Who-o-o-sh! Who-o-o-sh!* The shells flew overhead, landing with an explosion.

"Now there's nothin' for you to do," an unknown sergeant said. "Just hang around, an' keep your eye on the fortress there." I looked in the direction he indicated and could see nothing but grass and low winter-bare bushes stretching off to a haze.

"Every now and then you see the Jerries come out. You don't do nothin'. Your job is to keep them in there. Unless they start comin' out at you, you don't open fire on them."

With that, a shell came toward us, ripping through the air. It landed with a heavy smashing thud a little behind the trench, easily discernible to the eye—fat, silvery, gleaming among the brown leaves, the dead bushes and trees. Except for the sergeant and me, everyone in the trench and in the observation posts had crouched down. I didn't understand why. The sergeant started to speak and his teeth began suddenly to rattle and click. Afraid the shell would explode at any moment—a possibility that hadn't occurred to me—he abandoned his directions and scuttled off, crablike, to the opposite end. The shell was directly behind Dave Rossofsky and me, and we were at the dead end of the trench. When no explosion came, the others gradually straightened up, laughing a little but no one wanted to come down near our section.

Sometime in the afternoon, we heard that Captain Hillier, our Company Commander, had climbed up the cliff with the intention of inspecting us. Sergeant Brauer described the visit. "Dere he is vit a cane! A valking stick in his hand! Like a goddam tourist! He stands, smiling, looking all around. Then zoom! One shell comes over: he ducks and goes scooting down the hill. Vould not even come up as far as the trench!"

Captain Hillier was a tall, light-haired, well-built young man with decidedly almond-shaped blue eyes, knock knees and outturned lower legs. His pants were never bloused in the popular Zouave fashion over his leggings, but fitted tightly from the knee down, giving him the look of an overgrown Western Union messenger. He was always well groomed, well manicured, and clean-spoken. His voice was deep and resonant, and I felt he had taken a course in public speaking; but everything he said was paraphrased two or three times, and while addressing the men his oblique eyes were generally downcast. "You notice?" the men were quick to point out. "He can't look you straight in the eye. He don't dare, the son of a bitch!"

We heard he had played football at a small New England college, had taken R.O.T.C., and, upon graduation, had stayed on as an instructor in Military Tactics. "All he knows is in the book," the men said. When the war came, he entered the Army with a commission. He had good connections, it was claimed, and he was given a desk job in Division Headquarters. What happened there no one knew exactly, but he was demoted to being Company Commander of Regimental Headquarters, a step down but still a fairly good spot. "See, an' then he f---ed up there too, so they sent him down to us in C Company."

"Lieutenant McGrath might be one of those high-and-mighty bastards," one of the men said, comparing the two officers, "but at least he's a soldier. He's been in the Aleutians, and he knows what the hell it's all about. It's a damned good thing we got him along." This was grudging praise, for at the start Lieutenant McGrath had been almost

33

as unpopular as Captain Hillier. It was only now that his original haughty condescension was beginning to fade from him. He was tall and had a bored, good-looking Irish face with blue eyes and wavy dark-red hair. Some men said he had sold grain elevators in his native Oklahoma; others claimed he had been a professor and had taught philosophy in a Catholic college. He was about twenty-eight or thirty years old.

On one of our last days in camp I had been called down from the Art Shop to C Company, and half-Indian First Sergeant Tomkins told me to letter a new lieutenant's name and home address on an assortment of luggage I would find just outside on the company street. He gave me the name and the address on a card and a small can of black enamel, a cheap little paint-stiffened brush, and a piece of fatigue suit to use as a paint rag. It would have served no purpose to explain that I was not a letterer, that the brush was worthless. With First Sergeant Tomkins, one followed orders.

Outside I found a trunk, a crate, several footlockers, a valpack and a traveling bag. I lettered "Lt. John McGrath" and the address in Oklahoma on the footlockers, and a little group of men on their way to the mess hall stopped to watch me. It was not a particularly neat job: there were unavoidable blobs and dribbles, and every now and then sand blew onto the paint.

Suddenly a loud, imperious voice descended, crying, "Who did that? Who put that damned lettering on those footlockers? And on the *trunk!*"

The men fell away. "I did," I said, getting to my feet, seeing Lieutenant McGrath for the first time.

"Well, who told you to?" he demanded wrathfully.

"The First Sergeant."

"Oh, goddamit, I never saw such stupidity. Wipe it off!"

I looked at him. I had nothing to wipe the paint off with but the sandy piece of fatigue uniform.

"Wipe it off, I say!" he cried, so I did what he ordered and smeared black paint all over a corner of the trunk. He let out a choked cry and went fuming off to the company office.

The observers were content, pleased with the entire incident. "Gonna be real sassy, ain't he?" said one of them.

But here in Europe the change was becoming apparent: he started to think of the men before himself. For the three days that we were riding toward Metz in the splintery forty-

and-eights, he remained on his feet staring out the boxcar doorway hour after hour as the harsh plowed fields rolled slowly by. "It may be our only chance to see this country-side," he said, glancing around at the men lying dirty and careless on the floor. "Most of you are missing a big opportunity here." None of them budged. I happened to be sitting near him on the five-gallon can of water and he asked "Have you ever been to Europe before?"

"No, sir. Have you?"

"No. I never had the chance."

That ended our first unnecessary conversation.

Captain Hillier and I never spoke at all.

The long day in the trench went by, windy and cold, with the smell of damp dirt over everything. There was an artillery officer at the entrance to the trench, telephoning back, directing the fire, but it was dull to me because there were long waits and I couldn't see where the shells were landing. Once in a while the others claimed to see Germans walking about outside the fortress, working; and once during the afternoon a man near the entrance to the trench was hit with shrapnel: he cried out and fell back as if in a faint. We were ordered to stay in our places, and in time the medics came up with a litter and removed him. It was enough to make everyone duck down each time a shell seemed to be low. "Is that ours?" they asked. "Is that comin' in or goin' out?"

We talked idly.

"I hear these forts go eight floors down."

"I wonder how they know that."

"I don't know."

"These rations stink."

"Cheese isn't too bad."

But I didn't like it. And the narrow, hard, light-brown crackers I liked even less. They tasted as if they had been dipped in preservative, or a weak dilution of rat poison. You washed the cheese and crackers down with cold chlorine-tasting water; using the orange or lemon powder seemed foolish in that weather. You put the sugar in your pocket, ate the two caramel candies, and, when you finished, put the stick of gum into your mouth, lit one of the cigarettes . . . What a rotten life this was going to be! Always outdoors, always dirty, devitalized, tired from the broken sleep of guard duty. I thought of the men I had been with, making training strips, now in Camp Bliss, swimming after work, playing tennis, sketching and reading, or of those men I saw that one day in London who were stationed there, dining in the hotels, going to the dances, to the theater. And complaining, no doubt, of their lot in life. Still, obviously, someone had to sit in this trench, and I was tired and couldn't care too deeply. There was just a general feeling of depression, that flat carelessness that comes from knowing one has hit bottom and will stay there.

"Hey, Atwell, want to see where we're going to sleep?"

An opening had been hollowed into the side of the trench, like an oven, about six feet long and two feet high. The men before us had carted in newspapers and cardboard that was now damp and muddy. Lambert tried the place and slid out, saying it wasn't too bad.

Beginning, I think, at six o'clock, there came a change: one man slept for two hours while the other stood guard, facing the fort. It had grown colder and a steady rain came down. My blanket and equipment had been stowed in the dugout. Lambert and I stood guard while our partners crept in out of the wind.

"Cold."

"Freezing." But I didn't want to take my blanket out because it would get wet. We turned up the collars of our raincoats and sat on little facing seats carved out of dirt, our knees touching. Despondently I considered the rifle getting wet, rusting. Some men had fashioned caps of the waxed paper that came around the ration crackers; others used a contraceptive. Just before leaving the States, Lambert, or his wife, had made a reddish-brown canvas case that fitted loosely over the entire rifle, leaving only the stock outside.

The rain turned to snow—thick, furry, wet flakes, driven every way by the wind. They settled on my glasses no matter how I turned my head, and rendered them useless. I'd no sooner dry them off than they'd be wet and smeared again. I finally took them off; at night they were not of much use anyway. Lambert's shoulders and helmet had turned white. I could see that, come what may, he didn't intend to get his blanket out, but I got mine, wrapped it about me Indian-style and sat down again. The cold steel of my rifle came through my glove. And why hadn't the gloves been made with a gauntlet cuff on them? The wind on the mountaintop was bitter. We sat with our heads sunk to one side, shoulders drawn up, eyes squinting. Every now and then from a sense of duty I'd look up over the top, but I couldn't see three feet away, nor, above the wind, did I think I'd be able to hear anything short of a circus parade approaching. Since there was nothing to talk about, time dragged slowly and I began to feel like Lear out in the storm. At the end of our two hours Lambert went and awakened the relief. There was a wait while they pulled on their overshoes and prepared to come out.

I would have preferred almost anything to the dugout. Merkel was using mine with me. We sat at the entrance, took off our ammunition belts, overshoes and helmets, and stowed them inside. Then we locked our rifles and put them in down the center. He slipped in, his upthrust feet disappearing from sight; and I, rewrapping my blanket wet side out, crawled in after him and stretched out. A shower of dirt fell on my face. There was the close smell of earth, the feeling of being buried alive. Pitch-blackness. We had to lie like mummies; there was no room to move in any direction.

"Well, at least it's dry."

"Oh, *it* ain't bad," Merkel replied, sounding surprised that I should find any fault.

"Did you eat your supper ration?"

"No. Did you?"

By moving our arms cautiously, bringing down cascades of dirt and pebbles, we found our rations and struggled to open them. My raincoat was binding, twisted up under me somehow. By feel, I located the thick, hard chocolate bar, unwrapped it and began to gnaw on it, wishing it weren't so sweet. That smell of dirt close against your face, of airlessness, wet blankets, rifles . . . How I wished the night were over!

Two hours on, two hours off. And it snowed almost till morning. It was one of the long, sleepless, endless nights of the war.

Upon being relieved at eight the next morning, we came down the cliff and stumbled into the upset kitchen. Before we could get the muddy raincoats off to lie down, word came that we were to roll full field packs at once, to be ready to leave Metz.

"Take ya two blankets, ya extra set of long johns, ya OD

pants and shirt, an' any goddam thing outta ya duffel bag ya feel like carryin'."

The duffel bags were to be left behind—an unfailing sign that we were going into combat.

"When will we get the bags back again?" I asked, unpacking mine, coming upon the remains of a Christmas package that had been mailed on the fifteenth of October and delivered to me two days later at Camp Kilmer.

"I think in about four or five days," Husey replied. "As soon as you come out of combat, they bring the bags up to you."

We didn't see them again until June.

In the afternoon we quit the trucks that transported us away from Metz and started to hike along a country road; by evening we had settled on a sweeping hill going down into a cuplike hollow. The place, though lonely, was reminiscent of a golf course. There had been no houses, no sign of inhabitants for miles. We were in the Saar Valley. Our platoon had pitched tents and had dug gravelike foxholes beside them. The tents were widely scattered and we had been warned to stay apart from each other. "No bunching up!" you heard. "Keep your distance!" This we might do for the first five minutes, then we began to drift together again.

The night turned extremely cold. Everyone was on guard, two hours on, two hours off. The Germans were supposed to be all around us. Our squad had a long stretch of hedge to guard that ran up to the top of the hill, ending in a road that crossed at a right angle. Sergeant Danowski posted us, two men at intervals. We had each taken a blanket and wrapped in it, stood the length of the thorny, tall, bare hedge. There were chill bluish stars in the sky and a steady cold, black wind. The rifle became like a bar of ice to hold. We had to be completely silent, but once in a while you heard the murmur of a voice or the sound of someone spitting.

I was afraid to sit down for fear I'd go to sleep, but no such qualms deterred Dave Rossofsky. After standing a while, he'd sit part way in the hedge; a minute later he'd be asleep. This had been going on for some time, and while we were together I covered for him. At Metz, he had been teamed up with others who threatened to turn him in. "Goddamit, he doesn't fall asleep, he just *goes* to sleep! Suppose we all did that!" When there were two men standing together, I couldn't see that it made very much difference, but Lambert said to me, "If he goes asleep again tonight and you don't tell Danowski, I will! That's just rotten laziness on his part."

I heard Lambert coming down quietly to investigate and, knowing he'd hear me if I whispered, I reached out and touched Dave with my rifle. He awoke quickly and silently. "Everything all right down here?" Lambert whispered, shooting Dave a suspicious glance.

"What was the matter with him?" Dave asked when Lambert returned to his post. "I wasn't asleep."

"Well, then, stand up."

"No. I'm too tired."

On the next shift he sat down again and his head fell forward.

"Dave, are you asleep?" No answer. "Dave," I whispered. "Dave . . . Dave . . . Dave, get up."

He started up suddenly, throwing back his blanket. "Yes? What is it?" he asked aloud. "What's the matter? I wasn't asleep." But Lambert had arrived quietly in the midst of it and caught him. The grumbling against Dave increased.

By day there were tiny smoky fires of wet twigs, and men crouched low over them, tears from the smoke stinging their eyes. Someone, as usual, was trying to dry a pair of socks on a stick. Of us all, Smathers was in the best spirits and talked on with his flat Tennessee drawl, unaffected by the surroundings. Invariably, through clumsiness, Dave knocked into the questionable little fire, upsetting the one licking flame, the socks, the smoking drying twigs, and he'd be roundly cursed.

A man stopped by from another platoon. "Hey, d'you hear the big news? This is no s---. Listen. A German officer, a high-ranking officer they captured at one of the forts, said the Jerries are gonna give up on the twenty-second of the month! Their leaders and ours are together right now, talking over the armistice terms! They're trying to see if we'll give up on the idea of unconditional surrender—but anyway, no matter what happens, they're giving up on the twenty-second."

Everyone was talking suddenly about the news. It was now the fourteenth of December, if one remembered correctly. Then that meant in eight more days—if we could manage to hang on for just eight more days—what a magnificent Christmas all through the world! Dave and I jabbered about it excitedly, laughing, shaking each other's hand.

The rumor was tracked down to Jack Nugent, a college football player in the Third Platoon, and I saw men attacking him for his proof. He laid his hand over his heart. "Swear to God. Every word of it is true. It was a high-ranking officer, and he coughed up his guts. He said they knew they were licked and they decided to give up on the twenty-second." The men started to move away impressed and Jack Nugent bent over and laughed silently. "And if it's not on the twenty-second," he called after them, "then it's going to be the seventeenth of March!"

"Wha—?" They wheeled on him. "Ya sonofabitch!"

"No. No, I swear, fellows. It's the twenty-second of the month."

Rather than press him further, I turned away, only too willing to believe it.

Another rumor started up, and this one proved to be true. Upon leaving Metz, Captain Hillier had been relieved of his command, had been moved back to Division Headquarters again, and Lieutenant McGrath had been made Company Commander in his place.

"That bastard Hillier always had pull somewheres, and he knows when to get the hell out," a man was saying. "This whole deal don't look good to me. You hear about the 245th? I was talkin' to a jeep driver an' he says they been in combat two days an' they're gettin' the s--- kicked outta them."

Late in the afternoon there was a mail call. We were told to burn the letters as soon as they were read, for on no account was our address and APO number to be found on us should we be taken prisoner. "And while we're at it—all of you go through your pockets and wallets right now. Remove all your identification and burn it. Just your dog tags —that's all you're going to need." I had received no mail, but the others either burned their letters or the envelopes, and then the fires had to be stamped out. It was growing dark.

I looked around the hills where the entire battalion was bivouacked, at the hundreds and hundreds of soldiers moving purposefully around in the chill dusk, and I seemed to come sharply to my senses out of an anesthesia. What was I doing here? Panic came over me and for a wild moment I thought of marching into the new Company Commander's tent and saying, "Look. There's been some big mistake. I'm here, but I haven't had the same training as the others and I have no idea what to do in combat. What do you intend to do about it?" The answer, a cold "Nothing," formed with such promptness that I abandoned the thought, though unwillingly.

And a diversion came: we were told to get our mess gear out; we were going down to eat. The kitchen trucks were below in the center of the hollow with the blue gasoline lights under their ash barrels of boiling water, and from the ring of low hills snaking lines of men were converging toward them, rifles on their shoulders, the wearisome gas masks slung on, mess kits clinking and jangling. "Silence those goddam mess kits! You know how a sound can carry at night!"

We were lined up ten yards apart as a special precaution, ready to start down the hill, when the sky seemed to split violently apart. Four hurtling, screaming explosions landed in with a crash that stunned everyone. We had all fallen to the ground. I felt it thunder and shake and pound beneath me. There followed a long moment of silence. I lifted my head slowly, wondering if I were still in one piece. Then from all over there rose the cry, "Put out that fire! Put out that goddam fire!" Everyone was shouting it, but no one was moving or getting up from the ground. I looked behind me.

Up on the hill, near the hedge, there was a high flame leaping in the dark. How had it come there? Could one of the shells have caused it? When we quit the place only five minutes before, we had carefully trampled out the tiny fires; and since inhabiting the damp hill no one had been able to coax up a flame half that high. Realizing I was one of the nearest, I scrambled up and started to run for it. Antiaircraft artillery men on the far side of the hedge reached there just ahead of me and we stamped out the mysterious flame.

I ran back to the squad and we started down to eat. In a shell hole near the center of the hollow there were the stiffened bodies of three dead American soldiers awaiting the Graves Registration men. They had been there since our arrival, dressed in raincoats. On my way to eat I always looked the other way, but now I heard someone ahead of me saying, "One of 'em boys is got a nice gol' ring on his finger," and someone else said, "One of 'em got it right through the head. He was a sergeant." Without meaning to, I passed close by

41

and saw them in the ghostly light, stiff, no more convincing than the figures in a wax museum; the shoes and clothing were all that looked real.

On the nearby chow line the cooks were nervous and spooned the food out in a rush. They told us to eat and wash up the mess kits quickly; we were leaving the place at once. By the time our squad got its food, the last of the other platoons were washing their mess gear and hurrying up the hill. Smoke from the stacks of the water cans blew back down; jeeps and small trucks drove suddenly away; men ran by in the semi-darkness; a line formed somewhere, marching off; other men rolled equipment as fast as they could. The rush and excitement made me think of a circus breaking up to move before a storm.

Quickly, standing there, we gulped down the food—wet hash and coffee—and lined up, the last ones to wash the mess kits. We ran up the hill. "Let's go!" they were shouting in every company. "Let's go, let's go, let's *go!*" The food lodged at the base of one's throat. You wanted to smoke but it was too dark.

How quickly now you could unbutton the tent, roll and strap the muddy equipment!

"Hey, Les!" It was Dave. "See if you can fix my damned stuff! My hands won't—I can't get it together!"

"Give it to me. Quick!"

Then Sergeant Danowski: "What's the matter, Rossofsky? We're going! Come *on*, you two guys! All right, line up! Line up, Third Squad."

Without a moment to spare, sling on the pack and harness, buckle it. The heavy crisscrossing bandoleers of ammunition. Gas mask. Rifle. Race out to where the line was forming in the dark; start off. Almost running, we went down into the hollow where the battalion gathered awaiting the explosion of more shells. The kitchen trucks drove away fast. One wanted to leave, to leave suddenly, to be out of there! The rush; this waiting; the food lodged in one's throat . . .

Yes, here we go. Thank God, out of that clear cup into the heavy woods at the left. The officers were excited, running back a few steps, then running forward, urging us on to greater speed. The lines almost trampled on top of each other. As long as we're out of the open, I thought gratefully a moment later, but all at once the men started to complain loudly about being caught in the woods. The woods. The woods. The woods were the worst place to be. "I'd rather be caught in the open! What the hell are they doin' to us? You don't stand a chance in the woods!"

We halted, breathless. Lieutenant MacKenzie came running by and told us that the other two battalions of the regiment were already in combat, that we were the battalion in reserve, and of that battalion C was the company in reserve. Chris Taylor, who had worked with me in the Art Shop, was standing nearby on his line. There was just enough of the last streak of daylight to see him by. He smiled, his teeth glinting, his face silvery-pale in the dim light.

"How long will we be in reserve?" I asked him hurriedly.

"It depends. It can go on for weeks."

I thought again of the date on which the Germans were to surrender. The officers began to shout, "Get out of the woods! *Get* your men out of the woods! Hurry it up! On the double there!"

We came out into the open, ran panting up the hill and gained the road that was on the summit. From then on it was a steady rush, a forced march at top speed in the dark. Much of the time we were running to keep the ranks closed up. Weighed down by overshoes, the heavy stonelike full field pack, the overcoat, bandoleers and rifle, I was soon struggling for breath. It was too dark for me to see anything of the country road down which we were pelting. Part of the time we dropped back into a hurried walk, then almost at once started to run again.

After an hour or so it began to snow. Great swift flakes of it blew into one's eyes and into one's mouth as one gasped to breathe. I fell to the back of our line and then to the platoon behind us. We went up a long, long, deceptively gentle hill that soon had everyone panting and dizzy. Would it never end? Yes, here. Crookedly, with light uncertain legs, we ran along the top of the hill in blowing swirls of snow. Finally we drew off the road into a sloping pasture to dig foxholes. I paused for a few minutes to talk to Jack Nugent and Joe Vandendale as they dug, and we laughed about the officers leading us into the woods and then howling at us to get out of them. I left them, went farther down the pasture to where Dave Rossofsky was digging. "What happened?" he asked. "Do you feel all right?"

"Yes, sure," I said. "I just got tired back there for a while. Is this where we're going to stay for the night?" I had started to take off my equipment and suddenly I felt myself falling backward through space. The earth rushed up but there was no sensation of hitting it at all. Out of nothing the dark world seemed to begin again with the distant, tiny voices of men calling, "Medic! Medic! Hey, get the medic, quick! Someone get the doctor! It's Atwell!" I could hardly believe it: I felt so well, so completely peaceful. Then I heard something that sounded like a horse nearby breathing with loud effort and it took me a moment to realize it was I. In the meanwhile Dave and Sergeant Danowski were trying to loosen my clothes and get the equipment off me. Dave, I knew, had his knife out and was trying to saw through all the straps of my pack, but Farron, the young aid man, came along and pushed him out of the way. I passed out again and when I opened my eyes Lieutenant MacKenzie was there. "He's all right; he's resting now," Farron was saying in his quiet voice, kneeling on one knee above me, his hand on my heart. "His heart is—" I came to, completely, in embarrassment.

"It's all right," I said, aware of men digging about me. "Let me sit up. I'm really all right. If I could sit up, I'd be . . ." But the aid man held me down and remained beside me until the loud breathing gradually quieted.

In the morning I saw that Dave's foxhole and those about us had been dug in a sloping field that was bounded by stone fences. We were down near the bottom, and a valley, thinly covered with snow, stretched below. There was no farmhouse in sight. When we reached out for our leggings and overshoes, they were stiff with frost. Dave had left his canteen out and the water in it had frozen solid.

We had slept fairly late, for we awoke in daylight, and shortly afterward the sun rose. Before breakfast Sergeant Danowski came around and told us to hand in our overcoats and blankets. We had never done this before and, rather mystified, watched him tying them into large bundles which he marked "Second Platoon, Third Squad."

"What's gonna happen, Sarge?"

"We'll get them tonight." They were carried over and put on the trailer attached to the company jeep.

The day was cold and until the sun rose higher we stood in our foxholes, shivering, our hands in our pockets. I went up to the top of the hill to fill my canteen at the lister bag

44

and, on straightening, saw Lieutenant McGrath.

"Good morning, Atwell."

"Good morning, sir. I hear you've been made C.O. I'd like to congratulate you." He thanked me, smiled, and put forward his hand. I said, "Everyone feels very encouraged about the change."

"Do they?" He seemed surprised. "I hope things will work out. We'll see."

I turned and went down to the foxhole. We weren't to move till noon. We had rolled our packs and there was nothing to do. The snow was melting and in the wagon ruts, under the top layer of ice, you could see water. Tired of being dirty, I broke the ice in the deepest rut, knelt beside it and washed. My fingers froze at first but after a while I managed to work up a lather. My hands turned from mud color to bright pink with the ice water. I washed my face, neck and ears, and then, by feel, I shaved, using the brushless cream I had bought in England. Then more ice water, and by the time I had put on my outer clothing I began to feel pleasantly clean and warm. By now, like most everyone else, I wore the khaki towel over my head, with the helmet on top of it. The ends of the towel were just too short to be crossed under the chin and tucked into the collar of the field jacket, but it made a fairly good protection against the biting wind and felt strange only while it was still wet and smelled of shaving soap.

"Everyone! Off with your shoes and socks! Come on, start massaging your feet! Get busy there!" This we were supposed to do at least once a day for ten minutes as a hedge against trench foot or frostbite.

"Come on there, Rossofsky! You're not rubbing your feet! Rub 'em good and hard! An' don't bunch up. Stay apart, you guys!"

There was a strange, ominous silence over the slope. At times I had the uneasy feeling that enemy eyes were watching from the distant bushes. It would be so easy for a civilian to follow us through territory he knew and telegraph ahead our positions. My mind kept going back to the mysterious flame that had leaped up last night on the hill.

Rubbing our bare feet in the cold, calling across to each other, our voices sounded tiny and thin. Sometimes the wind swept them away. We seemed dwarfed, the sky was so vast and the hills so brooding at that time of the year. One felt it

45

was such an ancient battleground. *Omnia Gallia* was again divided, and, despite all brave hopes and ringing statements to the contrary, I could not believe we would be the last army ever to come there. Nations had fought since the beginning of the world, and doubtless would again.

Around noon we put on our packs and were marched away at five-yard intervals on either side of the narrow hilly road. We kept up a fairly brisk pace, and after an hour the weight of the pack, the bandoleers, gas mask, the ammunition belt with its dangling canteen and entrenching tool began to grow tiring. Another hour passed and the sun started to feel too strong. A glare came up from the mud. The scenery, at first beautiful, grew to be a blur. The speed was maintained; there were no rests, no sight of civilians. Occasionally we passed a deserted, ruined farmhouse.

"Left and right . . . Left and right." In a tired way, the cry was repeated, coming up from the rear, a sign to give way, to move farther off the road. The battalion jeeps, trailers and trucks, and soon the long hooded artillery pieces, began to drive slowly past between the lines of infantrymen.

"Sure we're a mechanized army," someone crabbed, limping along. "Look at us—everyone rides but the f---in' Infantry."

"Don't bitch, men. Transfer!"

By late afternoon there were longer spaces between the tired men; at the end of each platoon there were hobblers. The damned heavy overshoes sticking to the mud, I thought. The noncoms, goaded by the officers, set up a loud yapping, complaining at the men for not being in better physical condition. I felt myself frowning in resentment.

Toward evening, the footsore, weary company separated from the rest of the battalion, and in single file followed a path that led in among trees for a while. The trees left off and we came out on top of a hill similar to those we had stayed on except that this slope ran in the opposite direction; this one faced the German border. In the somber twilight we could see it before us: folding gentle hills, clumps of trees, a distant rolling horizon. The company scattered, the platoons stretched out, staying farther apart then ever before.

We began immediately to dig foxholes. "Dig 'em fast, dig 'em deep, and don't make any noise. No cigarettes, no lights of any kind. And everyone's on guard tonight."

46

"How long, Sarge?"

"The whole night. Two on and two off."

Even our foxholes were widely separated. Dave and I dug one halfway down the slope; Hepp and Husey were on an even line with us, about twenty yards away. While we were digging, Chris Taylor, my partner in the Art Shop, came hobbling up the hill, his face white and twisted, the equipment hanging from his arm.

He was twenty-four years old, an engineer who had majored in Forestry. When the Army Specialized Training Program was discontinued, he was sent to Fort Jackson, and his wife, Mary, an extremely pretty girl who had been in his class in college, came down to be near him. I had run into them at dinner in town several times and met them again on one of the last nights before we started for overseas. The three of us went to see Ingrid Bergman in *Gaslight*; Chris and I were still in suntans, Mary in a sleeveless dress, but late at night there was a breeze and a hint of autumn came up from the weeds at the side of the road. Mary was shivering.

"Les, I want you to be a witness," she said. "I've told Chris I'll never forgive him if he does anything wild or brave when he gets overseas. He's got to come back to me, I don't care how." The two of them had stood facing each other as she spoke. Her hair blew back in the breeze and the ruffles at her shoulders blew. He stared down at her, tall, slimly built, quiet, with regular features, a dark crew cut, glasses, an Englishman's mustache. "I mean it!" she said. "You've given me your word of honor."

"Of course," he said quietly.

"Anyway, I'm going with you," she said. "I'm going to be in the duffel bag."

"Your foot very bad?" I asked him.

"Killing me." Over a year before, he had had a growth cut out from the sole of his foot by Army doctors and it had never properly healed. On hikes it bled and was extremely painful. After one particular hike in England Lieutenant McGrath had examined it and had flown into a temper, demanding to know what anyone with a foot like that was doing in the Infantry. Hadn't the doctors ever seen it? How had they passed him for overseas service? The answer to that was simple: there had been no real examination; the Regimental Surgeon, by a sweeping edict, had qualified everyone, sight unseen, as fit for combat duty.

47

"On the road today McGrath told me to come and see him when we got here," Chris said, resting a moment beside our half-dug foxhole. "He says he's trying to get a job for me outside the company, back in the rear if he can."

We wished him luck. He limped past us to join his squad.

There were no roots in the ground and for once Dave and I had a respectable foxhole; the cold sods even came away in squares that could be placed neatly on the dirt banked up around the sides. Just before dark Sergeant Hill, the stutterer in charge of supplies, drove up with the blankets and overcoats and we fixed our beds for the night.

During this time we had no news of what was happening to the other regiments or battalions. We seemed like nomads, marching each day closer to the cold. Twigs and branches had torn our faces, and our woolen gloves had repeatedly become wet and, in drying over and over on our hands, had caused painful deep splits to appear at the joints of our fingers. These cuts, while they opened, did not quite bleed, but they made it difficult to button one's pants or do up the legging laces. Frequently men whose hands weren't affected had to perform those tasks for others whose hands were rendered powerless.

Preparing for sleep had become a complex routine. Before getting into the narrow sleeping bag, I'd dump anything hard or breakable out of my pockets: crammed wallet; cigarettes in one of those wonderful plastic cases—mine was red—; heavy, dull-bladed scout knife that some day I was going to sharpen; three pairs of glasses, all practically worthless; toothbrush; fountain pen; lumps of sugar; combination tool for the rifle; clips of ammunition; prayerbook; slips of Nescafé, bouillon, orange and lemon powder; K-ration crackers—everything went into my helmet. It was a clear night, so the overshoes could go outside. Right one to the right side of the helmet; left one to the left side. The leggings on top, also separated right and left, ready to slip on. Somehow we had not been issued the much more convenient and highly prized combat boots and had to stuggle, often in haste, with legging laces, eyelets, and hooks. All the preparations were performed in the cold dark; we would get up again in two hours to stand guard for two hours. Withal, there were rare moments of happiness when one would settle for the poor and insufficient food, the long hard hiking, if one could lie here, covered to the chin, looking up at the cold stars with the cold wind on one's face.

The next day, December the sixteenth, someone came over to our squad and told us that a rearrangement had been made in the company. All the men thought to be unfit for combat, and all those over thirty-five—evidently except me—had been transferred to other less arduous duties in companies behind the line.

"Did Chris Taylor go?"

"Yeah, he went. And the guy with the ruptures, Idell, he went; and Old Man Owens, Kemp, Shrimp Mitchell—a hell of a lot of them went."

"Hey," they were calling from foxhole to foxhole, "they got rid of all the unfit men! All the old guys too!"

"*Nu?*" Dave said to me. I was thirty-six.

"*Nu?*" was all I could say in return.

No fires were allowed. The day was so intensely cold and the wind so penetrating that we remained crouched in our foxholes. Our hands turned numb, and with the deep cuts it was almost impossible to strike a match against the little sanded strip on the package. Dave and I both tried time and time again, blowing on our powerless hands, holding them under our arms in between times. It took the better part of twenty minutes to light the cigarettes.

Lieutenant MacKenzie came along on a visit to the foxholes. "In ohll my life I've never felt such cold as this," he said, turning away from the wind. Under the helmet, his long soft scarf was wrapped tight around his head and neck, giving him the appearance of someone in a morality play. "We don't have it like this, you know, down in Georgia. Ohll the Southern boys feel it particularly." He stood shivering, his hands in his pockets. "If you happen to have any V-mail forms on you, you can write a letter an' I'll censor it right away for you; an' you can head it 'Inside Germany,' 'cause we are inside Germany now." He smiled. "We're really right on the border, but the dividin' line goes all in an' out here, so you can say we're inside Germany. We're one of the few outfits that are."

"That's cheerful news—'one of the few.'"

He laughed. "Atwell, I meant to ask you. Are you keepin' a diary?" I told him, truthfully, that I wasn't. "You can, you know. You're allowed, but you'll have to hand it in to be

49

censored once a week, an' then every month it has to go back to a base censor."

"I don't think there's very much of this I'll want to remember."

"Don't know whether I will either. See you boys again."

That night, led by Sergeant Danowski, in single file, with rifles on our shoulders, gas masks slung on, we padded secretly up to the top of the hill and into a thicket to eat. "No bunching up," he whispered. "Hurry up, wash your mess kits, get your chow, and scatter! The Jerries are all around here."

Burdened with the rifle on your shoulder, mess kit in one hand and collapsible canteen cup in the other, you performed quite a feat of balancing to lower yourself and sit in the stiff, crackling bushes. In the dark it was impossible to see where the stew and the potatoes were in the mess kit. For most of the meals now, like Chris Taylor, who had lost his other implements, I cut and ate everything with a large spoon.

In lining up afterward to wash the mess kits, Dave Rossofsky was ahead of me and as usual he had difficulty bending over with the heavy B.A.R. on his shoulder. The ash barrel of boiling water had been set up on a mound and the ground about it had become wet and slippery. Dave had climbed up and planted his feet on either side of the barrel; and as I approached to take the scrubbing brush from him, he slipped, lost his footing, flung out his arms, and fell back. The B.A.R. with its heavy steel bipods swung with sudden force in an arc off his shoulder and smashed me across the nose and cheek. I remembered in the midst of my surprise not to cry out, though I was staggered, and for a moment I didn't know where I was. A white flare seemed to go off inside my head.

"What—? What happened?" Dave was asking. "Did I hurt you?"

"Hurry up!" a voice in the darkness whispered behind us.

"What happened?" Dave asked again. "Are you hurt?"

"No. I don't know." I bent over and washed my mess kit and cup while Dave mumbled apologies. We started back together, he holding onto the sleeve of my field jacket. I put my hand up to my face, which both burned and felt numb in the icy air. My hand came away sticky with blood. I had a deep gash running across my nose and out to one ear. My nose was filling with blood.

Every two hours that night by turn one half of the company stood guard in a circle while the other half slept. "And listen, Rossofsky," Sergeant Danowski whispered, posting us, "stay on your feet! No sitting down. No sleeping, d'you hear?"

Each of us had taken a blanket to wrap around us. The night was Christmaslike, black, clear, with a steady wind that made a soft sighing through the pines, and there were myriads of stars, some sharp and brilliant, some powdery like silver dust. Dave and I stood in silence most of the time. One would yawn, setting the other off yawning too.

"I could go to sleep on my feet."

"So could I. If I just closed my eyes . . ."

Coming off one of our next shifts, Dave was staggering, more asleep than awake, following me down the hill. The sky had clouded over and in the dark I missed our foxhole and didn't realize it until I had walked into the next squad's territory. Bill Woods, seeing us from his foxhole, began to laugh. "Where're you two characters going? Off for a walk?" He directed us back, and on the way I made one of my usual night-blind blunders, and what I assumed to be a particularly dense shadow turned out, when I fell into it on top of my rifle, to be someone's empty foxhole.

After midnight Lieutenant McGrath, the new Company Commander, came around to talk to us, going from foxhole to foxhole on his way to check the guards. He had just finished his day's work and could have been asleep.

"How are you two men? All right?" He squatted down at the edge of the foxhole, speaking in a low voice.

"Yes, sir, we're all right."

"Pretty cold night. Have you just come off guard?"

"Yes, sir." We were lying down, looking up at him.

"Well, don't—don't let anything worry you. That's the main thing, not to—I mean, if you'll learn to take things as they come and not worry about what's going to happen—" What was he talking about? Was there something he knew that he wasn't telling us? "Anyway, try to get some sleep. Good night."

"Good night, sir."

Coming back from our next shift, we had got into the sleeping bags, had pulled the blankets and shelter-half up, and I had just started to go to sleep when Sergeant Danowski came running along, shouting to us to get up, to pack our

51

equipment in a rush. The overcoats, sleeping bags, shelter-halves and blankets were to be turned in to him at once.

"Why?"

"*Combat!* We're going *in!*"

Dave and I jumped out of the foxhole, stamped our overshoes on and began to fold the equipment in a rising high wind. The triangular far end of my shelter-half sailed up in the air and flapped hysterically against the dark sky. Guards, told to abandon their posts, ran past. There was excitement everywhere.

"Hurry up, you guys. Get your mess kits out and go down and eat. It might be your last chance to get something hot." The kitchen trucks had driven down into the hollow. Some men were packing, others running, it seemed, in every direction.

"Les, roll up my shelter-half. My hands—I'll be getting out your mess kit."

When we ran down to the hollow, Sergeant Hill was there, excitedly passing out ammunition to a line of men, holding a typewritten list up against his eyes, trying to check the names off in the dark. We went through the chow line, got our cereal and coffee and gathered in a large group about the company jeep, using the hood as a table. The five- or ten-yard interval was forgotten. "Hey, d'you hear? We're goin' into combat! We're relievin' the Third Battalion. They got the s--- kicked outta them."

Shivering, drinking the coffee in a rush, I found myself bending forward, trying to let the coffee pour over the rounded lip of the cup, for the coffee was always cooler than the aluminum rim which drew and held the heat. It was impossible; you'd always scorch your mouth. So that, I thought, if anyone ever asks me how I felt or what I was doing going into combat, I must remember: I was slightly nauseated and trying not to burn my mouth.

When we ran up again to our foxhole, Sergeant Hill was there, stuttering and shaking with nervousness, distributing extra ammunition to our squad. I told him I already had all I could carry, what with the two bandoleers and the filled heavy belt, but two hand grenades were given to me and to everyone else; they were hung from the lapel buttonholes of our field jackets. Clips of tracer bullets were stuffed into our pockets—I had no idea when or why to use them—and it suddenly evolved that I was to help little Louden carry some of the excess heavy B.A.R. ammunition. Then we were given two black canisters wrapped with yellow tape. I didn't know what was in them but rather thought it would be extra hand grenades. Along with this, three boxes of K rations were passed out to each man. I remarked to Dave that we should have been equipped like the Hindu god Siva with the sixteen revolving hands.

We were told to take with us merely a raincoat, gas mask, canteen, mess gear, wound tablets, ammunition and the tiny Red Cross pouch. The ammunition belt I had was too large and couldn't be further shortened; the weight of it pulled down over my hips and made walking difficult. I tied the two black canisters and two of the rations to my pack; the third was in my shirt front.

"Here," said Sergeant Danowski in the darkness.

"What's this?"

"An extra bandage. In case you get wounded."

We started out while it was still dark, with Sergeant Hill in a frenzy trying to distribute ponchos to each man. Between the extra weight, the rush, and last night's smash across the face which had filled my nose with coagulated blood, I was gasping within fifteen minutes. We were streaming along either side of a road, spread out ten yards apart, and after a while we began to climb uphill. For one of the few times I could remember, I developed second wind and started to feel quite well. We were scaling a small mountain as the sun rose. Because of our exertion, there was no sense of chill and the air felt fresh and invigorating, as if it could wash us. There was only our own company in sight.

Higher and higher we went, climbing along the arched spine of the mountain. The sky turned magnificent, with long dissolving streamers of flame and rose against brilliantly lighted opalescent banks. The sun gilded the edges of the men's figures standing out in dark silhouette against the sky and the mist-filled valley below. "You might know," someone said. "In camp we bust our b---s learning how to climb over a mountain so they can't see you; and look at us! *Targets,* for crissake, every one of us!"

Grasses and small bushes trembled stiffly in the breeze. When we had been hiking perhaps an hour, a rest was called and everyone dropped to the ground. Cigarettes were lighted, the canteens came out, and as a surprise the small company truck drove up and there was mail call. The only letter I received was from a girl I knew who, believing I was still in England, had written to ask if she could send me a box of oil paints, some brushes and canvas. We had to destroy the envelopes at once. I watched mine burn down, took another drink of canteen water, stood up, and it was time to continue. We came down the mountain, and the colors faded from the sky into an even pale gray-blue. At the bottom we went through woods, walking on either side of a winding path. Occasional shells sounded and everyone stiffened, ready to hit the ground. "Is that ours?" they'd ask.

"Yeah, that's ours. That's goin' out." Then one would crash much nearer. The men would drop into a crouch, wait a little and go on. We came out into clearings and plunged back into the woods again. The only sound was that of a twig snapping, a branch swishing against a steel helmet, feet scuffling through leaves. The day turned mild; the sun brought out the scent of the pine needles and of the dead leaves that were stirred up.

We came into a square open place, something like a room, its walls formed by trees. The grass was tall and we started to move through it on a diagonal. Lieutenant Sidney Ellis, known as the Child, was leading us, and I caught a glimpse of him looking nervous and high-spirited. He was gesturing in a gallant way, tossing his head, urging us on. With that, there was a stamping and crashing in the underbrush that bounded the clearing, and a furious red face emerged, the eyes strained and protruding.

"What company are you?" It was Colonel Mauck, the commander of our regiment.

"C Company, sir!"

"Well, who the hell is leading you? You're supposed to be going *this* way, not that way!" The diagonal line wavered in indecision. "Tell him—tell that goddam lieutenant to swing— Lieu*tenant!* Get your men over here! Over *here*, I say!" Still gallant, Lieutenant Ellis was leading off in the wrong direction. Someone told him and he turned in surprise to meet Colonel Mauck's oaths and shouts. "Goddamit, you're leading these men straight into the *enemy!* Get them in here, over this way!"

"Oh! Yes, sir! Yessir! Awright, men," came the singsong nasal voice. "This way! Follow me-e-e."

The line started to swing around, when there came at the end of a loud fast whistling scream a tremendous deafening

54

explosion, perhaps two of them. Everyone thudded flat to the tall grass. There was stunned silence for a moment, and then from almost at my elbow came the repeated cry, "Medics! Medics! Med-i-ics!"

I scrambled up, shaking. Little Louden, the ammunition bearer of our B.A.R. team, was lying on the ground, rolling in pain, grasping one leg. I could hardly believe my eyes. Two men bent over him and the aid man, Farron, came running up.

"Don't crowd up! Stay apart! No bunching up! Louden's hurt!"

"Hey!" Astonishment. "Lieutenant Ellis's hit too! Hey, Lieutenant Ellis's wounded!"

Lieutenant Ellis was some distance from me, near the screen of bushes and trees. With unbelievable quickness, both his and Louden's wounds were dressed—Lieutenant Ellis had been hit in the back—and both men were placed on litters. Colonel Mauck had withdrawn from sight.

"So long, guys!" Louden's tough little voice was calling as he was carried off; and then Lieutenant Ellis came by with: "A million dollar *wound!* I got a million dollar wound! I'm *out!*"

"All right, le's go, le's go!" Who was leading us now? I could see only Roger Betancourt, the Platoon Sergeant. Still shocked but eager to be out of that clearing, we rushed into the woods again, following a winding footpath. Who, I always wondered, would make such a path miles from anywhere, endlessly long? Branches hung low in places, and the men waited and held them for the next man; after Merkel, the last man, they'd swish back into place. As the rush continued I became overheated, struggling to breathe. After a half hour of fast hiking my head was light, spinning. I kept wishing the sun would go in; it seemed to make things dance. It bothered me that I was so tired before we reached the line of fire. We paused suddenly to rest with everyone panting and blowing. On either side of the footpath there was a ditch lined with trees. I put my hand out to hang onto a tree and found to my surprise that I had misjudged: there was no tree quite there. I fell over into the ditch and after a moment scrambled to my feet. Sergeant Betancourt came running along and joined Sergeant Danowski, who asked if I were all right. I replied that I was but I must have looked sick or very pale, for after a short consultation Sergeant

Betancourt told me to lie down. I protested that I was all right, but he cried, "Lay down! That's an order!" I complied—everyone else by then was lying down—and a few minutes passed. I looked up through the patterns of brown leaves at the pale sunlit sky.

Sergeant Betancourt came back and squatted beside me. "Listen, Atwell, you stay here an' rest about five minutes or so. We gotta move out fast. You stay here—right here—an' the next platoon'll come by an' you folley up with them, y'unnerstan'?"

With that he rushed away. The others had gotten up and started to move off, their footfalls fading through the rustling leaves. I thought, "Comrades, leave me here a little while as yet 'tis early morn—" Then I lay without thinking for perhaps two or three minutes. Suddenly it seemed my position was strange, even dangerous. What if the next platoon changed its course, just as we had changed ours? I got up, buckled on my ammunition belt, picked up my rifle and struck off down the narrow twisting path as fast as I could go.

After the distance of about three long city blocks, I came to a fork in the path. There was no sign which way they had gone. Now if I had been a Boy Scout, I thought . . . I looked for footprints and thought I saw signs of them on both diverging paths. The woods had dropped away into another clearing dotted with bushes, then far off there was a wall of trees. I thought I'd be forced to wait until the next platoon came up. Several loud near shells had fallen in the meanwhile. Others started to whistle overhead, but whether they were coming in or going out, I couldn't tell. I went back to a bend in the path to see if the platoon was approaching. No one. The shelling became much more frequent, almost constant, almost deafening. Too bothered about my own predicament, I paid scarcely any attention to it. The thundering explosions were nearby but not actually in sight. I returned to the fork in the path and was loitering there indecisively when two deer sprang past me so close I could see their wide frightened eyes. Bounding off, almost sailing, they were wonderfully graceful.

Now with the shelling the tops of trees were tearing loose and falling; and somewhere you could hear "Cr-r-r-ack!" as a giant tree crashed down. Then I heard a different sound: the popping of rifle fire off to my left, and a moment later,

56

breaking through the screen of trees into the tall grass, there was an American soldier, minus his helmet, running, looking back over his shoulder.

"Hey! Hey there!" I started toward him. In time he saw me and waited. I ran through the bushes and waist-high grass and by the time I reached him I was almost too breathless to talk. "Do you—" gulp—"know where—" gulp—"C Company is?" To my surprise, he was gasping as hard as I.

"Germans!" he said, staring. "Sniping at me back there!"

"What company are you in?" It struck me then that his stare was wild. He was light-haired and thin.

"Germans! Germans coming! German sniper—gonna get out of here! Outta here—"

Not right in the head, I thought, astounded. "Where are you going?"

"Gonna get out of here!" He started suddenly to run.

"Wait!" I called. "Wait a second." But he was running with his rifle held high, glancing back terrified over his shoulder, and he disappeared in among the trees.

Shells were now shrieking in and exploding with a continuous deafening roar. Rather dazed but sobered, thinking, I'm in the middle of an attack, I picked my way back to the fork in the path. On the off chance that there had been German snipers—I had heard small-arms fire after all—I took cover under the low sweeping branches of a hemlock and fixed my eyes on the spot where the man had emerged from the woods. Possibly four minutes passed. A cow, mooing loudly in fright, ran clumsily past. I stood experimentally tapping the ridge of dried blood that ran from my nose out to the far edge of my cheek. A little to my left my eye caught something moving, and when I looked I saw that it was four American litter bearers making their way, majestically it seemed, through the cleared space. The grass was so tall that I could see them only from the waist up. They were carrying furled litters almost upright and their white arm bands with the red crosses stood out in the sunlight. I quit my place and hurried after them.

One of the litter bearers, the leader of the four, I recognized. On one of my first days in the Infantry I had been on KP with him.

"Do you know where C Company is?"

His name was Johnston; he was a Canadian and spoke with a slight accent. "No, I don't know." They were on their way to D Company to remove some casualties. I told him I'd go along; I felt one company would be near another and I should be able to pick up a messenger running between the two. Johnston, though decent, was never very friendly. He shrugged: it was all the same to him. He said a moment later that he had only a rough idea where D Company *was*.

The five of us started off when there came through the air such a bursting scream and crash that we all fell to the ground. Laughing a little, nervously, we got up, went a few steps and there came a louder, nearer crash. This time we did not get up so soon, and then one towering, roaring explosion followed the other. They seemed to come in fours. There'd be that long wild shrieking, growing louder and louder—it seemed to be seeking you out, knowing exactly where you were lying. You gathered yourself, trying to shrivel. With the whole world filled with that sound, there'd be a split second of intolerable wait and then would come the enormous deafening smash of the explosion. The earth rose up and shook. Trees splintered, great branches fell. Then stillness, broken by what sounded like pebbles striking against the tree trunks. Leaves sailed down gently.

"Look at that! Shrapnel! It's red-hot. Boy, if that ever went through you!" "If it just nicked you—!" "It's air bursts —air bursts—" "Hey, let's get out of here! Let's—"

An officer in a green raincoat, small-waisted and neat-looking, ran into the clearing, followed by a sergeant. We had time only to look at each other when there started another shelling, this time not so close. The officer, though, threw himself flat down, shouting for us to do the same. After the four shells landed, we got up and started to approach him. The shells roared in again, this time pounding all about us. I fell down and was surprised to find my helmet lying before me, but far out of arm's reach. In a lull, I crawled forward and clamped it on. So many shells screamed in and crashed around us that for the next five minutes we didn't move or speak. Saying the Act of Contrition as hard as I could, I didn't even open my eyes. At the first let-up, the officer shouted, "Get out of here!"

Unencumbered by anything more than his carbine, he ran swiftly, lithely in the raincoat, and we lumbered after him. We were running in among some slender saplings when the shells came, seeming to follow us. Down again lying flat, panting, praying, eyes squeezed tight shut. Then up, running

58

farther on. Down for another ten minutes, and again, mysteriously, my helmet was off and far out of reach. "That's the concussion," the man next to me said.

I had been placing some trust in the thought of having an officer nearby, and then it dawned on me that he was paying no attention to us. He and his startled-looking sergeant stayed close together but had run off quite some distance by themselves. "That's Lieutenant Ragland, the Transportation Officer," Johnston was telling one of his men. Lieutenant Ragland looked like a poster of an Infantry officer, one of the keen-eyed, square-jawed, thin-faced type. He was conversing rapidly with the sergeant, who was the driver of his jeep. The jeep was some place nearby on a road behind us, and after the next spell of shelling—it was as if an enraged giant were hurling with all his force an entire string of trains, screaming locomotive and all, and we were reduced to the size of ants—Lieutenant Ragland quit us without a word, ran for the jeep and drove off.

"Pinpointing," one of the litter bearers was saying. "They're covering the whole place, raking it!" "Boy, them eighty-eights!" "They can drop them in your vest pocket!"

"Well, come on," Johnston said. "We might as well get the hell out of here before they start again."

We continued in the direction he had been leading his squad. It surprised me that I had held onto my rifle and that the hand grenades were still fastened to my lapels. The two black canisters were gone.

Hitting the ground only two or three more times, we came to a jeep and a stout driver stationary on a dirt road. I paid scarcely any attention; had it been an elephant and howdah, I wouldn't have blinked an eye. He directed us a short distance farther on to D Company. Before we quite reached it, the walking wounded reached us. A group of them was suddenly there against a bank of trees. Perhaps they had been waiting for us. There were evidently more than Johnston had expected, for he turned to me and said, "Hey, give us a hand, will you? Take this first one and help him down to the jeep."

The boy, who was about nineteen, light-haired and rather wild-faced, hobbled toward me. You could tell how shaken he was, how eager to get away. His teeth were chattering. One legging, shoe and sock were off, and a bandage, showing blood, had been wrapped around his foot and ankle. I slung my rifle to my left shoulder, put my right arm around him and started back to the jeep. His knee kept buckling under him; he'd put his heel down, wincing. "It's all right," I said, "you can lean on me."

"I'm not hurt as bad as some of the others. I ain't gonna lose my foot."

"No, of course not."

"I'm not hurt like them. Boy, some of them . . . Boy, am I lucky. Lucky to be gettin' out of this."

"Is it very painful?"

"Yes. No. Boy, though, am I lucky!"

"Did they give you a shot of morphine?"

"Boy, am I lucky!"

At last I delivered him to the jeep, where a few soldiers had congregated. They took hold of him; I turned back and retraced my steps to D Company. At the same point another walking wounded started for me, twitching. He was wounded in the shoulder and arm, bare on one side from the waist up; the rest of his shirt hung off him. He was shuddering and chattering in the same wild way.

"Well, at least you're out of it now," I heard myself telling him as we started down toward the jeep.

"Yeah. Yeah, I—" He was almost afraid to say it; then it came out in a rush: "I'll—I'll be going back to the States! Home! Me for home! Home!" I could almost smile. Home seemed so far away from me—so far, in fact, that I could envy him but distantly. I walked him down to the jeep, transferred him to the men—what were they doing there?—and heard him calling after me, "Thanks! Hey, guy, thanks!"

I brought back my third walking wounded, but a sense of unreality came over me so strong that I remember nothing of the trip at all. And someone must have told me where C Company was, for the next thing I recall I was walking up to where the Heavy Weapons Platoon was located. They were scattered about under the trees. I knew most of them by sight and a few to speak to. I was about to sit down when Lieutenant McGrath came walking briskly along. "Oh, hello, Atwell. I'm glad to see you." I explained that I had been helping the medics and would like to rejoin my squad. "Yes, well, they're ahead just a little. This platoon is going up in a few minutes, and I'll show you where to go."

It seemed to be past noon. I sat down with my back against a large tree. Most of the men were jumpy; each was near a foxhole he had dug, ready to leap into it should the shelling start again close to us. Every now and then there was an explosion. "Is that ours? Is that coming in or going out?"

I said thoughtlessly, "I don't give a damn whether it's coming in or going out. I'm hungry and I'm going to have my lunch before anything else happens."

"Lunch?" Sefton said. "God! How can you think of eating?"

I was already ripping open one of the packages. I ate part of the round of cheese and some of the poison-tasting crackers. A swig from the canteen, the two caramels, and then I lit a cigarette. Even sitting still, there was no sensation of cold. The sun filtered down through the bare trees; nearby, a little brook rippled and flashed where the sun struck it.

We were sitting very near a winding dirt road. Tanks had come through earlier and had churned immensely deep tracks through the thawing ground, making the road impassable for any other kind of vehicle. The ruts were as deep as any foxhole I could have dug and I planned on jumping into one should a new bombardment commence. But I was not as unmoved as I thought. When I got up later to relieve myself, I found I did not want to go too far off or even out of sight. I came back, flung myself down, yawning, wanting to sleep. Instead, I took up my equipment and tried to shorten my belt so that it wouldn't slip down. Lieutenant McGrath came along, saying, "All right, men, on your feet. Atwell, come along with me." The two of us started forward and the men got up reluctantly.

"Do you feel all right now?" the lieutenant was asking, when there came a loud near report like a *crack!* Men hurled themselves flat. Lieutenant McGrath looked all about him swiftly. I glanced up at a large tree, startled. Sniper! I thought. Then everyone began to recover. No, not everyone.

"Sir! Sir! It—it's Weems!"

Staff Sergeant Weems, in charge of the Heavy Weapons Platoon, was rolling on the grass, holding his foot, his face contorted. Lieutenant McGrath and I started forward, jumping over the tiny clear stream.

"What happened?"

"What happened?"

"Weems is shot!"

"Shot himself!"

61

"Through the foot!"

"Don't crowd up," the lieutenant said sharply but without excitement. "What happened here?"

"This—this—goddam grease gun—" Sergeant Weems ground the words out, crying. "I don't know how—I just went to—"

A friend of his managed to get the legging, shoe and sock off him and I saw the bright-red hole through the center of his thin foot. Someone was holding up the bullet between thumb and forefinger.

"Here. You pro'lly want to keep this."

"Yeah. Thanks." In tears, Sergeant Weems took it and put it into his pocket. He was explaining that he was unused to the grease gun and that it went off as he started to get up. A friend was applying the bandage over his foot. Then Sergeant Weems took his wound tablets and a gulp of water.

"Well, we've got to get him out of here," Lieutenant McGrath said, looking around at the men. "Does anyone know where the medics—Atwell? Do you know?" I said yes, I knew where to take him. Without warning, something strange had just happened to me: a fear of what was ahead had suddenly entered me, and I found myself glad, relieved to be selected for the job. "All right, Atwell, thank you. The rest of you men come along."

I had never liked the tall, twitching, rickety Staff Sergeant Weems, but here he was, writhing in pain, crying. I held him while the bandage was made tight.

"I hate to do a thing like this just when mah men are dependin' on me," he wept. His men, marching past in two lines at five-yard intervals, looked back over their shoulders, but not one exchanged a word with him.

"All right," I said, helping him to his feet and beginning the routine once again, "put your arm around me; you can lean on me."

He was exceptionally tall and he wrapped his long thin arm tightly around my neck. He hopped, dragging me continually off balance. My first walking wounded, who had been injured much more severely, had put his heel down, but Sergeant Weems would not try this and consequently our progress was very slow. He could hop just so far and then had to pause for rest. Over and over he asked what his men would think of him.

"Well, if it was an accident, what could they think?" I asked.

He hopped again, with me staggering under him like a badly angled crutch. The trees were so dense, growing thick to the edge of the churned-up road, that often we had to go between two trees sideways, or make long detours until we found an opening. Every now and then shells flew in with a screaming crash and he was all for flinging himself down prostrate. "For God's sake, you're already hit!" I said. "Lightning's not going to strike twice in the same place." I wanted to hurry him on, to be rid of him. "Can't you put your heel down? It won't hurt you to try." He wouldn't do it. Half strangling me, the injured foot held high, he hopped on. The trip seemed to be taking the better part of an hour. Here and there I noticed men, not from our company, passing us uneasily, going toward the rear. They appeared lost, yet there was something furtive about them; they had no purpose to be where they were, and some were moving merely for the sake of keeping in motion. Deserters . . .

At last we came to a broad dirt road that cut through the woods and we stopped to rest. There was a line of uneasy men along the road, looking as though they might be about to run. The Protestant chaplain's jeep was there, crowded with wounded men, some unconscious, fallen against the others. Some had blood-soaked bandages about their heads. The chaplain came toward us, his eyes staring.

"Can't I help you?" he asked, his spread hands making stiff side gestures like a football player about to go into a scrimmage.

"No," I said, "thank you; I can get him across."

"Here! Here! Let me! I'll give him a pick-a-back. You jes let me carry you across—"

Staff Sergeant Weems, the overbearing, the unnecessarily cruel, the snarler at men if officers were present, the toady if not, the shirker of hikes and constant consumer of coffee in the company office, now broke into a hoarse dry sobbing and permitted the chaplain, who was sturdy, to carry him across to the jeep. Weems's long thin legs hung down shamefully almost to the ground. I started back through the woods.

I had got back exactly to where Weems had had the accident when a procession came slowly through the trees—four men staggering exhaustedly with a litter. Two of the men

63

were medics; the other two were infantrymen, accompanied by friends who carried their rifles. I paused to let them pass by, unwilling to meet their eyes, sensing what was going to happen.

"Hey, Mac," said one of the litter bearers. Had he recognized me? "Mac, give us a hand here, will you?" I hesitated, not exactly wanting to take the easy way out, but what had been a slight unwillingness before about going forward had now turned into a positive dread. From what I had overheard from the men deserting, I formed the impression that we were in a trap, all of us, and that further ahead a withering fire was mowing our men down. "Come on, give us a hand. We got hundreds of guys to get out of here. They're all over the place a little ways back." He went on to add that the medics had been given the power to impress any infantrymen they saw to act as litter bearers.

Relieved to hear this, feeling the decision to go further suspended, out of my hands, I walked across and took the place of one of the medics at the back end of the litter; and what had looked like a funeral procession, accompanied by armed mourners, started off again. The man we were carrying was covered by a shelter-half. He was anonymous, a body; my mind did not go out to him, scarcely wondered about him; he was heavy to carry, that was all. We wound in and out between the trees, following the twisting road. Just when the weight became unbearable, we put the litter down and rested a few moments. The problem, though—whether I should, or could, go forward to where the company was— remained. "All right, men. Let's try it again." We stooped, picked up the litter and started off, blindly trampling down dry small bushes, cracking twigs beneath us. In time my hand ached and blistered; my shoulder felt as though it were wrenching from its socket. We were passed by more of the same uneasy deserters making their way back, and sometimes you'd hear snatches of their conversation.

"We're being murdered! There's only five guys left in my squad!" "Yeah, they got him; *he's* killed." "Gonna get the hell outta here." "F--- me. I'm not hangin' around here!"

Panting, resting now and then, pushing on each time with greater effort, we finally staggered out onto the road. Now the wounded were being piled onto a tank to be driven off, and the tank bore a grotesque resemblance to a float in a Mardi Gras. Figures were strewn over it, some sitting with their bandaged heads bowed. A wounded man, accompanied by a friend, hobbled toward it, white-faced. There were ten or twelve idlers standing about; they relieved us of the litter and lifted it up onto the tank. A jeep raced by. I turned around and started back once more through the woods. It seemed to be about twenty minutes to four: it had that feeling. In the dense shade there was something sad—no, more than sad: tragic, the sense of failure.

Again I passed the tiny stream, the bank under the enormous tree where Weems had shot himself, and this time went beyond it. A small wooded hill rose up; shells were shrieking in, exploding on the opposite side of it. My mind served up the picture of a hard dirt slope, men crouching in foxholes, and a withering crossfire spraying constantly, scarring the ground.

As I reached the base of that ridge I saw another litter procession coming toward me, seemingly in trouble. There were no medics carrying the litter; all four bearers were infantrymen. Seeing them, the wounded, lying in great numbers in a thicket on the hill, under nearby trees and bushes, half rose up, crying, "Medic! Medics, get me out of here. Medics. Water! Help! Medics!" They rose up out of the dead leaves something like rattlesnakes, all calling out at once. Their wounds had been bandaged and they had been collected there, waiting through barrages for someone to carry them out on stretchers.

The procession stopped near me and one man, carrying the back part of the litter, dropped it unceremoniously and bolted off. The two men at the front were Italians, broad and husky, surrounded by five or six arguing, squabbling little friends. The friends were obviously inciting the two front litter bearers also to desert; they'd run off a little, then run back, dragging at a sleeve. The men on the front wanted to leave but could not quite bring themselves to do it. One, a gigantic fellow, turned his head away, ignoring the excited babbling, yet he would not pick up the litter again.

"Hey, give us a hand!" someone cried to a passing soldier.

"Can't," came the reply, and the man skinned past, hurrying along to the rear.

"Hey, give us a *hand!*"

"I'm all beat up," another said in a grumbling tone, brushing past them.

"Hey, hey, someone, fer crissake— Hey!" They spotted

me. "Give us a hand here."

"I've got to get back to my company."

"We're licked," the big Italian said hoarsely. "Come on!"

"Well . . ." What was the matter with the companions? The man on the litter, heavy and light-haired, half conscious, was listening to all this. He was lying on his stomach, badly wounded in the back. His clothes were pulled away from the wound and you could see many bandages sopping up the blood. "I'll take it for a while," I said. "Some one of you take my rifle." I stepped around to the back and held my rifle out to the coterie. After a hesitation, a thin brown hand reached out and accepted it. The other man in the rear with me was quiet-looking, with a pointed, Austrian, dachshund type of face. He had not shared in the excitement, but had waited for it to end with a dry smile and a gleam of contempt in his eyes.

Now that we were proceeding slowly because of the weight of the wounded man, the jabbering little clique began urging greater speed. One member kept up a soft, steady stream of Italian, evidently telling the two men on the front that they were crazy for hanging on when they could have gone faster unencumbered. We could go no more than twenty paces, and then were forced to put the litter down. Almost at each rest the quiet man and I exchanged sides. The blisters on one of my hands had broken. Shells continued to scream and crash but not immediately near us. The little companions, though, grew more and more desperate; almost all had lapsed into Italian. The sun had completely gone and the day began to grow chill and morose.

At one of our frequent gasping rests the companions gave up their pleading and scuttled off. Then one of the men in the front, without a word, ran off after them, leaving the other big man with us.

"I can't take no more of this," he said in his coarse voice. "I'm bushed!" He wiped his sleeve across his face and remained looking off at the woods.

Afraid that he too was about to bolt, I started to call out to the men hurrying or stumbling past us. "Hey, give us a hand here! It's not far. Be a sport, come on." They went by without looking.

The remaining Italian, pretending to be more exhausted than he was, staggered off, his head lolling, but I noticed that he soon picked up speed and broke into a trot. The quiet man

and I exchanged a glance. There was no fear that he'd quit.
I told the man on the litter I was sorry we were giving him
such a bumpy ride. He said it was all right, that he understood how it was. It was growing dark rapidly. For five minutes or so we stood over him, embarrassed for his sake, begging anyone who came along to take hold of the litter.

"I can't." "Got my own f---in' worries!" "*No!*"

The Americans, I thought. I would not have believed this
unless I had seen it with my own eyes.

In the end, three men came past; two, disgruntled, picked
up the litter with us, and in a final burst of energy, resting
only a few times, we stumbled through the woods, gasping
and straining, and broke out onto the road. I had not seen
the little companion who had been carrying my rifle for the
past twenty minutes or so, but I saw a rifle stuck in the soft
dirt at the side of the road. There was a small truck there
with a Medical flag and the wounded were being piled into
it. Near the crossing, about eighteen or twenty exhausted
infantrymen were strung out along the edge of the road listening to one short man, who was giving them a half-
hysterical harangue. He stood in the center of the road, gesturing and shouting. We surrendered the litter and were told
that no more wounded men were to be gathered in that
night. Those still in the woods would be forced to remain
there.

I walked down to the lone rifle stuck in the dirt. 1277829.
Mine, and easy to remember because eight is my favorite
number, and twenty-nine the year I graduated from college.
I slung it on my shoulder and paused a little to one side to
listen to the oration.

"I tell you it's suicide!" the small private was shouting. His
eyes were wild in a face of extraordinary homeliness; his
mouth, without lips, was a trap, his skin pitted and bumpy.
"There's not ten men left in the whole of A Company.
They're all wiped out!" His listeners were lying or squatting
on the side of the road and one of them, chewing on a blade
of grass, said something to him in a voice too low for me to
hear. "All right!" the trap cried. "*Call* it desertion. Call it
any goddam thing you want. I'm not going back there. They
can line me up tomorrow morning and *shoot* me—I'm not
going back there to be killed!" I could feel myself smiling.
Tonight or tomorrow morning: what difference did it make
to him? "Don't you *see?*" he shouted, working himself up.

"Don't you see what's happened? They led us into a trap! They don't know what they're doing. They'll all be killed and so will we. What's the sense in that? We'll all be killed if we go back. It's crazy, I tell you! You can't do any good by going back. You can't *win* anything!"

The truck with the last of the wounded to be picked up that day started off slowly down the road. A few unwounded men swung up onto it; others ran or jogged behind, one holding onto the strap of the backboard.

"There! See that?" screamed the agitator. "They're *all* going!" He turned and ran and after a moment, like a flock of birds, the men rose up silently and began to trot down the road after the slow Medical truck with the wounded.

Exhaustion rolled up and struck me. I felt, if I sat down even for a moment, I'd go to sleep. Where the quiet man had gone, where he had been going, I didn't know. I was alone. I started back once more for C Company.

Darkness was coming down so fast that under the trees it was almost night. I had gone back and forth over the same ground often enough to know it by heart, but I had to feel my way along the side of the twisting road. Here and there a band of something white—a medical bandage—had been stretched along in the trees; I had not noticed this before.

There was the little stream once more, the big round tree, then unfamiliar darkness. Was the company straight ahead over that remembered rise? Now, perhaps because I was more tired, the dread of facing what was over that hill was gone. It was eerie, going silent and alone through the dense woods. Somewhere back I had lost the road and was going on doubtfully from tree to tree, one arm bent up in front of my face. I missed the hill and after a while, completely lost, I came to a halt in a small clearing. To drop down here and sleep, or go on? Go on, because the companies might leave their positions during the night. There were footsteps behind me and low voices, talking, fortunately, in English. A tall man separated some hanging branches and stepped into the little clearing beside me. I cleared my throat so as not to startle him and then asked if he knew where C Company was.

"C Company?" he whispered. "Hell no. I don't know where anything is. These goddam woods! I'm trying to get my men up to First Battalion Headquarters. We're mine sweepers." The other men came through into the clearing;

they had those long mine detectors with them. I told the sergeant in charge that I'd go along with him to Battalion and try from there to get over to my company. We set off with the men behind us. "Jeez, if I don't get these guys up there soon . . ." he was saying when a shell came screaming in and he hurled himself down. I flattened out beside him as several shells came in close. The earth seemed to smash apart, to be pounded and pounded again. When there was silence, both of us got up slowly, experimentally. Twigs and leaves were still falling in the dark. He was cursing to himself in a soft whisper. Then he turned and whispered over his shoulder, "Hey, you guys, come on. We gotta go." We started forward once more, whispering now and then, holding back branches for each other, and we had gone perhaps five minutes when he stiffened and paused.

"Joe!" he whispered. "Joe!"

"Wha—?" whispered a voice in answer.

"Oh. Come on."

"Come on where?"

"Come *on!*"

We had not gone far when he turned again to speak to his men, and found that the "Joe" who had answered him and was following along was not his Joe at all. It was someone who had heard the whispered command and had gotten up out of a foxhole.

"I'll have to go back and see where those guys are. They're probably back where the shelling was. If I've lost them, Jeez, I'll get hell. Listen, you wait here, right by this tree, and I'll pick you up on my way back. How'll that be?"

I felt he might not find the same spot again and asked him the general direction to Battalion Headquarters. I started off for it, wishing I had remembered to ask him the night's password. Because of the darkness I had to make my way by feel from one tree trunk to another; eventually I came out onto a dirt road, a continuation of the one I had been following before. Up ahead there were three or four jeeps fairly near each other. The drivers were waiting for something and were jittery, wanting to be away from there. I went up close to ask them if they knew where C Company was or Battalion Headquarters. Battalion, I was told in a whisper, was only a little farther ahead. Right through those pine trees. The driver sat cold, with his hands crossed under his arms. He answered in the lowest of voices, and when I asked him if

69

he knew the password, he whispered, "It's the same as last night's, I think, but I'm f---ed if I know it."

I came through the belt of pines without being challenged. The night sky had all along been paler than the dense gloom under the trees, and here it was like coming into a silvery, dimly lighted room. In the center there was a large, low mound onto which someone was tossing the last of some pine branches. At the moment it seemed the most natural thing in the world. Someone—an officer—rather testily asked me what I wanted. I explained, though I had grown tired of saying the same thing so often.

"There's Colonel Hessig. Speak to him."

Colonel Hessig, a tough, bulky, sagging man in his late fifties, was urinating to one side of the mound which did not extend more than two feet above the ground. There was a slotlike opening in it, and, as I approached, someone dropped out of sight into it. Colonel Hessig, buttoning his fly, turned to me. "Yes?"

"Colonel," I began, wondering whether I should have saluted or not.

"No!" He made hushing gestures. "No 'Colonel!' Forget that Colonel stuff. From now on, just 'Hessig.'"

I was too tired to smile even inwardly, but I had a dim desire to say, "All right, Hessig." I had to pay close attention or my words would spin out into jibberish. When I finished the tale, he said in a whisper, "I don't know where C Company is. Haven't *heard* from them. Tell you what you better do." He held onto my sleeve; he seemed to be just as tired as I, and to be having just as hard a time thinking and forming his words. "You—you'd better stay here for the night. Just—just dig yourself a foxhole close by here. Give your name to the sergeant. Tell him—"

"Yes, sir," I whispered. He moved heavily past me and I saw him crawl down the same slotlike opening. I felt my way around in the soft, low scrub pine, put my rifle on the ground, took off my belt, gas mask and bandoleers. It was as if they had been holding me up; I was unsteady as I fitted on the handle of the pick mattock. I took about two swipes with it and then I felt myself passing out, falling over backward into the soft little bushes. After a while I was looking up at the slowly revolving, dim, starry sky, listening to the wind. There was a sensation of rocking, like being in a vast cradle. Antiaircraft searchlights played restlessly across the sky and planes droned overhead. In a few minutes I was nearly asleep when someone stumbled over me and bent down.

"Hey, you're on guard here."

"Guard?"

"Yes. Everyone's on guard."

"What? For how long? I mean, how long will I be on?" I sat up.

"All night long. I'll be around every ten minutes to check you." He gave me the password and the countersign: it was something with Ws in it that I had heard the Germans had difficulty in pronouncing. Then he paused a moment. "Give me your name and company." I did. "Remember, stay awake!" The whispering ceased; he crept away. I saw no other guards. I felt around with my hand to see where I had started to dig, gave a few more halfhearted swipes with the little pick, encountered a mesh of tough pine roots and gave up. Somewhere I had lost my rations; I was chilled and had nothing to put on but my raincoat, the olive-green slicker. I wrapped it around me and huddled down in the small pines. Every now and then I'd almost go to sleep, but currents of icy air blew in where the raincoat didn't cover me. I drew my legs up, tried to hunch the coat further around me, holding it closed or tucking it under me. My head was bent down, my chin on my chest. The whispers, the air of extreme precaution, made me realize that the Germans might break through at any moment—I realized but couldn't bring myself to picture it, or care.

Now a hand on my shoulder. The password. The countersign. "What's your name?" A scrabbling of leaves; the sergeant moved away. By now I had the raincoat arranged to its best advantage; the slightest move disturbed it and let the freezing air in. What time could it have been? Nine o'clock? Ten? I tried to count back to when I had had the last full night of sleep uninterrupted by guard duty. Let's see . . . Last night was— Where was I last night? Oh, yes. Guard duty on the hill where Lieutenant McGrath came around to talk to us. The night before that—the forced march when it snowed: no guard duty but not a very restful night. The one before that was the thorny hedge place where Dave Rossofsky kept going to sleep. And before that, the snowy trench outside the fortress at Metz. The one before that had the pre-dawn all-out attack.

The next time the sergeant came around he asked where

71

my foxhole was. "Back there," I said. "Near enough for me to jump into." Sometimes the interval between his visits was longer than ten minutes. I dozed lightly and opened my eyes when I heard the leaves nearby ruffle or felt his hand on my shoulder. It would never do, of course, to fall asleep guarding Colonel Hessig.

Once during the night that seemed a month long, German shells screamed and crashed in, in a heavy bombardment that shook and pounded the earth, blasted and knocked down some of the trees that bordered the little clearing. When the barrage lifted, officers in numbers surprising to me jumped up from that slot in the mound. There must have been a sort of underground room, I thought, all covered over with logs and pine branches. The officers were talking in excited undertones, saying the Germans knew our position and were zeroing in on it. Then a clearer voice, but still by no means loud, speaking into a telephone or a walkie-talkie, using the code method of Rogers, I hear you well, over, and so on, announced that the Command Post was pulling out, changing its position. My heart plunged: that could only mean more work, digging another big room for the colonel. The voice stopped and there was a watchful silence. Nothing happened. "Are we really moving?" one of the dark figures asked.

"No," came the answer. "That's just to throw the Jerries off in case they're listening in on us." After a while the figures dropped back out of sight, and the guard duty, and the visits from the sergeant whom I never saw clearly and would never again be able to identify, continued throughout the rest of the night.

Daylight came so slowly that I was impatient with it. I'd close my eyes, hoping when I opened them that it would be perceptibly lighter and my impatience would force me to open my eyes in a minute or two. I was so bored and weary of maintaining that one cramped position that I almost didn't care whether I'd be freezing or not. The hours of silence now were broken by the first bird calls.

At last it was morning. I reached out and pulled my wet rifle close to me, along with the rest of my equipment. There was no stirring for quite a while. Then footsteps, crunching swiftly, approached. Two figures stepped into the clearing. I looked up and saw the Death's-Head, Lieutenant Millbank from C Company, accompanied by a messenger. Before I could speak, they dropped into that hole, out of sight. Lieutenant Millbank had been carrying a folded white paper in his hand.

I packed up and waited. Only a few minutes passed before they were up out of there again, Lieutenant Millbank looking somewhat distracted.

"Lieutenant," I said, getting to my feet, "good morning." He stared as if he didn't recognize me. "Are you going back to the company?" I asked, and once more he stared, his mouth hanging slack. "I'd like to go back." He shook his head a little at me. The messenger nodded, contradicting him, and the three of us set off. Lieutenant Millbank was almost running. He was a Southerner, in charge of the Heavy Weapons Platoon, a man in his early thirties, with tragic eyes and a down-turned mouth in a finely lined, sallow death mask of a face. In civilian life he had been a college instructor and football coach.

At first, rushing along, none of us spoke, then Lieutenant Millbank, talking to himself, said with a loud groan, "Terrible! *Terrible!* My God Almighty!" I looked over at the messenger, who with a forefinger described circles at his forehead and then pointed to the lieutenant. "Combat exhaustion," he whispered to me. All the way back the lieutenant kept saying, "God! My God! Horrible! *Horrible!*"

Within five minutes we found ourselves in C Company's area. It was on the crest of a rolling slope that led into a deep, narrow valley. Directly opposite, the mountain rose up again, heavily wooded. All along the slope the companies were stretched out in foxholes. Where this was in relation to where I had spent the previous day, I didn't know and didn't stop to wonder. I found Dave Rossofsky lying in a foxhole and I sat down beside it.

"Les! We didn't know what happened to you." His eyes were large. "We thought you might have been hit, or killed! What happened to you? Where were you?"

I was too tired to explain in detail. "Helping the medics and then I got stuck at Battalion Headquarters." I lit a cigarette. About me I could hear men saying, "Well, here's Atwell. Atwell's back; he's all right."

"What'd you do yesterday?" I asked Dave.

"Nothing. Just dug foxholes and got into them."

And yet Lieutenant Millbank had cracked up . . .

Lieutenant MacKenzie came along, smiling and bouncy as

ever, and I started to repeat my story for him. The particulars were not important to him; he went off to report to Lieutenant McGrath that I had come back safe.

And now I began to hear of the injuries suffered in the company. Except for little Louden, our own squad was intact, but a man named Bagnell had been killed; another, named Blasek, had been blown to shreds when a direct hit landed in his foxhole; Weems had shot himself through the foot, had I heard? The neat young aid man Farron had had his leg blown off and had died of loss of blood while Lieutenant MacKenzie was holding him. It had been his twenty-first birthday; he had been hit crawling from his own foxhole toward a man wounded in one nearby. Cornell had been hit, so had Braaf; Staunton and Hlavenka had become shell-shocked in the first five minutes. Lieutenant Giossi was in the hospital.

"And Major Debevois was wounded," Dave was saying. "They think he's going to die. And Major Pritchett, the Division Surgeon—he got part of his right hand blown away." Lieutenant McKenzie—the *other* Lieutenant McKenzie, who had been with us at Fort Jackson—had been killed. A Company, on our right had been almost wiped out.

"That guy Taylor in the Second Platoon is missing," I heard someone say. "They say *he* got hit."

"What the hell ya mean? There's Taylor right there."

I was relieved that the man was pointing to me. Because Chris Taylor and I had worked together in the Art Shop and went around together, many of the men had us confused in their minds.

In the wintry early sunlight men were stirring as far as the eye could see, climbing out of foxholes all along the rising and dipping crest of the hill. In the hollows the cooks were setting up the ash cans of wash water, preparing to give out breakfast. They had driven up in jeeps with vacuum-sealed jugs of food. In serving, they set the jugs fifteen or twenty yards apart; two cooks would drive up to a company and then recruit some of the infantrymen to portion out the food with them.

Only one squad ate at a time. Breakfast that morning was ground ration crackers made into a hot cereal by the addition of boiling water, eaten without milk, and a canteen cup of coffee. While eating hurriedly, one had to keep a wide interval from one's neighbor. "Listen," I called over to Dave, "if every day in combat's going to be like yesterday, no wonder they don't keep you more than five or six days in the line."

"The luckiest guy wouldn't last any longer," he replied.

Shortly after, to my amazement, we were told to police up the area.

"Police up," the men said in disgust. "What do you think of that?" "Police up, fer crissake!" "One thing's for sure, boys, this s---- must come to a screeching halt!"

As soon as we had finished picking up the stray bits of paper and I was hoping to be able to lie down, Sergeant Danowski came along with an order: our squad was to draw three K rations, make up a full field pack and be ready to move out at once. We were going on a reconnaissance mission.

By then nothing seemed to matter or to make sense. Feeling unreal with tiredness, I rolled up the equipment, put it on, and off we tramped, five yards apart, through the woods where I had spent the previous day. We moved along quickly, talking and grumbling. Everyone seemed to have accepted the day before, with all its wounds and deaths, as a fair sample of how things were going to be from now on: this was combat and they just hadn't told us what it was like. No one had seen any Germans. It was all artillery, mostly 88-millimeter shells. It seemed dehumanized to me, a matter of purest chance. Some men had been killed because they were in foxholes; some because they were not. Still others had been hit by our own artillery falling short of its mark.

"Tanks!" someone was snorting. "Tank destroyers! They're yella! What the hell were they doin', hangin' back there?" The only tanks I had seen had been hanging back where the wounded were being evacuated; still some had come forward and had churned up the road. I was surprised that we hadn't advanced under a wing-to-wing flotilla of planes. I had seen a few infrequently, and it made me wonder if we weren't magnifying our own importance. Perhaps somewhere else a battle ten times more important was being waged.

Everyone now was talking about million-dollar wounds. We had begun to feel that only a wound would get us out of this alive.

The day turned overcast, threatening to rain. After about twenty minutes of fast hiking we crossed a tiny dirt road in the woods and stopped. We were in a grove of bare trees on the edge of a hill that dropped steeply down into a wide valley.

Sergeant Danowski said, "All right, now listen, you guys. From now on no one make a sound. The Jerries are right down there in that house, right at the bottom of the hill. It's their C.P." I looked down and saw a white-walled, orange-roofed farmhouse with attached barns and outhouses. Smoke was coming out of the chimney. "That's the Jerry headquarters, that house, and we gotta set up an observation post and watch every move they make."

"Why?" I asked. "Why not just blow the damned thing to bits right now?" And get to sleep, I wanted to add. The suggestion, which seemed very sensible to me, was ignored.

"The orders are to dig a foxhole—every man—*or* you can dig a two-man foxhole, but dig it deep! Leave a step at one end; and over the top you got to put all logs, and then camouflage it good. Remember, don't go choppin' down no trees around here." Sergeant Danowski's English, normally good, accommodated itself to the Army when he was passing out orders. "You got from now till tonight. And remember, quiet!"

"Fires, Sarge?"

"No! No fires. What the hell's the matter with you?"

When American soldiers are supposed to be at their most quiet, it's been my experience that then they're most opposite. Here arguments broke out at once and loudly, about where the different men were to dig their foxholes. Some had started them too near their companions and the argument was: which was to move? A squad from another company came into the grove and they started to dig far behind us. In all, there might have been twenty of us there. As far as I knew, after that first glance at the German Command Post, no one ever looked down the hill again.

Dave Rossofsky and I started to dig fairly close to its edge —not through any choice; it was merely that we had been standing there. Our particular foxhole progressed slowly because I was dead tired and had only the little pick mattock to dig with. One man in each squad was supposed to carry that curious and useless entrenching tool; I was the man in our squad. Within an hour Hepp and Husey, digging rhythmically and tirelessly, had a respectable foxhole, knee deep. Ours was ragged, of uneven depth, with large rocks and roots still to be reckoned with, and we were taking turns, one digging and one sitting down.

Now and then spades struck rocks and the sound rang out on the still, damp air. Sergeant Danowski came over to exhort us to further efforts: we were the slowest of the lot. Then all about us men began striking water in their foxholes, which brought loud curses. The day, at the shortest period of the year, began to wane.

"The hell with this," I said to Dave. "Just let's even it off so we can lie down and we'll put some logs and camouflage over the damned thing and be done with it." He always agreed readily with time-saving steps. While we were off, ripping down a slender tree, it started to rain. We hurried back and tried to cover the hole over before the rain could settle in it. Other men had stout little sunken fortresses covered with logs, then with sods, then with branches and leaves. Dave was more for scattering over ours light, flimsy, thorny branches he had found. "Like we crisscross these," he said with his slight lisp, "and it will do just as good."

"The hell it will! These are no stinking good and get them out of here. I told you to get some logs!"

We had long since grown annoyed at each other's inefficiency. Our tempers were often short; doing any work, we snarled and snapped at each other. It was disheartening to find myself teamed up with someone even less adaptable to open life than I. Soon it would be too dark to work any longer. We declared an unspoken truce and sat down for our final cigarette. "I don't like to smoke all yours," he said humbly.

"It doesn't matter. Have you got anything to eat?"

"Only what's in the rations."

"I'll open a dinner, you open a supper, and we'll divide them."

We were cupping our cigarettes and from the next hole Hepp was complaining that he could see the glow. What the hell did we want to do, have the whole goddam crowd blown up?

With the arrival of darkness a complete and eerie silence hung over the knoll, broken only by the tapping of rain and the distant crash of a shell. Sergeant Danowski came around with his final instructions, delivered in a low voice. "All right, now listen, you two guys. We gotta be on guard here —on *special* guard—all night long. One hour on, and one hour off. At all times, one of you gotta be awake. You got to sit up on that little step there and keep your eyes peeled for the Jerries. On no account, no noise. You get that? No noise! We're a listening post here and if they start to clear out, we get the hell back and give the word. And don't shoot unless they come right at you."

"But from this hole we won't be able to see if they go or stay. I can't see over the other side of the hill!" I could no longer even see where Hepp and Husey were.

Sergeant Danowski appeared rattled. "W-well, if they start moving out, we'll hear them." I could not share his conviction on this. "If you want me for anything, I'll be right back there." He pointed behind him, gave us the passwords, arranged that we could borrow a watch with illuminated hands, and crept off. Faintly I could hear him mumbling and whispering to Hepp and Husey. The stillness returned.

I took first shot at sitting up on the little step we had left at one end of the foxhole. Dave lay outstretched with his feet toward me. We had placed our only logs at the far end of the foxhole, and over one's head they provided some shelter from the rain that pattered down through his arrangement of vines and leaves. After a while, sitting there with the unlocked rifle in my hands, my eyes grew somewhat accustomed to the dark and I could make out the trunks of nearby trees and the designs of paler sky between them. I was wrapped in my blanket, aching with tiredness, listening to the rain tap on my steel helmet. My eyes burned. I kept looking from the edge of the knoll to Husey's foxhole, hoping he was covering a different sector. The minutes dragged by reluctantly. How I envied the men sleeping behind the front lines! What a relief it would be to close one's eyes against the weight that was pressing them down! Too often I looked closely at the hands of the watch. Then I had to start pinching and twisting my face or my hand to stay awake.

At last it was time to wake Dave up. Clumsily he crawled forward, upsetting the covering of branches. He decided to use my rifle instead of the B.A.R.; I left it and we maneuvered past each other. I stretched out, looking up through the tangle of vines at the rainy sky, then quickly closed my eyes, trying to force sleep to come. After twenty minutes I was still awake, twitching every now and then like Sergeant Weems, I thought. Oh, well, it's not really night yet, I told myself; it's not even seven o'clock. Just as I was falling asleep, Dave told me the hour was up; did I want him to take two on and two off? I said no, and we crawled about and changed places. I borrowed the watch and strapped it on. But if it was this bad at seven o'clock, how was I going to get through until morning?

It rained continually, sometimes in a downpour, more often in a light pattering.

Part way through the night we did try two on and two off and once Dave woke me at twenty past the hour. Neither of us said anything, but it was obvious that he had been asleep those extra twenty minutes. Our blankets by now were wet and muddy. The one used on guard was soaked through. I was sitting wrapped in it like Saint Gaudens' statue of Grief when Sergeant Danowski suddenly whispered the password. I gave the answer and he, in a fury, complained that he had checked the other foxholes and had found three guards sound asleep. Two he could hardly wake up.

On another shift in the middle of the night I was startled by very near shots: a German machine gun fired and a B.A.R. flashed and chattered loudly on the road not ten yards away. I jumped up and threw the blanket back from my helmet. There was the sound of excited voices, of feet running. Someone, panting, was calling frantically to a man in our company: "Billings! Billings! For *Christ's* sake!" Then abruptly silence closed down. I waited, straining to hear more. A little later Sergeant Danowski crawled up to say that one of our squads on patrol had run into some Germans and Billings had opened fire on them but hadn't hit any. "Those Jerries'll be coming back now, so keep your eyes open." He went away to tell the others. Silence then, the drip of rain on the dead leaves, the tap of it on one's helmet.

On my next shift I was crouched in a half doze when I heard running feet approaching with such swiftness that I had no time to move. Someone leaping over the foxhole sailed over my head and continued on, running through the trees. Shocked as I was, I realized in the one glimpse of that silhouette against the rainy sky that the runner was a German. There was something about the helmet, the belted uniform, the boots seen in that one leap. The man had rushed down the hill. I got up to tell Sergeant Danowski, and somewhere nearby there was a rustling in the leaves. I froze.

"Hey! Psst! Atwell! Rossofsky!" It was Husey, crawling toward me. "Did you see that Jerry?"

"Yes!"

"He went down the hill. Right through us!"

"I know."

"What do you think we should do?"

"I don't know. Now that he's gone, nothing, I imagine. We're only supposed to do something if they start coming out. He was going back."

"D'you hear that firing before when Billings opened up on the burp gun? I don't like this damned place." Lying on his stomach, he waited to see if I'd have any suggestion or anything to say. "I think I'll go and tell Danowski," he said at length.

"Okay."

"Night." He laughed a little.

"Night."

"See you in the morning." He crawled off.

That was about one o'clock.

Dawn came with its usual maddening slowness. You'd wonder if it actually was coming on or if your eyes were merely growing more accustomed to the dark. I ached everywhere and spasms of twitching passed over me. How soon could you safely light a cigarette? I looked down at the rifle, which in the first glimmer of light showed pale-orange streaks of rust. The rain was stopping. After a short while the men began to stir, to get up out of the foxholes, to face a tree and urinate. Cigarettes were lighted. I folded the sodden blanket and looked at the white tag in the corner. Yes, it was mine we had been using, not Dave's. It would take days to dry out.

There was not much to talk about after discussing the Billings episode out on the road last night. The men looked ashen, dirty and unshaven. Everything was wet; there was no place to sit but on the fallen trunk of a wet rotting tree. Half the men in the knoll were strangers and one sat next to them without bothering to talk. There was nothing to look forward to. Dave awoke leisurely and crawled out of the foxhole. Now in the clearing daylight I was depressed to see how makeshift it was. In my mind, which seemed unusually dulled, there formed the idea of working on it further during the day, deepening it and removing the lumps. The ration of cold egg yolk and pork which I ate for breakfast

80

began to make me nauseated; I had to throw away my cigarette.

The morning went by slowly, a gray morning, and the ground did not dry, so that there was no place to lie down. Soon the men around me began to open their luncheon rations. At the first whiff of food, my stomach turned; I had to look the other way. Shortly after noon Sergeant Danowski told us we were to be relieved. The news came as a pleasant surprise. We had, he said, only an hour and a half to go.

Dave and I abandoned the work we had started on the foxhole and rolled up our soggy equipment. Everyone was played out, out of conversation. You found yourself giving slow consideration to the dullest, simplest observation, repeating it in your mind. The hour and a half dragged itself past. There was no relief. Another hour passed. And suddenly—I knew it was nervous reaction—the place seemed menacing, unsafe. I wanted to leave it. I knew I was going to be sick and I did not want to be sick here. Every minute intensified the feeling. Oh, please, you'd find yourself thinking, please, for God's sake—hurry!

Toward the end of the dreary, wet afternoon, when I had given up hope and was about to start again on the foxhole to prepare it for another night of one hour on and one hour off, the relief arrived. We slung on our heavy, muddy equipment, shouldered our rifles and started back for C Company. I was chilled and shivering and had to expend quite an effort to keep going.

We arrived at the exact spot in the woods where Weems had shot himself when an intense enemy shelling opened up. The same wild, screaming 88s flew in with a tremendous crash. The Fourth Platoon of C Company's men who were scattered about flattened themselves on the ground or jumped into foxholes. We flung ourselves down with them. Four shells landed with a deafening smash; a second later four more came. Four more, and four more, until there was a continuous shrieking, banging, upheaving and crashing, and in between the explosions you could hear giant trees cracking and falling. There came a momentary stillness and then an officer's voice cried, "The other side of the road! Quick! Everyone!" We jumped up and raced across. The distance was perhaps fifteen yards. "Spread out! Spread out! Start digging! Dig 'em fast, dig 'em deep!"

"Aren't you digging?" someone nearby asked me.

"No." I was lying beside the road where the tanks had cut the deep furrows. Now the ruts were partly filled with rain water.

"I dare not dig," said the excessively educated Everett Telford. He had a slight hollow already formed. Like many men who were afraid to dig standing up, he presented an odd picture, sitting down, panting, digging with the same motion one would use in paddling a canoe.

"How many did you dig so far today?"

"Seven," he answered.

The shelling then picked up on our new side of the road, but not quite so close. We ran back to our original side and fell flat. After ten or fifteen minutes there was a respite: the Germans were raking another sector. It was then late afternoon. We got up and our squad went forward; the next thing I recall was arriving at our foxholes on that crest that overlooked the valley and the mountain opposite.

Standing beside the foxhole, I began to shiver in my wet clothes. My teeth chattered; I became sick and dizzy; I wanted to lie down. I could hardly wait to unstrap the pack and spread out the muddy shelter-half and wet blankets. The chow truck drove up into the hollow, but at the thought of food my stomach revolted.

Sergeant Danowski excused me from guard duty that night and I fell asleep almost at once, but it was not a restful sleep. I seemed to be traveling swiftly back through wind and darkness, and when I landed there was the confused feeling of being in a recognized room with members of my own family, but somehow I was in the wrong generation. Great uncles I had hardly known were my older brothers; I was about five years old, not tall enough to see their faces. It was a dream in still life; nothing moved or unfolded. We were in a seldom used front sitting room on the third floor of the brownstone house where I was born. Sunlight came in through lace curtains. Someone had just spoken a sentence and the rest of us stood motionless, neither accepting nor denying it. I knew the tea cups and saucers on the mantel and the big picture above it, though I had not thought of them in thirty years and wouldn't ordinarily believe I could have remembered them.

When I awoke, alone in the foxhole, it was difficult to throw off the dream and realize where I was. I had to tell myself, and it came slowly—yes, you moved out of that house, grew up, went to school; now you're in a war. Your serial number is 32968894; your rifle number is— But I could not remember that. Antiaircraft searchlights were switching across the sky. Planes droned above; shells screamed and whistled and crashed, and there were splitting scarlet streaks through the darkness.

In the morning I awoke with a heavy cold as Dave was climbing out of the foxhole and I started to sit up, but neither arms nor legs obeyed any message to move. I seemed to be made of lead. I got Dave to drag me out and set me on my feet, but I had to call to him, for I kept stumbling down the incline toward the valley, my knees buckling under me. With his help I lowered myself into the foxhole. He brought me back some coffee from the chow line and as soon as I drank it I had to lie down again. Shivering, wrapped in his overcoat, he sat up on the edge of the foxhole, hugging his knees. The day was very cold. At intervals we talked back and forth.

"Dave, do you have any strong feelings that you'll live through this?"

"No, I don't think so."

"Will you mind very much?"

"I don't know. Would you?"

"It would be better than coming back with a serious head wound, but I'd hate to die here in Germany, dirty like this. If it were in France, somehow it wouldn't seem so bad."

Later in the morning he woke me by dragging out his equipment; he and the rest of the squad were going down into the valley and up the opposite slope to dig alternate foxholes. They were leaving me behind for a few hours. Though I knew I was incapable of going with them, I felt oddly ashamed.

In the afternoon Bill Woods, a young assistant squad leader, came over to give me my mail: two Christmas cards, one from a family I had met in England and one from Mary Taylor with a note enclosed asking me if I would tell her the details should Chris be killed. It sounded gruesome, she realized, but she would rather know.

In the late afternoon when the squad returned, Sergeant Danowski told Dave to go over to the medics with me and see what they could do. I got up, put on my gas mask and ammunition belt and slung the rifle on my shoulder. Going along the rising and falling crest of the hill, I remember the towel flapping in the wind across my face. I was getting sicker by the minute and the wind made me dizzy. I kept stumbling until Dave took me by the arm. It was my first visit to the medics since coming into the Army.

Their large olive-green tent was pitched in a hollow; the white flag bearing the red cross stuttered in the wind. "You'll be all right in a minute now," Dave said as we waited on line, but neither of us had high hopes. "Stay the hell *away* from the medics," everyone had always advised, and now a man came out of the tent and strode away, cursing to himself.

Going in, my rifle became caught in the canvas of the tent. "Can't bring your rifles in here," said a peremptory voice. "Leave your weapons outside there." I could scarcely hold my head up and was annoyed at the order, but we put our rifles down and stepped in out of the wind. I sat on a cot beside Dave, leaning against him. The towel, dropping down, cut off my view so that I saw only the dirt floor. Someone was having a hand bandaged, and then a voice asked, "Yes? What's yours?"

"This man is sick," Dave said. "The sergeant sent us—"

"What seems to be the trouble?"

Dave waited and nudged me. I said, "I think I have intestinal grippe."

"How do you know you have intestinal grippe?" a new, amused voice asked, and I realized I had made a mistake.

"I've had it before. It feels the same way."

"Ya bowels loose?" the first voice asked.

"No." I was about to add that that seemed to be part of the trouble, but I gave up the effort.

"Here, drink this."

Dave reached out and took the paper cup. I drank it. It tasted slightly familiar, cloudy, somewhat of licorice, and was immediately warming. Glad to be out of the wind, I remained leaning against Dave and after a little while realized I had drunk paregoric.

"Feel better?" asked the first voice.

"Yes—warmer."

"That'll fix you up fine."

After a pause Dave said in surprise, "Is that all?"

"Yup."

Starting back in the cold wind, Dave said, "They didn't do very much. They didn't take your temperature, listen to your heart, give you anything for your cold."

"They've seen so many guys blown to pieces, I suppose I was nothing." And the drink was reviving. In addition to that, it had been wonderful to get in out of the wind, even if only for a few minutes.

Back in our area the squad was ready to march off and spend the night in the alternate foxholes, and before leaving they gathered around to look down at me. Smathers and Lambert suggested that since they had a safer foxhole, I should use it. They reached down, lifted me up and helped me across to it. It was almost twice as deep as ours, on the far edge of the company line, and they had taken wooden ammunition boxes, filled them with stones and dirt and banked them in a double row around the four sides. They put down my shelter-half, sleeping bag and two wet blankets, and once I was lying down they marched off. I woke up through the night, delirious, coughing, very cold, missing the partial use of Dave's two blankets. There were heavy bombardments from both sides, the shells roaring and crashing, making scarlet explosions through the dark.

During a particularly furious barrage one of the guards named Lucky abandoned his post and crept over to the edge of my foxhole. In the flares of shell fire I saw his face, white and jibbering as he pounded the ground and ranted and howled back at the enormous explosions, screaming curses until the cords stood out in his neck. In between times he held a wild chattering conversation with me. He expected we would be both killed any second. What gave the thing for me the air of a complete nightmare was the fact that I kept passing in and out of spells of delirium when I'd be conscious of Lucky and try to answer what he was saying, and the next moment I'd blank out only to come to in confusion hearing the crashes again and seeing Lucky's flare-lit face shouting soundlessly in the din.

In the morning everything was calm, the sky pale and swept of clouds. There was a brisk crunch of feet on the frozen ground and Lieutenant MacKenzie, smiling, in good spirits, came along and, squatting down, asked, "Atwell, how're you this mawnin'? You have a bad cold there. I'd like to be able to send you to the hospital fo' a few days an'

85

you'd be all right again." I told him I wasn't sick enough to go to a hospital, that I thought I'd be up and about by noon. This I didn't believe, but I had heard the same reports about the hospitals that I had heard about the medics. He said, "Lieutenant McGrath's been tryin' to find you a good job back in Division, but they haven't got an opening right now." Embarrassment kept me silent. "There *is* a job open with the Battalion medics, but that calls fo' a noncom—a sergeant, someone to handle weapons—an', besides, he'd like to get you in Division if he could."

"I wouldn't want to leave the company and start all over in a new one."

"We'll see what happens."

I couldn't say too much because for all I knew Lieutenant MacKenzie might have been eager to be rid of me so that he could get a younger, better trained man for the squad.

The day was icy. Tiny fires were lighted all along the rim of the hill, with groups of men ignoring the five-yard interval, crouched over them for warmth. I had missed several meals, and in the pocket of my field jacket I found a brown paper sack of cocoa—a rare delicacy at the time—and several lumps of sugar. I got up stiffly, gathered some twigs, came back and started my first fire. The wood wasn't quite dry, and with the shortage of paper, the wind, the splits in my fingers and the difficulty in striking a match, one had to exercise considerable patience.

I had just put the canteen cup of water on to boil when Dave Rossofsky came back. I told him of the possibility of another job and realized I would be sorry to leave him. "If I do go and you have the chance to team up with someone else, pick someone who knows something about soldiering. That's the first thing I'm going to do. Would you like some cocoa? Got any water in your canteen?"

He added some until my canteen cup was almost filled. Silent at the thought of parting, we sat looking down at the slow bubbles rising to the top. Finally I dumped in the cocoa and sugar. To make the one cup of cocoa had taken in all about an hour. "Now," I said, setting the hot cocoa between us, "get out your cup." In reaching for it, one of his large feet shot out suddenly and knocked my canteen cup over. The cocoa ran away down the hill and steamed. Immediately we were back at our old stand, shouting at each other, and in the midst of it he was called away to rejoin the squad, ready to march off again to the alternate positions.

For want of something better to do, I went on tending the little fire, putting on a twig now and then, when suddenly Chris Taylor, my Art Shop partner, flung himself down. "Hello, sport!" he said, and we looked at each other and laughed. The same thought had struck us both: you're still alive. I asked him about his new job.

"Well, McGrath, you know, sent me back to Battalion Headquarters."

"Is it better there?"

"It's supposed to be better. Safer. Normally you're supposed to be out of the range of small-arms fire. Of course no one's safe from these goddam eighty-eights."

He had been placed in charge of the Battalion Command Post guards, most of whom were old and unfit for combat. His job was to arrange the shifts and post the men; and he thought in time it might lead to a sergeant's rating, though at present he was standing guard himself. I asked what he thought of the attack a few days ago.

"My God, it was awful. Colonel Hessig didn't know what the hell he was doing. He came up to relieve a colonel in the other outfit who kept saying, 'Get your C.P. right up there as far as you can. Right up front. That's all. Keep your C.P. up on the front line,' and with that he takes off like a great striped-assed ape. He had combat exhaustion and was out of his mind, but Hessig didn't realize it, so he kept moving the C.P. up and we were almost slaughtered."

I asked him what Colonel Hessig was like and he replied with feeling, "He's a *son* of a bitch! Each time he insisted the goddam tent be dug in to a depth of seven feet—and you know the size of that thing—and then it had to be all covered over with logs and branches. By around four in the afternoon the guards were caving in, poor old bastards, and then along comes Hessig. 'I want good hard Army digging here!' Chris could imitate the foggy voice perfectly. "'None of your goddam W.P.A. work! Get on those shovels and *dig!*' Well, we dug and dug till it was dark and the men were nearly dropping. The shovels began to freeze to their hands and finally I said to them, 'F--- it! That's enough. The hell with him. Go and get your own foxholes dug.'"

It didn't occur to me at the moment that he was describing what had transpired shortly before I had arrived at the colonel's Command Post in the pine clearing.

"Hessig came along when it was dark and says, '*Who* gave the order for you men to stop digging?' I said, 'I did, sir. The men are nearly dead.' So he yanks me off the job." Chris shook his head and laughed.

"And now what's going to happen?"

"I'm waiting to find out." With a remembered gesture, he flung his jackknife into the ground.

"Have you heard from Mary?"

"Yes. I just had a long letter yesterday."

"And I had a Christmas card from her." It was still in my pocket with her return address on it. "I must write sometime and thank her."

"Yes. Poor Toots would be glad to hear from you."

"I may not be here in the company much longer."

I repeated what Lieutenant MacKenzie had told me, and Chris said, "When I was leaving, saying goodbye to McGrath, he told me then he was looking around for a good job for you in Division. McGrath likes you." Chris glanced down and saw my canteen cup. "Who's been having the cocoa?" I told him about Dave kicking over the farewell drink. "Ass," he said. "My God. Well, I've got to get back and find out what they're going to do with me. See you again, sport."

Late in the afternoon Bill Woods came over to my foxhole and gave me two V-mail forms. "May be the last chance before Christmas to write a letter, At. I'll pick 'em up in about twenty minutes." The day had turned bitter cold and was growing dark. I sat on the edge of the foxhole, using the bottom of the mess kit as a writing desk. In the wind my fingers holding the pen soon became numb. I wrote first to Mary Taylor, telling her I promised to do what she asked, but was sure, now that Chris had been moved to a place of safety, that there'd never be the occasion. Then I started to write to my family, wondering what to say that would not give rise to worry, yet should I be killed could be reread and found to be of comfort. Other men had already written farewell letters and had given them to friends to mail in case they were killed, but partly because censorship imposed a constraint and partly because I never wrote in an extravagant fashion, I could think of nothing out of the ordinary to say in sending my holiday greetings.

After the letters had gone and I was feeling depressed—
alone, sick, far off from the rest of the company—Lieutenant MacKenzie walked over to tell me that Lieutenant Mc-
Grath had persuaded the captain in charge of the First Battalion medics to let me try the job even though I was not a
noncom. "So you can pack ohll your things an' move over
there. We'll keep you on our roster, but you'll be attached to
them." He was smiling. "It's not what Lieutenant McGrath
wanted for you, but it was the best he could do."

I told him I was sorry they thought it necessary and that I
was grateful to them for trying to do anything. Since it was
growing dark and I still could not walk very well—I could
not picture the new captain viewing me with enthusiasm—I
asked if I had to report immediately. He thought not, that I
could wait till morning.

I woke up the next morning discouragingly sick and shaky
again, but I emptied the canteen of ice water into my helmet,
washed my face and hands and shaved. In the little celluloid-
backed mirror I saw myself, gray, gaunt, hollow-eyed, with
one eye mysteriously blackened, and I had a long, thick
red scab running from the bridge of my nose out across
to one ear. Immediately after shaving I became so sick I
had to lie down again. I waited as long as I dared, then toward three o'clock I dragged the frozen, muddy shelter-
half and blankets out of the foxhole, rolled up my pack and
went over to thank Lieutenant McGrath and bid him goodbye. He was standing outside his tent and we talked for
about five minutes as equals, laughing now and then. In parting, he put out his hand. "Goodbye, Atwell. I hope you'll
come back and see us whenever you can. You'll always be
welcome here."

In my torn muddy overcoat, with the full field pack, gas
mask, ammunition and rifle, with the towel flapping in the
wind, I made my way through the adjacent company to the
hollow where the medics' tent was pitched. Several men with
Red Cross arm bands, sitting around the embers of a little
fire, looked up without interest.

"I was told to report here from C Company for a job."

A farmer's voice belonging to a heavy, red-faced, older
man with big ears and a snipelike nose said, "You the man

89

from C Company? Waal, ain't much fer you to do right now. Jes dig yerself a foxhole round 'bout here somewheres. Won't be nothin' much doin' till tomorrow. Name's Sergeant Campbell. You want anything, you jes come to me. I'm in charge of the litter bearers."

Was I to be a litter bearer? I didn't ask. The men glumly sitting around the embers watched while I started to dig a foxhole with the pick mattock. I exchanged a brief hello with Don Stoddard, who had been one of C Company's aid men in England. Sergeant Campbell came back with a large shovel. "This might make it a li'l easier diggin'." It was growing dark rapidly and the men had to stamp out the bright coals. With the shovel the foxhole progressed in a third its usual time, and by complete dark it was finished. When I was returning the shovel to Sergeant Campbell he said guardedly, "You got enough blankets?" We were standing beside a little truck, its hood marked with a large red cross.

I looked at him in surprise. "I have my two."

"Waal, medics got a lot of blankets. If you need more keep you warm—?"

"Well, yes, I . . . The ones I have are pretty wet."

"How many you want?"

"Could I have two?"

"Give you four; how'll that be? You return 'em firs' thing in the morning."

Four! Four warm, dry blankets! In the dark he seemed to be giving them to me surreptitiously. "Thank you. Do . . . Is there any guard here tonight?"

"Medics don't stand no guard. Line company boys, C.P. guards do all that. We ain't 'llowed to have no weapons."

Four dry blankets! No guard duty! I prepared my bed in the narrow foxhole, and once I was in it I drew one end of the shelter-half envelope-like over all. Warm for the first time in days, I went to sleep immediately without waiting for supper.

In the morning the shelter-half was frozen stiff and crackled when I moved it. Sergeant Campbell woke me, saying, "New man, time to get up there." Everything was white with frost, looking as if there had been a light fall of snow.

There were twenty medics in the group, twelve of whom were litter bearers, and they ate with the men of First Battalion Headquarters. While I was standing up having breakfast alone, Sergeant Campbell walked over and said, "Soon's you finish eatin', we'll be runnin' through a sick call here and part of your job is ter check the weapons outside. Can't bring weapons inside a medic's tent. Against the Geneva Convention rules. These boys come down to sick call, throw their rifles down any ole place, next man comes out picks up the wrong rifle, everyone gets all mixed up."

He went on to explain that I was to work with the officer in charge of battalion salvage and was to turn over to him the weapons and equipment of the men who were wounded or so sick they had to be sent to the hospital. In the attack last Sunday, he said, hundreds of rifles from wounded men had piled up outside the tent, as well as binoculars, pistols, grease guns and ammunition. The medics had been forced to move up several times and they left all the equipment behind in the woods since none of them was permitted to handle fire arms. "Jerries come along, pick up all them rifles, next thing you know they shoot 'em back at us." He gave his head a shake. "That's why we need an infantryman down here. You wouldn't mind loadin' up the ambulance or givin' us a hand litter-bearin' if we ever got stuck, would you?"

"No, I'd be glad to help."

"If y' want t' take anything fer that cold, jes see the sergeant after the sick call's over. Fix y' up."

Together we walked back to the large tent where the Red Cross flag snapped in the wind. The sun shone, but on an iron world; the frost remained dry underfoot. A line of sick men was already waiting outside the tent, hunched and shivering, turning their backs to the wind, comparing maladies. From inside the tent a voice called, "All right, firs' man." The first man started in.

"You can't take your rifle in," I said. "I'll check it for you out here."

"Wha—?"

"It's against the Geneva Convention rules to have arms inside an aid station."

"Jeez, check your weapons. It's like goin' into a dance hall."

And why were we obeying the rules so strictly? I was curious to see the captain and pictured him as small, eyeglassed, fussy and meticulous. I held the first man's rifle, then the second's, quickly gave that up and arranged five or six rifles in order along a fallen tree, noticing that whereas in garrison the slightest scratch on the stock would have called down

91

howls and punishment, here there were initials freshly carved, girls' names, hearts, notches and nicknames. When the men came out of the tent, usually making a shuddering, wry face after the medicine, I picked up their rifles and before giving them back, to make sure, asked them the rifle numbers.

Some distance off the litter bearers sat around their little fires, glum, holding out their gloved hands for warmth. Dave Rossofsky came over from C Company to stand talking with me for a half hour, and the long slow, cold morning went by.

I had said to Dave, "Have you any idea what the hell we're all doing here?"

"No." He looked surprised, as if I were expecting too much. "I heard someone say we should have waited for support on our right flank and we didn't do it, and that's why we're caught here."

"Are we caught? Is that it?"

"A frage! Who'd know?"

Out of the wind, protected by the tent, sitting before an upended box used as a dressing table, a serious young medical officer was shaving. I saw him in profile: dark, square-jawed, with close-cropped coal-black hair and a resemblance to a young Mussolini. When finally he stood up and tossed the soapy water out of his helmet, I received a shock. He was tiny, one of the shortest men I had seen in the Army, scarcely any taller on his feet than when he had been sitting. Sergeant Campbell had mentioned him to me earlier: Lieutenant Serletis, the Medical Administrative Officer, part of whose duties it was to censor our mail.

I became chilled standing hour after hour in the wind, and slowly the same sickness crept back on me. Around eleven o'clock, during a lull in the sick call, I walked inside the tent. It was dim and warm. A plump, firmly packed, eyeglassed sergeant asked in a Southern voice, "Well, Deac, whut kin Ah do fer yuh?"

"If you have a laxative handy, I'd like to take one. I don't know what's wrong with me, but I've been sick for a few days."

"Well, now, Ah tell you the truth." He shot me a glance over his GI spectacles. " 'Bout the only thing Ah got here's a brown bomber; ain't fit fer nothin' but a horse. Unless you're powerful constipated, don't think Ah'd advise it. Why don't you wait a while an' see how you feel?"

I did that, checking more rifles. The sun had broadened and up in the sky planes came out for the first time in days, buzzing and circling about. Everywhere along the hill heads craned heavenward. Almost directly above us a plane fight began and the men about the fires sprang to their feet and shouted encouragement. Several American planes circled and dived about a single German plane. Long silver streaks that looked like ribbons of shining tin foil spun out in arcs and hung against the blue of the sky as the planes, jockeying patiently for position rolled and circled and dived. "What's that?" the men were asking. "What's that silver stuff?" "Something caused by the *atmosphere?* Is that what you said? By the cold?" Don Stoddard, who had been transferred out of the Air Corps into the Infantry, seemed lost for an explanation.

Suddenly there were shouts. "Hey! Hey, look! That plane! He's hit! That's an American plane! That's ours!"

"The hell he's hit."

"The hell he ain't!"

He was, unmistakably. The one plane, pouring volumes of smoke, dropped down away from the others, quivering and listing. With its buzz turning into a deafening roar, it plummeted out of the sky, grew enormous rushing down and sent the men flying for their foxholes. Directly overhead the entire sky was darkened by its wings. Ready to crash on us, it skimmed up a little and, still pouring gray-and-white smoke, flew a short distance over the treetops at the crest of the hill. A split second later there was an explosion and smoke poured up.

"D'he crash?"

"Yep, he crashed!"

"Holy God! How far away d'you think?"

"Quarter of a mile, maybe less."

"Hey, guys, come on. Should we go over?"

"The ambulance! Get the ambulance!"

"Stay where you are!" noncoms and officers in the nearby companies were shouting. "No one's allowed to leave the area!"

Above, the other planes, dipping and circling, flew higher, grew tiny, gnatlike. The German plane escaped, and the American planes flew off in pursuit of it.

At noon when the sick call was over, I went back into the tent and told the sergeant who was called Preacher that I thought I had better take the brown bomber. He gave me two, dubiously, with a paper cup of water. I had no sooner swallowed them than someone put his head inside the tent and shouted, "Pack up! Pack up! We're pullin' out of here! we're being *relieved!*"

I tried to cough the pills up, but they had sunk past my throat. Preacher began at once to pack his medicine chests. "How soon will these pills take effect?" I asked.

" 'Bout half hour to an hour."

I went outside and heard, "We're movin'! Hey, guys, we're bein' relieved!" The word was spreading from company to company, and everywhere along the hill men stirred, began to drag blankets, sleeping bags and shelter-halves out of foxholes. Figures hurried. "Keep one blanket out! Every man keep one blanket out. We're going in trucks." "Hey, you hear that? We're goin' in trucks!" Now everywhere men were making their packs, kneeling, rolling forward on them. Wood was thrown extravagantly on the little fires and they blazed up high. Voices called back and forth. You saw smiles. Gloom was dispelled; for the first time there was bustle and liveliness along the hill.

The excitement in getting ready was premature, as we did not leave for several hours. Preacher was correct in his prediction about the brown pills, but the longer we delayed the safer I felt. The big trucks drove up within sight of the companies, and around three in the afternoon the first of them departed, filled with waving, cheering men.

Twilight came and on all sides of us now the companies had gone; the long hill was empty. The wood had been used up and the fires stamped out. The small group of litter bearers sat in silence, each man five yards apart from the other on the slope, waiting. The cold struck through all our layers of clothing. So far I had not talked to any of the men. Rather, it was the other way around. I had spoken to a few but had received scarcely any reply. Whenever one moved in the Army, there was always that awkward feeling of being unwelcome, the new boy in the school. Far off, behind a blur of bare trees, a low rift of somber winter red showed in the gray sky. I saw a three-sided carton blowing and tumbling end over end along the empty hill, got up, stopped it and sat on it, my lower back protected from the wind.

Soon we would go, we would leave here; another outfit would arrive and take over our foxholes, knowing nothing about us, nothing of the men who had died in the silent dark woods just behind us.

The last lone truck drove up to take us away. It was an open truck, unfortunately, and about forty of us—the medics and some men of Battalion Headquarters—climbed into it. We wriggled out of our packs, stowed them under the long side benches, wrapped the blankets about ourselves and sat down. Most of us arranged the blankets with a hood that we clasped tight before our faces to keep out the biting wind. At the final moment of starting in the dusk, a feeling of tremendous relief swept over me. I was glad to be leaving this position in the Saar Valley, glad to be sitting close to someone unknown, shrouded but alive.

Within an hour, riding in complete darkness, aches began: knees aching with cold, feet freezing, split fingers holding the blanket together stiff and powerless with cold, cold pouring up one's sleeve. Damn the designer of these short-wristed gloves! And why did this truck have to be open? Where was the tarpaulin that usually covered the top? Left off through the carelessness of the driver? What arctic gales poured down, lashing at us! In time we caught up to the rest of the division, driving slowly in convoy along back country roads into France, in whistling, freezing darkness, completely blacked out.

At about ten o'clock we halted for a few minutes—it was said to find out if we were on the right road or not. The dirt road beneath us, and the edge of the black fields, glistened under a film of ice. There were trees nearby in the dark and the wind roared through them. But aside from that, we were in France and there was silence, no scream or crash of shells. Hungry, stiff with cold, we started again to drive slowly through the rest of the night without stop. The men stood up on the seats to urinate as we rolled and bumped along.

"What time is it?" someone asked, and a man held a wrist watch up to his eyes.

"I got twenty after two."

Then this was the twenty-third—no, the twenty-fourth—of December. Christmas Eve.

In the morning just as dawn broke we rolled slowly through the streets of a small French town and came to a halt outside a court where two rows of pleasant-looking bungalows faced each other across their front gardens. We jumped off the truck on feet that had no feeling and began at once to light fires on the sidewalk and on the court paths, impatient for the flame to leap up and warm our hands. Someone smashed a kitchen chair and threw it onto a fire that had just started to blaze. "See that?" Sergeant Campbell said. "Now that's a good chair! No sense bustin' up a fine chair like that."

We opened our rations and began to eat, standing along the street. Milky-blue daylight widened overhead, and the orange light of the fires grew less pronounced. Remembering I had a ration slip of Nescafé in my field jacket, I heated a canteen cup of water, and when it began to simmer I searched all through my pockets and turned up nothing but orange powder—a great disappointment. However, I dumped it in and began to drink the hot orangeade. Before finishing half of it there was a great shouting of orders to line up; we were in the wrong town. We had to stamp out the wonderful fires, police the area, climb up into the trucks again and ride on.

By day it was not so cold; besides, one could smoke and look out at the countryside. We rode for hours—all through the morning. How could we have been as wrong as all that? The convoy, men were saying, had become completely lost during the night, leaving us more than a hundred and ninety miles off our course.

In the middle of the afternoon we reached the small village of Dieuze near who-knew-where, and as a magnificent surprise we were told that all of us were to have billets, to sleep indoors for the first time since leaving the house at the base of the cliff near Metz. The aid-station complement— the captain whom I had not yet seen, Lieutenant Serletis, the clerk, the two technicians and Sergeant Campbell—had already arrived in the heated ambulance and were established in one of the houses. The litter bearers and I were led up a side street toward our separate billet.

The houses we were passing were poor, flat, of pale plaster, each with one stone step leading abruptly off the cobbled street. Some had large barns or stables attached. A few streets over, a church spire rose up; our view of it was cut off as we turned into the house.

We went into a dark, narrow hall. A door, made partly of glass panes that had been painted over, led into a small empty living room, stone cold, with very dark green or brown varnished walls and dark shades on the two front windows. The owners of the house, a husband, wife and child, remained in the rear, in their kitchen, but had offered to turn over to us their living room. The men trooped in noisily and slung down their medical bags, full field packs, gas masks and clanking steel helmets.

In one corner of the room there was a stove lacking a pipe. One of the men went out and returned shortly with a few lengths of it. The owner of the house, a slight man in his early thirties, hearing the sound of hammering, rushed in alarmed, wearing corduroy clothes and felt bedroom slippers. He tried to remonstrate but no one understood French and he was elbowed lightly aside. Someone pointed to the stove pipe going up, the man shrugged, nodded his head in half assent and went back down the hall into the kitchen.

Some of us went out to scout for wood. The men were beginning to grow separate in my mind. A thin, rangy Irish-American named O'Rourke, and a tall Pole named Brudzin-ski appeared to be the unofficial leaders of the group. As we went out the door they were grumbling against a heavy, dark, eyeglassed youth who refused to get wood. I recalled being pinned down in the woods with him during the heavy shelling the first day of the Saar offensive.

We walked along the cobbled street, talking, they with their Red Cross sleeve bands, I with my rifle. O'Rourke asked my name, and though I told him twice he settled for Lee and so did I. We were gone about twenty minutes, picking up wood in yards or along the middle of the street, and when we returned the fire was already lighted in the stove, men were nailing blankets across the windows and someone had brought in a large, sweeping branch of Christmas tree which was left in a corner.

There was a rap on the front door and we were called out to eat. In the fading daylight we walked down the middle of the street, five yards apart, our mess kits rattling. The meal was slight, not worth carrying back to the room. We ate it in the street, a block away from where we lived, while the excitable captain in charge of First Battalion Headquarters shouted at us to maintain the five-yard interval. To-morrow we were having a turkey dinner, which accounted for the skimpiness of the supper: extra rations were going into the banquet.

Coming back in the chill dusk, I saw Chris Taylor alone, idling morosely on the street, and I fell into step with him.

"I have a new job," he said with bitterness. "I've just been made Captain Reddy's orderly."

It was hard to know what to say. "What's he like?" Captain Reddy was Colonel Hessig's assistant.

Chris shrugged. "He's all right, I suppose."

"You had no choice?"

"It was either this or go back to C Company. It's the only job they had open for me." A graduate engineer, I thought.

"Well, with your foot botched the way it is, you couldn't go back to C Company. I'll bet a lot of the fellows there would jump at the opportunity."

"Not many," he said. Limping a little, he walked up with me as far as the house where I was billeted. Under his field jacket, he seemed to be wearing a thin khaki blanket, sagging longer in the back than in the front. "It's the lining of a sleeping bag," he explained when I asked him. "One I found in the woods. There was blood on the outside—it belonged to a wounded guy. I ripped the lining out and cut off the bottom part with my knife. I have a scarf I've been saving for you." From inside his shirt he pulled out a length of white blanket with two red stripes running along it. He was wearing a similar piece around his neck. "A guy gave me a big piece of it." And this too he had sawed with his knife. It made a fine scarf, thick and warm and almost waist length.

Attached to the front of my house there was an empty cement watering trough, and in it, despite the approaching dark, he lighted the waxed cardboard of his K-ration box and tried to heat the little can of chopped pork and carrots.

Cold-looking stars had come out in the sky. We were staying here only a short while, he had heard.

"I wonder where we'll be this time next Christmas."

"Hell, next week," he said. "Or tomorrow night, for that matter." Thinking, I knew, of Mary, he stood watching the flame lick up around the cardboard and begin to die down. He opened the blackened can and scooped out the partly warmed ration with his jackknife. His hands, with the even nails that seemed to require no care, were, as always, lightly trembling.

"Are you in a house?"

"In a barn. The officers are in a house."

"Hey, Mac," a guard called, "put out that fire!"

Chris scattered the golden ashes and we stood watching them turn gray, quiver, rise in the icy air and blow away. I stepped on my cigarette and put out my hand.

"Well, anyway, Merry Christmas, Chris."

"Merry Christmas, Les."

I went into our room, into noise, warmth, smoke and laughter. A gasoline lantern was hissing on the floor. And there seemed to be preparations for a party. The captain had sent up some GI alcohol and one of the men came around gathering lemon powder and lumps of sugar to put with it. There was talk of midnight Mass if a way could be found to black out the high windows of the village church.

The men were taking their leggings and shoes off for the first time in weeks. The linoleum floor, which was like ice to touch, became one large bed as soon as the blankets were spread out. It was going to be a tight squeeze for all of us to lie down. We tried it, stretching out in a double row. Our feet met in a line down the center of the room and there was just enough space to lie flat, shoulder to shoulder. Once that was settled, everyone sat up, the drink came off the stove and was passed around, poured into the canteen cups. It tasted like scorched lighter fluid, but it was burning hot, re-vivifying. Cigarettes were lighted, and out of the din of chatter and laughter singing began. The mournful "I'm dreaming of a white Christmas"; "Silent Night"; "Jingle Bells"; "O Come, All Ye Faithful"; "Hark! the Herald Angels Sing"; "O Little Town of Bethlehem"; "White Christmas" again, and then, growing more secular, the Army favorites: "I've Got Sixpence"; "Someone's in the kitchen with Dinah"; "For Me and My Gal"; "When You Wore a Tulip"; "There's a Long, Long Trail"; "I'm going to buy a paper *doll* that I can call my own"; "Roll me o-ver in the clo-ver . . ."

Shortly after the singing had begun a friendly, pasty-faced little Southerner named Burrell, who claimed he would never grow accustomed to the cold weather, curled up on the floor very close to the stove. He fell asleep at once and about fifteen minutes later he startled everyone with his loud, anguished cries: he had rolled against the stove and burned his face quite badly. The others roared with laughter. "That's about the tenth time he's done that," one of the men said. The boy, frightened, still not wholly awake, with one hand up to his face, tried to join in their laughter, but even in the middle of it he sank down on the floor, and sleep overtook him again.

After a half hour of singing, "Silent Night" began again, wavered and stopped halfway. Most of the others were going to sleep. More than half the men, as everywhere in the Army, slept with their heads under the blankets. I was lying next to O'Rourke; the man on the other side I didn't know. The lantern went out, leaving a small warm ruby glow in the darkness from the open bottom door of the stove. On O'Rourke's part a guarded conversation started up: he wanted to know who was responsible for getting me my job with the medics. Except for the two of us, everyone appeared to have fallen asleep at once. O'Rourke, lonesome, spoke of Christmases at home in Syracuse, and then the door opened and two friends of his came in, having great difficulty finding a place to stand. They had brought him a drink and had come to wish him a Merry Christmas. He passed the bottle on to me. I took a swallow, and then the two dark, bundled-up figures, lighted by the dying glow of the fire, went out.

When everyone was asleep for quite some time, I sat up, feeling the chill coming through the wall, put my field jacket over my shoulders and lit a cigarette. I enjoyed the sensation of privacy in being the only one awake in the snoring crowded room. How lucky we were compared to the men who had relieved us in the Saar Valley, freezing tonight in the foxholes we had dug, standing guard or going out on patrols! They were troops even greener than ourselves and had, it was reported, marched in at attention to take over our positions wearing ties.

We were awakened perhaps at seven, in a dark icebox of a room, being called for breakfast. It still seemed strange not to wash before doing anything else, but we put on the shoes, leggings, all the paraphernalia, went out into the street with our mess kits and walked down to the corner crossroad.

"Merry Christmas, Atwell!"

"Merry Christmas, Husey! What are you doing down here? And Hepp!"

"We've been transferred to Battalion." They were both

100

radio operators, I recalled. "De Vroom came down with us too."

"Merry Christmas boys!" De Vroom, one of the tallest boys in C Company and the most cheerful, came along at that moment.

We moved up on the chow line, five yards apart, and received a larger quantity than usual of powdered eggs with bacon chopped into it, hot oatmeal and powdered milk, a slice of toast, and coffee. In the shadows between the houses there were drifts of snow, but everywhere else the ground was clear, frozen hard. The sun started to come up. On all sides you heard "Merry Christmas! Merry Christmas, boys!"

Coming back to the room after breakfast, I passed C Company eating in a large open stable. I stopped to exchange greetings and talk with some of the men, and one of the cooks came over to ask if I'd like to have Christmas dinner with them. The Mess Sergeant called, "Come along, Atwell, have dinner with us." It was very decent of them and gave me the sudden feeling of having more friends than I would have thought.

Back in the living room the litter bearers were wondering about the possibility of washing. There was no plumbing in the house, but might there be hot water? Who could speak German? "Schaeffer!" someone called. "Hey, Phil Schaeffer, how do you say 'We want hot water' in German?"

"You say, 'Heisses wasser, bitte.'"

"*What?*" "What the hell do you say?" "How do you say it?" "*What* is it? I can't say that! You go. You ask them."

For some reason he was unwilling to ask for more than one or two of the men, and the rest of us began taking turns going into the kitchen. Most of the men walked in and out in rigid silence. When my turn came, I went down the cold hall and knocked on the kitchen door; a voice said something in German and I stepped into a warm kitchen that looked out onto a back farm garden. On a pine chest between the steaming windows there was a small Christmas tree decked with ornaments and dull tinsel. A chicken was roasting. The husband, wife and eight- or nine-year-old son were in the room.

"Heisses wasser, bitte?" I asked, indicating my steel helmet and feeling like an amateur actor.

"Yah. Yah." The woman smiled, pointed to the dipper and the oblong enamel well attached to the stove.

. I ladled out some hot water, said, "Danke," and nodded toward the Christmas tree. "Schoen!"

"Yah." She put her hand on her son's shoulder and said something that I didn't understand. I gave the boy a bill, not knowing its value or whether he'd ever be able to use it or not. It was a large, bright, colorful bill of Invasion money. Smiling, he accepted it. The father and mother laughed and with mutual dankes we parted.

On the floor, the helmet of water had a tendency to roll and spill. Kneeling down, with one knee keeping it against the wall, I started to wash. Face first, and you tried in the process not to dislodge too much dirt from your hands. Ears, neck and hands last. Then shaving cream and shaving by feel, and drying your face on the brown towel, going outdoors to throw away the soapy water. Going out again with toothbrush, ribbon of tooth paste, canteen of water. One stood on the step, or a little down from it, in one's undershirt, and spat any place.

Then back again, stow away the toilet articles, put on the grimy, greasy-necked shirt, sleeveless sweater from home— my Army sweater had been stolen long ago—the field jacket, the scarf that Chris had given me. By daylight the white was a deep cream with dirt, but I was cheered by the double band of red. Now tighten the legging laces, light a cigarette, and one felt—almost wonderful.

"Mass! Anyone here going to Mass? Fall out!" The tiresome routine of putting on ammunition belt, gas mask, helmet, rifle—and out onto the road. Men were coming up the street in groups, all armed, with rifles, with here and there a B.A.R., a carbine, a grease gun, coming from houses, from barns and sheds. The church bells were ringing.

It was odd to see the door of a badly smashed house open and a little boy and girl, dressed in Sunday clothes, run out, followed by a neat woman in an old-fashioned fur-collared coat, beaver hat, and gloves. The children raced ahead to laugh and talk with other children, comparing, I supposed, what they had received for Christmas. There were men in overcoats, felt hats turned down all the way around, and stiff, high, polished shoes. None of the girls or women wore make-up. The civilians all kept to the sidewalk, while the soldiers roamed, talking, up the middle of the street.

The church property was surrounded by a wrought-iron

fence. You went up the steps, through a graveyard and into the vestibule. Helmets came off; rifles were stacked against the back wall. All the stained-glass windows were blown out and the still air was icy and damp. There were crystal-and-brass chandeliers and a worn, patterned marble aisle. Civilians sat on one side, we on the other. An organist played unfamiliar hymns. Out of the corners of their eyes the civilians watched us and we watched them. The first few rows were filled with children, then came a row of older boys, then girls, and finally the adults.

When the bell rang for the start of Mass, the parish priest came out in handsome white vestments, the two altar boys in red cassocks, starched white lace-edged surplices and white gloves. Blasts of frigid air blew in. The children sang hymns in French, but when the priest—stocky, middle-aged and dark—ascended the pulpit, the long sermon, surprisingly, was in German. He had a fine voice, deep and clear. Occasionally he gestured toward us, and the children all turned to look, then he gestured toward the crèche. The civilians received Communion, and then immediately after Mass our chaplain came out, gave conditional absolution, and asked the non-Catholic men not to come to the altar with us.

Getting back, I was a little late for dinner. I took my rifle and mess kit, went part way down the street and into the big barn that was C Company's kitchen. "Doubles!" the cooks were calling—they had been up all night preparing the food —"Doubles on everything today, boys. Eat all you want." I got on the end of the line, went through, and the mess kit was piled high with turkey, rice, dehydrated potatoes, gravy, fruit salad, a ration chocolate bar, a full cup of coffee. "More turkey here, anyone wants it. More turkey. Come an' get it."

It was a relief to be allowed to sit about close to each other on the barn floor. The wide doors stood open to the street. Some men wandered around, eating, going back every few minutes for more food.

"Swell, isn't it?" I said, sitting beside Dave Rossofsky.

"Swell."

Of course at times you considered: the turkey had been cooked the day before, had steamed all night and somehow didn't taste very much like turkey; and everything was plopped together in the mess kit, forming a stew, making me vow again, should I ever return to civilian life, to eat everything thereafter from a blue plate with its subdividing ridges.

But we were safe momentarily, sheltered; we had warm food to eat; we were still alive. And how quickly those who had been killed were forgotten! The tired cooks, scooping at the bottom of their pails, were offering more turkey, more fruit salad. They were smiling, grateful for compliments on the meal.

Lieutenant McGrath came in with Lieutenant MacKenzie, moving from group to group, rather gravely, I thought, asking the men how they were and if they had had enough to eat. They shook hands with me, exchanged Merry Christmases and invited me to come back and have dinner with the company whenever I could. Replete with food, Dave and I lounged on the floor, our shoulders against a large beam that formed the base for a row of stalls, gnawing contentedly on the thick, hard chocolate bars.

"Moving! Moving, boys! We're clearing out."

"Who said so?"

In the distance, drawing nearer, came a noncom's voice: "Fall out! Fall out for company formation!"

"Hey, Sergeant Danowski, what's going on?"

"Shots."

"Oh. Are we moving, though?"

"Yeah. Soon as you get your shots, hurry up back and roll up your equipment."

"Ah-h, hell. We're leavin'. I knew this was too good to last . . ."

After getting the injection with C Company, I went back to my billet. There the blackouts had come down from the windows, the blankets were being folded and men were rolling up packs. We were to travel in trucks, and to guard against frozen feet we were told to remove our shoes, put on an extra pair of socks and line our overshoes with straw. While riding we were to keep moving our toes to maintain the circulation. Some men, copying what we heard of the Russian soldiers, first wrapped paper around their bare feet. An armful of straw was thrown down in the room and we made innersoles of it, fitted them into our overshoes, slipped our feet in and then crammed in as much straw as we could. The straw stuck out in spots so that around the ankles we all looked like scarecrows. Just before leaving, some of the men took up a collection for the owners of the house, and everyone chipped in with cigarettes or chocolate, soap, lumps of sugar, a can of cheese. It was brought into the kitchen in a helmet.

By four-thirty the temperature had dropped to within a degree or two of zero. We came out of the house and walked down the cobbled street in the cold greenish twilight. The trucks were lined up—covered trucks, thank God, I thought, approaching them. Now, if only we weren't going to be too crowded . . . The hope died at once. We were crammed in, about sixty men to a truck that normally held thirty-two. Our particular vehicle had a thick coating of white ice on its floor, frozen hard, and at the rear, taking up valuable space, there were a number of five-gallon cans containing gasoline. I managed to get a space on one of the long side benches, but men coming in afterward were crowded double and triple on the floor all the way down the aisle. I wriggled out of my equipment and stowed it with my rifle under the seat, but I had to keep my feet tucked well in to make room for the men on the floor. Most of them were from Battalion Headquarters and unknown to me. The motors stared up, but at the last moment Captain Christoffsen kept rounding up extra men and packing them in, each one bringing a groan from those already inside.

The driver let down the back canvas flaps and the terrible jam of men, equipment, blankets, rifles and five-gallon cans started off.

"Nope, nope, we're not going back," someone was saying in the rear. "Least we haven't turned around yet. *No!* We're not! We're going in the other *direction!* We're going *away* from the Saar!"

All right, then, with that off your mind you could give yourself up just to being physically uncomfortable. We were wedged so tightly, each wrapped in a blanket, that it was almost impossible to move one's arms. Perhaps it was going to be a short haul. But inside a half hour one was chilled through, frozen. In the dark, gales of icy air blew up between the gaps where the canvas top met, or did not meet, the side of the truck. And the ice on the floor soon penetrated overshoes, straw and socks. From time to time I wriggled my toes, but it was not easy to do with someone sitting on my feet, unable to budge off them. The hours dragged past as if they too were frozen and could barely move. Five to six, six to seven, seven to eight, to nine, to ten, eleven, twelve: one's position was unchanged. The cold became

105

piercing; I could scarcely move my fingers. We were traveling slowly, in a complete blackout, through back country roads that had frozen into iron ruts.

For the most part we were silent, for to speak, to open one's mouth, let in frigid air that cut like a knife. But now and then a grumbling began somewhere on the floor, a cursing, a shifting about that brought more curses. Now all along the side benches men tried to move.

"Cold!"

"My God!"

"I think my feet are frozen. I can't move them."

"See if you can lift your arm; I wanna— Hell, never mind."

"Were you asleep?"

"Who the f--- could sleep?"

"I wonder if we're ever gonna stop."

"Hey! Hey, how about stopping the truck?"

"Hey! Stop this goddam truck! Hey, driver— Someone up front there, bang on the wall and tell the driver to stop. I gotta take a leak!"

A muffled voice from the cab of the truck informed us that he could not pull out of the convoy.

"Then let me up and try to get down the back. I gotta *go!*" Whoever it was stood up, but there was no way of getting to the back of the truck from where he was standing and he sat back again, groaning. Finally one of the men in the back emptied a five-gallon can over the tail board, spilling some of the gasoline on the frozen floor, and in the rear the can became a latrine.

"Hey!" There were cries. "Pass that goddam can up here! Pass that can! I gotta go!"

"Come on, hurry it up!"

We were so bundled up in blankets, in raincoats over overcoats over field jackets, and fingers were so frozen, so stiff with those deep painful cracks at the joints, that it was difficult to unbutton one's clothing. In addition, the truck, now reeking of spilled gasoline, swayed and jogged on the narrow, icy roads, and in the dark one could hardly see the opening of the five-gallon can. The men in the back had to hold the flaps down tight to prevent any light from escaping, while someone played a flashlight and still others held the can. The discomfort was so equally shared that everyone joined in the project willingly. It came my turn. Someone braced me while I stood; someone else played the borrowed flashlight. The five-gallon can was heavy, about to splash over. One man used it after me and then it was passed back, hand over hand, for the men in the rear to empty it. I sat down again, squeezing in, drawing the cold blanket about me. The can was returned to be used by someone on the opposite side, and a man up front, unable to wait, had used one of the waxed cardboard K-ration boxes.

"Pass it."

"Pass it."

"Christ! Hey, what the f--- goes on here?"

"Never mind. Just pass it."

"Pass it."

Intermittently the K-ration boxes were handed to you to pass. The five-gallon can was emptied and used again. The men in the back set up a howling that every time they closed their eyes someone gave them a brimming K-ration box to throw away.

Twelve to one, to two, to three . . . How long could one stand this cramping, this weakening, penetrating cold? My feet were so buried beneath packs and bodies that I couldn't move my toes at all; and, strangely, there was no sense of warmth arising from this closeness. It was as if one were clamped in a freezing vise.

By now men had started to cry hopelessly, without caring, without causing any attention or surprise. The first cases of dysentery became known and nothing much could be done about that either. The valiants in the rear had held four or five men over the back of the truck as we bumped and jogged along, but near me Husey began to shout, "Quick! Quick! Get off me! Let me get down the back! I got to s---!" But it took time for the crowd to unravel. Husey, cursing excitedly, began to claw at the men about him, then suddenly he gave up and started to cry drearily. A minute passed.

"Hey, for God's sake, some guy s--- in his pants."

"Ah, what the hell is this?"

Three to four.

"Hey, pass that goddam can. Let's have that can down here."

Four to five.

Someone in the impenetrable blackness on the floor had been blubbering and crying so long that I came out of the half doze into which I had fallen and asked needlessly what was the matter.

The voice said, "My legs. Someone's on my legs. I can't stand it."

"Well, here. See if you can drag yourself up here. I'll try to move a little."

"Where are you?"

"Here." I put my hand out. It was grabbed. Someone, pulling on me, managed to twist himself up out of the tangled mess. I gave him part of my seat—and where in the dark did I get? I seemed to get higher than the seat, to be crouched somehow on the side railing, in a fold of the canvas.

"God! Thanks." Whoever he was, he cried with relief and then fell asleep. At a bump in the road I slipped halfway down on top of his shoulder. And now I was more uncomfortable than before; at the time of moving I did not think it possible.

Five to six. I kept hoping my feet and legs would go to sleep to stop the pain in them, and at last they did. Frozen, no part of me seemed alive but my consciousness.

Those in the back announced that it was growing light. But even an hour later, when daylight did come, because of the gasoline that was spilled—no one knew whether it had gone into the blankets or not—we could not light a cigarette.

Out the back of the truck, where before there had been nothing but an early-morning winter-gray sky, low fields and a winding road, there suddenly appeared the gray stone walls of houses, a narrow street. The truck stopped. We were told to get down. It was about eight o'clock. We had been almost sixteen hours in the truck.

At first no one could move. Then slowly, stiff with cold, dazed, the men started to drop off the back, dragging blankets, equipment and dirty frozen rifles with them. Some men could not get to their feet and had to be pulled up by force. An officer's voice that I could dimly praise for its vitality shouted, unseen, "*Get* down! Hurry it up there! Leave your goddam equipment! Let the men get off!"

Now a noncom, also surprisingly vital, climbed up into the truck and started to lift frozen men to their feet, to throw equipment off into the street. When it came my time, I jumped down. There was no sensation at all to landing; I tumbled over and over. After a moment I knelt up, got to my feet. Gas masks, bandoleers and rifles were being sorted

108

out, and packs with the shoes dangling by their laces. "Who's
H-7175?"

"Here!"

"A-88— What is it? A-8894?"

"Here, mine." It was all there, entwined, except that
somewhere I had lost the bandoleers.

"On with your packs. Soon as you get your stuff, move
off to one side. Goddamit, don't bunch up there!"

A miserable ragged line formed to the side, awaiting de-
velopments. A shivering humorist piped up with "All right,
get these men out of the hot sun!" but we were all too cold
to laugh. I looked around for the litter bearers.

Yes, there was Sergeant Campbell, like a large, homely
mother hen, rounding us up, counting. "Arright, men, this
way. Follow me." In giving an order, he always lowered his
voice to a confidential level, minimizing the military aspect.

"Sergeant Campbell, we gonna have billets again?"

We were. What a feeling of relief! "Right over here, men.
Bear over to the lef' a li'l there."

The town appeared to be stout, fortress-like, with its
rows of citified gray stone houses and narrow streets set
down in a plain. We were led into a large barn beneath a
high stone house. The barn ran through the narrow block;
a quick glimpse out its back doors showed a row of flat
houses opposite and up at the corner the bowed front and
flapping sign of a wine store and delicatessen.

" 'Fore any of you start looking around, you got to get the
station set up," Sergeant Campbell was saying. "Get this
whole place clean."

Since there were only a few twig brooms to sweep with,
and one shovel, all the men could not work. I had been
given a broom, but I told O'Rourke and his friend, Nick
Nichols, about the wine shop and asked them to buy some
loaves of bread and some wine, offering to pay for them.
They hesitated about accepting the money and finally went
off without it.

It took very little time to sweep the grain from the floor.
"Might jes as well clean up that courtyard too," Sergeant
Campbell said in a tone that made light of the extra work.
The men cursed under their breaths, but Sergeant Campbell,
a farmer in civilian life, was a strong willing worker and
never asked anyone to do what he himself wouldn't do.

We started to sweep the cobbled courtyard while Sergeant

109

Campbell was setting up the drum-shaped Army stove. Outside on both sides of the street men were being billeted in the rows of houses by their officers. A few pale Frenchmen stood in the cold sunlight, hands in their overcoat pockets, smiling at us and occasionally taking their hands out to make a V-for-Victory sign, but for security reasons we were forbidden to talk to any civilians. There was a sixty-five-dollar fine for doing so.

Happy American faces appeared at the upper windows of small houses that were topped by chimney pots.

"Yoo-hoo! Hey, look where I am!" "Hey, Roy, I'm da-a-ncin'!" This was a tag line from a USO show that had played in the apple orchard. "This is some deal! We got beds! How many rooms you guys got?" All along the street windows burst open outward. Heads crammed close to look out. In one attic window a man leaned out to wave. He had found a woman's straw hat and had jammed it on. At that moment I noticed a thick authoritative roaring on the street.

"Get out! Get out of those goddam houses! *Who* gave you permission to go into those houses?" Two generals, fat, glaring, beefy-red, bristling with rage, were striding down the middle of the street in beautiful smooth, clean overcoats. The stars winked on their shoulders in the sunlight. "Get out!" they shouted cholerically. "Get out of the houses!" They were looking for an officer to fall upon. The men gaped down, incredulous at first, then they began leaving the houses.

Unconscious of the disaster, the man in the woman's straw hat was still waving across the way.

"Yoo-hoo."

"*Soldier!*" The generals came to a stout, important halt and glared up. The street had become suddenly quiet. The soldier looked down and his eyes popped with amazement. "Soldier, what army are you in?"

"W-w-w-why—" he gulped and pointed tentatively to General Purvis—"why *yours*, sir!"

"Then get that goddam hat off your head and *act* as if you were! Get back into uniform! The rest of you, *out* of those houses!"

"Arright, me-e-n," Sergeant Campbell was saying, "get your 'quipment on an' get right out. Hurry it up."

"What? After cleanin' up the place? Aren't we gonna stay?"

110

"Get all the men together. Get out."

The thick roaring continued down the street. I took a glimpse outside and saw Lieutenant McGrath, bareheaded on the steps of a house, his dark-red hair catching the light, firmly and coolly arguing with the two generals. They cut him short in the middle of a sentence and strode on. The men came tumbling out of the houses, dragging their unfolded blankets, their rifles and full field packs. "What the f---'s goin' on? We in the wrong town, or what?"

The litter bearers, similarly loaded down, walked out of the courtyard and joined the throng of soldiers in the street. The trucks were parked up at the corner, and above rows of helmets I saw the first line of men climb up. It was an open truck and there seemed to be some confusion, a countermanding of the original order: the line of men, high in the truck, turned around and got off again.

"What's goin' on? What's up?"

"Beats the s--- outta me."

We stood crowded on the street, waiting. Then came stentorian cries: "C Company men, *line* up!" "A Company—" "First Battalion Headquarters, *line* up!"

"They said we didn't line up fast enough," a man was saying on his way to the formation, "so now we got to walk."

Still not sure, feeling perhaps we were in the wrong houses and were going only a block or two, we didn't bother strapping on our packs but carried them in our arms, the shoes dangling, gas masks hanging, blankets trailing on the cobbles. Falling in on the end of the battalion line, we walked to the corner, turned right, walked two short blocks and at once found ourselves outside the tiny village. A long, perfectly flat road stretched before us, dwindling to a vanishing point on the horizon.

"Hey, what the hell is this? Where are we going?"

Off the road, on the hard, frozen ground, the trucks began to rumble past, empty. From a nearby company came gripes, curses, a loud voice leading the familiar chorus: "Som-m-me s---!"

"Silence, there! Silence! You're marching at attention!"

A jeep with the two angry generals standing up in it like charioteers now rode out along the flat frozen ground, reviewing the troops. The wind blew and the unfolded blankets blew; towels flapped about haggard, dirty, unshaven faces. Open overcoat pockets bulged with ration boxes, bottles of wine, a loaf of French bread. Someone was carrying a little chair; another man was eating. The lines were uneven; some men, carrying their overcoats, showed a dangling line of socks beneath the bottom of their field jackets. The whole effect, what with straw showing above overshoes, was raffish in the extreme.

Colonel Hessig, doubtless goaded by the two generals, now was the one to fly into a passion of rage, quitting his still-moving jeep to run alongside the raggedy lines, screaming at the men, at the noncoms and officers.

"—want you to act like soldiers and *look* like soldiers, or by God, I'll—" The rest was lost, torn away by the wind. "Straighten up there! Now march them at attention. I want to see some—"

A yapping cry was taken up by noncoms and officers. "Hup, tup, trip, fo! Hup, tup— Straighten up those lines! Straighten up those rifles! You're marching at attention! Hup, tup, trip, fo! Marching at at*ten*tion!"

We were also marching at top speed, in cold whirling clouds of dust, and the road, frozen in ruts, struck painfully through overshoes and straw. Exhausted after the all-night truck ride, without sleep or breakfast, one soon felt the awkwardly distributed weight of the pack and rifle.

At the end of an hour, men had started to collapse, to fall out of line onto the ground. There were perhaps forty or fifty of them lying by the wayside. Colonel Hessig, still howling, had driven up again in his jeep and once more he began to rant and shout at the stragglers, the nearest of whom got to their feet and fell in near us at the back of the line. Chris Taylor was one, and when we saw each other we burst into laughter. "Listen to the old bastard," Chris said, limping. "If he had to do this, his ass'd be dragging on the ground."

· "If it kills every *one* of you, you're going to march like *soldiers!*" he was screaming, and the men, too tired to care, went stumbling past him, their faces slack. "Throw down that equipment. Throw *down* those goddam blankets! I'll have someone pick them up later! I want to see you *march!* Here, what's the matter with you?" This was to a man sitting beside the road with a few others. The colonel bent down, ear turned in the attitude of the deaf, awaiting the answer. Whatever the answer was, he suddenly roared, "*Get* up on your feet every goddam one of you! Get up!

Get along there! Here, *you!*" This might have been to me but I didn't glance over to see. "Throw down those packs and blankets!" Some men did so, but, pretending not to hear and at the same time trying not to laugh, I hung onto mine.

The village we had left was on the outskirts of Rheims, I later discovered. When we had marched six or seven miles beyond it, we came to a small pine woods where, amid caved-in trenches left over from the First World War, we were told to dig foxholes and put up our tents. In this activity I was teamed up with one Dick Gann, a medic whom no one else appeared to want. He was a freckled, loose-mouthed, stupid-looking boy with a perpetually running nose and GI glasses that had a greenish bloom of grime on them. When he spoke, it was slowly, blurred, like someone under an anesthetic. Nevertheless he dug a good straight foxhole and managed with me to put up a good straight tent.

"Now, every man," said Sergeant Campbell, "they want yer ter take a shave and clean up. We got some wa-a-ter over here."

"Be goddamned if I'm going to shave." O'Rourke, the thin, nervy Irish-American, rebelled against any order on general principles, and his friend Nick Nichols followed his lead. They were careful, though, to grumble out of Sergeant Campbell's hearing; all of them, I discovered, lived in fear of being "sent out as aid man" to live with the line companies. Nick was a quiet, neatly made young man, perhaps twenty-three, an egg candler in civilian life. He had the square, blond, Norwegian type of good looks one saw in skiing advertisements. He was seldom found, even indoors, without the little peaked wool-knit cap, and on him it had a jaunty air; it also had a purpose: he was going prematurely bald and was self-conscious about it.

Resenting Sergeant Campbell, most of the men sat over their little fires, talking in low voices about their experiences in the Saar Valley.

"One of the guys saw Ned Farron just after he died," someone was saying. "Didn't have a wound on him." This was directly opposite to what I had heard in C Company, where the young aid man had bled to death while in Lieutenant MacKenzie's arms. "He was just dead white. Must have had heart trouble or maybe it was concussion from a shell. They had him lying in a foxhole."

113

"And poor Allen. God, you'd wonder what happened to him. Last anyone saw him he was running and he didn't have any helmet on. Someone yelled, 'Hey, Allen!' but he ran right past as if he didn't know where he was going."

Another litter bearer had cracked up that Sunday and had been sent back to Regimental Headquarters by Captain Stettner. "One Jew," said O'Rourke sourly, who hated them, "stickin' up for another, that's what it was. Friedmann was nothin' but a yella bastard."

I filled my helmet with water and went off a short distance to wash and shave at the edge of the trench that formed a boundary for our particular group. The sun was going down, staining the shingled trunks of the pines with its cold winter red.

"Put out the fires!" an officer called, coming through from First Battalion Headquarters a few yards away. "All the fires go out promptly at four-thirty. Put 'em out, men."

Sometimes the men scattered them so there'd be no blaze and the embers glowed on red-gold in the dusk, but O'Rourke, who took the four-thirty curfew as a personal affront, persisted with his fire until the officer came back and spoke to him several times.

When darkness was complete, we were called by Sergeant Campbell or by Mike Nowak, the tall, eyeglassed assistant squad leader, to line up for chow. There'd be a dive into the cold, pitch-dark tent for the mess kit and gas mask—and in my case for the rifle and ammunition belt—and then we'd line up, shivering in the increasing cold. At a signal, we'd wind in and out among the pines to join the long line waiting to wash mess kits.

Captain Christoffsen, the Company Commander of First Battalion Headquarters, a long-waisted, short-legged man, brisk of gesture, former owner, it was claimed, of a delicatessen, would be striding up and down the line, shouting, "Five yards! Keep five yards apart! Goddamit, can't you understand plain English? *That's* not five yards there. Lieutenant! Lieutenant, keep those goddam men from bunching up there. Make 'em back up. This whole line, back up! Christ A'mighty, you ask them to stay five yards apart—"

Sergeant Askew, in charge of mess, the owner of a lined, lugubrious India-rubber face and a helmet so large that it came down to his eyes and forced him to lift his head back like a turtle, would be standing there, gloomy and cold, trying in the dimness to peer into the face of each man who went past. Food was extremely scarce at this time, and men from the adjacent companies would often sneak onto our line for an extra meal.

Because of the shortage, there were only two meals served each day, and the cold made everyone's appetite increase. For the main meal in the evening, one would get a tiny dab of stew or very limp corned-beef hash, two narrow ration crackers, a cup of coffee and, with luck, a single spoon of canned fruit salad. For breakfast we would be given a cautious serving of hot cereal without milk, or two very small pancakes with watered syrup, and always a cup of coffee. The men complained constantly and tried to be picked to serve the food so that they could give themselves and their friends larger portions. "Oh, well," others said bitterly, "we can stand it. Just as long as they're getting it on the home front." There was also a sudden shortage of cigarettes, and as time went on men took to smoking the ones they had, secretly, for fear a friend might ask for one.

After the unsatisfactory supper I noticed that most of the men repaired to the captain's large tent, but so far none had shown themselves to be friendly, so I went immediately to my own tent and prepared to go to sleep. It was too cold to stay up any longer. Dick Gann, mumbling to himself, turned in too. On first acquaintance, I thought him unusually morose and slow; now I realized he was a mental defective of sorts, well enough disposed toward me, but he held violent and often unreasonable dislikes for the others. I'd hear him talking to himself and muttering curses, but when I asked him what the trouble was, he was never able to say. It took him a long while to crawl into his sleeping sack; there were all sorts of mysterious precautions: hiding his wallet, fountain pen and knife from me; crawling around outside on his hands and knees, testing the tent pegs, hammering them with a stone, retying the tent ropes. When finally he was in his sack, I'd ask him if he wanted a cigarette. We were hoarding Fleetwoods and other little-known brands that came in the K rations and had been begged from the nonsmokers, and I'd hand one over to him in the dark.

"Y'know, s-s-some—some of these—of these—of these gar-dam—some of these guys here th-th-think they're so— so f---in' s-mart—"

You'd never know what the story was. It was probably a grievance against Big Steve Brudzinski, who baited him by the hour.

In daylight, Dick smoked a cigarette much as one would a cigar, seldom removing it from his mouth. A long bent ash formed; the part in his mouth became wet and disintegrated. His nose ran unevenly, just so far and no farther. His co-ordination was bad; he lurched and staggered rather than walked. I admired Sergeant Campbell for treating him well and keeping a protective eye on him.

In the morning we awoke to a world stiff and white with frost. The fire-making began at once. What were we doing here? I knew we had fallen far back, but that was all. Some said we were awaiting reinforcements before going back into combat again.

Immediately after breakfast men started coming to sick call and I took up my place outside the large tent and started checking rifles. When there was a break near noon, I went over and sat for a few minutes near O'Rourke's fire. He was still distrustful and not quite free to talk against Captain Stettner for fear I'd carry back tales, but when I told him that I had had no pull in getting the job of outdoor checkroom attendant—in fact had never yet seen the captain—he thawed somewhat and offered me a piece of advice.

"Lee, come 'ere, listen. You want to hold onto this job here, you play up to the cap'm, see? Hang around, try to get in good with him." His face was dour.

"How? I'm not very good at that."

"Well, to stay here you got to get on the right side of the sonofabitch. You watch some of these guys. You'll see how it's done." Fiercely he held himself aloof from that. He and Nick exchanged a glance. By effort, I thought, Nick remained expressionless and looked off. Plainly he thought O'Rourke foolhardy for offering advice to a possible spy. "Don't say I said anything," O'Rourke added. "It's only a hint."

"Oh. Well, thanks."

Some line-company men started across to the large tent and I got up to intercept them before they went in with their rifles. As I was setting their weapons down, a tall, thick-set, unspruce young man stepped out and I caught the silver flash of captain's bars on his shirt collar and, through the camouflage net, the white bars painted on his helmet: Captain Stettner.

"Are you Atwell?" he asked with a smile. He was olive-complexioned, dark-jowled, with a long, heavy, intelligent face, the most notable feature of which was a pair of puffed and watering brown eyes set almost flat on the surface. He looked to be about twenty-seven and had big, solid, sloping shoulders, heavy hips, heavy, clumsy legs and feet. "Yes?" he was saying. "Well, Atwell, how are you gettin' along? You like it here with the medics?"

"Yes, very much, sir." Unable whenever it's necessary to create a good impression, I could feel myself going stiff and poker-faced.

"Who are you teamed up with?"

"Dick Gann, sir."

He gave me an odd, surprised look. "Do you get along all right with Dick?"

"Yes, we get along very well." My mouth refused to smile and I realized I had missed an opening: he had been ready to laugh about Dick Gann. His tone changed.

"There's something I'd like you to do for me, Atwell. I have a carbine I picked up. It's a good little rifle and I'm savin' it to go deer huntin' when I get back to the States." He smiled and gave his head a shake. Here was another chance for me to smile, to show some interest, but I couldn't manage it. "I'd like you to keep it in good condition for me. I want you to clean it as often as you clean your own weapon."

"Yes, sir." That would not be too often, I thought.

"How often do you clean yours?"

"As often as it needs it, sir."

Hedging about, we looked at each other.

"Well, I'd like mine cleaned every day," he said, inching in. Something told me then that he knew less about weapons than I, and I said I'd take care of it for him. He called to one of the men named Russell, told him to fetch the carbine from the medics' truck, and, turning back, he said, "You do a good job of cleanin' on it and then you show it to me."

"Yes, sir." There was no point, of course, in telling him I didn't know how to take a carbine apart. Russell, who went off to get the rifle, handed it to me. Unsure of each other, we exchanged a level glance.

I brought the carbine over to one of the fires. Mike Nowak,

the tall assistant squad leader, sitting there in a rabbit-lined German jacket, said, "What's he want you to do? Clean his f---in' rifle for him?"

"Yes. Do you know how to get it apart? I was shown how once, but I've forgotten."

The two of us, by tugging, wrenching and pressing various parts, managed to take it down. With the oil-and-thong kit from my own rifle, I cleaned it, got it together again and then rubbed some oil into the wooden stock.

When the captain came out a half hour later, I showed it to him and he eyed it appreciatively. He was uncertain just how to examine a rifle for inspection, not knowing whether you held the bore up to your eye like a spyglass, or whether you held it down from you and let the light shine through it against your thumbnail. He had the nerve, however, to try both ways.

"Sure you got it all clean?"

"Yes, sir."

He turned it over in his hands. "Look at that grain!" His smile widened. "That sure looks good. That's really swell! You did a good job." There was a canvas cover for the rifle. The captain buckled it on and then handed the weapon over to Bob Russell. "Every day now, you get this rifle from Russ here. He takes care of it for me."

Russell, a swarthy, muscular young Southerner with dark eyes and a dark mustache, accepted the rifle, and when the captain turned back to the tent we exchanged another glance, and this time Russell permitted himself a string of oaths as he walked off to the truck to put the rifle away.

The next time I saw the captain that morning, he came out of the tent to ask me to chop some wood that was too large for the stove. With misgivings I picked up the ax and said, "I may not be particularly good at this, but we'll see."

Within a minute or two we did see.

"Here," said one of the litter bearers who had been watching, "let me trah that." He took the hatchet, upended a log and, holding it with one hand, split it neatly into a series of even, pale pieces. The captain looked on, lazily amused.

"What's your name?" he asked.

"Sam Benton, Jr., sir." The reply came smartly, the name pronounced all as one word.

"That's the kind of a man we need in a place like this," the

118

captain remarked, and, with another indulgent smile, went inside.

Sam Benton, Jr., was unfailingly good-natured. Evidently he had arrived just a little ahead of me to join the litter bearers—I believe he was replacing Friedmann—and he spoke to everyone, smiling and friendly. He was fairly tall, slender, blond, pink-cheeked, blue-eyed and good-looking; better looking on first sight than on second, and younger in appearance than he actually was. He looked, you thought, nineteen; he was twenty-seven. A second glance showed laugh lines high on his rather dry pink cheeks; his eyes were a faded blue, his teeth slightly yellow. He'd take a look around at the men grimly crouched over their little fires and say rapidly in a Kentucky accent, " 'Bout lak Valley Forge, guess." And he'd give a laugh. Perhaps five minutes later, behind you, somewhere out of sight, you'd hear it again: " 'Bout lak Valley Forge, guess." And there would be the same laugh. Twice in the space of the one half hour, he said, "Yes, sir, I'm from Colfrey, Kentucky. Kentucky hillbilleh, an' I'm proud of it. Colfrey's garden spot of the worl'. No place lak it, no sirree! Got m' girl down there, Miss Lucy Lee, an' evra time I drive nearby her house, it makes mah heart go pitteh-pat."

The second time I heard this I was walking past O'Rourke's fire. "Crissake," Nick was mumbling, "you ever notice about that new guy we thought was going to be so good? Every f---ing thing he says, he repeats over and over."

The others, however, were still congratulating themselves on getting a man with such a friendly, winning personality into the group.

Calluses on my feet had been giving me trouble for the past few weeks, and now, wearing only overshoes with straw in them seemed to make the condition worse. I had heard Preacher, the medical technician, telling men who had come to him with the same complaint that he was devoting the afternoon to the care of feet: removing corns, calluses, tending ingrown toenails and so on. Late in the afternoon, when the line of men was finished, I presented myself as a patient. I had washed my feet in cold water and had put on clean dry socks.

"All right, Deac, let's see 'em feet of yours." Preacher looked over his GI glasses, moon-faced, with light close-cropped hair, blue eyes and a broad upturned nose. He told me to lie on one of the cots with my feet extended, and when

I had done so he gingerly touched the calluses. "Got some real dillies there. Corns underneath. We'll see what we can do. Yes sirree Bob, some real dillies." Lips compressed, he gave his head a decisive shake. "Mm, *mm!*" Both shake and exclamation were to become familiar. "Now I got me a way a cuttin' out a callus I picked up from a doctor in Camp McCain, an' I never found none better. Might as well tell you, 's gonna hurt, but after four, five days you'll be walkin' on air."

I told him to go ahead and secretly I hoped it would take considerable time: it was so pleasant to be in the warmth. He sat in such a way that I couldn't see what he was doing, but within a few minutes the operation became so painful that I burst out into a sweat and had all I could do to lie still. In about ten unbelievable minutes it was over and he sat looking at my feet.

"Well, now, Deacon, I'm jes gonna tell yuh. To get these here things out, I cut deeper'n I should. See, mah way's not jes to slice the top off; it's to cut like a V till you get the whole thing out, an' as I say, I went in purty deep on you. Went right to the bone. Drew blood, of course."

I could feel my feet dripping and bleeding, but the relief that the gouging was over was so great that I lay back silent and the sweating began to stop.

"Now Ah'm gonna dress these things here an' Ah want you ter report in an' get 'em dressed twice a day till 'ey heal up." He put dressings in the incisions, then bandaged and bound adhesive tape tightly around my toes, and then round and round my feet. I put on my three pairs of socks, my overshoes with the straw, and tottered out to sit by Green's fire and smoke a meditative cigarette.

O'Rourke and Nick whispered together, then Nick went into the tent, returned and from inside his shirt drew out part of a large loaf of bread they had bought in the delicatessen in town. Nick whittled off two generous slices and paused. My mouth suddenly watered. "Want some?" he asked, but so painfully that I quickly said no, although I would have given him twenty dollars for a slice. Relieved of a great weight, suddenly friendly toward me, he put the bread back in the tent. The two of them hunched far over the coals, like misers, toasting their bread on sticks, looking guardedly about for fear that others might see them.

You could begin to tell the new men one from the other.

120

Just before dark, Chris Taylor dropped by to talk to me. We went over and sat near my tent. It was turning very cold. You could hear the first jingle of men getting out their mess kits. While talking, I told him about the minor operation on my feet.

"Good God, man, you didn't let those butchers at you! You're crazy! I had them cut out that wart or whatever it was on the sole of my foot and the goddam thing's never healed up since. What I wanted to ask you—how's your job here?"

"There's nothing to it. It seems too good to be true."

"Well, you know it's not steady—"

"I know I'm here on trial."

"That's not what I mean. You know Captain Reddy's Hessig's assistant, and I overheard the two of them talking today and Reddy wants someone else to have your job. You remember that guy in C Company with us? Rodriguez? One of the Mexicans who can't speak English? Well, he had a year in med school and since he's no f---ing good to the company, Reddy thinks your job should have been given to him. He saw Stettner about it, and Stettner says he doesn't want to change you."

"For God's sake!" I couldn't imagine either of them bothering his head one way or the other. "Is it settled? Am I leaving?"

"No, it doesn't seem to be. Or at least not yet. But Reddy doesn't like to give in once his mind is made up. Stettner said, 'What's to happen to the man I have?' and Reddy says, 'Atwell could go some place else.'"

"Back to C Company, I suppose."

"Well, I don't know but I thought I better tell you."

After he left I sat wondering why Captain Stettner would oppose Captain Reddy on my account. Through friendship for Lieutenant McGrath? Because, as a doctor, he wanted to show that he'd brook no interference from the military? Because of a little oil on the stock of his rifle?

During the night there was a fall of snow, and after checking the rifles the next morning at sick call and having the incisions in my feet dressed, I hobbled to the edge of the trench that marked our boundary and saw three of the litter bearers down in it, stoking a fire they had built in the remains of one of those ovenlike hollows I had slept in near the fortress at Metz. One of them was Ted—it evolved Teddy Jameson, the litter bearer O'Rourke and Big Steve Brudzinski had complained about because he wouldn't gather wood for the fire. They called him Mabel.

"Come on down!" he called and, hampered by my bad feet, I slithered into the gulley, gained speed, couldn't stop myself and ended up by falling into their midst, knocking the three of them off balance and surprising them by what must have seemed an excess of boisterous spirits.

"I wanted you to see our fireplace," Teddy said, recovering himself and straightening his helmet. "Yesterday we had a wonderful fire in it, didn't we, Phil? Better than anyone else's. They all said these weeds wouldn't burn, but they did! They burned—ooh!" His skin was dark and oily, with flat dark moles. Behind GI glasses, his eyes were large, black, with a slight cast. Thick black eyebrows; a flaring nose; small, petulant mouth and sloping chin. He slumped badly and had round, though heavy, shoulders. He was heavy throughout, with a small waist, wide hips and curiously broad, bearlike feet.

His inseparable friend was Paul Clifford, a former dairy hand from a religious family in Kansas, a fairly strong boy of his own age—nineteen, I believe. Clifford was quiet, uncomplaining and rugged. He stood braced on wide-spread legs. His head sagged forward, giving him at times a hangdog air. He was brown-haired, with almost imperceptible freckles, good features and large greenish-blue eyes, one of which was either greener or bluer than the other, slightly opaque, and turned out. Very often he listened, his head half averted, then: "*Good*ness sake!" he'd exclaim, the nearest he came to profanity.

The third member of the group, Phil Schaeffer, was older —twenty-seven—and better educated than his companions. He had a stiff, skinny build, flat and high-shouldered. He wore GI glasses patched with a piece of adhesive tape, on a long chinny face, light reddish in color. Already at twenty-seven there was something dried-out about him, something puzzled and reflective. He was forever attempting to be fair and impartial in groups seldom bothered by such scruples. He smoked a badly lighted pipe and gestured with it stiffly; and, in a way that amused me, he showed himself to be wholly inefficient in tending to the fire. The trio, with my tentmate, Dick Gann, comprised one of the three litter teams.

Yesterday they may have had a good roaring fire with the

weeds, but today they had mostly acrid greenish smoke. The comforts of a fire were less important to Phil Schaeffer than to most.

"That's all very well," he was saying, talking of the scarcity of food here, "but you mustn't forget this: a man can exist on half a slice of bread a day."

"Yes?" replied Ted Jameson. "Well, I'd just like to see you try!"

"Sergeant Askew's a good man. I'm sure, under the circumstances, he's doing the very best he can."

"Sergeant Askew's just a mean old fart, that's all he is!" said Teddy, unimpressed by Phil's attempt to give the Devil his due.

Cliff listened with a faint smile on his face; his head was turned away so that he stared into the wind.

"Now, I don't know; I don't agree there." Phil frowned seriously, shaking his head.

He asked where I had come from before joining them, and the conversation reverted to the Saar. "We were at Saarbrucken," Phil recalled. "The name of the nearest town was Gross Rederching. That was the objective. We were pointing toward Echternach, the southernmost tip of the American line. We were supposed to have the 245th on our right flank and we should have waited for them, but instead we went *in* and caught all the Eleventh Panzalehr Division could throw at us. We had over twelve hundred casualties in one day. Of course," he continued after drawing on his pipe with compressed lips, "what made our particular job so bad was those tanks coming up around midday. They churned up the road there where we were to evacuate the wounded by jeep and no vehicle could get through from then on. No doubt you heard about the wire Colonel Hessig sent back around that time?" Phil knew it by heart: "'Heavy casualties in A and B. B Company's commander killed. A Company 49 per cent casualties. Continuing the advance. Hessig.' Blithering idiot! What the hell did *he* care?"

I found myself grinning foolishly at the outburst.

"Ooh, that was terrible there!" Teddy said, giving a shiver.

"Had hit the ground 'bout every twenty feet," Cliff recalled with a deepening of color and a smirk of embarrassment at speaking.

"I imagine all of you saw plenty of work?"

"'Member, Phil, that first casualty we had?"

123

"That was awful." He turned to me, frowning, deeply troubled. "The first man we picked up died before we could get him to the collecting point. It was the first death I really ever saw."

" 'Member he started to look awful white while we were carrying him," Cliff said.

"I didn't know what to do!" Phil cried. He was the leader of the four-man team. "I knew he died, but we carried him on for a while, and then I said, 'No. This isn't right, we can't—' So we dumped him off, but I hated to leave the poor guy there in the woods. I covered his face with my towel and Cliff and I put our raincoats over him. Of course, by the end of the *day*, that was nothing! Nothing!"

"By the end of the day," Cliff said, "my wrists and legs— did they ache! When it got too dark to get any more out, I went back to the aid station and I was too tired to dig in. Just went to sleep on the ground."

"Yes, but you could *go* to sleep!" said Ted, flashing his eyes.

"Oh, well, Ted here had it worse than any of us that night," Phil explained, turning to me. "By dark, the woods were still full of wounded men lying there. The captain gave the order to stop litter-bearing till morning, but he said someone would have to go on out back there again to stay with the wounded."

I couldn't tell from the account whether Teddy had been selected for the job or whether he had volunteered; at any rate he had made his way back to the wounded and had remained with them all night. He sat and talked to the men and told them he'd be with them until they were evacuated. No one perhaps could have done a better job of talking: observations flowed from him easily and comfortably, accompanied by all manner of little settling motions, clearings of the throat, coughs, conjectures and confidences.

"I helped them move if they got tired in one position, and gave them sips of water—like some couldn't move their arms —and I just talked to them 'bout any old thing. But it was awful cold out there—and scary, ooh! One time the moon came out clear and I looked in front of me— I thought it was a round rock all the time and it was a man's head blown right off! It was right near my foot! And there was someone's legs there too—I nearly died!" He let out a high, nervous whinny of laughter and shivered. "And then a lot of shells came in—" A split second later the whole thing had left his mind. "Cliff, let's get some more weeds. Don't be such an old slowpoke. Come on, the fire's dying down."

That was my introduction to the three. I climbed out of the trench, repeating their names to settle them in my mind: Phil Schaeffer; Cliff; Teddy. Then there was Sam Benton, Jr., Big Steve Brudzinski, O'Rourke, and Nick Nichols . . . Sergeant Campbell, Mike Nowak, and Preacher in the aid station . . . The captain and little Lieutenant Serletis . . . Bob Russell, who drove the truck and took charge of the captain's rifle, and Burrell, the boy who burned himself rolling into the stove, and Don Stoddard, who had been one of C Company's aid men in England, and a young Mexican named Pancho . . . Gradually one grew to know them.

Leaving Phil Schaeffer's weed fire, I was on duty again, checking rifles for a while. The Protestant chaplain who had carried Sergeant Weems across the road on his back was inside the tent, arguing loudly against being sent to the hospital with a serious kidney condition. For as long as possible he had hidden the fact that he was sick and in intense pain, but sleeping in cold foxholes had made the condition worse, and his assistant had finally reported the case. The chaplain begged to be kept on, knowing there were only two others, one Protestant and one Catholic, for the entire regiment of approximately five thousand men, and replacements were almost impossible to procure. In a short while, however, he was carried out to the ambulance, driven off to the field hospital and was never returned to us again.

How long we were staying here outside Rheims, no one knew. There was one rumor going around to the effect that we, or our superior officers, had made so many errors in the Saar Valley that the division was in disfavor and would never again be committed to combat. Another claimed that there had been an enormous German break-through.

"Sure! Didn't you know that? They're tearin' like hell, bustin' through the line everywhere. They expect to be in Paris by New Year's. We're in a holdin' position in case they come this way."

"Listen to him; he talks like a man with a paper ass."

"Yeah? Well, you know that fifteen miles we gained in the Saar?" What fifteen miles was this? I wondered. "Well, the outfit that relieved us, they got the s--- kicked outta them and they lost all that land."

"I heard we made the deepest penetration into Germany of all the outfits along the line."

"Deepest penetration my ass. We f---ed up, but good!"

"Hey, I hear the rations are coming up. They're counting them now!"

That report at least was true. Joe Mortara, the Supply Sergeant for the battalion medics, passed out the rations with Sergeant Campbell. The day was extremely windy and snow blew off the ground in great sheets that eddied up until one felt caught in a wild, stinging blizzard. Each man received free of charge a carton of cigarettes, seven candy bars, two packs of chewing gum, razor blades, soap, toothpaste and shaving cream.

My pockets and the front of my overcoat bulging, I started to limp back to my tent, and I had gone only a few steps when I stopped and gulped down a candy bar. In civilian life the idea would seldom occur, but here the taste was delicious: a chewy center, with peanuts, covered with milk chocolate. I had no sooner finished it than, shaking, I undid another bar and ate that too, though originally I had planned to make the seven bars last a week by eating only one a day.

I put the rifle and rations in my side of the tent and suddenly, while I knelt there, before I could stop myself, I ate another candy bar, wolfing it down. Surprised at myself, I took a pack of cigarettes, a stick of gum, and stumped off through the blowing, stinging clouds of snow to stand near Phil Schaeffer's fire in the ravine. The first rumors of moving were afoot, and we wondered whether we'd go toward or away from the German break-through. We had not yet heard the words "Battle of the Bulge." Someone passing along the crest of the ravine called, "Be movin' soon, boys. The two-and-a-halfs are comin' up."

On the chow line that night, after a long delay and a vast amount of talk, preparation and excitement, the enlisted men received their first monthly ration of wine. I believe it happened only once more. There was a moon behind drifting, fleecy clouds, and its dim, greenish light filtered down through the pine branches onto the snow, gleaming here and there on an aluminum mess kit or a canteen cup as the men went forward on the winding line. Dip, splash and jingle of mess gear in the ash barrels of boiling water. The wet hash

126

plopped into the wet mess kit; two K-ration crackers; a spoon of fruit salad, mostly juice, poured carelessly over the hash, and then: "Whaddya want, cawfee or wine?"

"Wine."

The dully gleaming cup was filled almost to the brim while Captain Christoffsen stood watching closely.

"Hey, how is it?" someone was asking eagerly of a man already served, and the answer came back, "*Lousy!*"

As I carried the food and wine back to our own section where the scattered embers of O'Rourke's fire was still smoldering, a voice was asking, "What the f--- kind of wine *is* this?"

It was very thin, very cold, very sour wine, and tasted as if it might have been half water. At the same time it was enough like alum to dry and pucker one's mouth. Any expectations of being thawed and filled and warmed by a rich heavy wine, any hopes of a pleasant relaxed numbness, were dashed at once.

"Ooh, this tastes awful!" Ted Jameson was saying somewhere in the dark. "Cliff, are you going to taste yours?"

After a pause, Cliff, who neither drank nor smoked, answered, "Naw."

"Is this how wine always tastes?" Ted was asking. "If I drink it, will I get drunk?"

In moments like that the youth and inexperience of many of the men sent over into combat were startling.

That night when the men started to crowd into the medics' tent, I went in too. The light from the hissing gasoline lanterns was so bright after the darkness that at first I was blinded. The tent was baking hot. There were the two cots, but only the initiate sat on them: the captain, Lieutenant Serletis, Sergeant Campbell, Preacher, Big Steve and a few others as yet unknown to me. The rest of us stood close, sometimes off-balance, smoking a final cigarette. And what I disliked in the usual relationship between officer and enlisted man held forth here too, for even though the captain and the tiny lieutenant were both friendly, they were, in a sense, royalty: they introduced the topics of conversation, bantering with this one or that, while the others stood listening with forced, subservient grins. No one ever bantered back, ever took the same liberties or asked the same sort of personal questions. You sensed it would even be impolite to turn to someone nearby and start a quiet conversation that would not include the two officers. Still, to feel the warmth soaking through . . .

"Now, I'm gonna show you boys a map," the captain said, getting to his feet, finishing a can of hot C-ration stew. With his helmet off, he was better-looking. He had heavy, cleanly parted black hair and a well-shaped head. Unfolding a large map and bothered slightly by indigestion, he gave a brief, clear description of the German bulge, pointing on the map to the enemy infiltration with a finger that for a doctor and a big man was tiny, unclever-looking, nicotine-stained and dirty. Everyone pressed in close to see.

"Up here's Germany. This is Belgium down here." The finger with its nail bitten down described a long loop on the green-spotted map. "They poured in all through here." In the heat, with the lanterns hissing, making sharp shadows against the side of the tent, we all looked at the bulge. "An' this is where we're goin', somewhere up through this part of Belgium, near St. Vith and Bastogne." He had a bad sinus condition that clogged his nose and made his eyes puff, redden and water. He kept interrupting the little talk to clear his nasal passages by snorting through them and he had a restless way of lumbering about as he spoke, padding heavily up and down. "We'll be pullin' out of here tomorrow morning, goin' back now into action. An' this time we're really gonna smack those Krauts." He looked around with a little smile at the group of unsmiling, watchful faces. "Are there any questions before I put the map away?"

There was a long moment of silence and then a voice spoke.

"Yes, Cap'm." In surprise I saw it was O'Rourke. "I'd like to—I'd like to study that map if it's all right. I—I always like to get the territory clear in my mind."

The others remained looking rigidly before them. The captain handed over the map and O'Rourke sat down on one of the cots and puzzled over it. The conversation again became bantering.

Soon, all in a moment, by some unspoken word, it was time for us to leave. The air outside was stinging sharp and clear and cold after the closeness and heat of the tent. We separated and went to our shelter-halves for the night.

The next morning we struck the tents and by eight-thirty had boarded the trucks and were leaving for the long ride up

128

into Belgium. It was a magnificent winter day, very cold but brilliantly blue-and-white, with the sun dazzling on the snow. The trucks were uncovered and again we were wrapped in one blanket. I had managed to get my shoes on over all the adhesive tape and the sensation was not too bad. Riding along, we were forced to sit with our heads turned away from the wind, gazing out the back. Everywhere you looked there were views similar to the photographed Christmas cards entitled "Winter Wonderland," "Snow Scene," "The Brook in Winter." Now and then a pine branch let go its weight of snow and sprang up, and the air about it turned all crystalline and rainbowed with the flakes. Ours were the only vehicles ever on the roads and we rode fast, down steep hills, past tall craggy gray stone castles, through icy forests, through cold blue shadows, up into the chill sunlight again. At some point in the afternoon we crossed the border into Belgium.

We had been given C rations for the trip. For each meal there were two cans. One, the dry ration, contained round crackers, the slip of Nescafé and three or four hard candies; the other, a slightly larger can, held stew-and-vegetables or hash. There was no way of heating this, and toward three o'clock I tried to eat the stew cold. It was frozen solid and didn't taste very good. After eating about a third, I gave the rest away and put the spoon back into my pocket. A shivering man nearby finished a can of stew that had slivers of ice all through it.

Some of the litter bearers were riding on the long bench opposite, and I noticed that the small, pasty, light-haired boy named Burrell was asleep most of the time, his head fallen forward. Now that I placed him, I remembered him Christmas Eve night falling asleep in the middle of the singing and burning himself against the stove. As darkness came on over the snowy Belgian fields, his head nodded, dropping farther forward till you could see his bare neck in the back, and I wondered that the collar of his overcoat didn't choke him. Finally his helmet fell off onto the floor of the truck and he started up with a scream.

"My head! My *head!* Oh, my God, my *head* is blown off! Oh, my God, my God!" He tried to scoop the helmet up and get it back on.

Those around him looked at him in astonishment and then broke into laughter. Sam Benton, Jr., laughed so hard he had to stamp his feet and pound his knees.

"Ha-ha-ha-ha! Ole Burrell—his helmet drops off an' he thought it was his head! Oh, m' gosh, thought it was his head. Thought his head come off. Ha-ha-ha-ha-ha!"

Burrell came out of the nightmare abashed, smiled around uneasily and a few minutes later was asleep again, his head beginning to nod and fall forward.

"Isn't there something dead wrong with Burrell?" I asked Phil Schaeffer, who was riding beside me.

He looked concerned, not liking to admit what was painful but obvious. "Yes, there—there is something wrong there, I'm afraid. He seems to have a form of sleeping sickness."

Sam Benton, Jr., was still laughing about it. "Ha-ha-ha-ha! Ole Burrell thought he had his head blown off. Was tryin' to stick it back on. Funniest thing Ah ever saw!"

Nearing eleven o'clock that night we got down off the trucks, moved off the road into the snowy woods, dug fox-holes and went to sleep. Very early the next morning we were up and climbing into the trucks again. The day was dark; it felt as though it might snow at any moment. I rode again with Phil Schaeffer on one side and this time with Ted Jameson on the other. Both were considerate of what little space there was, and both were easy to talk to. In Ted Jameson's case, it was more a matter of listening, for in a few minutes his life story voluntarily poured out.

He came from Lynsdale, a very small town in Pennsylvania, and he had a sister, Janet, who was still in high school. Their mother died when Teddy was about eight, but he still remembered her. "She was very pretty," he said, "but always sort of delicate. She was a little bit hunchbacked on one side, but she wore little capes so you'd hardly notice it at all."

After she died he, his father and sister went back to live with his maternal grandparents; his father at the time had a job traveling. The grandparents, considered well-to-do in the neighborhood, were domineering and stingy, Teddy said. They owned a big farm and in addition the grandfather worked on the railroads. The grandmother, Winnie, was a cruel martinet. Once a year she and her husband put on evening clothes and went to a railroad organization dance where they climaxed the evening and brought the house down by doing an exhibition Charleston.

Phil Schaeffer was shocked and exclaimed, "My word, Ted!" He looked around to make sure.

130

"And then," Teddy said, delighted with Phil's reaction, "one time my father came back from a trip on the road and surprised us all by bringing home a wife. Very pretty and about nineteen years old. She was an Italian and her father was a barber—"

"Was she nicer to you than your grandmother?" I asked.

"Oh, sometimes she was and sometimes she wasn't. She used to bang our heads together and she'd lock Jan up if she cried. She had a terrible temper, I remember. Other times she'd take Jan and stand her on a table and dress her all up like a doll. But she was from a big city, from Pittsburgh, and she didn't know anyone in Lynsdale, and, like in winter, there was nothing to do: my father would be away on a trip and we'd be snowbound. She had a big fat sister used to come over once in a while, and *she* was nice to us; she'd talk and cook big spaghetti dinners for us and all, but she could never stay for very long. She used to try to advise my stepmother. I always remember her in the other room, talking and talking to her. But after about a year my stepmother just suddenly ran away with some man."

"Ran away!" Phil glanced around again, frowning with astonishment. His own background was quite different from this. His father was a newspaper editor and his mother, who wrote to him daily and sent profuse clippings marked with a blue or red pencil, collected early-American glass. Phil himself was a graduate of Rutgers; he had never worked and before joining the Army had spent his time taking graduate courses. He was interested in history and politics.

"And you know what?" Teddy asked with a smile, pausing for dramatic emphasis. "A few weeks later she was found murdered."

"Murdered! Good God!" Phil looked in alarm at me.

"In a hotel room some place. And they never found who did it. So then we had to go back and live with my grandmother again, and she was mean to Jan and that made me mad, and oh, I don't know, you always had to work. Before going to school you had to get up at five o'clock, chop the wood and all that."

"Hard work . . . never hurt anyone," Phil said, but in a faltering voice, as if all his previous convictions about life were being undermined.

"And then one time, I don't know what I was doing—" all this was told with a faint, smug smile: it didn't affect Teddy

131

nearly as much as it did the sheltered Phil—"I was reading and my grandmother asked me to do something and because I didn't do it right away she got mad and pulled my hair—I was about eleven—so I reached over and pulled *her* hair, good and hard. She slapped me, and I slapped her back, just as hard. Sure!" He smiled, still satisfied with the encounter. "And that night she told my grandfather on me, and the next day he told me to pack all my clothes and he drove me down into town to this lawyer's house, and I lived there with them for a couple of years in return for my work."

"What?" Phil asked sharply. "You mean your grandfather made a *deal* with this lawyer and turned you *over* to them—"

"Well, of course." Teddy's smile asked, hadn't Phil ever heard of such an arrangement? "I was to look after the kids and keep them from always fighting; I had to help out around the barn and go on all the errands. I wasn't allowed to go back and see Jan and that was the bad part, but the people were better to me than my grandmother and grandfather, and the oldest boy, Keith—that's the one I write to in the Army—when we were growing up we were like brothers. He was taking piano lessons, and when he used to be practicing he showed me how to play a little. He was going to college when he was drafted. Of course, we weren't such good friends after we grew up and he went away to school, but I lived there in their house about three years, and then one night—it was in June—I was in bed, my grandfather drove up, and they had a long talk downstairs, and then he came up and told me to get up and pack my clothes, and I went home with him again. He never said why or a thing."

"And all that while, all those three years," asked Phil, horrified, "didn't your own father *object?*"

"Well, no."

Phil could only make a crowing noise in the back of his throat. The men opposite us in the truck sat with their blankets pulled down over their heads. The convoy rumbled through a snowy village and out into the blowing white country again.

"Winnie and I," Ted continued, "got along better then. I was older and bigger, and I guess she was afraid of hitting me, and it was nice being back with Jan. Jan's nice. See, so then there was this woman who used to be a friend of my mother's, Clara." He pronounced it "Clair-a." "Her husband died, and she has three children. She's sort of plump and nice

132

and motherly, and then my father married her." Phil gave another start. "That was just a few years ago, just a little while before I came into the Army, so that's where we live now, with Clair-a, in her house."

"Well, that makes it nice for your sister," I began optimistically, but Ted, a realist, had to weigh this for a moment, lips pursed.

"Well, not too nice." Life went on; there were no easy, happy endings. "You see, Clair-a's got a daughter, Sue Ann, a year older than Jan, and I mean she's sort of spoiled and jealous. Sue Ann has to come first with everything. She's very pretty and all—she's going to be a beauty-parlor operator—but people somehow like Jan better and she has to be careful so Sue Ann doesn't get jealous of her. That's why, like when I was going home on furlough, if I brought something for Jan, I'd have to bring something just as good to Sue Ann; or if I took Jan out some place one night, I'd have to take Sue Ann out the next."

"What were you doing at the time you were drafted?"

A little ashamed, he said, "Well, I was left back in my last year of high school and I was making up some subjects. I was taking a commercial course, typing and all that. I never *wanted* to, but my grandfather—see, we were living with him at the time—he made me. He said I had to take something practical, 'cause that's how he is."

Like a dragonfly, Teddy darted from subject to subject, making the switch without preamble. "In my last letter, Christmas, I wrote and asked Clair-a to make me some cupcakes with icing on them. I don't think she'd mind, do you? She wrote me a letter and signed it 'Mother,' so I think she'll do it for me. I thought if I could just taste a cupcake with some icing . . . If she sends them, I'll save you one. You know, I did work for a while. My grandfather got me a job in this factory he has an interest in. A canning factory, and I was the only boy in the whole place. They were all old, old ladies." Here Phil nudged me so violently I kept toppling into Teddy. "But we got along all right; they talked to me and— It was like downstairs, and we had to bring our lunch every day, and they'd make tea and we'd all eat it together. Did I tell you Winnie belongs to the Eastern Star? Every year they get all dressed up— They all have the same evening dress: it's lace, and every year they change it a little so it's in style, and they have little corsages on it, and then everyone says

133

how young Winnie looks, and she does!" There came another switch. "The last time I was home on furlough, I got off the train about four o'clock and walked down to where my father works. I saw his car parked there, so I thought I'd wait and drive home with him. Well, the car was locked, and while I was standing beside it, waiting, a lot of men came and they looked out a big window—it's on the second floor—and they called down, like, 'Welcome home, Ted!' and 'How does it feel to be in the Army?' It was nice, you know? And then I heard one of them say, 'Go and tell Ted Jameson his son is out there waiting.' So they went away and after a while my father came to the window and I yelled, 'Hello, Dad!' and I waved, but he just stood there looking down at me with his hands in his pockets. He just stood there and never said a word. I don't know why. Then he walked away again. It made me feel so *funny*. Ooh, it's cold, isn't it? I'm going to put my head inside."

Snow was blowing up from the ground in great storming clouds and practically everyone had his blanket pulled down over his face. To the Belgians, we must have looked like doomed prisoners on their way to be executed.

Sitting facing me on the floor of the truck was Old Man Owens, formerly of C Company and now one of the Battalion Command Post guards. All during the cold ride yesterday he had sat, the last man on the row, like a fierce-eyed old rooster, the only one in the truck who had not bothered to wrap a blanket around him. Somehow one could never feel sorry for him, though no one ever spoke to him or he to anyone, save when he would ask a question, usually ten minutes late. "Goin-n-n-g-g-g to move out-t, ar-*r*-r-re we?" he'd ask with astonishing articulation. Back at C Company and now at Battalion Headquarters men went about imitating him: "Goin-n-n-g-g to move out-t, *ar-r*-re we?"

He was a rifleman, forty-two years old, small, rigid-looking, square-faced and gimlet-eyed, one of the first to be inducted into the Army. There was a rumor that because of his age he could have got out but had refused the chance. Against me he harbored a bitter resentment. On one of the few occasions when I heard him speaking to someone, it had been in the dark, and he was complaining that by rights he should have been given the job I had with the medics. Along with having once worked in a PX—no one could believe this

—he claimed in the first year of the war to have worked in a General Hospital too.

Now, looking at each other in silence, we rode hour after hour in the blowing snow. At around two o'clock I ate the dry part of the C ration—the crackers and the three hard candies—and had a swallow of cold water. That had been my breakfast too. Though hungry, I couldn't eat the frozen stew.

From inside his coat Old Man Owens pulled out a heavy ration chocolate bar. In the apple orchard Captain Hillier had permitted him, in view of the supposed experience in the PX, to portion out our rations, and Chris Taylor told me Old Man Owens had a wealth of chocolate bars cached away. Thinking I could not see him through the slit in my blanket, which I had pulled down over my face, he gnawed rapidly at the bar. He had extra-large teeth and badly chapped white lips; trying to bolt the candy, chocolate-colored saliva drooled from the corners of his mouth. I would have given him twenty-five dollars for one of the bars, but I knew even if he had not disliked me that he would have denied having any, for he was strange and secretive. My blanket suddenly blew back and left us staring at each other, he with the chocolate bar halfway to his mouth. Giving me a bitter glance, he closed his teeth around the block, snapped it off, and had great difficulty thereafter in maneuvering it. I felt my stomach rumble emptily and had all I could do to keep from begging him for a bar at whatever price he'd name. I lit a cigarette. Everyone else sat shrouded in a blanket.

An hour or so later Owens took out another thick chocolate bar and snapped off a corner with his square teeth. Knowing he'd prefer me to look the other way, I had my revenge by watching him, unblinking, until he had self-consciously and uncomfortably finished the last bit of it.

Nearby us on one of the long benches there was another C Company man, a sergeant called V.D. because he had contracted a venereal disease while we were back at camp. He had wild, fixed, blue eyes in a face that had once been burned away in a gasoline explosion and then was rebuilt by plastic surgeons. His lashes were gone and his skin in patches was a bright pinkish-red. The features, though good, even fine, seemed unsubstantial and corrupt, as if with a push one's hand could go through them. His lips were thin, very red; they pulled back into a wide, mirthless smile during which the lost, lashless blue eyes continued to stare wildly, as if from behind a mask. I found it difficult to look at him. One night, I recalled, at Stone in England during our month's stay, while I was on guard at the entrance to the mews where we were billeted, he went past me on the dark street, chasing a skittish young prostitute. He was chuckling and the coins jingled in his pockets as he broke into a run, keeping close to the shadows of the buildings. He caught up to the girl at the corner, and in the moonlight she saw his face. She gave a scream of terror that could have been heard for blocks. There was a scuffle and I heard him cursing. The girl, gasping, broke away from him and took to her heels. A few minutes later he came past me, walking slowly into the mews, crushed, his hands in his pockets. As a staff sergeant in the United States, he was the cruelest I had encountered. While undergoing treatment, he had been broken to the rank of private and worked in the Supply Room. He was friendless, and if men jokingly reminded him of his disease, he said, "Hey, how's about gettin' off my back, hey?"

Sitting beside him now on the truck was a very young, lonesome farm boy, a replacement who had just joined us. He was carrying with him a battered package from home. There was cheap, hard Christmas candy in it and a crumbled layer cake with icing that had violently colored dots on it. To open the package made him homesick. Without speaking, he offered the box around to those whose faces were not covered with a blanket, and they, not knowing him well, turned strangely refined and in constrained silence each took one tiny thing. Not so V.D. He slung his arm about the boy, put his blanket over both their heads, shook it down well over them and in about ten minutes the blanket came off. The empty box was tossed over the side.

The appearance of the countryside began to change: stretches of bare frozen earth showed through the snow, then gradually the snow left off entirely. We were riding along a dirt road that tunneled through a deep woods. The afternoon was declining. The trucks stopped; we climbed down, buckled on our equipment and marched a short way through the woods into a clearing, our feet scuffling through deep drifts of brown leaves. A steep hill rose up, shutting off the wind. The place seemed ominously silent. When I looked behind me, I saw that, aside from the medics, there was only a platoon from Battalion Headquarters in our group. The trees soared up, huge and bare, with greenish-gray trunks that were covered with moss on one side. Sergeant Campbell came along with little Lieutenant Serletis trotting at his heels. "Medics, this way. Follow me. No noise."

We started up the steep hill, weighed down by our overcoats, overshoes and full field pack. The climb became difficult, but spurring one on there was a sense of escaping from danger. Shortly the trees with the silvery-green trunks fell away below us and thick, almost impenetrable pines took their place. Now and again we came upon a narrow, meandering, orange-colored footpath and scrambled up it.

On the top of the hill we separated from the Headquarters men and, led by Sergeant Campbell, pushed our way through the tough pines, and there, in a thicket, were told to dig in.

"Dig 'em deep," Lieutenant Serletis warned. "Don't make any noise, and no matter what you do, don't go lighting any cigarettes. No lights of any kind! The Jerries are all around here, all over the place. When you get your foxhole dug, cover it over good with logs. Good heavy logs. We don't know *what's* gonna happen."

The typical arguments began, in by no means quiet voices. "*We* had this place!" "Git the hell outta there, *we* had it. Go find someplace else."

Dick Gann and I started to dig where we were and almost at once struck a tough, tight web of pine roots. I hacked at them with the pick mattock, wanting to get as much done as possible before dark, for then I could never see where or what I was digging.

"I want—I—I w-want this—be good an' deep," Dick was saying ten minutes later. I worked too fast, grew winded and was forced to sit down. Then Dick became tired and rested while I used his little shovel.

When it was almost dark, I said, "The hell with digging any more, Dick. Let's hurry up and roll the stuff out."

But Dick was not to be dissuaded. "I—I want—I'm—I—I'm not takin' no—no chances on eighty-eights."

It started to snow. Great thick flakes came swirling down. I ripped open my pack and hung my rifle upside down on the limb of a tree.

"Dick, the snow's covering the bottom of the foxhole; we can't bother getting logs or anything else. We'll have to put a shelter-half over us and trust to luck."

137

Grumbling, he gave in. A high wind was now blowing and it was difficult to see. We took off our overshoes, shook the snow from our field jackets, and crawled into our sleeping sacks.

We were lying down perhaps ten minutes when muffled through the shelter-half I heard Lieutenant Serletis' voice crying, "Let's go! Let's go, let's go, let's *go!*" He always said it rapidly and desperately. "Come on, you guys, let's go there!" I didn't know whether it was he or someone imitating him, but I threw back the corner of the shelter-half and heard voices: "Go?" "Go where?" "What the hell is this 'Let's go'?"

"Let's go-o-o-o!" he cried somewhere in the snowstorm. "Let's *go,* you guys! We gotta get *outta* here!"

I jumped up and started to roll my equipment, and my hands turned powerless with the cold; it was a race between the numbness and pulling the straps tight. And why couldn't the straps have been made an inch or two longer? A genius had gauged them so that they would just barely meet the buckles, but he had not taken into account the fact that equipment was not always rolled under perfect garrison conditions, that snow enlarged everything. Damn everyone in moments like this! Now where were my overshoes?

"Let's go!" Sergeant Campbell was crying. "Line up, me-e-n, we're movin' out!" Motors had started up somewhere, and Battalion Headquarters men began to rush along the road, almost running. I got into my overcoat, buttoned it, clasped on the heavy ammunition belt, put on the pack, the gas mask, and was about to run and join the others when I remembered, and missed, my rifle. I should have taken it into the foxhole with me. I knew I had hung it upside down on a tree, but now the trees were furry with snow and unfamiliar, and the air was thick with swirling flakes. As I rushed about from tree to tree—like old blind Pew, I always thought—I could hear Sergeant Campbell calling the roll. I was about to give up when a last despairing search produced the M1 entirely camouflaged by snow. I grabbed it and ran out onto the road just in time to fall in on the end of the line as it moved out. For one of the few times that I could remember, Sergeant Campbell forgot that I was attached to the medics.

On the double, at break-neck speed, we rushed down the narrow road, slipping and falling in the hurried descent.

"Where we going, Sergeant Campbell?"

No answer. No knowing why, how far, what was going on. Nor, as far as I was concerned, was there anything to see but the dim bulk of the man hurrying ahead, the dark line of footprints in the snow, the white branches whipping against shoulder and face. Down, down the hill, and at the bottom running and trotting in all the heavy equipment along fairly even ground through the snowy woods, then suddenly up another steep hill . . .

At the top we came to a halt and were told to dig in again, to dig deep, keep quiet and cover the foxholes once more with heavy logs. Without proper food for the past few days, I was dead tired, and since, with the little pick, I was more of a hindrance to Dick than a help, I told him to dig his own foxhole and I'd dig mine. The snow blew from every direction. We were in a more open place, on flatter ground, and I could hardly see the two nearest men bending and rising with their shovels. I made a pretense of turning over the ground with the pick mattock, waiting for the others to finish so that I could wrap myself in the shelter-half and lie down. It was in emergencies like this that one saw the advantage of youth. Bob Russell and Don Stoddard dug like tireless mechanical men, working evenly and neatly.

Within an hour they were all settling down to sleep. I had a shallow excavation made and I wrapped myself up, pulled the triangular flap of the shelter-half over my face and lay down, trusting no truck or jeep would mistake me, covered with snow, for an unimportant log.

Once more I had just closed my eyes when Lieutenant Serletis started crying, "Let's *go!* Let's go, let's go, let's *go-o-o!*" There were oaths and curses all about. "What's the matter?" the little lieutenant was shouting. "Don't you guys hear me? I said, 'Let's *go!*' "

"Can't he say anything besides 'Let's go, let's go'?" someone was asking. "Gives me a pain in the ass, 'Let's go' all the time."

There was the same rush, the same frenzied difficulty with frozen fingers trying to make the snowy straps of the pack meet around the snowy roll. At last I was into my harness; I had kept my overshoes on; the rifle was on my shoulder. And then there was an hour-long delay. "Just like the Army," someone was saying. "Hurry up and wait. I'll be goddamned!"

To get out of the falling snow, we withdrew a little from

the clearing to the edge of a grove of beech trees. They were enormously tall; one seemed to look up a quarter of a mile to their top. While we stood there, stamping in the snow in little groups, careless of the five-yard interval, the vehicles pulled out. The conversations going on had, as usual, very little to do with the situation at hand. Phil Schaeffer, Ted Jameson and Paul Clifford stood near me talking idly; small bursts of laughter went up. Whatever the strain or sense of urgency had been felt at the first "Let's go!" now had evaporated. The higher-ups might have been in a sweat at the moment, and doubtless were, but this was the time to be without responsibilities, a private.

Out in the clearing the snow gave off light, but here the huge, bare trees cast a dim shadow and seemed to keep off some of the wind. In the stillness between conversations, you could hear the snow, sounding like intent but distant hail. A half hour passed. I asked the three boys to gather around me, then I bent over, stuck my head inside my overcoat and lit a cigarette. Cupping it in my gloved hands, I began to smoke it. Nearby someone else lit one, then someone farther away. Other men cursed and grumbled at us. The line-company boys started to rush past, and suddenly a tall stranger came galloping across the clearing toward us, and I recognized Lieutenant MacKenzie's voice asking, "You medics? Who's got the cigarettes lit here?" For a moment no one spoke or moved. "Atwell?" he asked, looking around for me.

"Yes. I have the cigarette."

"Then fo' God's sake, give me a drag. Where are you?"

"Here."

He came close, and while I shielded him he bent, took two long drags, said, "Thanks!" and went rushing off across the snow to rejoin his men, blowing out huge plumes of smoke.

"Here's old Campbell," someone said. "Better get rid of the cigarette." I bent down and plunged it into the snow.

"All right, you me-e-n, gonna take off now. Only one squad kin fit in the ambulance. Rest gotta walk. Got a long hike ahead of us. Everyone sure they kin make it? We don't want nobody fallin' out."

There was a little silence. "How far is it going to be?" I asked.

"'Bout fourteen, fifteen miles, maybe. *You* can do it, can't you?"

I said I could, which relieved him, and with that, those of us who were walking lined up and fell into place just behind Battalion Headquarters.

The snow by then was fairly deep, and it was tiring to keep up the fast pace in overshoes and overcoat. The cutting wind blew snow steadily in our faces so that everyone on the two lines marched with his head down and turned to one side. I kept hoping the road would swing abruptly, but even when it did about a half hour later, the wind still continued to drive into our faces. We had to keep brushing the snow from our eyes. Plunging along either side of what was now a fairly broad road in snow growing ever deeper, we looked like the Dispossessed.

Mile after mile after mile . . .

At the start it was not too bad. Though the wind buffeted us and the snow blew stiffly, we grew fairly warm with the speed, the exertion and the constant effort not to slip and fall; and the men talked back and forth quite cheerfully.

It was beautiful countryside we were rushing through: forest, hunting lodge, sweeping hemlocks weighted down with snow, large country houses set down in their parks . . . Passing one such house, a man overtaken with dysentery asked permission to drop out. "If it won't take too long," Captain Christoffsen said; and almost before the words left his mouth, the man handed over his rifle to the next man and had started to run for the waist-high stone wall that surrounded the place. With one wrench, still running, he had his pack and ammunition belt off; just as he came to the wall, he ripped off his overcoat. Continuing his uninterrupted speed, he scaled the wall, unbuckling his pants; the overcoat, sailing in the wind, was just settling near the road. The performance was so expert, it brought a cheer and a roar of laughter.

At times, warned to be absolutely silent, we hurried through a sleeping village, passing beneath its tall elms, leaving no trace but our footsteps, which the snow would soon fill and obliterate.

The hours of continued speed became exhausting, and now, through tiredness, one began to feel the cold again and the weight of the full field pack. "How many more miles?" the men started asking. "Hey, for God's sake, how many more miles?" And here and there a man stumbled out of line, rocked and dropped over, too spent to go any farther. You

141

saw them, dark lumps in the smooth, untrodden snow at the side of the road, a helpless aid man bending over them.

Three o'clock passed. Three-thirty. Four. And now that one was so tired that it no longer seemed to matter, the snow grew finer and began to let up, though the wind continued its icy force. All talk and laughter on the lines had stopped long ago, and the men, their heads bent lower, trudged doggedly on, slipping more frequently, jolting suddenly awake. The smallest hill presented a great obstacle and forced one to keep awake, to struggle. It was only on level stretches or going down long, easy slopes that there was any rest. Then, eyes closed, snatching a few winks of sleep, I could march by memory, waking up when I stumbled or when my head dropped too far forward.

Four-thirty. Five. Toward five-thirty in the morning trucks and long, covered artillery pieces started to roll past. Without waiting for orders or invitations, the men began to move out toward the middle of the road. Like frozen, clumsy crows, they moved up to the rolling equipment and attached themselves to it silently. I walked out into the middle of the road. A truck came by me, very close. I ran a few steps, placed both hands on the snowy fender, took a jump and landed up on it. The assistant driver poked his head out to say I was blocking the view: could I bend down a little? I could.

All the vehicles then started to speed up. The wind tore past me; I had to shut my eyes. I was hanging precariously by one hand, holding the rifle in the other. In a short time the hand that was hanging on and its exposed bare wrist began to freeze. My feet were only a few inches from the speeding wheel. At the first stop, about a mile farther on, I slid off. "Gonna start up again, Mac," the driver called down, but I was too chilled to hang on any longer. I walked stiffly around to the back, and someone in a voice hoarse with laryngitis croaked, "Want to get in? Come on then." It was a two-and-a-half-ton truck with the high back guard up, and it started to move before I was halfway in. A pair of hands grabbed me and hauled me aboard. They belonged to Chipman of C Company. The truck was piled with bulky machinery, and Chipman and I crouched on it, our knees wedged tight against the tailboard. Several other men, too tired to care that we were sitting partly on them also, were stretched over the equipment. "Isn't this a bitch?" Chipman croaked, going into a series of shivers. At camp in South Carolina, Chipman, who was neat-looking, sturdy yet nervous, had aped the tough members of the outfit: the two recalcitrant Smiths who had deserted at the Port of Embarkation rather than come overseas with us, and Braaf, his staunchest friend, matching them curse for curse, and swearing he would obey no order. Here, shivering and with laryngitis, his nervousness was more pronounced and the boastfulness was gone.

After a mile or so I noticed the convoy was breaking up: trucks and jeeps were turning off in different directions. We stopped to be directed by an MP stationed on the road. The driver called back to ask where we were going; an assortment of voices asked where he was going. He was going up the hill a little way to where C Company was to be stationed. I said goodbye to Chipman, climbed down, and he passed my rifle out to me.

A town, ringed close by hills, lay before me in a long hollow, the houses dark squares in the snow. It was just before daylight. Even now there was a break in the dark sky and a thin banner of pale gray was spreading. "First Battalion medics?" I asked an officer standing beside the MP.

He pointed down the hill toward the town. "And hurry it up," he said, shivering. "Get off the streets as fast as you can."

It was only a short distance down into the town of Rondu. I seemed to be the only one abroad at first, but in the middle of the town—a very pretty one with substantial gray stone houses set down in wide snowy lawns and gardens—an excited officer popped up and shouted at me to get off the street, to get out of sight, to get in anywhere. In the middle of his orders, little Lieutenant Serletis came running toward me in an overcoat that reached almost to his heels.

"Atwell? Is that you? Aren't you our new guy?" He appeared lost, frightened, and he looked up at me beseechingly. "Where the hell are the guys?"

"I don't know, sir. I hitched a lift for a while. I lost them."

"Oh, Jesus, this is all f---ed up. No one knows where anyone is! Oh, holy God!"

The excited officer shouted to the two of us that the Germans were on the hills, that we were to launch a surprise attack; at any moment it would be light enough for them to see us. "Now get out of here! *Scatter!*"

143

Lieutenant Serletis raced down one driveway while I ran down the next one. A garden separated us. "Atwell, if you see any of the guys, tell them I'm in here," he called. I planned on hiding in a sheltered side doorway I saw ahead, but when I reached it, it was not as sheltered as I thought. Standing against it, I was in plain sight of the nearby hills. Why hadn't I run in with Lieutenant Serletis? Because the officer had said, "Scatter!" and I had obeyed instinctively. Then, realizing that everyone was indoors somewhere, I turned the knob behind me. The door swung in, and, rather surprised at myself, I stepped into a black hall that had a rough tile floor. There was a comfortable, clean smell. It was too dark to see anything, and while I was moving quietly forward, my hand up before my face, I heard the mumble of voices. I waited a moment and discovered with relief that they were American.

I made my way toward them, found a door, pushed it open, and saw by the flare of a match someone was applying to a cigarette that the room was crowded with soldiers lying on the floor. The match went out. I stepped on someone, then over someone, and, feeling an open space, let myself down. My God, at last, I thought, out of that freezing wind. At first I lay as I was, bound in all my equipment. I was lying on a cold tiled floor in a room that was blacked out. I wanted a cigarette, made the effort, unbuckled my ammunition belt and worked my arms out of my pack; then I found the red plastic case, took out a cigarette and lighted it. Across the room Ted Jameson's voice said, "There's Les Atwell!"

"Is that Ted? Are the medics here?"

Several of them, including Sergeant Campbell and Mike Nowak, answered. I told them about Lieutenant Serletis being lost, and they burst into laughter. Sergeant Campbell asked if I'd go over and tell him where they were in case there were any casualties.

By the time I made my way out of the house, I was surprised to see how the sky had lightened. Racing back into the house after delivering the message, I found my place again on the floor of the kitchen. "Yeah," I heard a worried voice saying, "we're jumpin' off at ten o'clock."

"The Jerries got the high ground, I hear."

"What time's it now, I wonder. Anyone got the time?"

Someone said it was almost seven o'clock, and for the first

time I began to see just how lucky I was. I would have no active part in that attack or in any other as long as I was kept with the medics. Everyone appeared to be as exhausted as I was; after the grueling night, I wondered where and how they found the stamina to face the thought of an attack.

Above us in the dark house a door closed, the stairs creaked. Everyone became still. Soft-soled footsteps descended, came along the tiled hall. The kitchen door was pushed open; a man, blocking it on our side, had to move out of the way. In the silence that followed his moving, we heard the sharp intake of a breath. Whoever it was—a woman—retreated swiftly and went back up the stairs. The door remained half open and in the upper hall we could hear voices whispering as a family consultation was held. By this time one of the men produced the stump of a candle, lighted it, and, when some wax had melted, he set it on the kitchen table.

The woman came back cautiously, yet it was brave of her, for she couldn't have known whether we were German or American. Perhaps at that it wouldn't have mattered, for surely the family had discussed the alternatives. Holding her breath, her eyes enlarged, she stood looking into her kitchen, a large, stout, light-haired woman in a long woolen dressing gown. Someone finally said to her, "Guten morgen." She stepped into the room. Sprawling legs were drawn back to make room for her to pass by; some of the men lounged to their feet.

"Guten morgen," she whispered back, and said "Ach!" to the condition of her floor, wet with melted snow puddles. She crossed over to the stove, shook it down and began to light the fire. In silence, she filled the kettle and set it on one of the rings. Most of the men got to their feet and moved over to the stove, drawn by the flickering orange light. The woman, staring at the flame, stood hemmed in close, and at first her breathing was shallow and frightened; then she relaxed as the men began to warm their hands and set their little cans of K ration on the stove to heat. Someone offered her a cigarette. "Here, Mom. Want a butt?"

"Danke, nein," she declined, pressing her hand to her bosom.

Now her husband came into the kitchen, a tall, thin, light-haired man, middle-aged, smiling but not quite likable: I could not forgive him for sending his wife in first. A tall blond boy, sixteen or seventeen, in a heavy embroidered sweater, plus fours and stocking feet, followed immediately after the father; his manner was more open, more genuinely friendly, almost exhilarated. He kept smiling broadly, shaking hands, making stiff little bows, and he began to speak a few words in English: "Welcome. Welcome. Pardon—I do not speak—good. Welcome to Americans. In school I learn the little—no, *a* little English." He laughed. "But not—" He meant that he had lost what little fluency he once might have had. "Yah, school," he said, shaking hands with one of the men. "High school, no? United States soldiers good. Friends. Friends to come to us." He accepted a cigarette and beamed.

The father had gone out and returned with a loaf of dark bread, at the sight of which my hunger grew suddenly boundless. He stood beside me at the kitchen table and started to cut through a slice, smiling and looking at me inquiringly. Though I didn't like him, I smiled back, nodding my head. He had not cut all the way through, and now he paused and raised his light eyebrows. I fished out my wallet, took out one of the bills, not knowing whether it was two and a half, five or ten dollars, and gave it to him. Then quickly he cut through the rest of the slice, went out of the room and came back with it spread with pale butter. It tasted delicious.

The rest of the men began to offer him cigarettes and cans of ration meat for a slice of bread, and a thriving business went on until a loaf and a half were gone. The rest of the bread suddenly disappeared, and when the men asked for it the owner of the house pretended not to understand. He lifted his thin shoulders, spread out his hands continuing to smile.

The son, in the meanwhile, embarrassed by the father's business transaction, moved about, an ambassador of good will, shaking hands when hands were offered, saying, "I like United States," and refusing cigarettes because he still had one.

Smaller brothers came down into the kitchen, which now was beginning to grow warm. It was the sort of kitchen, pine-paneled, with old hand-painted chests and simple furniture, that was becoming increasingly popular in the United States. The indoor wooden blinds now were opened and fas-

146

tened back against the wall, and a snowy light filled the room. The candle was blown out. Everyone seemed to draw a breath; the sleepless night was over and one was awake for the day.

The younger boys, smiling and excited, were of assorted ages, coming down, I imagined, to seven or eight; and there was a tall, pretty, athletic-looking daughter of about fifteen who appeared briefly, spoke to her mother in a whisper and was sent immediately upstairs again. The family seemed to be in comfortable circumstances; the father was a professor. The little boys, quickly popular, trying not to smile in anticipation, watched all the preparations for the soldiers' breakfast: wrappings coming from crackers and lumps of sugar, cans of cheese being opened, sticks of gum appeared. The men offered the woman and the little boys wedges of food on the blades of dirty pocket knives. The tastes were strange and delicious to them, particularly the orange-colored pork-and-carrot which most of us disliked. "You can eat it," someone told me, "if you sprinkle the bouillon powder all over it. It kills the taste."

While eating, the men continued to mill clumsily about in their open overcoats, helmets and overshoes. As soon as the ration was eaten and the hot coffee drunk, the warmth of the kitchen made everyone tired. Yawns were catching. The talk and movement gradually died down. Thin sunlight was filtering through the milky fog. The men, already bored with the family, left the woman to gather up the ration boxes, the wrappings and greasy empty cans; they slumped down on the floor and most of them fell asleep. A few cleaned their rifles. The hour for the attack grew nearer and nearer. I could almost feel sorry for the family of Belgian boys who had enjoyed their moment of popularity and now could not understand the sudden loss of it. Ignored, they looked at each other, ill at ease.

Within a half hour word came that the attack had been called off; mysteriously, the Germans had retreated.

"Oh," the men said dully. "Good. God. Thank God." As opposed to what I had heard or read, there was no great jubilation, no cases of taut nerves snapping. In fact, there was hardly any reaction at all. They slumped back again and went back to sleep.

An hour or so later we had to pack up and leave the house.

147

Late afternoon of the same day found us riding in open trucks again. Too cold any longer to look out at the snowy gray and white and black countryside, I drew the blanket down over my face and held it closed. When the truck stopped, I thought it would be for only a moment or two, but a voice cried, "All out! This is it, boys." I threw back the blanket and saw a few cheerless frame houses on either side of a country road.

We climbed down and started to walk along the road leading past the small farmhouses out into the country. In the distance there was the sound of shelling.

"Hey, medics, we're in here," called Mike Nowak's voice. "Here" was a cheap little green plaster house, the last on the road which turned at that point and stretched off through a thin woods. The barn was situated on the turn of the road. "The aid station's set up in the barn. Come on in the house and get warm."

We went in the side door, along a narrow hall into a dining room that had lace-curtained windows looking out toward the barn. The captain, Lieutenant Serletis, Sergeant Campbell and some of the others had just finished looking at a map. They sat at the table in the thin, dark warmth, silent, all with their helmets on. Outside in the snow, trucks lumbered past empty and a line of infantrymen went straggling by. This was, one gathered, a temporary halt, yet there was an air of worry in the room. They did not tell us what it was and somehow one could not ask. In fact, we new arrivals were not quite welcome. Not daring to take a seat, we stood about in silence just inside the door.

Someone hurried along the hall to announce that there was a casualty being brought in. The captain and those around the table got up hastily. Since my job was to take the equipment from the wounded, I followed after them. We crossed the frozen yard and went into the barn. It was dark in there and chill, with a hayloft and cows in their stalls; vapor came from their nostrils. One of the men was trying hurriedly to light the lantern. Just as he had it going and the light began to fan out, four litter bearers, straining, breathing hard, came in swiftly with a man on the litter and set him down on the straw. Everyone else crowded around, but I did not want to see the wound. My one unwilling glance had shown a thin, dark boy, perhaps twenty years of age, with cheekbones standing out and dark, frightened eyes trying to focus, to understand where he was and what had happened to him.

"Get out! Get out, all of you!" Captain Stettner cried, suddenly ill-tempered. "Everyone clear out of here. Only the ones supposed to stay, stay."

A group of us stumbled out. I remained outside at the barn doors; the others returned to the house. Presently someone hurried out of the barn and sprinted for the house; Lieutenant Serletis trotted out after him on his little legs, his dark face serious. They went in the side door and came running back shortly after, carrying something—a jar—passing me in silence.

A few minutes went by, then the captain and the five or six who were in the barn came out. "God *damn* it!" someone was saying, and Bob Russell, coming toward them from his truck in the gathering dusk, asked, "What hap—?"

The answer came back: "Dead. He died."

A shock ran through me. In that short time, I thought. A life had gone out of earthly existence forever, and might now have been judged for eternity, a life that had been aimed like a guided missile at this moment, through childhood and school days, through the first pair of roller skates, the first two-wheel bike, through Christmases at home, through high school and baseball and first dates, to meet death here, frightened and bewildered, among strangers in a dark barn, on New Year's Eve in Belgium.

Lieutenant Serletis was visibly more affected than the others; he kept muttering curses to himself and shaking his head. I trailed after them and near the house heard him explain to someone, "Goddam blood plasma was frozen! Couldn't thaw it out, couldn't *give* it to the guy. Might have saved his life. Yeah, well, it's a lesson. After this, I guess they gotta be sure the stuff's not frozen." The others said nothing. Separate from each other, they continued to walk over the trampled-down snow toward the house.

I assumed that the convoy had run into some resistance and that the line-company men were clearing the path. Actually, an attack was in progress on the town of Remange about a half mile away. Artillery shells crashed and exploded in the woods.

My God, I kept thinking, how lonesome that death was a few minutes ago! No chaplain near him, no one to offer comfort, to take a last message. What could the boy have thought of, being carried jolting on the litter? Hadn't part of his mind hoped for a hospital bed, for clean sheets, warmth, skilled hands, a ship home, only to find a dark cold barn, a row of cows, a hissing lantern, unknown faces, bungling hands, a frozen bottle of blood plasma?

In a few minutes, more wounded men, victims of mines or shrapnel, were carried into the barn. I waited at the door till they had been treated and bandaged, then went in and from the straw gathered up what equipment had been ripped off them: ammunition belts, bandoleers, hand grenades, steel helmets, gas masks—in some cases slippery, blood-stained field jackets. Looking surprisingly peaceful—even relieved —the wounded lay on stretchers, covered up to the chin with army blankets, waiting for the ambulance to drive them to the field hospital.

It was then almost evening. Stars came out, and in the bitter, cold dusk a soldier approached me uncertainly. When he was close, I saw that his eyes, pale in a dark-complexioned face, were fixed and dilated. He was talking in French, as if in a daze, then, half whispering, half aloud, drawing the word out, he said, "Noi-i-se! The noi-i-se!" His eyes became even larger and he started plucking at my sleeve.

A distant shell exploded. He moistened his lips, then harkened, one finger raised. I could think only of a moving-picture actor giving a fairly good, not wholly convincing performance. Whispering in French, he started to go past me into the barn, but I said, "You can't go in now; there's a wounded man being bandaged." Then, thinking I might be misjudging him, I asked, "Would you like a cigarette while you're waiting?" I had been smoking my last one before dark, cupping it.

"Yes," he said. "The noise . . . The noise, you know."

I said, "You'll have to cup the cigarette," and I gave him a light from the tip of mine. He bent toward it, his hand covering mine, and in the act his face was absorbed; it had lost its vacancy of expression. There was a heavy college ring on his finger. Once again the cigarette was going, he said, "The noi-i-se!"

I remained silent and he stood a short distance away, his

collar turned up, hunching over to inhale. From inside the barn Preacher called, "Anyone else out there?"

"Yes, there's one," I said.

With that the man stepped on his cigarette, began his delirious talk in French and went inside the barn.

About five minutes later I heard the captain's voice saying near the doorway, "Take this man over to Battalion Headquarters and tell them I said to let him rest up a few days around the kitchen. He'll be all right."

Resting up around any kitchen meant working as a KP. The man, who was about twenty-four, was led out past me by a medic, whispering, "The noi-i-se. The noi-i-se!" The two figures went down the road and disappeared into the gloom.

A Third Army rule forbade the men to sleep in billets, but the captain went over to Battalion Headquarters and stated that during the bitter cold weather he could not run an aid station outdoors. His tent was not large enough at times to hold all the wounded, and as a consequence, some of the men had to be left lying outside in the snow while waiting to be treated. He insisted that he needed some kind of shelter, and preferably one that could be heated.

That night he and the aid-station complement slept in the farmhouse. Under the law, the litter bearers and I were supposed to be out in foxholes, but instead, we slept in the barn. The men said, "Sleeping in the hay! Boy, that's a good deal! Nice and warm in the hay."

It wasn't warm at all. The hay was like ice; in turning it over, it gave out a cold breath, and drafts of icy air blew up through it all night long. However, we were infinitely more comfortable than the men in the line companies; there was a roof over us, and it was a quiet night. No shells were falling. "They took the town," Captain Stettner told us, "and now they're all buttoned up." The straw scrunched and rustled as the men settled down in the dark, and now and then you heard the animals pawing and moving in their stalls.

"Well, men, it's a hell of a way to celebrate New Year's Eve," said O'Rourke's voice, and for a moment, like a fireworks flower, I saw a New Year's Eve party from a few years back: a room with a lighted Christmas tree, people in paper hats gathering with champagne glasses for a toast, and a girl in a silver-and-white evening dress pulling a cord that

151

sent draperies rocking back from the windows, so that out-side you saw the lights of New York, and all the horns and whistles and church bells started.

The dark, cold barn was completely silent, and just outside it in the snow a dead man was lying.

1945 January

New Year's Day, when one of the other battalions passed through us and took over, we came back to Rondu. Toward evening, with some of the Battalion Headquarters men, we left in the first of two open trucks and, with a jeep leading us, rolled out of the town, taking a road that tunneled through the forest. I heard Don Stoddard saying to the man next to him, "This is called the Forest of the Ardennes." The cold evening air, the snow, the trees—everything turned blue, as if all about us deepening veils of that color were sifting down. Somewhere in the distance shells were falling. The road turned and we emerged into a small, flat, open stretch of country. In almost a cowardly way, the trucks began to slow down. A roaring explosion went off. There was a confused outcry from the men.

"Hey! What's happening here? Look at that! 'Way out there!" In the indigo twilight, something burned red-gold, like a cannon ball. "That's an ammunition dump!"

"The hell it is! That's one of our ammunition trucks—it hit a mine!"

The little convoy came up to an open crossroad and halted.

"Road block ahead! We can't get through!"

A barrage of tracer bullets streaked over our heads, and there came the whistling, loud crash of a German shell landing very near us in the field.

"Hey, get us out of here! Hey, driver! *Driver!*"

While the enemy shells continued to come in, the two big trucks began to execute a full turn on the narrow icy road, going into reverse, coming forward, going into reverse, coming forward. At last, at snail's pace, the trucks headed back out of the clearing. Some of the men had dropped to the floor; others, standing, pounded on the side rails, shouting for the driver to get up speed. The trucks went only a short way toward the tunnel of trees when the order was changed. We turned around once more and started back under enemy fire across that same open stretch like ducks in a shooting gallery. Indecisiveness at the helm was communicable. There was no plan. No one knew what to do. My stomach suddenly went into knots. In the same place as before, the trucks halted and waited stupidly.

"What the f--- is this?" the men were shouting. "They're zeroing in on us! Let's get the hell down!" A few started to climb over the side, but another barrage of tracer bullets drove them back to a crouch.

From below us on the road an officer's voice cried, "Don't get down! Stay where you are!"

Large shells whizzed and smashed about us, sending up explosions of snow and great spinning clods of earth.

"My God! Don't you think we'd better jump down?" I asked Phil Schaeffer. I began to tear the blanket off. "It's safer on the ground!"

Someone hopped into the lead-off jeep and it suddenly spurted ahead, bumped off the road into the field, cutting a wide curve in the smooth snow. With one arm raised, the driver made circles over his head, looking drunk or highly nonchalant. After an astonished moment, I realized it was a signal for us to follow, for we started up and lurched crookedly down off the road into the field with half the excited men yelling, "Yay! Yay! Get us the hell *out* of here! Get goin'!" while the other half shouted frantically, "No! No! For crissake, they're taking us right *into* it!" The truck, carefully following the curving lines made by the jeep's tires, headed for a narrow line of bushes and saplings that bordered the intersecting road. If we can only make those *trees,*

I found myself saying. If we can only get out of *sight!* Behind us the barrage had intensified. "Yay! Yay! Faster! *Faster!* Come *on!*"

We smashed through the bushes and bumped crazily down onto the other road. A little farther on, a low hill formed slowly on either side, shielding us at last from sight.

For me, following upon any such unexpected crisis, there always came a space of mental blankness. Around me the men were still chattering excitedly, holding a post-mortem. "We ran into our own road block!" "It was that truck that blew up!" "The whole road must have been mined!" Darkness came fast, but we continued down the side road with no plan, it seemed, except to set as much space between us and the German artillery as possible. Gradually everyone settled down.

Somewhere, later that night, we found the rest of the blacked-out battalion convoy and rode along in line. Over that silent, frozen countryside the sound of the motors, I thought, must have been heard for miles. In the bitter cold the thin blanket and one's clothing seemed to absorb and hold a glacial iciness. There was no experience in civilian life to compare to this, no too prolonged stay ice skating after dark, no winter ride in the rumble seat of a car. Nothing went on like this, unrelieved, hour after hour in the wind's steady buffeting.

For no apparent reason, the convoy halted but the motors kept running. A rumor began, spread by our driver, who had hopped down to speak to the driver ahead, that the whole convoy was lost.

At first it seemed no matter where we went that night in the trucks, or where we stopped, the Germans were there, waiting to fire at us. Here two shells flew in, and the trucks immediately started up. We rolled for another half hour. There came another halt, a wait in the blackness, and after a few minutes bright-orange tracer bullets blazed in dying arcs above us. The badgered trucks pulled out again before the German artillery could zero in.

A few miles farther on there was another halt in a long defile. When the clouds parted, the moon could be seen riding pure white and cold in a clear, dark-blue field, and the stars were brilliant, bluish, and sharp-pointed as crystal. An officer on foot hurried down the long line toward the rear of the convoy. Men called down, "Hey, sir, where the hell are we?"

The bothered officer never replied beyond saying, "Oh" or "Ah." This was a wait of perhaps twenty minutes. Then a jeep doubled back from the head of the column with officers in it, driving swiftly past us.

"They're gonna try'n find the way."

"Now we'll get *real* f---ed up. Leave it to those stupid bastards."

A half hour of sitting still in the truck. Well, at least the wind was not as cutting when one was stationary; it didn't feel as though it were blowing directly through you. What silence! Not a sound but an occasional cough, and, when the wind blew through the stiff bare trees, the boughs groaning, rubbing, stiff with ice. Most of the men sat like chickens cold on a perch, heads drawn in, eyes closed.

At last, here was the jeep speeding back. The men, reviving, gave rusty, jeering cries of encouragement as it went by. Another long wait, and then a signal, and all along the line the motors started and slowly we began to roll.

"How's it going?" Phil Schaeffer asked.

"Fine. Only all this damned fresh air's going to be the death of me." Before my mouth, the blanket was covered with drops of ice where my breath had congealed.

The trucks rode on along straight roads, up steep, snowy hills, along winding roads, while the night grew colder and colder. No one spoke. To breathe in this coldness was painful. This time, past midnight, when the trucks halted, there was no reaction or comment. An officer, hurrying along the road, told everyone to get his equipment and get off.

"This looks like it, boys," he said encouragingly.

"This looks like s---, boys," De Vroom's good-natured, clear young voice repeated in the same intonations.

"Dig in," someone said in disgust, anticipating the usual command.

Dropping off the back of the truck, we were stiff, careless, incurious. But now another officer joined the first, imparting better news, which we overheard: "Just get them in anywhere to get warm for a while. Any of these houses. Bust down the doors if you have to."

Houses? Yes. I looked around and made out the silhouette of a row of houses and a side street going uphill. Then in the dark, Sergeant Campbell's voice said, "Medics, over here. Over here, medics. This way, me-e-n." As he pronounced it, it was between "men" and "main."

He led us up the front path of a house, up the step, into a hall and then to a dim, peaceful living room. The lantern, turned down low, was set on the floor. It was too dark to see very much. Sergeant Campbell spoke in a whisper; those who worked in the aid station were already asleep. "Jes bed down here any place for the rest of the night. Here's two blankets each."

The house, though not warm, was not stone cold. Smiling to myself with tiredness, I sat down on the floor, unbuckled my overshoes, got them off, closed my eyes, felt around for my legging laces, untied them half in my sleep, and remembered to take the glasses, lumps of sugar, fountain pen and plastic cigarette case out of my pockets. I stretched out on the floor, still in my overcoat, drew one of the blankets over me, and fell asleep at once.

In the morning we awoke in a house that was clean, spare, somber, almost ugly; the living room was pure 1914: dark woodwork, lead color in the wall paint, shining floors, straight chairs set back against the wall, no lamps; an involved grillwork arch of dark wood separated living room and dining room. There were many small stuffed animals and birds in glass-fronted cases. The cold, snowy light from outside was reflected on all the glass panes, the waxed woodwork and floors. About the house there was an air of thrift, soberness, and childlessness.

The owner of the house—taxidermist by avocation?—was an underground worker. I caught only a glimpse of him, a serious, dark man in his middle thirties, standing in the dining room talking earnestly to the captain in German, trying, it seemed, to explain quickly a complex situation. His wife appeared briefly, a thin, pale woman with straight, glossy black hair combed back into a knot. She wore a heavy jacket over a clean, faded cotton dress, and moved quietly through the room, not meeting our eyes. She went upstairs again and remained there.

We went out the side door of the house and up the road with our mess kits to get our breakfast. We ate out in the snow, came back, folded our blankets neatly, "policed" the living room, and then sat writing V-mail letters, waiting incuriously to see what would develop. Outside a light, powdery snow began to fall.

We left at lunchtime, and after riding several hours deep in the Forest of the Ardennes, we came to a halt and started to hike through the snow. The sky was dark gray and the forest gave off a cold echoing silence. As we advanced, the denseness of trees fell away; the atmosphere lightened, became that of a vast park. Unexpectedly, in a clearing, the chateau came to view, large, forbidding, too high, of flinty gray stone, with no foundation planting to break the severity of its rise from the snow. A long flight of snowy steps led up to high plate-glass doors protected by a black iron filigree.

We were halted quite a distance from the building, told to scatter and wait. An officer nearby was explaining that this was the only house for miles about. It was not shown on any reconnaissance maps and the Germans did not know of its existence. An empty truck drove up to the door, and men, not of our outfit, began to leave with their equipment. In the sub-zero cold we stood watching, leaning against the trees, our equipment in the snow. There was an hour's wait, and then finally, yes, thank God, inside for the night. We went up the ice-coated flights of steps into a wide vestibule, then up two more long marble flights leading to a pair of tall glass doors at the top.

In the main hall the walls were decorated with the bleached skulls and antlers of deer, each bearing a tiny black card with a name and date in gilt letters. We went through a door and climbed a narrow servants' staircase, coming out into a dark drafty hall on the third floor that reminded me of a large old summer hotel: straw matting, glass-fronted bookcases, turn-of-the-century prints of croquet games on the walls. It was too dark to see anything distinctly.

Of the three bedrooms that had been allotted to the litter bearers, one was off by itself, a small square corner room that lacked a stove and was as cold as a refrigerator. The other men were not interested, and I was glad to claim it for myself. As soon as I put my equipment down, I joined them in one of the other rooms down the hall where the fire was going and red serge curtains had been pulled over the blackout shields. An officer came through with instructions that nothing was to be destroyed or taken: we were to leave the place exactly as we had found it. The blackout regulations were to be followed with utmost strictness. We were a few miles from Bastogne and might be staying here for several days. The Germans were feared to be about to break through the St. Hubert-Tillet line and our entire regiment was stretched out to its utmost in a holding position.

Chow was announced by someone bawling that one word through the drafty hall. We got out mess kits and filed down the dark staircases, down the two flights of marble steps, down the outer two snowy flights and out between waist-high banks of snow onto the main drive. Wash the mess kits, move on to where the frozen cooks, half covered with a snowy blanket, crouched over the pans of food. *Plop*: C-ration stew or hash. Dry ration crackers. A spoonful of fruit salad. Coffee. Then quick, indoors with it and up all those flights of stairs, stumbling in the dark on the wedge-shaped turning steps, along the chill black hall into the warmth of the candlelit room with the red curtains. Sometimes there was space at the round serge-covered table and I'd sit down to eat; at other times I stood and ate from a white marble-topped bureau while my canteen cup of coffee reheated on the tiled stove. A cigarette, and then on again with the gas mask and rifle and ammunition belt, and down through the drafty dark stairwell, the hall, the marble stairs, the icy steps, and out on line to wash the mess kit.

By nine-thirty, everyone went to sleep. In my own frosty, dark room, which was furnished with odds and ends, the windows had been nailed shut. On the first night there I slept in one of the twin beds—my first real bed since leaving the United States. It had a double red mattress, but something was wrong: I had grown too accustomed to sleeping on the ground. The softness kept me awake. Outside, the wind sounded like the long drawn-out howling of wolves.

Unwilling to leave the bed for the floor, I lay trying to imagine who had slept here before me in peacetime. Some not quite important guest? A nephew? An aunt? A tutor? And would there ever again be large house parties lighting their way upstairs by candles? It was a relief being alone, not hearing anyone snore. By the starlight that pierced the lace curtains and shone faintly in the mirrored front of one of the clothes presses, I could see, on the marble-topped commode beside me, my steel helmet holding all my possessions, and my rifle leaning against the dim white wall.

During the greater part of the ten days we spent at the chateau, I was stationed in the front hall just outside the aid station, guarding the rifles and pistols of the men going in. I was glad I was not outside the building in the snow. Upon reporting for work the first morning, I opened the tall door and stepped into a large, handsome room with a high ceiling, an enormous crystal chandelier, and tall arched windows looking out onto falling snow. The walls, wood-paneled half-way up, were painted a deep red above. The round Army stove, placed on four bricks, had been set up on the black-marble hearth. Most of the furniture was gone, and what remained—two Empire sofas upholstered in yellow velvet and some matching side chairs—had been pushed back against the walls. There in the far corner on a gleaming mahogany table stood the familiar olive-drab five-gallon can of water, the one large and one small box of medicine, splints and dressings.

My day started before eight in the morning and lasted usually until ten or eleven at night. When officers started in, I said, "I'll take care of your weapon, sir; you can't bring it inside the aid station." More than half of them turned on me an abrupt, outraged stare, and strode past with their light carbines on their shoulders. The officers who knew me by sight, or were in and out of the station frequently, surrendered their weapons without protest, though plainly they thought the whole thing as foolish as I did. As far as I knew, ours was the only aid station in all the E.T.O. to have an infantryman in attendance, and that had been at the captain's request.

"What's the idea?" one officer asked me. "You stand out here guarding weapons and the captain walks around inside with a forty-five stuck in his belt. How d'you explain that?"

"I don't, sir. You'd better ask him."

The captain's penchant for weapons was becoming well known and was the subject of favorable talk among the infantrymen, several of whom came to the chateau pleading illness, only to try to sell him a German Lüger once they arrived. The bargaining sometimes went on for days; at the time the asking price was around seventy-five dollars. The captain was fascinated by pistols but knew nothing about them, and I doubt if he had ever fired one. He came out one day and asked me to clean and oil his American pistol, and I told him I didn't know how.

"Didn't they teach you? Couldn't you get someone to show you how?"

"I could probably, but it would take a long time. For a full month I was like a monkey with a puzzle, trying to get an M1 apart and together again."

He looked at me a moment, bobbing the pistol up and down in his hand. Then he smiled, accepted the refusal and went inside. If I gave in on everything, I felt, I'd gradually become his orderly.

During all our stay there, the weather remained bitter cold, with below-zero temperatures, fog and iron-gray skies, and snow fell unendingly. The line companies, holding a road that led to St. Vith and Bastogne, were in snowy foxholes where they froze and stood guard and went on patrols day and night. Their chapped hands split open, their lips cracked, their feet froze. They had heavy colds, chilblains, pneumonia and dysentery; they became exhausted and stiff from too prolonged exposure, but they could not be relieved. They stepped on mines and had their feet blown off, or they were ambushed on patrols through the forest, and shot down and killed.

Larger and larger numbers arrived daily on sick call. After trudging several miles through deep snow or through a blizzard, in they came, their uniforms white with snow, their faces pinched, astonished, red or mottled. Even the very young looked old. Gasping, winded, they handed over their rifles to me, and, glad to be rid of them temporarily, sank down on the wet tiled floor.

When C Company's sick call arrived, there were familiar faces and friends to talk to: Dave Rossofsky, my former tentmate, here with pains in his appendix, with hemorrhoids and dysentery; Gramling, who had had so much trouble getting his men off to town on a Saturday night, who now could only whisper with laryngitis; Boudreau and Ciani, with wracking coughs and dysentery; Telford, with his delicate voice, his sighs, his dysentery and laryngitis; Pop Evvers and Smathers, and Ahlhauser and Sergeant Danowski . . . All dirtier, rougher and more battered than when I had been with them in C Company.

Their talk was brief, embittered. They envied those who had been wounded and sent home, and in an uncritical way they talked of men deliberately freezing their feet, leaving them outside the covers at night or even holding them in a helmet filled with ice and snow.

"I wouldn't do nothin' to bring it on," said Atanasio, who was particularly subject to dysentery, "but I'd settle for a frozen foot to get out of this."

161

"Yeah, but you might have to have your foot cut off."

"So maybe you'll get your whole leg shot off if you stay. Lots of guys'll be goin' around without a foot when this is over."

Unlike fiction, conversation on any one point was never long sustained. Someone would change the whole trend by remarking, "I got a letter yesterday. My sonofabitchin' brother-in-law's still home!" The listeners, shivering, digested this in silence and permitted the talk to lapse.

By now through all the line companies, when the need was most acute, some men would have only one glove, and often their overshoes were ripped or worn through, and evidently there was no way of getting new ones. In the foxholes, the blankets were stiff with ice.

From the men now who were evacuated for any reason—wounds, pneumonia or frozen feet—I removed the overshoes and dry socks and paired off odd overshoes that were not too worn, to give out to those who needed them the most. Usually I had five or six stiff, snow-encrusted overcoats that I took down into the unheated, potato-smelling cellar and beat with the stock of my rifle to dislodge the ice, and sometimes I had dry rifles to give out in exchange for frozen ones clogged with mud and snow. I ran an informal supply room with the used overshoes, socks, extra gloves, a sweater, a whole but bloody field jacket. Word of it spread and men in foxholes sent down requests by those coming in on sick call. "Hey, the guy in the foxhole with me wants to know if you got a left overshoe, size ten. Just the left one." "You got any dry gloves I can take back—'bout four pair? The guys need 'em." "Save me the next carbine that comes in?"

The Mosaic floor of the hall was always dreary and black with puddles of melted snow, for Message Center was here in the chateau, and in the room adjoining the aid station the Command Post for the battalion was set up so that couriers and officers came and went all day long. I caught only glimpses of the Command Post. It was in a room that was smaller than ours, with emerald-green walls and a larger crystal chandelier. Officers sat talking around a long, gleaming table where maps were spread out, and empty ration cans were piled with cigarette butts; the room was thick with drifts of smoke. Clerks with their backs turned sat at smaller tables or window sills, typing, filing and telephoning.

Because of the endless traffic, both inner and outer plate-glass doors were always open, and blasts of snowy wind blew in. It was always cold enough to see one's breath. The C.P. guards were on duty at the doors, but they grew tired of closing them. It was like standing hour after hour in an ice-house.

After we had been there two days, like most everyone else, I developed dysentery that lasted on and off for weeks. I was standing in the hall and slowly I began to feel nauseated; my stomach rumbled, turned soft, seemed to cave in. My head grew light; by turns I had chills, then fever. By four in the afternoon I was at my sickest, head ringing, shivering, longing for ten o'clock to come so that I could go up to bed.

There was, as far as we knew, but one toilet—not a bath-room—in the entire chateau. It was situated off the broad landing on the main staircase, and after the first day of con-stant use, it was reserved for officers and declared off limits to the enlisted men. It became a courtmartial offense for the latter to use it, but several I knew, overtaken by dysentery, dashed in there when the long trip outside seemed too much of a risk.

The latrines were at quite a distance, around by the serv-ants' quarters, in a side garden under some low-hanging ap-ple trees. There were four or five long trenches, close to-gether, and sometimes on a twig a roll of sodden toilet paper. Nearby were filled-in trenches, bearing crudely printed wooden signs: Latrine closed, 1-9-45. "Eighth time I been out here today," you'd hear.

"Eight? You're a lucky bastard! You ain't got nothin'!"

By day, you were in plain sight of the servants, who merely had to glance out their windows to see you. The fall-ing snow was our only screen. No one cared particularly. Europeans, I used to figure, are closer to the soil anyway; and not knowing them at all, not speaking the same language, seemed to make the performance impersonal.

There were possibly fifteen servants and their children staying in the chateau, along with its owner, his family and a friend or two. The family kept a suite of rooms on the main floor, and once when the door opened off the hall I saw a comfortable sitting room where a log fire glowed in a white-marble fireplace. A tufted red velvet Victorian sofa was drawn up to it, and on it sat a very old woman. An old man, a girl in her middle twenties, a nursemaid holding a baby and several men well on in years were all talking excitedly. The door closed.

There was a story that an advance party of men belonging to the outfit that preceded ours had come upon the chateau and asked if they might stay there for a while. Permission was granted; then, fearing the presence of American soldiers would bring the war into their very home, the family and servants hastily bundled up, packed some things, and drove off in two large sleighs. They had gone down the road half the distance to St. Vith when they saw the German Army coming at them. Turning the sleighs about, they lashed up the horses and sped back to the chateau to give the alarm. There was only a handful of Americans in the house, and the Belgian family and servants, women included, asked for rifles and ammunition, prepared to fight for their lives. The soldiers had no weapons to spare, so with hunting rifles the civilians joined the few soldiers and stood guard all that night at the long windows, waiting for the Germans, who, for some mysterious reason, never came that far.

A few days after our arrival, the family and servants ran completely out of food and had to eat what we ate. The baby was not well, nor was the owner of the place, a man in his late seventies. Each morning, before attending to sick call, the captain paid the family a professional visit. The owner of the chateau had a friend staying with him, a man of his own age, fine-looking, thin, erect, with silvery-white hair and rosy skin as transparent as gelatin. He could speak a little English and often dropped into the aid station to talk. He wore a stiff collar, a tie with a ring and a suit of purplish tweed, cut like a business suit except that the trousers came down to a broad tight cuff about the ankle; with this went heavy white woolen socks and ski boots. He was present on one of the few occasions I was inside the station, and we talked a little when I offered him a cigarette. He accepted it with thanks and apologies and told me till the present he had smoked nothing but a pipe.

"Do you—does the family here have a radio?" I asked. "Do you get any news at all? I'd love to know what's going on."

"I come in *here* looking for news." He laughed. "Sometimes your drivers have a radio in their truck. I hear very little. No newspapers."

He was from Brussels and had come to stay with his

friend, "to be out of danger." This made him smile. "Why I should care, I do not know. At my age, you see." In Brussels, his house, all his family and then his place of business had been blown up by bombs dropped from German planes. "Of all the family now I am the only one—an old man."

But he was a shrewd and civilized old man, interested in finding out for himself what the Americans were like. I was embarrassed about this because after once getting his story, none of the others bothered with him again even to the extent of concealing their lack of interest, and after the first few days he stayed away. The war seemed to affect many of our men that way. Nothing went deeply; no impression remained. Just get the main facts as quickly as possible, then the hell, forget it, move on to something else.

Under Colonel Hessig's patronage, there had just been formed, through volunteers from the various line companies, a special group of men called the Tiger Patrol. They were to go out on highly dangerous scouting missions into enemy territory, and in exchange for this they were to work only every other day. On their free time they were to have no duties, the best possible food, and were to be quartered indoors. Braaf from C Company was one of the first men to sign up.

"What the hell, Major," he said to me in the hall, "it's only every other day. Back in the company I was out *every* day on patrol, every night too. Ran my f---in' ass off, so I might as well be down here." He laughed—a strained, hoarse chuckle.

Braaf was about twenty-four, of average height and muscular, with light wavy hair. He had a round neck supporting a square face; his features were broad, almost Negroid; his skin was pale, his eyes a light green. He had a harsh, husky voice. In a rough way he had, at the start, gotten along well with most of the men in the company, but he made no close friends. The first evening that I was sent to C Company, Braaf was there, having just arrived himself. While being transferred into the Infantry, he had gone over the hill for some time and was waiting to see what disciplinary action would be taken. I remembered him sitting on a footlocker upstairs in the barracks, in suntans and cheap, wrinkled low-cut shoes, flicking cigarette ashes freely on the floor, laughing his hoarse laugh, his head jerking around every now and then to look down to the Company Office to see if anyone was coming for him. Outside in the hot summer sunset you heard *click-click-click*: the men, lined up, waiting for Retreat, taking a last look at their rifles. With that strained harsh voice, he went on talking, explaining the predicament he was in, laughing. I did not like him.

I still did not like him much later in the summer. There seemed something ruthless and violent about him, but banked, controlled under a laughing exterior. I avoided him and he realized it; we never spoke to each other. Then late in August, Pop Evvers told us all one night that Braaf had a furlough coming up and that, if he had the money, he could go home and get married. Pop Evvers was taking up a collection. At first I said no, then later went over and gave Pop five dollars. He wrote my name and the amount on the envelope and turned the money over to Braaf. Nearing midnight, Braaf started off with everyone sitting up in the double-deck bunks shouting good wishes after him. He yelled his thanks, waved, and rushed down the stairs to pick up his furlough papers. Very few men thought he'd come back. But he did, and after a few days he came to me to thank me for lending the money, and said he'd pay it back as soon as he could. I told him there was no immediate rush and not to worry about it. I offered him my congratulations and we shook hands.

Since coming into combat, I had heard C Company men talking about him. He had already been slightly wounded that Sunday in the Saar, had been granted the Purple Heart and had been returned to the company, where he became suddenly unpopular because, they claimed, in attacks he stayed low in his foxhole and wouldn't advance with the rest of the men. Later, he'd rejoin the company, claiming he never heard the order to go ahead, or he'd get conveniently lost.

At the time, I never formed absolute judgments about things like that, for different men had different breaking points, and it was not always a matter within their control. Some with the best of intentions, like Hlavenka or Lieutenant Millbank, would go to pieces in the first big attack, perhaps in its first five minutes. Other men were extraordinarily brave for weeks, then one day a German 88, no different from any other, no louder or closer, would land and the unprepared man would turn sick in heart and mind, craven from that moment on.

In Braaf's case, I felt his reasons for joining the Tiger Patrol were mixed, perhaps not fully understood by himself. For one thing, he wanted to clear out of a company where, after an early popularity, the men had soured on him; then there was a glamour about the Tiger Patrol and only the wildest and most fearless had volunteered for it. Braaf, in joining up, would seem to be re-establishing himself. And there was sense in his theory about working only every other night; he figured it automatically cut down his chances of being wounded again by half. "A patrol from here, a patrol from the company—what the f---'s the difference?"

Another who joined the Tigers was the ex-sergeant from C Company with the hideously burned and rebuilt face, the man known as "V.D." His rank was restored to him and he was put in charge of the Tiger Patrol. It was a sort of Foreign Legion within the battalion: every one of its members had a different reason for joining it.

At first the Tiger Patrol went out only at night. Very often our litter bearers were out, making long, dangerous hauls, bringing back someone shot up on a patrol or blown up in a mine field, and I waited up in the station for their return to take the equipment from the wounded men. I was there one night at about eleven o'clock when the door opened and the Tiger Patrol came trooping in. Both our lanterns had been turned very low; at the far end of the room the technicians, the clerk, the captain and Sergeant Campbell were sleeping, the captain on a sofa, the others on the floor. I looked at the Tiger Patrol in astonishment, without recognition at first. They came in silently, in the shadows, some wearing white sheets as capes; others had pulled on long light-gray GI underwear outside all their other clothing, imparting to them the lumpy appearance of some modern sculpture. Pieces of torn white sheeting were clamped over their helmets.

"Hello, Major," came Braaf's hoarse whisper. "We come in here an' wait aroun'? Get warm?" The lights were out everywhere else in the chateau.

No matter how much one wished to think otherwise, many of the Tiger Patrol were tough little exhibitionists. Every gesture, boast and act proclaimed it during the hour's wait before they set out on their mission. Consciously or unconsciously, they resented the fact that the medics were sleeping and they themselves were not the center of atten-

167

tion. There were a few fine, high-principled men on the Patrol, among them Carraher from C Company, big and affable and well educated, who, up to this point, appeared to suffer from an excess of energy and a lack of suitable outlets.

Shortly before midnight the connecting door to the emerald-green room opened and a stream of bright light fell into the dim aid station. Colonel Hessig entered, gathered the Tiger Patrol about him and in a whisper gave them a final briefing. They set off in single file, the white sheets making a rustling whisper, their feet in the rubber-soled overshoes almost soundless. Some carried in their hands the long hunting knives that they had sharpened during the hour's wait.

After they left I sat silent. Colonel Hessig remained on his feet, his head turned in a characteristic listening attitude. A long moment went by. Then he crossed the room, woke Preacher up, and a curious, secret and pitiable little ritual took place. Colonel Hessig, who did not in any way wish to appear old, sat down to have his varicose veins bound up before he went to bed. Preacher attended to him in sleepy silence and the colonel sat rocking back and forth a little, sighing deeply, and rubbing his knees.

The colonel and I furthered our acquaintance in the chateau. One day a jeep drove up into the courtyard bearing under guard a wounded German prisoner—the first German soldier I had seen at close range. It was at dusk, lightly snowing, and the man was gigantic, hatless, dressed in the long German overcoat and black boots. His hands were raised up over his head. He had been wounded in the eye and had a bloody bandage tied roughly and crookedly about the upper part of his head. He towered—about six feet five—as he stood up in the back of the jeep, and had to be assisted down. I was returning from one of my frequent visits to the latrine, and his captors were asking where the medics were located. They also wanted the interpreter brought in; they felt that they had a prize. I led them inside, held back the army blanket over the door, then, annoyingly, because of their rifles, I had to wait out in the hall. News that a German prisoner had been brought in spread rapidly up through the chateau and brought crowds of men down for a look. Those who had seen the German were astonished at his size; he looked more the way we pictured the Russians.

He was inside the station only a few minutes when the

168

door burst open and Colonel Hessig appeared in the hall, demanding with oaths to know who had brought the prisoner in here. Technically I had, but, hearing his tone, I did not bother to tell him so. Everyone stood looking at him, dumbfounded.

"Don't they know any better than that?" he cried. "This place is secret! We don't want the enemy to know it even *exists!*" He went into the aid station and came out a minute or two later. "Who's Atwell out here?" My heart plunged as I stepped forward. He put his hand on my shoulder. "Atwell, I want you to go outside and tell everyone—everyone out there to stop talking, to keep quiet. Not a move or a word out of them till we get this prisoner out of here." Then he raised his voice to a shout. "Now I want *silence* in this hall! All of you who don't belong here, clear out!"

The men scuttled—I was reminded of army roaches when you put the light on—and in the silence I walked down the hall and started out the long flight of steps. Below in the snowy court there were three or four jeeps lined up with their drivers and assistant drivers standing about talking, and a few men were coming back from the latrine. Raising my voice from halfway down the steps, I gave the message that they were not to move or speak till the prisoner was gone. The little procession then came out and down in complete silence, Colonel Hessig leading, and a guard on either side of the shuffling prisoner, whose head was tipped back, the same bloody bandage tied securely over both his eyes. They crossed the courtyard; the enormous German was put into the jeep and driven off for further questioning at Regimental Headquarters, his bare hands lifted over his head.

I was standing outside the aid-station doors late one afternoon when a C Company man came in out of the snow. He didn't answer my greeting, but said, surrendering his rifle to me, "Lieutenant McGrath's been hit."

"*What?*"

"Yeah, God." He lifted the army blanket and went past me into the room. I put his snowy rifle down beside several others I was guarding and after a few moments heard the connecting door of the Command Post thrown open. With a clatter of chairs and feet, the Headquarters officers rushed into the aid station. When four litter bearers were summoned from upstairs, I followed them into the station.

The Headquarters officers were down at the far end, silent, grouped in silhouette against the tall, bare, arched windows. Captain Stettner was talking to Tubby, the stout jeep driver, while the messenger from C Company stood by.

"So all right, Tubby, what do you say? How's about takin' a run up there as far's you can and let the boys walk the rest of the way—how's about that? You know the way, don't you?"

"Sure, I know the *way*." Tubby's voice was a doleful chirp.

The captain pretended to take the answer for a willing assent. "Good," he said. "Then you run the boys up there."

Rotund but nervous, Tubby took a breath, turned and set off with the litter bearers and the C Company man. When the footfalls went out, no one moved or spoke; the officers maintained their grouping. Then Sergeant Campbell walked toward me, took the lid off the stove and threw in a few chunks of wood.

"Is Lieutenant McGrath badly hurt?" I asked in a low voice. One's tone took its cue from the others in the room. Sergeant Campbell was quite hard of hearing and didn't like to admit it.

"Lieutenant McGrath, C Company, shot up," he whispered out of the corner of his mouth as he straightened the woodpile. "Out scoutin' where he was sendin' a patrol t'night. Boys goin' up there now."

Before I could learn anything else, someone blundered into the room with a rifle on his shoulder. I walked over, took the weapon from him and brought it out into the hall, closing the door behind me.

In the twilight, just before supper, Tubby and the litter bearers came back, passing me in silence. I followed them into the station.

Captain Stettner sprang to his feet. "What'd you find out?"

Warren Troy, the clerk, was pumping up one of the lanterns and his hand paused. The answer came: "They got him all right; he was dead."

"Oh, God *damn* it! Oh, God!" The captain swung his head away for a moment. Then: "What about the others?"

"They got Sergeant Howell too. He was killed. The other guy wasn't there. There was a lot of blood around in the snow."

"Yeah, there was a lot of blood and we followed it. It went off into some bushes and stopped 'bout fifty yards from the jeep."

170

Lieutenant McGrath had been found lying in the snow where he had fallen out of the vehicle. The jeep on that side had been riddled with bullets. Most of his wounds had been in his leg, they said, as if he had started to jump out, putting his leg forward, when the fusilade struck him. Sergeant Howell had toppled out the opposite side.

"We don't know about the third guy," they were saying. "The blood—the trail stopped there in the bushes. We looked all around for him. He might ha' bound up the wound, stopped the blood and escaped, or maybe he was taken prisoner. The snow was all roughed up there; you couldn't tell what the hell went on."

Depressed and saddened, I went up the dark staircase to get my mess kit, remembering Lieutenant McGrath at the doorway of the forty-and-eight, looking out hour after hour at the melancholy French fields and hills, saying, "This might be our only chance to see this countryside"; remembering him the night before we went into combat in the Saar, coming around to talk to us in the foxhole . . . There was his kindness when I was leaving C Company, and the memory of him arguing coolly with the two generals as they were ordering his men out of the houses near Rheims.

Ordinarily when a man was killed, his body was left where it fell until the Graves Registration Squad came along, but the officers of the battalion felt so bad thinking of their friend's body in the snow, an exception was made, and a detail of men went out to bring the body back.

When I started to the latrine at about ten o'clock that night, the bluish stars were shining frostily. On my way back, I noticed a little group of silent jeep drivers staring at the ground in the shadow of the front steps; I walked over and asked what was the matter. Someone said, "That's McGrath's body." A shock ran through me. It looked like a log wrapped in a frozen, snowy shelter-half, tied with rope. I remained looking down at it with the jeep drivers, in silence. How far from the classroom where he had lectured on the philosophy of St. Thomas Aquinas, I thought, turning away, oppressed by the terrible, careless waste. A young college professor lying here; Sergeant Howell, a decent man, father of a young family, lying out in the snowy forest beside a riddled jeep.

In the morning Lieutenant McGrath's body was gone.

The litter bearers, except when they were sent out to carry in a wounded man, remained upstairs in their two rooms, reading, talking, taking sponge baths out of helmets or the large washbasins, shampooing their hair, playing cards and writing letters home. Phil Schaeffer used to come down once in a while into the station and I'd see him prowling about, shoulders hunched, looking for a copy of *Yank* or the *Stars and Stripes*, sitting off by himself reading it.

The litter hauls they made were long and dangerous. Tubby would drive them up the road as far as other jeep drivers had told him it was practicable to go. Then the boys went the rest of the way on foot, sometimes, Phil told me, plunging hip-deep in drifts, looking for guards posted against their arrival, and expecting to be blown up by mines at any moment. They had a sled which they sometimes used to carry the wounded men back on, but they could never decide whether it was helpful or not in the denseness of the forest. When parts of the route lay through territory known to be under enemy observation, Captain Stettner requested two armed guards from the line company meet them half-way, bring them to their objective and escort them back; and the litter bearers had an odd story to tell about this. Almost invariably, when they were accompanied by the two armed infantrymen, one leading, one bringing up the rear, the Germans fired at them with burp guns; yet when they crossed the same territory alone with the wounded man, the enemy rifles were silent.

This was not a hard-and-fast rule. No sooner would they ask the captain to let them go and come unescorted than four of them and the man on the litter would be subjected to a merciless cross-firing. It seemed to depend on the individual German soldiers and on how they felt at that particular moment. The same could be said for our own men: some would let wounded or surrendering Germans through; others mowed them down. "The boys ain't takin' any prisoners to-day" was a fairly common statement, and there was never any doubt as to its meaning.

Chuck Cornell joined us as a litter bearer for a while at the chateau. He had been an infantryman in C Company with me, had been wounded in the Saar attack and had been sent to a hospital in France. There, in talking with a doctor, it was discovered that he had had some pre-medical training and the doctor suggested that by transferring out of the Infantry

172

into the Medics, Cornell could make himself far more helpful to his friends back in C Company. Stirred by this, he permitted the transfer to go through.

When we were back in camp, his *esprit de corps* was striking and rivaled even that of Gramling and Pop Evvers. Days before I met him, I had heard of him; he was a legendary character. "You don't know *Cornell?*" someone asked me, astounded. "He's about the smartest guy in the division! College guy. He wrote a book!" "His old man's a colonel, only he don't speak to him." "He's going to be a doctor." "He can speak Japanese! The only guy in the whole division can speak Japanese."

Naturally I was eager to meet him. It was early in the summer and the division was being repeatedly drained of seasoned infantrymen to make replacements for outfits overseas, while new men kept coming in from the Air Corps, Basic camps, Antiaircraft and the Army Specialized Training Program. Many of the new men had high I.Q.s and college backgrounds and they were bitterly resented by the remainders of the Old Guard, in which group Chuck Cornell had occupied an almost unique position.

I discovered who he was one day when the company returned from a field problem, exhausted, red-faced, bitten by chiggers, covered with sweat and sand. They crashed up the staircase, shouting and talking at once, beginning to rip off their torn and raggy fatigues. "Joe! Joe, how are you?" one of the group was asking. "Sure you're all right?" He stopped the man and put the question seriously, his hand on the man's arm. A moment later he turned to someone else. "Michael. How's your foot? I'll take a look at it in a minute. Bill! Are you all right?" He went from one to another, questioning, encouraging, later giving his head a slow pessimistic shake.

"That's Cornell now," someone said to me.

In appearance he was rather colorless, with a small head, small, sharp features and GI glasses; his body was long-waisted and muscular. At the moment, and at most moments in the barracks, he wore a sweaty, torn undershirt, sagging, wrinkled wet shorts, and unlaced GI shoes.

At the start, through his choice, we were not very friendly. The division was soon put on the alert, and because he could speak Japanese he was transferred to Regimental Headquarters, where life was cleaner, somewhat more intellectual and less arduous. He did not like it and was back

173

in C Company every night, looking after his men and complaining about the softness of his new berth. "A pack of phonies over there, half of them going to work in suntans, for crissake!" When he came into our barracks, he took off his own suntans and sat around in a dirty undershirt and the sagging khaki shorts. Addressing me directly for the first time, he said, "I got to come over here for a relief from all that chicken. I want to be with the boys. I want to help them all I can."

He never mentioned his book to me as we became friendlier, but he told me he had picked up conversational Japanese by playing with Japanese children in California. He was so unhappy at Regimental Headquarters that at his request he was sent back to C Company just before we left the States, when it was clear that we wouldn't be shipping to the East and his services wouldn't be used as an interpreter.

Now, returned from a hospital in France, wearing a new Red Cross brassard on his arm, he had the same complaints about the litter bearers living in the chateau that he had had about the men at Regimental Headquarters. "Look at 'em," he said to me. "A laugh, isn't it? Shampooing their hair. Sleeping indoors. Four blankets. I don't think I can stand it. Do you know the guys are *crying* in the foxholes? Sitting there at night, *crying!* God! If I could only be there *with* them!"

"What good could you do? You couldn't make them any warmer."

"No, but I could *talk* to them, I could—I could do *something!* Just to be there! I feel *guilty* hanging around this place when they're suffering like that."

I did too, but evidently to a lesser degree. And there was no point in sneering at the litter bearers. They did what was asked of them. Had they been told to sleep outdoors, they would have done so, but Chuck Cornell soon developed a contempt for all of them; he found something wrong with their most innocuous statements, felt that I shared his convictions and sent me disgusted glances, snorted, shook his head and laughed scornfully.

His dislike was more pronounced for the aid-station group downstairs; he found them unfeeling and abrupt with the line-company men reporting on sick call. "It's that cold, lousy *callousness*," he complained to me. "How can anyone be that way? To their own men, suffering and dying for them! They come here sick, all beaten up, and these guys treat them like animals. Hand them a couple of pills and send them out again."

I couldn't go with him all the way on this. I had watched Preacher working and found him to be conscientious and fair at all times; he did the best he could with his limited supplies, and was fast but gentle with the wounded. The other technician, Charley Heydt, was just as adept, but his attitude was impersonal; it might almost not have been a human being he was working on. Finishing the job of bandaging, he got up, walked away; and seeming to forget the wounded man at once, he returned to his continuous ragging.

Captain Stettner came into the picture only when there was a very serious wound or an involved diagnosis to be made. His manner with the men on sick call could have been construed as offensive, though he did not intend it to be so. He had an amused smile he wore at such moments; he answered few questions and gave no explanations. The smile remained. To me, it was as if he had assumed an attitude prevalent among officers, that the enlisted men in the Infantry were all Willy-and-Joe characters out of Mauldin's cartoons, ignorant, incapable of meeting him on an equal plane, funny even while sick, a race apart. With officers he was all solicitude.

Chuck Cornell watched him smiling, refusing to answer an infantryman's question, and he cursed him steadily under his breath. He was in the aid station frequently, asking the captain to send him out to C Company as aid man, for here he did not feel he was doing enough. Captain Stettner put him off several times and tried to reason with him, but Cornell, in a half-concealed, sullen way, made it clear that he did not like any of his present companions and, in fact, held all of them in contempt. It seemed to dawn on the captain that he too was included, and quickly he gave in. Chuck Cornell filled his medical pouches, slung them on his shoulders and went out to live with C Company in their snowy foxholes.

Late one afternoon a truckload of men was delivered to the courtyard of the chateau. They were clerks, KPs, assistant artificers and mailmen rounded up from the various line companies. I saw Ayres, the mail clerk from C Company, and asked him what he was doing here. Almost too sick with dysentery to answer, he said he didn't know but that he had been told to take his rifle, mess kit and ammunition and climb on the truck. "Maybe they're sendin' us back for a rest," one of the shivering KPs said hopefully.

In the aid station, I heard there was a big enemy break-through expected that night, that rosters had been combed and every available man, sick or well, was being pressed into use.

As an extra precaution, a litter team from the 210th Medics, who were attached to our division and who worked back at Collecting and Clearing, had been sent for, and they arrived, four of them, rather jittery at being so close to the front, and they were assigned to the room I used.

I was on duty downstairs outside the aid station. The chateau, totally blacked out, was silent and empty with all the First Battalion men outside on guard. At about ten o'clock, Sergeant Campbell told me to go up and sleep for a while, that he'd call me as soon as I was needed. I went up and stopped off to see the litter bearers and smoke a final cigarette. They were spreading their blankets on the floor, hoping against hope that there would be no calls for them that night.

I went from their hot room, through the chill black hall, and entered my own room. The four 210th boys had put a blackout up and had a single candle burning on the bureau. They were stretched out, two men to a bed, and when I came in and introduced myself, they asked politely, beginning to sit up, if one of the beds was mine. I said no. After the first night I had given up sleeping in the bed and used my shelter-half and a folded down-comforter on the floor. They gave up the red comforter and asked what my job with the medics was.

"Oh, I was *wonderin'*," one of them said when I explained. "I knew this room was for medics, and I seen the rifle there in the corner."

The candle was snuffed out and they settled down, hoping there'd be no call for them either. Worried, they talked in low voices for some time. The man who had asked about the rifle was the oldest of the four; he had an Irish name and came from Jersey City. The three others were quite young and had formerly been in A.S.T.P.

"Before we say good night," one of them said, "I think we all ought to say our prayers. How about it?"

"Yes, I think so too," replied one of the others.

"All right," said the first voice, "I'll begin." There was a momentary pause and then: "Almighty God, our Father, we put our trust in Thee. Protect us this night, keep us in Thy loving care, and return us to our families safe and sound. Amen. Dave?"

Dave's voice then offered up a similar prayer for protection during this period of special danger, and at the conclusion the third boy began. "We place ourselves in Thy care, Almighty God, beseeching You to spare us—" and so on. Remembering the Irish name, I waited.

"All right, Conneally, come on now, it's your turn. Don't be a louse."

"I don't say them kind of prayers," Conneally said. "I got me own prayers. I say them to myself. We don't pray like that out loud."

"All right. Just as long as you're sure you say them!"

"I say them. Say them every night."

There came a pause during which I thought they might be going to ask me.

"Well, good night, then. Good night, Dave. Good night, Steve. Good night, everyone." I was "everyone."

We went to sleep in a few minutes. They were not called out during the night, I was not awakened, and the next day went on as usual. I didn't see Ayres or any of the clerks again, and I never knew what, if anything, happened outside the chateau.

The tension, however, still held. The 210th boys stayed till the afternoon when they were relieved by four others from their detachment. The new four, heavily equipped—with duffel bags, I believe—and just as nervous as their predecessors, cooked their own food up in the room, but they did not pray aloud.

There was a brief wintry twilight one of the few days, if not the only one, when the sun came out at all. In its descent, it turned the snow a glazed frosty pink. There was excitement among the guards hurrying toward the chateau; they were bringing a group of Free French scouts—a sort of French Tiger Patrol. I saw seven or eight of the Frenchmen standing to one side of the chateau in the snow, against a sky with long red banners in it—men in berets and tam-o'-shanters, in parts of uniform, who, with vigorous Gallic gestures, were urging some of our Tiger Patrol to accompany them at once down the road to St. Vith; they could not understand any delay for the sake of darkness. The Tiger Patrol came away whistling, awed by the daring of the French scouts.

Nightly, as everyone was going to sleep and lights were put out, the Tiger Patrol came into the dimmed-out aid station. Some still wore the long light-gray underwear stretched to the bursting point over their uniforms, but most of them had given up wearing the white capes and sheets because they caught onto bushes and branches as they tracked through the forest. The original promise that they were to work only every other night had not been kept. Or at least so Braaf told me. Frequently they were sent out coming on toward evening, and then again the same night near twelve o'clock.

Though many still looked on them with admiration, almost from the beginning I heard line-company boys say, "Yeah, sure. The Tiger Patrol goes out and they come back and say, 'No resistance.' Then *you* go out and *bul-luum!* You run right into it." Whether this was true or not, the Tiger Patrol rapidly suffered many casualties. The leader, V.D., was wounded badly the first or second night, and the big, goodhearted, high-spirited Carraher was put in charge. A few nights later there came a call for the litter bearers: Carraher was wounded and lying out in the forest. Four litter bearers were awakened and sent out to find him. The directions that had been telephoned in were vague, and Captain Stettner remained awake, pacing up and down the half-dark room, worrying about his four men.

An hour passed. Suddenly the door burst open and, much to our surprise, Carraher walked in, accompanied by some of his patrol. He was laughing, highly keyed up, and with a wound in his forearm. Captain Stettner was furious.

"I wasn't going to wait out there with just a little wound like this," Carraher was saying, laughing. "Hell, I can walk."

"But how about my men out there looking for you?" the captain cried. He did not like Carraher to begin with. Carraher was sure of himself, and, though well mannered, polite and friendly, he treated the captain as if he were merely another individual. "If there was any mistake," Carraher said, laughing good-naturedly at the captain's tantrum, "it was made by whoever phoned in. Hell, I didn't ask for any litter bearers." His tone relegated them and their captain to an extremely minor place in his scheme of things. The captain went about blackly threatening to bring court-martial charges against someone, while Carraher, still in the best of spirits, was driven off to the field hospital.

The large number of casualties sustained by the Tiger Patrol and the frequency of the missions began to get on Braaf's nerves. Then one night the Tiger Patrol came in and reported him missing. Five or ten minutes later, he came in alone, saying he had lost them somewhere in the woods. This happened a second time, and the first suspicions were aroused in his teammates.

The next afternoon he came looking for me; he was in his stocking feet. "Major—" he laughed—"you got a pair of shoes 'round here, size 8-B? Those ones I got are killin' me; I can't wear 'em." While he stood by, I looked through the shoes I had in the salvage heap under the stairs. Something in his manner made me think he had already gone through the pile while I was inside the station and that he had made sure there'd be none to fit him. He went on to explain that his shoes had become wet, and, in drying before a fire, they had cracked and shrunk so that he couldn't get them on his feet. That night when the Tiger Patrol went out on a mission, he couldn't accompany them.

He had, in the meanwhile, become fast friends with another Tiger Patrol man very much like himself in a superficial way: both were light-haired, stocky, not tall, and tough. The other had a crooked, slow grin and some teeth missing in the front. I also recall he owned and sometimes wore brass knuckles. He swaggered when he walked and was a favorite with Captain Stettner, who called him "Tiger." Tiger was in the aid station frequently with cut and infected fingers that he had to soak for half hours at a time. The big difference between Tiger and Braaf was that Tiger was unendingly tough and fearless, whereas Braaf by that time was devoured with fear.

The second or third day Braaf came to see me about the size 8-B shoes I knew there was something very wrong. I had the impression he had just arranged his square-jawed face and that he was forcing his light-green eyes to look clear and honest. Both of us went through the rigmarole of searching through the salvage for those small shoes. Several times I felt he was on the verge of blurting something out to me—his worry and fear would come that close to the surface—but when I looked up at him, his face would clear by effort.

"Well, thanks, Major. Wish I could get me a pair of shoes."

In his socks he started up the main staircase; part way up, he shuddered and began to hop two steps at a time, as if in relief.

By then Tiger began to be not so friendly with him. Tiger was in the aid station one afternoon soaking his hands in a little pan of hot water. "They'll never clear up, Tiger, if you don't keep 'em clean," the captain was saying, and Tiger grinned, showing the black space between his teeth. Braaf, in socks, came in to say something or other to his friend and Tiger gave him the cut direct. He looked at Braaf a long contemptuous moment, did not answer the question and, with a roll of the shoulders, turned his back. Braaf, looking as if he had been slapped suddenly across the face, hung around for a moment or two and then padded out. I never saw them together after that.

That night while the Tiger Patrol was out on a mission, Braaf, minus his shoes, sat up on the floor in the litter bearers' room, his back against the wall, knees drawn up, laughing and talking in his husky voice. The room was smoky and hot and crowded with messengers, jeep drivers and men sent down to the chateau to rest up for the night—the flotsam that was generally around Battalion Headquarters. The litter bearers were tired of all the guests they had; they wanted to go to bed but the extras hung on, talking and talking, recounting their most dangerous experiences. A truck driver who had held an audience spellbound earlier in the evening was now launched on the same harrowing story but telling it to a dwindling, yawning little group. Braaf, sitting on the floor, made sporadic attempts to establish himself as a member of the Tiger Patrol, but its stock had gone down, no one was interested, and there came into the room a Sergeant Demorest, a slim, black-haired young Southerner from C Company who knew Braaf's background and reputation there only too well. Braaf got up in his stocking feet to leave and I saw his face contorted when he thought no one was looking. A moment of desperation had come over him; frowning hard, he bit on his lip, then made his face clear and he padded out of the room.

The following night Braaf was given a pair of shoes and ordered to accompany the Tiger Patrol on a mission into St. Vith. When he dropped out and became "lost," he was expelled from the Tiger Patrol and sent back in disgrace to C Company.

Gloom and a sense of strain hung over our entire stay at the chateau, and I was glad to see the trucks pull up to the door to carry us away.

Through a great part of January it seemed to me that we never met the enemy head-on as we had in the Saar Valley, but instead we always appeared to be traveling through heavy snowstorms to get to some point, and once there to hold some line, or to back up another division that was bearing the full brunt of the fighting a few miles ahead. The section of Belgium we were in, however, was so overrun with German troops that there were constant clashes, attacks and withdrawals, and our men were being wounded and killed in great numbers. The battalion was on the line and taken out of the line to go into reserve and thrown back into the line again with bewildering frequency.

After we left the chateau we stayed for a few days in a large monastery where our men looted the place, breaking and throwing the books all about, where Nick Nichols was sent back to Regimental Headquarters as a jeep driver, much to Tubby's chagrin, and where O'Rourke, the chip-on-the-shoulder littler bearer, crossed words with Sergeant Campbell and for his rashness was sent out as aid man to one of the rifle companies. That the others looked upon as a death sentence; all that was lacking was the date of execution.

Very often, moving into a town, we gave little thought to the fighting that had taken place just previous to our arrival. A battalion, having finally wrested the town from the Germans, would withdraw, battered and exhausted, and we would move in to relieve them.

Tillet was an attractive little place, very much like Rondu, with sizable gray stone houses and gardens. Snow lay heavy everywhere. We were quartered in a small private schoolhouse. Classes had been held in one large room, a wing attached to the house, overlooking the walled garden. All the little old-fashioned desks with attached benches and a scattering of household furniture had been thrown out into the garden, and it had snowed upon them.

The schoolmistress—or wife of the schoolmaster—was a thin, straight, middle-aged woman in severe high-collared black clothes. Her hair was arranged in a pompadour, but not modishly so. As we came into the house, her daughter was helping her scour the stairs; they used **twig brooms** and pails of boiling water. The girl, who was light-haired, perhaps seventeen, and pretty in a blurred way, was frightened and retiring, but she could speak a few words in English. She and her mother, she explained, were cleaning up after the German soldiers. I gathered that both had lived down in the cellar during the long German occupation, the bombardments and the street fighting that finally drove the enemy out of the town.

The large schoolroom now was taken over for the aid station, and the litter bearers had been told to occupy two rooms upstairs in the house for sleeping quarters. When we went to take a look at them, the unsmiling mother forced her way past us and barred the doors by flinging her arms dramatically across them, speaking to us in streams of Flemish and pointing with a straight stiff finger at the straw on the floor. Someone finally understood what she was trying to tell us. The German soldiers had carried the straw in and had slept on it, and since they had been infested with body lice, she did not want us to go into the rooms until they had been scoured. She kept up her diatribe, making gestures of shoveling the straw out the window. Save for the huge clothes presses, a heavy marble-topped bureau, a green tiled stove and several holy pictures, there were no other furnishings left.

I understood what she wanted but I reneged at touching the lousy straw. A few, braver than I, got rid of it for her, and then she and the daughter went in, in boots, with buckets of hot water, the twig brooms and strong disinfectants. A half hour later, grim, unsmiling, she turned the wet, reeking rooms over to us. Conversation with the daughter, as she went up and down with pails of water, had produced the information that the father was a prisoner of the Germans and the twenty-year-old son was in Africa somewhere. Both had been active in the Underground forces.

The mother made us understand that we—the group I was with—were occupying her son's bedroom and that we were to take excellent care of it. His photograph as a schoolboy was framed in the center of a diploma on the wall, along with pictures of the Sacred Heart and the Blessed Virgin. The wallpaper was mottled gray and white. The glazed tile stove stood in a niche with an arched window behind it, and you saw bare chestnut trees and a gray winter sky outside.

The stove smoked badly for the first few days that we were there; after that we gave up and used the room unheated.

Down in the schoolroom, the black iron Army stove that Sergeant Campbell admired so had been set up on bricks in the middle of the floor. The wall behind the teacher's desk was covered with a blackboard, and there hung a large canvas map of Europe that rolled up and down—a simple, pleasant, nostalgic one in blues and pinks and greens and yellows, showing Europe before the First World War.

"Not," Phil said to me, "a very progressive school."

But who had progressed? We stood smiling, looking at the Good Old Days.

The litter bearers had roamed out to look the town over while the rest of us struggled with the blackouts, and some came back favorably impressed. Ted Jameson, Paul Clifford and Sam Benton, Jr., had encountered two friendly young girls on the street, had been invited into their house to meet the family, and had been given bread and butter and coffee with cream in it.

"They can speak a little bit of English," Ted reported. "Oh, they're so glad the Germans have gone! One's name is Ma-rie and the other one said her name is Pee-you. Yes, that's what she called it, didn't she, Cliff? Pee-you?" Cliff guffawed. "Pee-you can speak English a little better than the others. And she said there are two girls she wants us to meet who were in America."

Ted could be perfectly contented one moment, uneasy the next. A rumor had spread disquietingly that one of the litter bearers would have to go out as aid man, to live with the rifle company and move with it unarmed through each attack, and he was afraid he'd be sent.

The next day Big Steve Brudzinski came down with a heavy cold and a slight fever, and he lay stretched out on a litter near the stove, covered with blankets. "Big Steve's one of our best men," Captain Stettner said—erroneously, it proved. "We can't let him get sick on us nohow!"

I noticed that the captain's manner of speech was changing. He was developing a very marked Southern drawl, though his home was in New York. He began to say, "This-a-way" and "that-a-way" and on the telephone he had worked up a pat little singsong. "Cap'n Stettner speakin'." It finally dawned on me: normally he overaccented his final

183

"ng" sounds and he avoided this by dropping the "g" sound entirely.

Through the day, the uneasiness as to which man was to be sent out as aid man increased. Ted Jameson asked me to spy and see what I could overhear each time I came into the station. He was a mass of worry and hand-wringing. Several times on trumped-up excuses he came downstairs to ask if I had found out anything. I hadn't. He had also put Warren Troy, the clerk, to listening in for him.

Testily Warren said, "No, I haven't heard a damned thing! There's no use *worrying*. If it's going to happen, it's going to happen!"

"I don't believe Steve Brudzinski's sick at all!" Teddy whispered to me pettishly. "He's just putting on so the captain can't send him out." Lazier than most, Ted now began bringing in armsful of wood for the fire. He'd go upstairs and be down ten minutes later with the excuse that he was looking for a V-mail form. Passing me, he'd whisper, "Hear anything?"

"No."

"Oh, I'll die if he sends me! Pray that he doesn't. Keep listening. I'm going out for a while with Cliff and Sam. We have a date to meet Pee-you and her sister."

At about five that evening he came into the schoolroom and told Preacher he too was sick and wanted to have his temperature taken. He stood slumped, shoulders sagging, stomach protruding, his head bent back on his neck. Annoyingly enough to Preacher, who did not like him, he did have a temperature and was bedded down on a litter in the far back corner of the room. You had only to give him an inch and he could produce any number of other infirmities: a frozen toe where he had had a nail removed, a good rousing cold, headache, sick stomach, diarrhea.

He realized he was unpopular and for that reason his position was shaky, yet he called out whenever anyone passed by asking for more blankets or to have the blankets rearranged on his sore toe, and he thoroughly and comfortably enjoyed his illness. Once he called me over and said, "Pretend you're doing something for me. Listen: he could never send me out now, could he?"

When chow was announced and everyone started to rush out, he set up a piteous caterwauling from the litter, asking who was going to get his dinner, demanding that Warren

Troy use only half a mess kit and donate the other half to him. And when Warren did so and brought him back something to eat, he complained to me that he hadn't got any fruit salad. "How I'd love some fruit salad! Just had my mouth all set for it. Would you help me get up? I'm going outside to the latrine. Just hand me my overshoes there. I'm too sick to get my shoes on."

I was standing in the center of the room with a group of the others when he returned. He knocked against me and would have fallen had I not grabbed hold of him. He was in a half faint with a cold sweat pouring off him. No, he said, when the captain asked, he had no idea what had made him so sick; he had eaten only a tiny mouthful of dinner that Warren Troy brought in on half his mess kit. But later, with a grin, he confided to me that at Pee-you's house he had eaten twenty or thirty pancakes and had drunk eight cups of coffee that was half cream. "Oh, it was so delicious, I couldn't stop. Don't *dare* tell on me."

In the end it was Burrell who was sent out as the aid man, Burrell, the nervous, blinking, pasty-faced little Southern boy with the friendly puppy smile who had fallen asleep on the truck ride where his helmet had fallen off and he thought his head had been blown away. He seemed an odd choice for the new job because he fell asleep everywhere we halted and often had to be shaken and slapped to be roused to his feet. He had become friendly with Sam Benton, Jr., and he had a pleasant singing voice. The two sometimes harmonized on "Then He walks with me, and He talks with me, and He tells me I am His own. And the things we share as we tarry there . . . none other . . . has ever . . . known."

No one ever liked to be around the man packing up to make his solitary departure. "Good luck, kid," the other litter bearers said gruffly. "Come back an' see us when you get the chance."

"Sure. Sure." Burrell blinked and smiled glassily. "I'll be back. Can't keep a good man down. Listen, guys, if—if any letters come here from my wife, see that I get them, will you? Send someone over with them."

After he left, the others sat plunged in gloom.

In Tillet, a wave of self-inflicted wounds broke out. Time after time, men were carried into the aid station from nearby houses, wincing with pain, shot through the foot. Each swore it was an accident. "I was cleaning my rifle—" Sometimes the wounded man would say, pointing to a friend, "He can tell you. He was in the room with me." And often on the face of the friend there would be a look of duplicity as he backed up the story. The circumstances were almost always the same: the man was alone in a room, or a foxhole, and at most in the presence of his best friend; there would be the one shot, the cry for help, the wound always through the foot. Everyone naturally wondered why there were so many of these accidents in Europe when men were thoroughly accustomed to their weapons, whereas in the United States, on firing ranges, such accidents were almost unheard of. There had been so many self-inflicted wounds since the day Sergeant Weems shot himself through the foot that word was read out that every man similarly injured would have to face court-martial charges.

On the day that the order to move out of Tillet was given, two men from one of the nearby houses went out together to the latrine. As always, they brought their rifles with them. Their latrine had been dug in a snowy little truck garden. One man had pulled down his pants and was straddling the trench; the other man, talking to him, tossed his rifle sling over the bare branches of a bush. The rifle slipped, struck a rock and fired twice, shooting one man in the heel, the other in the seat. In the aid station we heard the sharp near reports breaking the stillness. "*Uh-oh*, another guy cleanin' his rifle," Charley Heydt said, and we waited. But there was silence for the longest while before someone cried, "Medics! Medi-i-ics!"

Four litter bearers ran out and brought the men in. Both kept up a steady nervous chatter, swearing the thing was an accident. At first it looked suspicious, but three men had seen the incident from the windows of different houses and came down to testify.

One of my clearest memories of Tillet is of cramming myself with difficulty into one of those tiny school benches attached to a desk, in the little chill hall outside the classroom, with sick line-company men crowding in to escape the wind and the snow, waiting their turn to go inside. Like someone running a checkroom, I had just got my duplicate sets of numbers arranged early one morning when Jack Nugent, known for his rumors at C Company, came in quickly.

"Here, Les, hold these for me, will you?" He grinned his

crooked little grin and gave me a package tied with string that contained his writing paper in a broken portfolio, his toilet articles and a pair of low-cut shoes.

"Where are you going?"

"Home, I hope," he said. "I have a pair of winners here. Two frozen feet. Can I go in?"

He came out about twenty minutes later with an evacuation tag tied through the buttonhole of his overcoat. I gave him his belongings, we shook hands, and he climbed into the ambulance.

"*He's* a lucky bastard," the men from C Company said when they came in on sick call. Atanasio, who still suffered with diarrhea and now had a heavy cold and looked gaunt and worn, said to me, "It worked for Nugent, and there I was, leavin' my feet out, stickin' them into ice water, tryin' everything. They *wouldn't* freeze!" He shook his head.

The others accepted the whole thing philosophically. How strange though—"It worked for Nugent . . ." No one standing on the line criticized Nugent for deliberately freezing his feet, yet from what I heard, feeling was mounting steadily against Sergeant Weems for taking a similar way out of combat. Wherein did the difference lie? In the fact that Jack Nugent, with his genius for starting rumors, was likable and popular and Sergeant Weems was not? Or was it that Sergeant Weems had shot himself through the foot on the first day of combat, whereas Jack Nugent had gone through attack after attack, patrol after patrol, and had come at last to feel, as most of them felt, that his chances for survival were fast running out?

At lunch the day before leaving Tillet, I heard that Teddy's friends—Marie and Pee-you and three or four girls they knew, all friends of the daughter of the house—were coming over for a party that night after dinner. The captain had given his permission, though strictly we were still not supposed to fraternize with civilians. A sketchy collection was made of K- and C-ration crackers, a few cans of cheese, some chocolate bars and a package of gum. After supper, the floor of our bedroom was swept, the blankets folded and arranged into seats along one bare wall, and two kitchen chairs were produced. A lantern was borrowed from the aid station and placed on the floor in the middle of the room. In its light it was cold enough to see your breath when you talked. The men in our room washed and shaved out of their helmets, dumped the water out into the snowy garden, and combed their hair, working seriously on it before borrowed little mirrors, arranging an artistic tangle of curls over the forehead. They shined up their shoes a little by rubbing them on the backs of their leggings, and straightened their uniforms as best they could.

The girls came trooping and laughing up the dark staircase, chaperoned by the stern mistress of the house whose eyes, it seemed to me, glinted with even more purpose than was usual. The girls walked into the room, smiling, dressed in heavy shoes, ski pants and winter coats. They were all in their teens, rather pretty and innocently flirtatious, their hair arranged in high pompadours in front with long back curls. The cold walk over to the house, escorted by Ted and Cliff, had made their eyes shine and their cheeks glow brightly with color. Ted introduced us by first names, and the girls went into peals of soft laughter. " 'Ello," they said. " 'Ow do?" Two of the girls, sisters, had been to the United States to visit an uncle and to see the World's Fair. Both had felt they could speak English fluently, until the moment they tried with us, and then they had sudden surprising difficulties. You could see the blank disappointment come over their faces when the sentences emerged mostly in French.

They all had dropped the woolen scarves from their heads, but it was too cold for them to take off their overcoats. A sudden shyness struck them. They sat in a row on the blankets, all on one side of the room, and we sat on the other. We grinned at each other. The chaperone, thin-lipped, unsmiling, on a chair in the middle of the room, did not relax her iron vigilance; and seated next to her on another kitchen chair, ready to spring from the room, there was a large, completely silent, expressionless girl of fifteen. She did not smile or draw in that ready foot, or change her position once during the entire party. She appeared never to look at us, or be aware of our presence, and instead she fixed her gaze on the wall straight before her. The large social evening was a great strain on her; she seemed relieved, yet sorry too, when it was over and, she gave us a large, damp young hand in parting.

All had lived and slept for weeks on end in their cellars through countless bombardments by planes and artillery.

Their eyes glared when someone mentioned the German soldiers.

Now that they had arrived with their hair so carefully arranged, there was very little anyone could say or do. The two girls who had been to America asked halting questions, often after conferring with each other in French as to how to form the words in English. Finally one said, "Do you know a song, 'Tanks for . . . Memory'?" Off key, she hummed a few bars.

The boys started to sing it and the girls listened delightedly; they clapped their hands when the chorus was over and asked for more. A songfest grew up with all the old reliables: "Someone's in the kitchen with Dinah," "For Me and My Gal," "Show Me the Way to Go Home," "There's a Long, Long Trail A-winding," "Moonlight Bay." Then we asked them to sing.

There were giggles, conferences in French, bursts of laughter, and at last they began. Evidently they belonged to a choir, for they sang in parts, in light young voices. They sang well—much better than we—and imparted to all their songs a chiming bell-like quality. Finishing three or four songs, they struggled to find something we could sing with them. Some knew the tune of "Way Down upon the Swanee River," and at last someone thought of "Alouette," which everyone sang over and over. I asked if they knew "Lili Marlene," which we had heard in England. They were shocked. "That's a bad song, 'Lili Marlene'! A German song!"

There was time-out while the girls ate the ration food, giggling and whispering about us among themselves. None of them smoked. "Sing again more American song," said one of the sisters who had been to the United States. She had evidently told the others about American dance music and wanted us to give an example of it. During all this, the mother sat like a stone woman, or a referee, with her young friend beside her still ready to bolt at the first sign of danger. The lantern threw huge shadows onto the wall behind the girls, and glinted in their hair, in their clear eyes, their teeth.

Warren Troy, the clerk, had come up from the aid station, but Big Steve Brudzinski and his boys, and the ambulance driver, Silly Willie, and his assistant, clustered around the open door, looking in at the girls and discussing them, but they would not come into the room or join in the singing.

Clearly it was not their idea of a party.

During a final exchange of singing, I noticed that our fast songs seemed to exasperate the chaperone. "Pistol Packin' Mama" made her head swivel toward us in annoyance; she had a poor opinion of us and our songs. I said to Phil, "How about something for the old girl? Try the 'Merry Widow Waltz.'" We began to hum it, the girls joined in, and a change came over the mother. Streaks of color rushed up into her face and slowly, almost painfully, she began to smile, then to sway her head. Her hand waved back and forth, keeping time for us. At the conclusion, she beamed and became friendly for the first time, requesting a second chorus, into which she herself joined with a piercing, nasal soprano. That broke up the party and the girls got up to leave. They came around in turn, each one shaking hands and laughing, thanking us and wishing us good luck. Teddy and Cliff walked the block or so home with them past the guards.

Early the next morning we left.

In the afternoon of a very cold, still, dark day, we dismounted from the trucks somewhere deep in the woods. The medics, following a bend in the road, arrived at the only building anywhere visible—a long, low, weather-beaten taproom set down in a little clearing. In the United States it would be called Dave's Place and it would have a lonely neon sign; here there were no advertisements and the dark, chill forest grew close about it. The interior was bare except for a long empty bar and a few wooden benches and folding chairs. Enemy artillery shells crashed now and then in the forest.

We had been there only a short while when the telephone rang and Warren Troy answered it: "Half-Blood-White-One-Six. . . . A Company. . . . I see. Yes, right away." He looked over, impervious, California-big, light-haired, serious, eyeglassed. "Casualty at A Company."

"All right, whose turn to go out?" the captain asked. The litter bearers shifted uneasily. Someone stood up; the other three members of his squad put on their helmets, slung on their medical pouches. Perhaps Tubby, the stout jeep driver, would run them part way to their destination.

Because some officers came in to get warm and to talk to the captain, I went outside and stood in the vestibule, keeping an eye on their carbines. Both outer doors were missing and the cold night air swept in. Standing in the dark, I turned my back and was looking at the crack of light under the inner door when I heard footsteps approaching, crunching on the snow, and a remembered voice said in a half whisper, "Noise! The noi-i-i-se!" The voice then lapsed into French. I turned around. It was, of course, the same man with the frightened stare. Two men had come with him. They had him by either arm, and they went past me into the lighted taproom.

The two men came out almost at once and walked off in silence. Ten or fifteen minutes passed. The officers came out, picked up their carbines, and I went inside. The captain was saying to Noise, "All right, go get your personal belongings —writing paper and toilet articles—turn in your rifle and ammunition, come back here and wait outside there for the ambulance." Starey-eyed, unshaven, in a daze, the man left to obey. The door closed quietly after him. "What the hell are you going to do with anyone like that?" the captain asked. "Intelligent man, college trained—no damned good in an attack. Cowers in his foxhole. They can't get him out. He can't remember his name. He's worthless as a soldier! Back in Regiment, in some clerical job, I suppose he'd be all right." He paced around, lumbering in a circle. "If I thought he was putting on that act though . . ." The sentence went unfinished.

Once more I was standing outside in the dark, icy vestibule. Noise came back with his personal belongings, wearing his overcoat. I said nothing to him, but I didn't realize he was unaware of my presence till I heard him whisper to someone passing by outside, "Hey! Psst! Hey, boys, I *made* it! I'm going back to Regiment! Isn't it *wonderful?*"

"If I were you," I said, "I wouldn't be so loud about it. You're not back yet."

"Oh!" He jumped and turned to me, confused. "Thanks! I . . . the . . . the noise, you know."

When the ambulance came, he rode back murmuring in French with some wounded men.

After dinner, there were many casualties. All three litter squads were rotating on the hauls, and every now and then the walking wounded came in under their own power, with an arm, or a leg or a hand bandaged. Preacher and Charley Heydt, the two technicians, working under the lantern light, removed the bandages, shook sulfa powder into the wounds, applied splints and rebandaged, while Warren Troy bent over the litter in the midst of the work. "Could I have your name,

191

please? And how do you spell that last name? What's your rank? Serial number? What company are you with?" The captain would be standing there, supervising, giving the diagnosis which Warren wrote on the tag before tying it firmly to the man's field jacket. That man was carried to one side, to make room for the next litter under the glare of the lanterns. Contrary to what I had read and expected, there was seldom a great deal of blood; the technicians were never drenched with it, nor was the floor ever slippery because of it. As soon as the bandaging was done, I moved in, picked up the equipment and carried it outside. If there was time, I'd quickly sweep up the pieces of torn and bloody clothing and bandages, swabs, Carlyle bandage boxes, and burn them in the stove. The litter cases were attended to first, then came the patient walking wounded.

"Well, what's the matter with you, Deac?"

"Got shot in the ass."

"Take down yer britches, and les have a look."

There were few tears, few big scenes, seldom any cries even when the pain must have been outrageous. When, as frequently happened, the litter bearers brought in compound fractures, sucking chest wounds, shattered backs, shoulders, necks and so on, Captain Stettner gave over his supervision and worked on those cases himself. In a respite, he sometimes delivered a short, clear explanation to the two technicians on the nature of the wounds they had just dressed. During the little lecture, he kept up the roaming back and forth, back and forth, the one heavy foot slinging in pigeon-toed.

When the ambulance drove up, I'd lift one end of the litter and carry out the wounded man with anyone who happened to be standing about. As soon as the four litter cases were in, the walking wounded were led out and crowded in along the floor of the ambulance.

This was not a large-scale attack, but for hours that night the litter bearers kept carrying men out of the snow-covered forest, across a square moonlit clearing, and up into the beer hall. At about nine o'clock Sam Benton, Jr., returned from a haul, his face scarlet with the cold, and told the captain that he had seen several rifles stuck up in the snow "raht at the end of the woods. Jes standin' there clear as day. American rifles." He pronounced it more like "raffles."

"How many?" the captain asked.

" 'Bout five, six. Mebbe more, sir."

The captain turned to me. "Do you think you'd better go out and pick them up? It's not your job now." He smiled. "You're not supposed to go out in the middle of an attack to gather up stuff, but what d'you think?"

"Well, I don't mind going—but I don't want to be searching around." I turned to Sam Benton, Jr. "Exactly where are they?"

"Raht at the edge of the woods."

"Sam, you go out and show him."

I put on my helmet and gloves and we stepped out a back door. The cleared sloping field stood out silvery-white against the dark background of trees.

"Raht *straight* down there," Sam Benton, Jr., said, pointing. "You can almost see 'em. *See* 'em?" I didn't. "Well, come on then." As soon as we reached the edge of the woods I did see two M1s, their butts stuck in the snow. Why had they been left there? Had the walking wounded abandoned them, seeing the aid station in sight? "An' see, there's another one down there near that tree. An' there's two more. There's a pack an' a gas mask. Want me to take back some of these things?"

"Yes, if you would. I'll take the rifles; you take some of the other stuff."

There were hand grenades placed at the trunk of a tree and, farther in the woods, another rifle. Sam Benton, Jr., went back and I became aware of one of C Company's platoons moving with great caution all through the woods about me. Each man was separate from the other, advancing in what I thought must be the diamond formation, holding his rifle down loosely across his thighs, ready to lift it at a moment's notice. "Flushing the woods." The words formed in my mind as I gathered up the rifles and pressed down the frozen locks. Artillery shells were falling, but not nearby. I was somewhere in the middle of one of the advancing diamond formations, and the man named Lucky, whom I remembered mainly because he had appeared one night during a great barrage, gibbering and shouting on the edge of my foxhole in the Saar Valley, was moving abreast of me, turning his head nervously from side to side, trying to keep track of the two men ahead, one to his right, the other to his left. He was whispering the foulest curses, calling himself the most loathsome and hated names, as if he mortally

193

dreaded every forward step he took and had to force himself on. Suddenly, quite close, there broke out the mechanical chattering of a machine gun, and streaks of tracer bullets pierced the dark woods.

Everyone became tense. There was a watchful halt, and silence. Over to my right a twig snapped loudly with a sound like a pistol report, and Lucky instantly brought up his rifle. Had he fired it, he would have shot my head off. Even in that sub-zero cold I could smell the heavy odor of sweat and fear that came from him. Deciding to get out of there as fast as possible, I picked up a few snowy bandoleers, left the hand grenades at the base of the tree, and, with my arms loaded with rifles, started to hurry back, thinking, So that's what it's like flushing the woods. A loud chattering of small-arms fire began as I broke into the clearing, and going up the incline, across the moonlit field of snow, I knew I was an easy target if anyone had been looking in my direction. Weighed down as I was, I couldn't run, and the field seemed endless.

When I sat down again in the beer hall and resumed the letter I had been writing, I heard Sam Benton, Jr., sitting nearby in the circle, say, "Cliff, Ah'm tared. Write a letter for me, will you?" Cliff was always agreeable, and when he finished his own letter, Sam dictated slowly and distinctly: "Somewhere in Germany. Dear Mother and Dad: Ah am well. Today Ah read Isaiah, chapter ten, verses one to twenty-two. With love, your son, Sam." The other pens had all become still. Eyes slid around to meet other eyes, but no one said anything.

We were still in the beer hall the next afternoon. Chuck Cornell had come in from C Company, unshaven, sick-looking, hoarse with laryngitis, the Red Cross brassard dirty on his arm. At the moment Captain Stettner was out, and Cornell hung around waiting to see him. "Oh God, it's awful out there," he said to me, whispering with effort. "These guys back here have no idea—suffering—" Part of the time his voice failed him completely. "I got to have *relief*. No one could stand—" After he had pleaded so to be sent to C Company, I was shocked by this sudden reversal. "I'm sick," he said. "Ought to be in the hospital for an operation." He flung himself down near the fire and borrowed my canteen cup to make some hot bouillon. I found the cup later, dirty, thrown under one of the benches. The litter bearers eyed him uneasily, wondering if one of them might have to relieve him at C Company. He dozed off, his head hanging.

The captain came in and Cornell woke up and went over to speak to him. There was a gathering of litter bearers around the captain and the usual hangers-on from First Battalion Headquarters. The captain sat relaxed in their midst on one of the long benches. Chuck Cornell asked to be evacuated to a hospital because of a hernia that was troubling him. The interview was made awkward by Cornell's laryngitis, the captain's smiling, professed inability to understand the whispered voice, and by the presence of the little audience.

"Well, let's take a look," the captain finally said with his humoring smile, and Cornell dropped his pants and drawers. "Nope," the captain said after a brief examination, "you haven't got a hernia."

I had walked away, but Cornell, who had studied medicine, said something and the captain examined him again, this time more thoroughly.

"There's a weakness there, yes. But it's not bad enough to evacuate you."

With his clothes still down, with the despised audience listening, Cornell began to argue his case in the whispery voice. Captain Stettner, smiling, continued to shake his head. Cornell persisted, and suddenly all pretense of good humor disappeared from the captain.

"That's enough now. I said no! I been pretty patient with you, Cornell. I been hearin' a lot of bad reports about you not doin' your job, an' if you want to steer clear of a courtmartial, you get the hell back to C Company an' stay there!"

Cornell's face and neck turned fiery red. He started to remonstrate, but the captain silenced him. "That's enough! Get out of here!"

Hot-faced, guilty-looking, Cornell had to dress himself and return to the company he had once begged permission to rejoin.

What had taken place inside him? What loss of illusion brought about this collapse of his famous *esprit de corps* all within a few weeks? He had wanted sincerely to be with the men of C Company, to be allowed to encourage and comfort them, to share their sufferings—and now he would abandon them without a thought; he would neglect them even when they were wounded. And again, why? What caused it? Was there some unsuspected point in almost every man beyond which his courage would not and could not carry him? A point reached sooner in some than in others? And if he had been brave and enduring up until that point, was he to be held accountable for it when it came? I could not answer the question; I did not know.

The next time I saw Cornell it was a few weeks later, from a truck. C Company had led off in an attack, and the aid station was the last of the battalion to leave the town. I happened to turn my head and look back and I saw him sneaking out of a demolished house where he had been hiding.

The following day there was a long, bitter-cold ride out of Belgium into Luxembourg, ending in the town of Consdorf. The battalion was in reserve, but I was sent six miles ahead in the jeep with Mike Nowak, Charley Heydt, Phil, Teddy, Cliff and Dick Gann to establish a forward aid station.

The house that Mike picked out for us, with a narrow central hall, had a slice of a room on the right and a small living room on the left boasting a floor-to-ceiling pier mirror; the kitchen was in the back, and the two bedrooms were upstairs. The aid station was set up in the living room, but most of the time we sat across the hall in the narrow room where there was a Morris chair, a white-covered square table and a phonograph that was broken but which could be played by twirling the turntable with one finger to produce faint scratchy renditions of *Carmen*, the carol *"O Du Froeliche"* and several German marches. All day long the fine snow fell.

In departing, the owner of the house had left the place in charge of one Dominic, an overseer, a Pole, with whom Mike Nowak struck up an immediate strong friendship. Dominic was a tall, dark, cavernous-looking man in a cap, knitted muffler and dark corduroys. Most of the time he was drunk. In return for conversation with Mike, cigarettes and a few rations, Dominic scoured the neighborhood and came back with apples, potatoes, drippings, and sometimes with that rarest of delicacies, a half a loaf of dark bread.

"Arbeit, arbeit, *arbeit!*" he complained whenever I saw him. He was always promising to go out and arbeit, but each time he delayed to down quantities of hard cider with Sam. Still, unbidden, he rigged up a simple but comfortable toilet for us in the barn that was piled high with cut wood, farm machinery, hay, and—oddly—two or three crated porcelain bathtubs and washstands—more, one would think, than would ever be used. Often if you were out there, Dominic would be working among the animals, pitching hay to them, stumbling and staggering about and talking to himself. You'd catch the words "Arbeit, arbeit!"

Aside from C Company's cooks and some artillerymen, we were the only soldiers in the town—in fact, almost its only inhabitants. We had a telephone rigged up and could communicate with the rear aid station; and frequently in the afternoons Tubby would drive up to see how we were and to give us our mail. The trip was extremely dangerous and he always came in blowing, looking surprised, giving vent to his usual observation: "Phew! Things are gittin' rough in the E.T.O.! Roughtie-toughtie, hey, Phil?"

"Right, Jim, they're rough," Phil always replied. He seldom used nicknames.

Tubby's wife had sent him a coonskin cap, which he wore with the ear flaps down and his steel helmet on top of it. During a long jeep ride in the snow, one of the ear flaps had become soaked, and it had dried stiffly, curled up permanently like the end of a Dutch girl's cap. Tubby had been rotund, but now in these days, though far from thin, he could show you, by the voluminous waistband of his pants, how much and how fast he was losing weight. His face, small-featured and blue-eyed, that once had seemed to be bursting, was shrinking and disclosing a tiny pointed chin with a dimple in it.

"Yeah, you guys," he said to the litter bearers in his tight, squeaking, comical voice, "you take *turns* goin' out, but goddamit, I'm out *all* the time! 'Drive this one! Drive that one!' Don't see him stickin' his nose out, do you?" Tubby answered his own questions. "Goddam right you don't!" He'd stay a half hour or so and then drive back just before dark.

All of us enjoyed having the house to ourselves. Mike Nowak was content to sit and spin the victrola by the hour. I was surprised to hear that he was married. "Ah—I don't like to talk about my wife to all these guys." Her name was Frances. He showed me some snapshots. She was a very pretty girl. Yes, she got along well with his family; they were all crazy about her. But then everyone got along with his father. "Fatty Nowak"—the name was on the door of his office— was a foreman in a steel mill in West Virginia. Mike and his three brothers, both sisters and perhaps Frances all worked in the mill. On Saturday nights they piled into their cars and went out to a Slavic club, where they danced the polka hour after hour. Fatty Nowak could dance his sons down, strong as they were. It was pleasant and reassuring to hear of a family so attached, so happy and decent, such an odd mixture of Americanism with their cars and radios, and Mike a basket-ball and football player in high school, Frances so modish and well dressed—and of Bohemia, with their polkas, their long Christmas celebrations.

"Is your family Catholic?" I asked.

"Sure! Good Catholics."

"Aren't you?"

"Aah, I go to church when I'm home—but what the hell. You know how it is."

Even in our own small group there were several Catholics in name only, and there had been many in C Company. I often wondered how the comfortable expression grew up: "There are no atheists in the foxholes."

During the ten-day stay in "Dominic's house," Dick Gann, away from Big Steve's ragging, seemed to improve a little. At times he stared emptily through his dirty eyeglasses, but he spoke more freely and easily; he was included in conversations; and once, laboriously, with great twistings of his tongue, he wrote a letter home to his married brother with whom he lived and in whose short-order restaurant he had worked. "Will ya—will—will ya read—read this an'—and see if I got the f---in' return address right?" he asked, showing me the V-mail form. He had it almost right.

He was a heavy burden to Phil on the litter hauls, I discovered. "He *tries* hard enough," Phil said in his worried, "reasonable" tone. "Dick tries hard, but he's always stumbling and falling, and he pulls the litter down *with* him, giving the poor bird on it a terrible jolt. Of course, by rights, he shouldn't be here. He doesn't know how to protect himself at all. He doesn't know enough to get down when shells come in. You see him lumbering along as if nothing were happening."

"Does the captain know?"

"I *feel* he does," said Phil, scrupulous. "I know he tried to get *rid* of Dick, to leave him behind in the States, but Major Pritchett certified everyone as fit for overseas duty. I don't know what we're going to do. He's getting worse all the time!"

Phil's squad was not called out during the nights that we were there, but that did not mean the nights were quiet. The artillery boys had set up two Long Toms in the garden of our house, and when they went off, the ground, the house and everything in it shook with the tremendous blasting roar. The first night that it happened I nearly jumped through my skin.

"Of course," Phil said when he told me what the explosion was, "those Long Toms shouldn't *be* this close to an aid station. It's against the Geneva Convention. And another thing I'm thinking—as soon as the Germans find out where those Long Toms are, they'll be zeroing right in here on us." Throughout the days and nights, the Germans did shell the town, but not constantly. The 88s and 150-mm. shells smashed and crashed in the streets and houses about us, and then the Long Toms retaliated. Sometimes after their explosions went off, there'd be silence from the Germans.

Because of the intensity of the enemy barrages that began to open up at night, we moved our blankets downstairs and slept in the aid station. Just after dusk one evening a man from C Company walked down from his snowy foxhole on the outskirts of the town leading a private named Staunton, whom I had known by sight at Fort Jackson, a quiet, sturdy boy with dark wavy hair. The man explained that Staunton had been evacuated for combat exhaustion during the Saar campaign and had just been sent back to the lines that afternoon. He seemed to be cured, but then an hour or so afterward a German 88 had screamed in and exploded near him, and Staunton had gone out of his mind again. While this was being explained, Staunton stared blindly before him, his square jaws clenched. Every now and then a shudder ran through him.

Back in camp, I had never heard him speak. When we passed on the company street, he looked at me with recognition but never said hello. I thought he was surly, and then I heard someone say he had a slight stammer. Now he seemed embarrassed about the shudders and was trying to control them by twisting and knotting his large fingers together. The man who had brought him turned around and left.

Charley Heydt telephoned the rear station and asked if the ambulance could come and pick Staunton up. The answer was no, it was too dangerous; we were to bed Staunton down until morning, and in the meanwhile Charley was to give him a shot of morphine. There was a little uneasiness at the thought of Staunton spending the night with us, for he looked as if he were under tremendous pressure and might fly off the handle at any moment.

Shortly after nine, we prepared to turn in. Staunton, squeezing his hands, was lying next to the pier mirror on a litter, staring at the ceiling. I glanced over at him as one of the Long Toms went off with a deafening roar in the yard. Staunton jumped so that his entire body seemed to shoot into the air; he cried out incoherently and started to pull and tug frantically on his fingers. Sweat broke out on his face.

"That's ours, Staunton." I went over and squatted down beside him. "That's going out. It's a Long Tom in the yard. There's nothing to worry about."

He thrashed around and bit on his lip until I thought his teeth would go through it. Every now and then some stammering story tried to force its way out and he kept choking it back, rolling from side to side, pulling at his fingers, making the joints snap loudly.

"Staunton!" I said. "Say whatever you want to say. Yell if you feel like it. We won't care." Most likely we wouldn't have heard, for now the German artillery had opened up and the shells came screaming and roaring in. "Go ahead, yell! Good God, we'll all yell!" The explosions were so close, the others had jammed on their helmets.

There came a blast from the Long Tom that shook the house to its foundation; the pier mirror rattled loudly in its gilt frame and I expected it to crash and splinter on top of us. This time I had to hold Staunton down on the litter, and I turned around to ask Charley if he couldn't give him more morphine. He said that he couldn't, and somehow Staunton became my patient.

I lit him a cigarette to keep him from clutching at his hands. I noticed that they were black and blue and badly swollen. He had evidently been wrenching at them for hours. "Th-th-th-than—th-*thanks!*" he said. "S-st—st—s-s-sta— St—"

"Yes, I'll stay. I'll be right here." I made my bed up next to his litter; Phil was lying beside me. When Staunton finished the cigarette, I squashed it out in the top of a ration can. Immediately he grasped onto his hands again. I gave him a towel with a knot in it, but he threw it away. Charley was about to put out the lantern.

"Charley, just a minute," Phil said. "I have to find a receptacle." His kidneys were weak, or weakened by the cold, he said, and he never went to sleep without a pitcher of some sort within arm's reach.

The lantern was turned out. I could hear Staunton tossing and cracking his knuckles, but I was about to fall asleep, convinced that the shelling had ended, when one of the Long Toms let go again with a fearful thundering roar. This time Staunton jumped up, shouting incoherently, and I threw myself over on him to keep him down. I kept talking to him, telling him all the shells were ours, that he was safe, he was going to the hospital, he was going home, these were the last shells he'd ever have to hear, but in his delirium he couldn't even hear me. The morphine, or perhaps exhaustion, overtook him a few hours later; he drifted off into a heavy sleep.

In the morning the ambulance drove up before breakfast. We got up and took the blankets down from the two windows. It was dark out, snowing. Staunton was hauled up from the litter and his overcoat and helmet were put on him. He could not speak and had no memory of the room or of any of us in it at all. Silly Willie, about to lead him out, said to him, "Hey, you wanna take a leak before we go?" Staunton didn't understand him. "Don't you want to take a leak? Hell, I'll take him outside anyway."

"Yeah, go ahead. You go with him," the others were saying, and Staunton, helpless, without will or understanding, let Silly Willie lead him out the door.

It snowed throughout the morning. I went into the narrow room where Mike Nowak was twirling the turntable with his index finger. "O du froeliche, O du froeliche," sang a distant German soprano. "The hell with this! Here's the one *I* like." A Viennese waltz, thin and sad, scratched out. He and Charley Heydt had been talking about Captain Stettner. Charley mentioned Sam Benton, Jr., and Mike said witheringly, "That Conchie!"

"*What?*" I asked, startled.

"Sure! Sam's a conscientious objector, didn't you know that?"

"No!"

He looked around cautiously before adding, "Phil Schaeffer too."

"You're kidding!"

"Swear to God!" He went into a burst of laughter. "You don't believe me? Go ahead, tell him, Charley."

"Yep, Phil's a Conchie," said Charley Heydt, sitting there with his Red Cross brassard on and a pistol stuck in his belt.

"Is that why they were both put in the medics?"

"Who the hell knows?" asked Mike, whose conviction it was that there was no reason for anything in the Army.

From the kitchen, Ted Jameson called, "Les, come here a minute." I went out. "We're making French-fried potatoes again, and listen, I found some flour. Least I *think* it's flour. Maybe it's starch or plaster. Can you tell?" I couldn't. "Well, anyway, I'm going to make some pancakes." He had only the dubious flour and water and a little dish of grease Dominic had brought in to cook them with.

"Isn't that going to make library paste? Flour and water?"

"Well, I don't know, but I'm going to try. I'll eat the first one. Here. Have some potatoes. I'm cooking these for lunch. Cliff, peel some more and don't slice them up so fine this time. It just makes potato chips."

Toward the end of the ten days when the rest of the litter bearers and the aid-station complement moved up, First Battalion Headquarters came into town too. Our house was overcrowded. Phil, Ted, Cliff and I moved our things into the kitchen, which had a stone floor, and we slept there at night. As soon as the fire died down in the stove, the room became cold enough to freeze water left near the windows.

Upon arriving with the others, Captain Stettner displayed a great and genial interest in the frying of potatoes. With a smile and a nod of his head, he said, "Sure like you boys to fry *me* a batch." I was in the kitchen at the time, and when I made no move to join Cliff and Ted, he asked, "Aren't you any good at this cooking?"

I said no. All day long the two boys washed, peeled and fried potatoes. The captain sat inside and ate them with his fingers, calling out for more before more were cooked, inviting any officers who happened to stop in to have some with him. "Fry up a plate for Lieutenant Hoppe!" "Fry up some good and brown for Colonel Hessig! Bring 'em in as soon as they're ready."

The two boys worked hurriedly. "Haven't had *one* for myself all day long!" Teddy whispered to me. "Never says 'please,' never a 'thank you,' and he leaves all the dirty dishes

202

in there for us to bring out. Hurry up, Cliff, he'll be after us again."

Around five o'clock the captain came out to the kitchen, and, after a glance at the piles of potato peelings, the greasy brown paper and pans of dirt-colored water, he said, "*We* can't have a kitchen lookin' like this! Quit what you're doin' and clean this place up. And when you get finished, *keep* it clean. Supposed to be an *aid* station here." With that he walked out. The boys looked at each other and began to clean the place up. The good old days had ended, and I went back to standing in the dark narrow hall, checking the weapons of men going into the living room. I kept waiting to see if the captain would notice and tell me to check the weapons outside in the snow, but he seemed to have forgotten his concern about that, and we gave merely lip service to the rule.

Back in the rear station two new litter bearers had arrived. "Did you meet them?" Ted Jameson asked, pleased with any innovation. "They're very nice and friendly, especially one. His name is McDunn or McDonough or something like that." Accuracy was not Ted's forte. "He's about thirty something, and sort of fat and lazy and good-natured. The other one I don't know so good. His name is Lawlor. He's young and very polite. I'm glad we have them with us 'cause they're not like Steve Brudzinski or any of them."

I was brought inside to meet the new men. Jimmy McDonough, who was stout and just beginning to go gray, had blue eyes in a likable, easygoing face and a helmet that seemed too small perched high on his head, showing his ears. Tom Lawlor, part way through college, was tall, with a young football build and a schoolboy's face, snub-nosed, Irish, clear-skinned and large-eyed. Sam Benton had been elevated to squad leader in O'Rourke's place, and the two new men were assigned to him. Both were decent, clean-spoken, friendly and unobtrusive and, as Ted Jameson had noticed, the tone and balance of power among the litter bearers shifted, with Big Steve Brudzinski taking a minor place.

At the same time one of the medics who had been in the hospital with pneumonia, which he contracted before I joined them, was now returned to duty. His name was Howard Mason and he was about twenty-five years old, a heavyset Southerner with dense, wavy black hair and a handsome, crowded profile that looked as if it had been drawn by a cartoonist's thick pen. He relieved Bob Russell as the driver of the little truck; and, unhappy about the change, far more worried than I would have expected, the stocky Bob Russell reverted to his regular job of litter-bearing.

Still in Luxembourg, we moved on to Berdorf, an almost completely smashed-up town in the snow. It appeared to have been a resort or a health place: probably a little spa. Soon after landing in it and while waiting for the line-company boys and First Battalion Headquarters to arrive, Phil, Cliff, Ted and I went out to get firewood, and we took the sled along with us. A powdery snow was falling in the silence. We were the only ones abroad. It was odd to see garden chairs and tables strewn everywhere in the snow.

Ted was pulling the sled, walking ahead of us down a narrow street with houses and little hotels smashed to splinters on either side of it. He was complaining about something and then, characteristically, a moment later, he was singing, jitterbugging by himself. Immediately after that, by an equally swift transition, he was pining because he was so out of touch. Here he didn't know the words to any of the new popular songs; he—nor any of us—had ever heard "Don't Fence Me In," which "everyone was talking about back home."

"I asked Jimmy McDonough to sing it to me," he said, "and he said he heard it, but it was just like any Western song. There was a time when I knew the words to every song on the Hit Parade. Everyone in school used to come to me for the words to the songs. That's how you get to be popular, you know."

Phil and I broke into laughter. To Phil, he was a constant source of puzzlement, annoyance and amusement. If Phil mentioned a novel, Teddy, in good faith, would invariably say, "Oh, yes, I saw that in the movies."

"Well, my dear Fatso," Phil would point out, "that was also a book first. *How Green Was My Valley* was actually a *book!*"

"*Was* it? Was it, Les? A book first?" Before you could give your answer, he switched to something else: "Doesn't Phil look like old Franz Schubert? *Doesn't* he? *Just* like him. Phil, you must be a relative of old Franz Schubert." Whereupon some excess of animal spirits led Teddy to push Phil into a snowbank, to fall on him and start to wrestle.

"Damned annoying young one!" Phil cried, struggling to his feet, shaking the snow off. "*When* will you grow up?"

Ted and Cliff collapsed with howls of laughter.

"Ooh, I forgot," Teddy said a short distance up, "I have some pictures of my girl to show you. They came in a letter." They were snapshots of a pretty, smiling girl clowning in the snow—one with her arms around a snowman, another showing her wrapped only in a large bath towel and coming out the door into the sunlit snow, laughing. "Her name's June," he said. "And she's married. Mmm. See, she used to be my girl, sort of, when we were in high school, and then she got married, and when I came home last time on furlough, why, she made a big fuss over me at a party—her husband's in the Marines—and I didn't ask her to, but she said she was still my girl. If I go home again, I don't know *what's* going to happen!" He was pleased.

"You know," Phil confided when I fell back beside him, "I'd say it'd be better if Ted *didn't* go back there to live. I've been thinking over that grandmother of his—that Winnie—and I'd say she was a frightful old bitch, wouldn't you? I think we ought to talk to Fatso seriously, and try to get him to go to college on this GI Bill and *learn* something once this war's over. I'm afraid all he knows about is the *movies*. If it's in the movies, Ted understands. Otherwise, it's meaningless."

"Well, that's Young America. Whenever you read about the New Young, they always know the score, they know just how to set the world straight. They're clear, fearless thinkers, rising up in all the plays and books to tell their elders what a mess they've made of everything, and how, from now on, they're going to take over. But from what I can see, the young are pretty much like Ted and Cliff, or any of these kids. Give them a secondhand car to repair, lots of comic books, and a Betty Grable movie once in a while—that's all they want, and all they're interested in."

"Do you really think it's that bad?" Phil stared at me.

"Well, almost," I said, laughing. "Don't you?"

"I don't know!" he said, worried. "I'd hate to think that."

There were no civilians left in Berdorf; the only people you saw were soldiers, looting. Here, perhaps in revulsion from wearing khaki so long, an epidemic of colored scarves suddenly broke out. Men made them from any bright material they could find in the houses. You'd see sleazy, printed rayon dress goods, drapery material—anything as long as it was colored. Phil, whose face was long and reddish, had one scarf of shiny pale-pink silk; another of grayish lavender.

Silly Willie, the ambulance driver, made a scarf from the bright-red silk of a parachute; he worked hours fringing the ends and knotting them professionally. The thing was highly praised. "Let's go out and get scarves," Teddy would cry, and Phil was always ready to accompany him for this. Anything, he said, to look unmilitary.

The battalion quickly took on a gaudy, musical-comedy appearance. Men wore many cheap little rings, some that fit only to the first knuckle; they wore little rhinestone pins on their lapels; some wore one earring dangling from a lobe. Then one day the stout, dreamy aid man, Pecassi, showed up with stark black-and-white accessories. The men were awed to silence. Around his plump neck he wore a large white scarf; a piece of white lace curtain had been stretched tight over his steel helmet; and—the crowning sartorial touch, striking envy everywhere—a pair of large black goggles, I think from the gas mask, were fastened on top of the white lace of the helmet.

"Boy! Do you look sharp!" someone finally said in whole admiration. Pecassi could hardly unbend to us.

"White lace is the perfect camouflage for the snow," he informed us without a smile, his eyes narrowed, bored and vain.

Everyone then, the Tiger Patrol included, broke out in white lace helmets, and that, plus the jewels and the colored scarves, made the outfit look so ludicrous, a rule came down that everyone had to get back into uniform again. Not long after, warm, fleecy, khaki scarves were given out to the men. In quality, they were the finest article of clothing we were issued. But why, why hadn't we been issued combat boots, especially when we heard that men in other divisions, even those back in London and Paris, in desk jobs, all were wearing them? It was a continuing source of irritation to our men, many of whom felt, for this reason, they were in an inferior, underprivileged outfit.

In Berdorf we were in a static position, and the litter bearers and I were quartered in the cellar of a small bombed-out house. The cellar had a low arched ceiling—you could stand upright only in the exact center—damp walls and a cold, damp dirt floor. I disliked all cellars, but most of our men felt safe only when they were in one.

At times the cellar gave me a smothering sensation, but I was glad that was all that bothered me, glad that time and the winter were passing without any major fighting on our part. Silly Willie and his pale, callow, red-haired assistant sat in the cellar all day long, writing letters by candlelight, asking how to spell the most commonplace words. Indoors, Silly Willie still wore a number of cheap little rings he had picked up on his looting expeditions. He was about twenty-seven, tall and thin, and his flat hair was a greenish-yellow, his face narrow, his parrotlike eyes piped with red, his upper lip sunken in as if he had no top teeth, and yet you could tell he rather fancied himself. He showed me a six- or eight-piece tortoise-shell desk set he had just picked up. "A thing of beauty," he said reverently, taken with the phrase, but not quite sure what a desk set was: the long letter opener and the rocking blotter were mysteries to him. He showed me also two gilt-edged missals with red velvet backs and ivory covers carved with chalices and roses. They looked as though they had never been used, and the script inside was in Latin and German. What Silly was going to do with them, he didn't know, but he and his assistant had "bags full of stuff" out in the ambulance, the cab of which was plastered with reclining pin-up girls, all legs and brassieres; the wife of neither was anywhere in evidence.

Almost everyone had loot of some sort. Even Phil had an onyx inkwell he had picked up in a previous town. Its penholder was formed by the brass antlers of two stags' heads. "What am I doing taking something like this?" he asked after having it a few days. "Am I a *thief?*" It was his only piece of loot and he abandoned it, disturbed by the thought that he could not return it.

Usually, leaving a town, the infantrymen were loaded down with bottles of wine, books they could not read, clocks, statuettes, pictures. They'd carry them along, and then as the hike grew lengthy, they'd begin to drop them. For miles in the snow on the sides of the road, you'd see a trail of books, ornaments, carving sets and little clocks. In the next town, the looting would start up all over again. Generally, the officers were just as avid and as guilty as the men. Advance housing parties made hay while waiting for the battalion to arrive; then the line-company boys poured through the houses, working excitedly in teams, ripping out drawers and scattering the contents on the floor, smashing locked chests with the butts of their rifles, overturning tables and bookcases. By law, men were allowed to take as souvenirs only captured German army equipment, but frequently, with a

207

superior officer's connivance and signature, chests of silverware were sent home, silver dishes, banquet cloths, mother-of-pearl opera glasses, cameras, jewelry, ancient dress sabers —everything from paintings to thimbles—and this while we were still in Allied territory.

The aid station at Berdorf was in the cellar of a building on a main street, quite a distance from the one the litter bearers used. It was much larger, better lighted, and had an even red-brick floor. I reported there after breakfast every day and sat or stood around till five in the evening; there was little for me to do aside from checking the rifles of men coming in on sick call.

The *Stars and Stripes* gave such encouraging news of the swift Russian advance that Germany's fall was expected any day. A system of three-day passes to Paris and twenty-four hour passes to Luxembourg City was worked out, and officers and top three-graders began to leave in high spirits. Perhaps in the anticipation of such a pass, Sergeant Campbell spent a morning washing out his khaki wool shirt and undershirt and drying them over the stove. Phil Schaeffer walked in.

"Waal, Silas," said Sergeant Campbell, "what kin I do fer yuh?"

"I was just looking for—" Phil frowned for a long moment —"a copy of *Stars and Stripes*." He seemed lost, preoccupied.

"One right over yonder. Help yerself." When Phil walked off, his shoulders stiff and high, Sergeant Campbell said to me, vigorously wringing out his shirt, "I call him Silas 'cause that's how he seems ter me, like a Silas, 'n' not like a Phil. You know Silas got a college education? Done a lot of readin', I guess, but you know well's me, old Silas ain't much good for nothin' but books. Lotsa men in the worl' like that." It made Sergeant Campbell feel good. "What you learn in books ain't everything—that's what *I* allers say."

I smiled a little but didn't answer, and then, turning around, saw that the captain had been listening. I walked over and stood near the wide flight of snowy steps that led up to the street. After a while the captain came over, smiling.

"Are you always as reserved as this?" he asked.

"Yes, I believe so," I said.

"In civilian life too?"

"Yes, sir."

He gave his head a shake, smiled, and lumbered off.

In the afternoon Sergeant Campbell came back from a

meeting at Battalion Headquarters and announced that a truck would pick men up in the morning to take them into Luxembourg for a shower. The litter bearers were all called in and there was a draw from a helmet. Only two men could go. I was very surprised when, with Paul Clifford, I won. Immediately after breakfast the next morning, dressed in our overcoats, with gas masks and one blanket, with soap and towel and one ration—and I with rifle belt and a carbine—we climbed into the open truck. There were about twenty of us from the battalion.

It was a piercing cold day, still and gray, ready for snow, and by the time the truck got going the one blanket was no more protection than a linen handkerchief. It was too cold to open one's mouth and talk. We rode for three or four hours at top speed through beautiful, clean countryside—pine forests weighted with snow, farms, hills, valleys—into the city of Luxembourg, and paused there for a while, looking for directions. It had started to snow. We were in the center of a square near a monument; rococo gray stone buildings ringed the place. A horse-drawn sleigh went past and an unmade-up woman went by in a long fitted coat and large beaver hat, pressing a muff against her lips.

The driver climbed back onto the truck and we rode on, down a steep, steep hill, continued straight ahead instead of turning back at the bottom, and drove for miles into the snow-swept, hilly farm country. An hour or so later the mistake was discovered, and we had to turn around with great difficulty and danger on a narrow, icy ledge that ran without a railing along the side of a precipice. As we retraced our way, we opened the ration boxes and ate with numb fingers. The snow had stopped again.

"There's the place!" someone finally called. "There it is, down in the valley."

The setting was superb, a bath, or resort, in a deep chasm amid pines, shielded from most of the wind. There were rows of well-designed bathhouses opening onto a promenade that surrounded a huge swimming pool, now drained. An electric motor chug-chugged and somewhere you could hear water being pumped. The Army had set up two large tents, and we waited on long winding lines to come up to a ticket-chopper's booth. As you went in, you surrendered your towel, received a clean one and a fresh set of long underwear.

The first big tent was for undressing. Many wet feet before

209

us had turned the dirt floor into mud. There were rough wooden benches to put your clothes on, on which men stood dressing or undressing. The bodies of those just out of the hot showers steamed in the chill air that whipped in the tent openings. From the adjacent tent you could hear distant shouts and laughter, the hiss and splash of water. A sergeant came in and called out the rules: "Y'llowed five minutes under the shower. When four minutes is up, I blow the whistle. A minute after, the water shuts off, and everyone leaves the shower room. Keep it neat in here." We had our clothes off by then, and stood shivering, waiting to go in, clutching a bar of soap. It was the first shower I had had since—when? The shower in Stone, Thanksgiving night, the night we left England. How many weeks or months was that?

The whistle blew in the shower tent, bringing cries of dismay; a minute later the water turned off. The men started back into the dressing tent as we started forward, skinning past each other. Between the two tents there was a short space open to the sky that was like a dip into an icy bath; then we came into the warm, steaming shower tent with its slippery, soapy duckboards placed over the mud, its narrow pipes overhead. There were not enough shower heads for each man to have one, and we had to double or triple up. We waited, looking up tensely like basketball players. The hot water came out, spraying and splashing with no great force. Elbows banged and collided.

"God, this is good!" "Oh boy, feel that hot water!" "First shower in *months!*"

Everyone worked fast—only the water seemed to come too slowly, at leisure. I had completed one over-all soaping, rinsed off, and started to lather again when the nozzle above spluttered and suddenly went dry. The three of us scattered and crowded in under other bursts of water. A man in my new group dropped his soap under the duckboard, couldn't fish it out, and in sudden desperation begged to use mine. I gave it to him and a second later the whistle blew. A short minute after that, the water stopped. "Ah-h-h," everyone said.

"All out!" cried a voice. "All out! That's all."

We hopped back across the open space, ducking down as the cold air from above touched us, found our clothes and began to towel vigorously. Grinning, looking at each other with bloodshot eyes, we were a cleaner, fresher color. The long underwear of cream-colored wool, I heard, belonged to the English Army. The buttons on the drawers were of brass. Mine were several sizes too large in the waist, but fortunately I had a safety pin to pin them in the back. How clean one felt! And how disinclined to put on the dirty uniform, the battered shoes, the worn and permanently wrinkled leggings!

As soon as we were dressed, we started back for Berdorf. The cold afternoon was drawing in. In the front of the truck, an extra tire was lying on the snowy floor and I sat on it, hoping the cab would fend off some of the wind. Paul Clifford sat beside me. Since morning he had said scarcely a word. "Pretty cold— What, are we lost? *Good*ness sake! Like to take a trip sometime in this Army without gettin' lost— That shower sure felt good." That was all.

Climbing down out of the truck, frozen, in the lonely evening light, no one thought to complain of the length of time consumed. It had taken more than eight hours to stand five minutes under the shower. Everyone agreed it was well worth it and would have gone back the next day for more.

On one of the last days there, Phil Schaeffer came down to the aid station to wash out the khaki cotton shorts he wore under his long drawers. What with washing and drying, and spells of abstraction, the project took him the better part of the day.

"Do you notice Phil getting absent-minded?" Ted asked me. "He's a regular absent-minded professor! I think he acts so funny! You speak to him and half the time he doesn't know what you're saying."

I did notice that day he seemed disorganized, but it was only when I recalled meeting him for the first time in the trench near Rheims that I realized how he had changed. He had begun to mumble to himself; he was indecisive, often forgetting what he had started to do; and sometimes it took him quite a while to answer a question. "What?" he'd say. "Oh, yes, yes! Yes." But he'd have no idea what you had asked. These changes had come upon him so gradually that we had grown accustomed to them and looked upon them as slight and harmless eccentricities.

He had gotten the pair of shorts dry and was about to leave the aid station when the telephone rang announcing a casualty in A Company.

"All right, Phil," said the captain. "I think it's your turn. Get your squad out."

Instead of rushing out, Phil stood at a loss, looking through his patched glasses that now had a length of green string for an earpiece. "Yes, sir," he said. "I—I'm just going to change my underpants."

This answer was so astonishing that everyone stared and a little stillness fell. Phil looked back, perfectly serious.

The captain put on a smile. "Hurry *up*, Phil, hurry up! We can't wait for you to change your clothes. There's a man wounded!"

"*Oh!* Oh! Yes, sir! I— Right away!" He turned and went up the stairs, and for a moment or two no one spoke.

"Boy!" someone said. "Going to change his *underpants!*"

"Ole Phil Schaeffer seems to me's *slippin'*," Preacher said.

I looked at the captain. He still had the half-smile on his face, but he had seen, I think, better than we, what was happening to Phil.

Coming on toward morning, we were in a small farmhouse on a road just beyond St. Vith. A blizzard was raging and the line companies were "jumping off": the term was always used, and hadn't you seen the performance, it would have created the impression of greater readiness and snap than was ever actually the case.

For the first time, and much against their will, the three litter squads were leaving the aid station to follow the line companies throughout the attack. They much preferred remaining in the comparative safety of the station till a call came in for them. Captain Stettner was the originator of this system, but the company commanders asserted their men would feel much safer if they knew the litter bearers were close by at all times; and since that was how the medics worked in the other two battalions of the regiment, the company commanders brought pressure to bear on Colonel Hessig and his assistant, Captain Reddy, who in turn brought pressure on Captain Stettner which, until now, he had resisted. He claimed that his system was the more effective of the two, since the line companies did not come equally under shell fire: usually one company at a time sustained the brunt of an attack—why, then, scatter the only litter bearers over the entire battalion? He kept the aid station moving up until it was almost on the line of attack, and the moment the telephone call came announcing a casualty, Tubby rushed the litter bearers up in the jeep, then sped back to be ready to shuttle another four up when the next call was received.

A rather peculiar situation, though, had started to develop. Little Lieutenant Serletis, the Medical Administrative Officer, was slowly cracking up. His face had turned the gray of cigar ashes; he had lost weight and he couldn't eat. He smoked and worried constantly. I saw him always looking up, turning his head nervously from one man to another, asking, "Any news? What's the dope?"

From the beginning he had neglected, or avoided, much of his actual work—that of locating the companies in an attack, establishing "collecting points" where aid men and litter bearers could first bring their wounded before carrying them into the station, and going forward, when we were about to move, to find new billets. Fear kept him indoors a greater part of the time. Captain Stettner was aware of this, yet seemed to have a condescending fondness for little Lieutenant Serletis, and as time went on, he became more patronizing and careless and Lieutenant Serletis took on the role of the captain's body servant. It was he who ran out and brought in the captain's food from the chow line, and ran out and washed the mess kit afterward; it was he who always set out his own soap and shaving equipment for the captain, who had a curious disinclination ever to use his own. And when the captain was finished, the soapy gray water, the clouded brush, the unwashed razor and the towel were left for the little lieutenant to put away. I watched to see what the captain did about brushing his teeth. He didn't. He rubbed them and his gums with a little wad of toilet paper.

Of course he could have turned Lieutenant Serletis in and gotten a better Administrative Officer, but I think partly he was sorry for Lieutenant Serletis and partly liked having someone so under his thumb. "Nick," he'd call, "run down to the C.P. for me an' see what's goin' on. See what information you can pick up." Sick at the thought of going out, Lieutenant Serletis would put on his helmet and trot off on his tiny legs.

While this was progressing, Sergeant Campbell was becoming more and more useful to the captain, taking over more and more of the lieutenant's duties, so often now it was he who went down to hang around the Battalion Command Post to gather information. Soon the litter bearers began to say, "Old Campbell is after Serletis' job. Sure! The son of a bitch! He thinks if Serletis cracks up, they'll give him a battlefield commission." I believe this is exactly what Sergeant Campbell did think, for he spent all his spare time at the C.P. and began to act increasingly important in the aid station. Captain Stettner, who was acute, appeared amused at the by-play.

Chris Taylor, who was Captain Reddy's orderly, had told me that down at the C.P. Sergeant Campbell would listen to the officers complaining that Captain Stettner ran his aid station to suit himself, and time and time again, to ingratiate himself, he promised to use his influence on the captain about sending the litter bearers out with the companies. The litter bearers watched this uneasily. Captain Stettner continued to shake his head in refusal, but it was apparent to everyone that Sergeant Campbell was nettled; he had given his word and was ambitious to succeed in the matter and build himself up in the eyes of those who might be instrumental in bestowing on him a battlefield commission. The weight of the argument became too much for Captain Stettner, and finally Sergeant Campbell had his way. In his usual quick, low voice, he gave the orders for the litter bearers to go out with the companies that morning.

Cursing Sergeant Campbell up and down, carrying extra stretchers, they set off in the snow. Lieutenant Serletis, aware, I think, that Sergeant Campbell was taking over, sat with his head in his hands. The captain was out. Preacher, also aware of the shifting of power, sat in the neat, warm little farmhouse kitchen with his hands folded under his stout arms. From time to time he glanced at me over his steel-rimmed glasses and then at Lieutenant Serletis. Sergeant Campbell, hiding a smile, was particularly busy, bending over, moving equipment about unnecessarily. I got up and stood looking out the window at the double file of infantrymen going past the door in the great blowing clouds of snow. There went poor C Company's Second Platoon: Smathers, Gramling, Ahlhauser, Dave Rossofsky, Lambert, Sergeant Danowski. There came the long wild scream and crash of a German 88, and the double line, thin-looking without overcoats, indistinct in the swirling snow, wavered and sank down flat, then struggled up and went on, heads bent against the wind.

This was "jumping off"—this cold, plodding, unwilling, ragged, double line plunging up to their knees in snow, stumbling, looking back at the last farmhouse in sight with the Red Cross flag planted in front of it.

While the two thin lines struggled forward against wind

and snow, a jeep drove up before the house and deposited a small figure burdened down with the new heavy pack that replacements were given. Lopsided, he carted it up the path, knocked on the door and came in. "Medics?" he asked.

"Yup," said Preacher. "What kin I do fer yuh, Deac?"

"I'm—I was told to report here," was the glum reply. "I'm a replacement." He was a small, thin-faced, pimply boy with a pinched, cold, lugubrious face, light hair, and red rims to his eyes. "Name's Jenkins," he said in answer to the question. "No, I just come over. They tol' me to come in here."

"Guess he better go right out with A Company," Sergeant Campbell said in a quick, businesslike tone, still working about. "Jenkins, you jes throw your stuff over there in the corner. Jes wear your fiel' jacket, gas mask, helmet, brassard—"

Jenkins was shivering. A hopelessness, a great weary disgust, held him in thrall. "No, I never done none of this," he answered listlessly. "I always worked in a General Hospital. I just come over—"

"Preach," said Sergeant Campbell, "better check over his supplies, see he's got everything he needs."

"All you got to know, Jenkins," Preacher said, looking through the bag, "is how to put on a Carlyle bandage and give a shot of morphine. You know how to give morphine?"

"N-n-no. I never gave it." This I didn't believe, but Preacher showed him how to use the syringe, gave him a supply of ampules, cautioned him about keeping them on his person, secret, tied the brassard on his sleeve for him, shook his hand, and off Jenkins went into the snow.

That night in the aid station he told me he had just caught up to A Company and had gone only a few feet with them when a German 88 screamed in and exploded nearby. There was almost at once the long cry, "Me-e-ed-ics!" He waited, and when no one appeared, he got up, shaking, ran over through the snow and saw a man with most of his back blown away. Not knowing whether he was going to faint or vomit, Jenkins sank to his knees, and when he did neither, he began in a daze to apply bandages; then he gave the shot of morphine. Before he could get to his feet, there came another shattering explosion and there was another casualty. "I didn' seem like myself," he said. "I got sort of in a daze, puttin' on bandages, stickin' the needle in."

He came from Long Island City and had been a cabinet-

maker's assistant. "This guy was makin' bars, like out of mahogany an' all, an' he was showin' me the business. Yeah, I
sort of liked it. Before that I was in the three Cs."

"The what?"

"Three Cs. C.C.C. It stunk."

Jimmy McDonough's initiation was somewhat the same.
"The first shell comes in and blows a guy's legs right off.
Jeezus, I nearly die. Then after I get him fixed up with one
of the other guys, someone yells 'Eighty-eight!' an' believe
me, by that time I *knew*. I starts diggin' in the snow like a
bastid. I didn't know whether to keep my helmet on my head
or stick it on me ass."

The next day we moved on to Shliebach and were quartered in a long, empty beer tavern facing the road on a slope
that led down into town. Approaching it on foot, I had the
odd sensation of having been there before; then I realized that
it was almost identical to the place where Cornell came to
see the captain about his hernia. Instead of being surrounded
by a forest, though, the ground here was hilly and fairly
open, with fields and farms and stone fences covered with
snow. German shells were shrieking in, exploding in the
fields, and one of our men said, "What the hell is *that* over
there?" In an open field there appeared to be eight or nine
tall spears, inclined all at the same angle. "They're German
aiming stakes!" someone else replied.

"Why doesn't someone rip the damned things out?" I asked,
struggling up to the tavern with an armful of blankets. For
that matter, I thought, why didn't I rip them out? The shells
were crashing in so fast that I didn't want to go even that
short distance into the field. It was a dark, snowy day.

Inside, we set about at once blacking out the windows; the
lanterns then had to be lighted, and a blanket was hung on
the inner side of the door. There was a long bar with dry
beer pumps that everyone tried. Above it there was a beer
poster, quite old, a few faded framed picnic photographs and
two plates with strawberries painted on them. Near the bar,
three wooden steps led up to a little railed-off platform
where there were bare round tables and wire soda-parlor
chairs. There were many windows up here to cover, and the
men, fearful of flying glass, if not of a direct hit, began looking for the cellar. Behind the bar they found a trap door that
led down into a waist-high pit that might, with crowding,

hold three or four men, hunched down. Across the room, a flimsy green door that was locked on the far side led to the owner's quarters. Someone said the family were Germans. The men did not like the place because it lacked a cellar, but I liked the feeling of space and air.

Casualties had become so much a part of our life that one scarcely noticed the wounded coming in or being carried out. While they were being bandaged, the litter bearers sat about talking and laughing. It was only when a particularly bad case came in that an uneasy silence would fall.

One was brought in now.

"Cap'm!" Preacher called out—sure sign of a difficult case. Laughter and talk in the room almost died down. Howard Mason, walking around, went on sudden tiptoes; passing someone, he pulled down the man's helmet and you heard a snicker from him, a whispered curse as the man made a wild swing at him.

The captain, Preacher and Charley Heydt had gathered about the litter, blocking it from my sight. Bandages were torn hurriedly out of the square gray cardboard boxes; strips of adhesive tape were ripped off. Four or five minutes passed with the three figures intent, serious, working almost in silence. "All right, we're finished here," Preacher said. "Someone, quick, hand me a blanket there."

The captain started to get to his feet.

"What?" he asked of the wounded man, who had whispered something. "Yes, he's here." He turned around. "Atwell, friend of yours wants to see you."

I got up and walked over. It was Dave Rossofsky.

"Can I speak to him a minute?" Dave was asking in a whisper.

"Sure. Go ahead." They walked away. Except for Dave's extreme pallor and graveness, you wouldn't know he had been wounded. I bent down and he looked at me for a long moment.

"Hello, Dave," I said through a sore throat. "Are you badly hurt?" Pictures of the misty, rainy apple orchard came back, the smell of wood fires smoking, and the sagging, upset tent we had had.

"Yes." He looked at me soberly. "Intestinal wound." The words were whispered. "I mustn't have any water."

"Oh, I'm sorry, Dave." I struggled for something to say. "They'll fix you up."

"Yes," he said gravely, not at all like himself. There came back the day his foot had kicked over the canteen cup of cocoa and I had shouted at him. "Les, could I have a cigarette?" He asked it hesitantly.

"Of course." I was glad for any normal conversation, any activity. "I'll have one with you. Can you smoke it, or should I hold it for you?"

"Hold it." A whisper.

I put the cigarette between his colorless lips, waited a moment, drew it out. He blew forth a faint trickle of smoke, then lay perfectly still.

"More?"

"Yes." The whisper was fainter. In silence he took two more drags and then said, "That's all, Les." His eyes, fixed on me, changed, grew dim and began to close. I thought he was about to lose consciousness, even to die, but his eyes opened again.

"Dave, you'll be glad to get home. You'll be all right."

"I don't know," he whispered. He had been partly planning on becoming a doctor and knew the seriousness of his wound.

Warren Troy came over to the other side of the litter. "Name?"

"David Rossofsky," I said, spelling the last name.

"Rank?"

"Private. C Company," I said.

"Serial number?"

Dave didn't answer. His eyes had closed.

"I don't know it." We both reached to unbutton his shirt and get at his dog tags when Dave whispered the number.

"All right," I heard the captain say behind me to the ambulance driver, "get this man back as fast as you can."

"Goodbye, Dave. Write and tell me how you—"

But he had lost consciousness. He was carried out into the ambulance. I got up.

"He was a swell fellow," I said, but no one answered or cared. I said to Preacher, "Was he very badly wounded?"

"Yes. Wouldn't you say so, Cap'm?"

Captain Stettner nodded his head several times, slowly. "Very," he said.

"He'll live though, won't he?"

"All depends. They'll probably fly him to England."

Just after dark we heard the jingle of mess kits on the road as First Battalion Headquarters lined up in single file. "Back up there!" a muffled voice was shouting. "Don't crowd up."

"Hey, chow!" someone inside the station said, and there was a dive for mess kits and canteen cups.

"Wait till you're called outside," Sergeant Campbell said. Then there came straight at us a wild long shriek and the jolting explosion of several German 88s. Everyone had cowered back from the blanket-covered windows and a few had fallen flat on the floor.

A cry went up from outside and footsteps thudded up to the door. The door was flung open and behind the blanket a voice bawled, "Medics! Medics! All out. Hey, *Medics*." Other voices from the road were shouting and groaning, "Medi-ics! Oh-h-h! Oh-h-h! Help! Medics, I'm wounded!"

"Quick! Out there!"

The mess kits clattered to the floor.

"Watch that goddam blanket! Don't let the light out!"

There was confusion while the litter bearers raced out and the first wounded were carried in, or staggered in alone, unbandaged and bloody. The barrage had killed two of the men on the line and had wounded nine others. With supper forgotten, the captain, the two technicians and several of the litter bearers worked over the wounded while more shells smashed and crashed outside. The ambulance raced back to the rear with the first litter cases. About a half hour passed. I swept up the bloody swabs and pieces of uniform, burned them in the stove and threw the salvage equipment in a heap near the door.

Almost as soon as the last of the wounded were driven away, there came a knock on the heavy wooden door and we heard, "Medics? *Chow!*" For a moment no one moved.

"You goin' out?"

"I don't know. Are you?"

A few of us picked up our mess kits, grinning, but at the moment of starting out a great unwillingness took hold of me.

"Hey, don't be crazy!" Jimmy McDonough said. "I wouldn't go out there for a million dollars! The hell with eatin'! *I* can miss a meal."

Some of the others sat in a row, shoulder to shoulder, expressionless, worried, not saying anything. Then the door opened, the blanket moved and writhed, and Sergeant Concannon, the new mess sergeant, struggled in with those round, aluminum covered pans containing enough food for all of us: boiled potatoes, pork chops, dry bread and lukewarm coffee. Nervousness made us eat quickly. Somehow one wanted to be finished, to be ready for the next huge explosion. Sergeant Concannon came back to pick up his pans and received a rousing thanks for bringing the food in and saving our faces.

"Boy, oh man," Bob Russell said about ten minutes later. "Ah've been puttin' off goin' out ohll day to take a s---." Sadly he shook his head. "Now Ah'm gettin' *pains*, Ah ain't kiddin' you. Ah gotta go so *bad!*"

"I have to too," I said. "I'll go out with you."

At the moment there was silence outside.

He smiled, walked around in a circle, paused, scratched his head. "All right, Les, come on. You come with me."

We waited till we were both behind the blanket, then we opened the door and stepped nervously outside into the dark. Damp snow was falling lightly, but it wasn't cold; the air smelled of thaw, of wet bark, of shellfire. Our feet went through the top crust of snow and sank down. We turned the corner of the building and walked beyond it. "I don't know where the slit trench is," I said, "but I'm not going very far to find it."

"Boy, me neither! Here. Right here, Les. This far enough." The damp night wind blew. We separated from each other, dropped our pants. Instinctively both of us faced the direction from which the shells had come.

I was finished before he. "Les," he said suddenly, "don't go!"

I was buttoning my clothes. "No," I said, laughing. "I'll wait."

With that there came toward us, as if splitting the night sky, an enormous gathering shriek and a jolting, deafening crash. I had taken a few steps on hearing the scream begin; as usual I was looking for a comfortable place to fall. But the scream had come like a thousand furious whistles, so fast and loud, I fell over any place, landing on my side, burying my head in my arm. The explosion pounded me and the earth all about. I had time afterward to say, "My God! Russ, are you—?" when another long, flying scream started through the sky, coming straight down at us. I banged my head into the snow as the explosion roared out with a blinding light and with what seemed like a great hissing of the snow. For a moment I waited, holding my breath, hearing the shrapnel flying angrily about, striking the building and the saplings around it.

"Les? You all right? Stay low-w." He reached out and grabbed my wrist. "Stay down. Stay low. Stay—"

Another shell had started for us and I found myself trying to shrink through the snow, to press my body by main force down into the earth. The roaring, rocketing explosion jarred and deafened me. Shrapnel was flicking and pinging against the trees and the building, dropping into the snow. There was a long moment of silence.

"Russ—?" I wondered if he had been hit this time.

"L-Les, d-don't move!"

"Another's coming!"

His grip tightened on my arm. We ground ourselves down, then held on. Though I had shut my eyes tight, I was aware of the burst of light that came with the blasting roar. Then darkness again and absolute silence. Experimentally I lifted my head, waiting for pain to strike out through some wound. The last shell had been the closest.

"Get out of here," I said with a wobbling jaw. "Quick! Before another—"

"Come on!"

We jumped to our feet and, as usual, a momentary paralysis held me before I could start. Wanting to start too quickly, I couldn't move at all. Suddenly both of us were running as fast as we could, our knees going like pistons, our feet not gaining proper traction in the snow. How long, endlessly long the entire length of the building seemed once we were abreast of it! I was running so fast through the saplings that when we started to turn the corner and get in the door, I had to execute a wide semicircle, trying to make up with extra speed for the extra steps. I was surprised to find myself laughing.

We flung ourselves at the oak door and burst into the blanket, then the lighted room, both chattering at once. Russell, buttoning his pants, stuffing his shirt inside, began to curse loudly and freely as if in a heated argument. Afterward he went over and flung himself face down on the stack of blankets and put his head in his arms. His body began to shake. I sat down and roared with laughter, realizing I was only a short step from hysteria.

Many of the men were nervous about sleeping in what they

221

called "the open," and some stretched their blankets behind the bar or under it. Phil and I, Ted and Cliff slept up on the little balcony, against the railing, as far away as possible from the windows. Just before we lay down, Phil started crawling about in his stocking feet.

"What are you doing, Phil?" Ted called.

"Looking for a receptacle to pee in!" came the reply which invariably sent Ted into a whinny of laughter. Then:

"Ooh, I hope we're not called out tonight. I *hope* we're not."

Frequently they were. Their litter squad, or some other; some nights all three squads had to go out. Phil's was called out that night. I woke as soon as he started to get up. In the silence I heard them buckling on their overshoes in the impenetrable dark.

"Phil, do you have everything?" I asked.

"I don't seem to have a helmet, damn it. *Had* one."

"Use mine." I reached out in the dark and dumped the things out.

"Les—" Ted's whispered voice— "could I borrow your scarf too? It's so cold out." He leaned over to get it. "Say a prayer we'll be all right. Oh, how I hate to go—just feel it's going to be my unlucky night."

"Are we ready, men? Where's Dick Gann?"

"L-l-l-lacin' my—my Gah-damned—"

"Ready, Cliff?"

"Yep. Wait a second. Hey, Les, do me a favor? Hang onto this fer me?"

"What is it?" It felt like a folded silk handkerchief.

"It's a—Nazi flag. I don't want to carry it roun' with me."

"Oh. Sure." We had heard that any of our men taken prisoner and found with German souvenirs on them were shot at once.

"Les, don't forget. Say a prayer, and if you can find anything to eat, save it till I come back. How I'd like a nice hot cup of cocoa to look forward to."

"I have a fruit bar from a breakfast ration."

"All right. Save that. Oh, how I hate to go."

I'd fall asleep, enjoying the full width of the blankets, hoping it wouldn't be a long, dangerous haul for them.

In the morning, after breakfast, the captain and most of the medics moved up to the next town. Unsure whether

222

they'd be able to stay there, they left five or six of us behind to hold the tavern. Every now and then an 88 landed in.

"Don't *like* this goddam place," the men said. "Wish we could get outta here! Boy, I'm going to take another look at that cellar place in case any more of 'em shells come in."

No one investigated the green door that connected with the rough little farmhouse, but after a heavy shelling had passed, the door unlocked and the frightened, stout, middle-aged face of a woman peered in. The door closed quickly and the bolt shot back into place. I heard the woman clumping down the stairs to her cellar.

At about ten o'clock, the front door opened and a young woman came in with a baby in her arms. She was pregnant and breathless. The child was wrapped in a blanket; she herself wore a heavy coat and a white knitted scarf over her head.

Phil Schaeffer had gone with the captain; there was no one in the place who could speak German. I had memorized most of the German words and phrases in the little booklet the Army had given us, and it suddenly developed that I was the only one in the place who had done so. I had to come forward as interpreter. The girl assumed that I was the doctor in charge and poured out a soft stream of German, indicating her baby.

"What's she say, At?" Preacher asked while the others stood and gaped.

"I don't know, except the baby's sick." To the girl I said, "Meine frau, bitte sprechen sie langsam. Langsam . . . Ich kemmen nicht sprechen Deutsch goot."

Again she began, but she was breathless. I led her over to a chair. She sat down and rocked the baby back and forth, sighing over it. Again she explained. My ignorance must have been irritating; it took a long time, with many questions, gestures, lifts of the shoulders, pointings to various parts of the baby, to find out it had a bad sore throat, a heavy cold, fever, and that it had not eaten for three days. It was very languid. She lifted up its little hand and showed me how limply it fell. The child, who was about a year old, watched her drowsily with eyes that started several times to roll up in its head. I put the back of my hand against the baby's cheek, which felt hot.

I went over to Preacher and explained what I could.

"Trouble is, At, we jes ain't got any medicine you could

223

give a baby 'at young. Stuff Ah got here's fit fer a man, mebbe, or a horse, but I'd be right afraid to give it to a kid."

"Don't you have aspirin? You can give a baby half of one."

"Don't have a single one here. Don't have no paregoric, nothin' but these here big sulfa pills an' a bottle of brown bombers. She better wait 'n' see when the cap'm comes back, let him look at the baby. Ah don't know nothin' 'bout 'em."

"*Is* the captain coming back?"

"He said so."

Hating to disappoint the girl, I went over to her.

"Meine frau—Ich bin *nicht* ein Arzt. They are not doctors either—nicht Arzt: Sanitaters. Der Arzt vieder kommen ahere—"

"Yah? Yah?" she asked eagerly.

"Warren," I called. "When is Stettner expected back?"

Imperturbable, he answered, "He said around two o'clock."

"Der Arzt vieder kommen back ahere in feer hoor. Fersthayenzee? In feer hoor. Der Arzt. Das medicine? Ahere, goot feer soldaten, feer menchen?—nicht goot feer kinder. Tsoo gross."

She said something that I took to mean, Would it be all right if she stayed and waited for the doctor: she had come such a distance with the baby and there was so much shelling going on.

I said yes, and since truck drivers were coming in and going out, gaping at her, and since she was sitting in a constant draft, I led her farther down the room, up the three steps onto the little balcony and sat her down at one of the tables. She shook the scarf back from her head. She was blond, pretty in an unemphatic way, gentle-looking. Whispering something to the baby, she kissed it, and rocked with it.

I asked, "Haben sie etvas-tsoo-essen today? Breakfast? Kaffee?"

She looked startled for a moment and then said, "Nein," and led me to understand she had been too bothered about the baby's illness. I offered her a cigarette, which she accepted with a smile at herself; I lit it for her, and then went down and made her a cup of Nescafé in my canteen cup.

"Ach, danke, danke!" she said when I brought it to her. I told her it was hot and gave her my spoon and two lumps of sugar. I found a few K-ration crackers, but she shook her head: she did not want to eat. She took sips of the hot black coffee, and tears came swimming to her eyes. I could tell what it was—worry about the baby, her own condition, the long, dangerous walk through the snow, and now, sitting in a bare tavern among foreign soldiers. She tried to give the baby a few sips of coffee from the spoon, but the baby turned its head away and began to cry. She herself drank about half the coffee and put it down. I could see that it immediately made her sick. We had taken the khaki blankets from the windows and a stack of them was near her on the floor. I spread some of them out and asked, by gestures, if she wanted to put the baby down or lie down herself. She said that she didn't.

I left her and went down into the main part of the taproom. The rest of the men accepted her presence without comment or curiosity, without even interest. She was my patient and responsibility. Battalion Headquarters moved out of town and about five minutes passed when suddenly, with hideous whistling screams, German 88s started to come in, crashing one after the other all about the tavern. The place shook crazily. The men, startled at first, made a wild, panicky dash for the trap door behind the bar. I turned and looked for the girl. She had jumped up and came running toward me through the shaking beer hall, screaming, "Keller! Keller!"

"No cellar! We have no—" I couldn't think of the German words. All I could see was the men crowding behind the bar, tearing at each other to get into the square hole. The girl, though shouting something hysterically, took in the situation at once—women and children were *not* first here—and before I knew what had happened, she had given me her baby, thrust it at me to hold. She herself then started to faint so that I was trying to hold onto both of them. The shells smashed in with a horrible banging roar. The girl, crumpling, sagging, became almost a dead weight and her head fell against me. Her forehead was covered with sweat.

"It's all right," I heard myself shouting to her over the din while I tried to maintain my balance in the shaking room. "Don't worry, it's all right!" It seemed the most absurd thing in the world to be saying at the time. One more shell came in, exploding with a frenzied blast, and then there was absolute stillness. For a minute no one moved. The half-fainting girl and I, with our arms about each other, were the only ones on our feet. Warren Troy lay nearby beside the telephone.

225

The green-painted door leading to the farmhouse was within arm's reach. The shuddering girl, opening her eyes slowly, took the baby back and held it. With one arm still about her, I reached out and started to pound on the door. "Open up!" I shouted. "Open the *door!*" It was a flimsy door with a few cracks in it, but the lock held. I began to kick at it, shouting, "Open up! Herein! Herein!" I don't think I expected anyone to come up out of the cellar of the house, but surprisingly the bolt shot back, the door opened and the pale, terrified face of the stout woman appeared. I pushed the girl and the baby toward her. "Im keller! Keller! Schnell!"

"Yah! Yah!"

The girl stumbled through. The door slammed and locked again. My knees then began to shake so I could hardly stand up.

Gasping and exclaiming, the men got to their feet and started to come out from behind the bar. Everyone was chattering, laughing nervously, talking all at once. The two little white plates with the wreaths of strawberries were still on the wall, but the pictures and the poster had fallen, leaving brown oblongs on the faded tan wallpaper.

"The communication line's still open," said Warren Troy, who could be maddeningly matter-of-fact at such times. He stood listening with the earphones clamped on. The others, recounting their exact emotions, were laughing, letting out whistles. Suddenly Warren Troy said into the mouthpiece, "Yes! Half-Blood-White-One-Six! Half-Blood-White-One-Six. Yes! Yes, I hear you." He listened, said, "Very well," and turned to us. "The captain wants us to move up at once—to clear out of here." He stood listening a moment longer. "They're taking out the line. That's the last message to come through."

Everyone rushed to grab up the equipment, the boxes of medicine and dressings, the blankets. "The stove!" someone cried. "Gotta get the stove down! Quick! You take the blankets. Load 'em up in the truck any old way. Get the litters!" In the haste, the sudden confusion, the hurried trips out to the truck and back, there was only a moment to think of the girl and the sick baby in the cellar waiting for the captain, and to hope that the German woman and her family would treat her well. At the last minute, about to slam the door, I saw the heap of salvage equipment. Making several running trips, I pitched it—rifles, unlocked grease guns, bandoleers

226

and all—into the back of the medics' truck. Howard Mason took off at top speed. The jeep was crowded. I jumped up on the snowy hood and we raced down the long hill and through the smashed-up town.

There was a temporary halt at Houem, but I have no clear memory of it. The litter bearers were out following the companies through the attack. Phil Schaeffer, with Ted Jameson, Cliff and Dick Gann, were trailing C Company, which had been ordered to capture the last of four defensive towns. The Germans knew of the proposed attack, and, with vastly superior numbers and equipment, were hurling in 88s and Screaming Meemies.

"It was an *impossible* position," Phil told me when he came in that night, "and Lieutenant MacKenzie got on the phone and told Colonel Hessig so. I was surprised! They had a terrific argument and MacKenzie came right back at him. Told him the whole company'd be wiped out and that he refused to give the order to attack, Hessig could court-martial him or any other blankety-blank damn thing he wanted. And Hessig finally gave in. We withdrew."

When Phil walked away stiffly, Ted Jameson said, "Lieutenant MacKenzie is going to put Phil in for a Silver Star. There was a man, a sergeant, I think, caught 'way out in a mine field, wounded. Ooh, and there was the most awful crossfire coming in. Lieutenant MacKenzie said he couldn't *ask* us to go out there and get the man. We could all see him but we couldn't get out to him. It was up to Phil, whether he wanted us to go or not. And finally Phil said, "No. You wait," and he went out by himself—crawled out—and bandaged the man out there and then dragged him back. And just as they got *out* of the mine field, the Germans started sending in mortars like mad, exploding all over. Ooh, were we glad to carry the man back, to get out of that whole place!"

We moved in the morning to Schonberg, a once pretty, now smashed-up village on the Belgian-German frontier. It was the 31st of January. Schonberg had become the crossroads for several divisions, and all day long in the fine-falling snow, traffic rumbled past: miles of supply trucks, jeeps, tanks, tank destroyers and huge artillery pieces shrouded in tarpaulins. On the streets you saw shoulder patches different from ours, and strange faces. You had to edge your way through the press of men. In the courtyards of jagged, snow-

227

covered, skeleton houses, little bonfires glowed; the looters were out; you saw someone going past with a bottle of wine.

At the main road sweeping out of town, C Company's Second Platoon was waiting to cross over; a long line of tanks was clattering past. Ahlhauser, the man in my old squad who volunteered for the Army because his young brother had been killed in the Pacific, left the line and came over to speak to me. I remembered him at Metz telling me he was going to try for a battlefield commission, and I saw by the sleeve of his field jacket that he had risen as far as sergeant. It was raw and cold, near evening.

"And how's Sergeant Danowski?" I asked after shaking hands and talking a few minutes.

"Danowski! I'm disgusted with him," he said bitterly. "He's gone to pieces. Completely gone. No one has any use for him any more. I admit he has his troubles, but Christ, a man's got to forget them."

"What kind of troubles?"

"Oh, his wife. She doesn't write to him and he nearly goes nuts. He—he actually—" Ahlhauser hardly knew how to say it. He looked around first to see if anyone might be listening. "He actually had an idea in his head of—of going over the hill! *Deserting* to get back to her! I talked him out of it. She's expecting a baby, see, sometime soon, and she wrote once to say she had a bad fall. But that's all. He didn't know whether she was writing from the hospital or not. He's never heard from her again and he's going crazy."

"And how about you?"

"Me?" He remembered then telling me his plans for getting ahead in the Army by taking on responsibility. "Hell, I don't know. All I can think of now is taking care of myself. You know, they'll use you here, use you and use you till you're all worn out. In the end you crack up or you get killed; another guy comes up and takes your place and it starts all over again. The only thing I have to hope for—" he bit on his mustache—"is to pick up a wound that's not too serious. I know that's the only way I'll ever get out of this alive."

While he was talking, I was aware of Braaf standing off a little to one side. He waited until Ahlhauser walked away before stepping forward smartly, clicking his heels and extending his hand. "Hello there, Major!" he said in his harsh, husky voice, laughing. "Good to see you. How the hell are you?"

"Fine. And you?"

"Oh, usual." His square, pale face was mottled and blue with cold, and as he smiled, not quite at ease, he was shivering. His eyes seemed to be searching to find out if I had heard how he had come to be expelled from the Tiger Patrol and, if so, if it would make any difference in my attitude toward him. I had the impression that he was lonesome, that no one on the line was talking to him.

"Been working hard?"

"Workin' hard! That's all I been doin'. Come back to the company here—" the words were rushed, slurred together— "they been workin' my ass off ever since." He gave a bark of laughter. "The guys takin' a grudge out on me. Every f---in' patrol that comes up, Brauer picks me for it first one. Never get any rest, gives me the lousiest f---in' missions." He laughed once more. The platoon started to cross over. "I'll say goodbye, Major. See you again!"

I turned around and found little Burrell, who had been sent out as an aid man, smiling up at me, waiting to shake hands. For the first moment or two, in the falling dimness, I didn't recognize him.

"How are you making out with the company?" I asked.

"Oh, pretty good. It's tough, but I can't complain. The guys are all right." His pasty face twitched and he blinked even as he smiled. "The only thing—I'm always afraid I'll fall asleep somewhere and they'll all walk off and leave me. You know how I gotta have my sleep. But so far I've been all right; I told the guy in my foxhole and he makes sure I wake up. Look, I just got a picture of my wife. First one she ever sent me."

He had married her shortly before we left the States, and she had sent him a snapshot of herself and a girl friend. Neither of the girls, in bobby socks and saddle shoes, looked more than fourteen. They were standing beside a bush. On the back of the snapshot Mrs. Burrell had written, "Joan is on the right. The other one is me," and signed her first initial.

The men were all paid the next afternoon, but I was told I'd have to wait till we were situated somewhere near C Company, since I was still on the roster there. Phil Schaeffer had sent most of his money home in a postal order, or so he thought.

229

"D'you mail your money order home, Phil?" Ted Jameson asked.

"What? Oh, yes. Yes. Yes, of course. Mailed it this afternoon."

"No, you didn't. 'Cause here it is! I just picked it up off the floor."

"What?" Phil jumped up and looked at it in astonishment. "Oh. Thanks," he said. "Thank you. I—" His eyes blinked. Bothered, he walked away, sat down again against the wall and continued reading a letter from home. Soon he put down the letter and began to mumble to himself, holding a debate.

"Look at Phil!" Teddy squealed.

"Boy, he's a corker, isn't he?" Jimmy McDonough said, laughing. "A real corker. He fights with himself! Ah, it's a damned shame."

The phone rang; there was a casualty at C Company, a man with a broken leg. Would the litter bearers come at once? It was Phil's squad's turn, and as they prepared to leave, I asked Captain Stettner if I couldn't go along and pick up my pay: I was tired of being indoors and wanted to go for a walk. The captain, who was just leaving, entrusting the aid station to Preacher and Sergeant Campbell, gave his consent and the five of us—Phil, Ted, Cliff, Dick Gann and I—set out, with Cliff carrying the furled litter up across his shoulder.

There had been a thaw at midday that was beginning to freeze over now that night had fallen, and a fine rain was turning into sleet. We left the town behind and were walking along in the darkness, talking and laughing, beginning to slip now and then on the glossy surface of the road. Starting up a long hill, Dick Gann lost his balance, crashed down on all fours, picked himself up, slipped again immediately, this time off the road, and had to be hauled back. Almost with each step our footing became less secure.

"Coming back with a man on the litter isn't going to be so easy," I said.

"The one *I'm* worried about is Dick," Phil said in a low voice. "Look at him! He gets worse all the time!"

Lumbering along like a mechanical man whose machinery was running down, his arms sawing out in a stiff, ungainly fashion, Dick kept stumbling off the road and regaining it with difficulty. Because he didn't like Ted Jameson, he walked a little apart from the four of us in silence, but now and then you'd hear him mumbling, "Gar—dam!"

"*Why* don't you speak to Stettner about him?"

"Oh, he must know," Phil said pessimistically. "He *must!* He's not blind." Down Dick went again and lay like a dead man for a long moment, holding one arm up stiffly out of the snow.

"Are you all right, Dick?" Ted asked.

"Lemme alone. Jus' lemme alone. Don't—d-don' want you to—"

"Here's the thing," Phil resumed as we struggled on upward. "We really need two strong new men on this litter team. Ted's infernally lazy, but once the wounded man is on the litter he's all right; he's young and he's strong. And of course Paul Clifford's an iron man. However, *I'm* no good any more! I can tell it by the way an 88 affects me! I'm losing my *nerve*, and for another thing, physically I'm knocked out. I don't know how much longer I can keep this up. As the head of a litter team, you've got to set a good example or the thing's all shot to hell."

"I don't care," Ted was saying as we paused for breath, slipping back a little on the steep icy road. "There's no one very brave any more. Big Steve Brudzinski's a complete coward." Phil winced, hating the truth to be dragged out in its ugliest fashion. "Every time he goes out on a litter haul, he goes and hides under a pine tree. That's why he always comes back now and says, 'We were pinned down; we couldn't get out there.' And the others don't tell on him because they're right there, hiding under the tree with him—all but Pancho. He's the only brave one on that squad. I found out Don Stoddard's just as scared as anyone else. And so is Bob Russell."

I did remember now seeing Big Steve come back three or four times without his wounded man; and I had heard ugly complaints from the infantrymen that sometimes the litter bearers never tried to reach the wounded, but cowered in cellars, leaving the riflemen to carry in their own casualties as best they could.

"And what's this I hear about you, Fatso?" I asked Ted. "Sam Benton tells me when you're out on a litter haul at night everyone knows it for miles around by the way you go shouting, 'Cliff, Cliff! Wait for me-e-e! Cliff, where are you?'"

"That's all right," he answered, unabashed, as we climbed on again. "I just don't want to get left any place, do I, Cliff?"

Cliff looked away, laughing silently.

The road by now had turned to glass and one had to zig-zag up, cutting in on the very outsides of one's feet. We reached the top, winded, and started along a dark lane with bare trees and dense wet thickets growing up on either side. Out of the blackness a guard rose up and challenged us, throwing us into nervous laughter. "What the hell is the password?" we were asking each other. "We don't know the password. We're the medics from First Battalion. Is C Company around here?"

"First house you come to on your right."

In the darkness, the farmhouse loomed up against the paler sky like a cottage in a Hans Christian Andersen fairy tale: old, cluttered, bulging, with thick mullioned windows, chimney pots, plaster and dark beaming. No light showed anywhere. A guard at the door admitted us.

From the first moment of entering the long, narrow, dark hall, one caught the impression of terrific overcrowding, of a house straining at the seams. C Company men were standing talking in the hall, as crowded as in a subway train. Light came from a partly opened door at the far end of the passage. The stairs too were thick with men, some sitting, some coming down, others going up, tousle-haired, in their stocking feet.

Phil went up the stairs to see the wounded man, Dick Gann got lost in the crowd, and Ted, Cliff and I squeezed into the overcrowded kitchen, where three candles burned on a disordered table. A new company commander, Captain Liebert, sat at its head, staring into the candlelight, elbows on the table, one hand rubbing over the other, up before his chin. First Sergeant Tomkins sat behind him, straining his eyes over reports, working at a crowded dresser; the company clerk sat facing a dark corner, earphones on. Several sergeants were there, arguing and talking in the cigarette smoke as one cleaned a carbine.

I collected my pay from Sergeant Tomkins, signed for it and wormed my way over to an empty kitchen chair in the far corner; Ted and Cliff came with me. Men came in with messages and went out again. There was a wrangle about guard duty. The captain's head jerked around sharply as he rapped out a question; then it swung back and he went on staring into the candlelight, a muscle leaping in his jaws. His face showed deep lines, although I don't believe he was over twenty-eight or thirty. The sergeants and stocking-footed privates were carefree by comparison. Was there a patrol out about which he was worried? Was he thinking of his predecessors, two of whom had been killed in action? Thinking of his wife? His children? Did he feel that at last everything was closing in, that the camps and OCS, officers' clubs and salutes and all the little privileges and rackets led down to this, where he was backed into a dangerous, narrow corner, with no way out? The candlelight made his staring eyes glitter.

Phil came in, working his way over toward us. "Listen, this guy upstairs hasn't got a broken leg; it's a broken arm! I don't think it's a bad break and he says he's not in any great pain. There's a splint on it, and I think he ought to stay here till tomorrow morning. If we try to get him down the mountain, one fall on that arm will fix him."

He went over, rang up the aid station and started to explain, but Preacher had his instructions: the captain said the man was to be brought in, and that's all Preacher knew. He wasn't goin' to go changin' what the cap'm said. Phil turned around and explained to me. I told him to speak to Sergeant Campbell and ask if Tubby could drive up for the injured man. Tubby, it seemed, could not: driving was too dangerous, and Sergeant Campbell too thought we had better bring the man in.

The company commander paid no attention. At that moment a sergeant led in a group of new replacements loaded down with clean equipment. The company commander looked around at them, the muscles leaping on his jaws. He moistened his lips, about to say something to the astonished greenhorns, but he was exhausted, disgusted, worried. "Report to Sergeant Ziegler." He was finished with them, and went back to staring into the candlelight. More bewildered than ever, they picked up their heavy packs and bumped their way out.

We stood up to go.

"Hell, you can't get that man down tonight," Garfield, the clerk, said. "Not on *foot!* Can't you get transportation? Ambulance? Jeep?"

A big red-faced truck driver who had just come in said transportation was coming to a standstill. All vehicles were being called in. Garfield, a neat, pleasant man, got busy on the phone, calling all over the battalion, and finally caught onto the trail of a lone jeep that was still out. He telephoned messages wherever he could to have the guards halt the jeep and send it on to C Company's C.P.

After a twenty-minute wait, the lone jeep driver, red-faced and puffing, came in to pick us up. The injured man came downstairs, his arm in a sling, his overcoat on his shoulders and half buttoned, his helmet on crooked. He carried his toilet articles and writing materials. He had been a recent replacement, and he stood for a moment in the crowd as if he wanted to shake hands with someone or make some gesture of farewell. The captain did not look around, and Sergeant Tomkins dismissed him with a rough "So long" and went immediately back to his work.

The man then turned to us and we edged our way out of the kitchen with him, out through the dark, narrow hall.

"D'you guys know the way back where you wanna go?" the jeep driver asked when we were outside. Phil explained that we knew the way straight down the mountain. "I don't wanna go straight down no mountain," the driver said. "Too goddam slick out."

"We want to get to Schonberg," I said.

"I don't know where the hell that *is*."

"It's the next town back."

"I only know one way. It goes roun' an' round and comes out in some goddam li'l bitty town—I'll take you boys down that way and we'll see. Hop in."

We helped the injured man in and sat in the back of the jeep, three on each side. I was next to the injured arm. We started off with such a lurch that the man toppled against me.

"Wanna git back before this whole goddam thing freezes over like ice," the driver called over his shoulder, and with that we raced with astonishing speed, taking a road that kept circling around the mountain. No ride in a roller coaster could begin to compare with it for wildness. We seemed to fly over the ice, making hairpin turns at top speed, crashing down now and then into an unsuspected hollow filled with slush, racing through it with such velocity that huge fins burst up on either side of us as high as our eyes. We struck long descending patches of ice where we skidded crazily, the back tires swinging from side to side. Once, in making a long, fast, screaming turn, the jeep threatened to turn over; the injured man let go his toilet articles and clutched onto me. Our side dipped far down. I turned my head away and saw a snow bank rushing past not two inches away from my face; I could feel its swift, damp closeness.

"All there?" the driver called cheerfully, but not really caring. I was about to say, "Yes, all here," when we hit a mighty bump and shot into the air. Phil, Ted and Cliff, high off their seats, seemed to hang higher than us in mid-air for a split second before crashing down into us, threatening to hurl Dick, the injured man and me over the side. And somehow in landing, my hand had become badly pinched under the railing.

"Are you all right?" we asked the injured man.

"Y-y-yes, I—I think so."

By this time I could look back and see that we had reached the bottom of the mountain, and except for a few more sickening skids, and one quick figure eight, we were all right. We had come in by a back way to Schonberg. The driver let us off at the door of the aid station and went whizzing off.

While Preacher was rebinding the man's broken arm, the captain came back from an officers' meeting at Battalion Headquarters. It was decided that since the driving was so dangerous, the ambulance had better not go back to Collecting until the morning. In the meanwhile, the C Company man was to be bedded down on a litter beside us. "The Army way," Phil said. "Hurry up and wait again."

The captain was telling us that the Siegfried Line lay just ahead, and the attack that was being mounted would, once it was launched, send the Germans reeling and provide the finishing blow of the war. It was hard to tell whether he believed this or not; there was a little half-smile on his face and he kept lumbering up and down the room, rolling from side to side as he walked, throwing one foot in. It was hard to tell whether the men believed it either. At the mention of the Siegfried Line, their eyes became still and round. Each stood, or sat against the wall, watching him in silence.

February

The next day around noon we prepared to leave Schonberg and cross the border into Germany. We were going on foot and orders were given for the medics to lead off.

"All right, me-e-n," Sergeant Campbell said in his low voice, "line up there now. Try 'n' look good. 'Ten-shun! Lef' face! Forward—march!" Unmilitary, not quite in step, we struck off, passing the Headquarters men, who hooted and cheered and roared with laughter.

The sun was shining, the earth was moist, showing in long, wet streaks through the snow. It was the first real break in the weather and everywhere there was the loud, quick tap and drip of melting snow, the smell of slush, of mud, distantly the scent of spring. There was no momentous feeling crossing into Germany for the second time. We smoked, talking back and forth, and everyone seemed to be in good spirits. Swinging downhill into the next town, we crossed a rustic bridge beneath which ice was floating swiftly away.

At dusk winter returned again. We marched into a town called Aaw, and there as everywhere were signs of destruction: pitted and chipped walls, stark shattered trees, bomb craters, crashed-in roofs and blown-out windows. In the fields, horses and cows, stiff in death, were lying on their backs, all four legs raised. For a while there had been an impressive, gloomy sunset with piled-up, powerful-looking gray and brown clouds. A limestone church rose up undamaged, with the gilt cross on its steeple piercing the last patch of daylight left in the sky. We halted near the church, waited a while, then went through a victory garden and entered the priest's house.

Immediately one was aware of cleanliness, waxed floors, peaceful bareness, a slight but pleasant warmth. "Boy, how clean everything is! Cleanest place we ever been in!" And yet there was nothing newly painted or papered.

The priest, a large, bearded, jovial man in his fifties, stood in the little hall wearing a cassock, smiling and nodding his welcome. His sister and her husband, who were his housekeeper and sexton, had been allowed to remain in the house with us because it had been established to the advance billeting party that they were not Nazis. Everywhere else in town where the soldiers were to stay, the families had been routed out and crowded into a country school.

Phil and I were putting our mess gear away that evening up in the unlighted bedroom when Ted and Cliff came up to see where we were staying. "Ooh, listen, I'm learning how to talk German," Ted cried. "The priest is teaching me, isn't he, Cliff? I know the word for 'table'—that's 'tish'—and 'ceil-

236

ing,' and 'nose' and 'chin.' I can say some words in French too! 'Bonjour' and 'como talley voo'—that means 'how are you?'—and 'caffay' or 'caffee'—that's 'coffee'—and 'choco-lette' is 'chocolate'; 'beaucoup' is 'a lot.' And now I'm learn-ing German!"

At once he and Phil fell into an argument over the Ger-man word for 'chin.' Phil might have studied German in col-lege and his family might have been able to speak and write it at home; Ted was not impressed with that. "But, Phil, that's what the priest *said*, isn't it, Cliff?"

Like one of Dickens' rural characters, the stalwart Cliff smiled. Not as progressive as Ted, he never entertained the idea of picking up any German words. He had asked me how to say, "I am a medic": "Ich bin ein Sanitater," and he repeated it several times until he had memorized it. He wanted to know it in case he was captured, but beyond that he had no curiosity.

The next day was one of complete peace. The wind surged, and the sunlight was fitful; the bare branches tossed outside the diamond-paned windows. I took a sponge bath, shook the unpleasant grayish lice powder on myself and into the seams of my clothes, wrote a few V-mail letters, and lay about on the floor, enjoying the sensation of snugness and quiet. It was Ted Jameson who again found Phil's money order on the floor. Phil looked startled, then he became wrathful because Teddy laughed. "Silly child! What differ-ence does it make anyhow? Fifty dollars, or a hundred and fifty, or a thousand and fifty. What's money in a holocaust like this? Go away! Don't bother me with trifles!"

"What's a 'holocaust'?" Ted asked me in an aside.

"A holocaust is what you're *in*," Phil shouted, "but you're too much of a dunderhead to realize it!"

Little Lieutenant Serletis came in. "Anyone want any packages? Here! Eat it up." He had received two of them from home, but his nerves, in a worse state than Phil's, would not permit him even the comfort and relaxation of eating. I thought: how sick he looks! His face had grown small and haggard, and his eyes were rheumy with dark circles beneath them. He still ran out on his tiny feet—feet that were as sure as a goat's, and encased in wet little combat boots—to get the captain's meals, but he himself seemed to live on ciga-rettes. If anyone came into a room where he was, he jumped up nervously, expecting bad news. When the captain came in, he trotted over and stood looking up apprehensively. "What's up? What's up, Captain?" If he never had to budge outdoors, I believe he would have felt easier. As it was, he faced a thousand deaths when the captain said, "Nick, run down to the C.P. and see what's goin' on." I think he even worried that he wouldn't be able to pick up any information, or that he wouldn't remember it correctly; and adding to the agony nowadays there was always Sergeant Campbell. "Want me to go along too, Cap'm?" Sergeant Campbell would ask, looking like a shrewd rube, dependable and strong. It would be Sergeant Campbell who would bring back the news.

"Lieutenant, come on, let's make you up a bed," the men sometimes said. He'd be lying, shivering and wet, in a corner.

"Nah, nah, don't bother. You guys look after yourself. I'm all right here." But when the fire in the stove died down and chill drafts blew in, he'd try to creep under a loose edge of someone's blanket. One night I heard Mike Nowak wake up and say, "Here, for cris*sake*, crawl under and git warm."

"Jesus," Lieutenant Serletis said in tears. In the morning he'd wake up, remember he was an officer—one who was not doing his job—and he'd feel ashamed.

There were moments, as now, when he could carry the tenseness no longer. Throwing himself down beside us, he began to talk about his family, who were coffee merchants in New York, and about his convertible, his sports coats.

Don Stoddard, who was engaged to a pretty girl in New Hampshire, came into the room to sit down, and Lieutenant Serletis said, "Jeez, that was some letter you wrote, Don: 'My dearest, sweetest, most beloved—'" Then he remembered he wasn't supposed to discuss our mail. He began to talk about his own girl, Angie, a beautiful blonde who appeared to care nothing about him. "I spent plenty of money on that son of a bitch. Gave her plenty of presents too, and now she's runnin' around with some other guy. Atwell, how about you sittin' down sometime and writin' me a swell letter to her? You know, crap it up with a lot of big, fancy words, make it real literary."

"Sure. We'll collaborate sometime." He had already asked me to do this several times, but I always put it off. "Won't you have some of your cake? Or candy? It's good."

"Nah." Reminded of home, he turned his eyes away, sagged, began to worry again. "Oh, Jesus, this is awful. This

238

is terrible, isn't it? D'you guys think it'll ever end?"

"Ever *end!*" Don Stoddard, with a piece of layer cake in his hand, began to swear. "Didn't you see *Stars and Stripes?*"

"You mean about the Russians bein' so close to Berlin? Yeah, looks pretty good, hey?" He revived a little. "They could almost hike it!"

Don was staring at him. "Hike it, hell! It says right on the front page the bulk of the troops here, once this war ends, will be shifted over to the East!"

"It doesn't!" I was appalled.

"Swear to God! 'The bulk of the troops.' "

"But they can't! That's not fair! There're infantry divisions in the United States that have been training for years and have never seen *any* action!"

"What do they care? We're 'battle-seasoned troops.' "

"But . . . But *anyone* could be battle-seasoned. If we are, so could they be! How the hell long are they training replacements nowadays? Eight weeks? Why not turn around and train all the perfect specimens they got at the start of the war and stuck in office jobs, in places like Washington and . . . There are *millions* in the Army who never see combat! Why use the same worn-out ones over and over?"

"Don't fight with *me,*" he said, laughing. "I'm only telling you."

People speak of the bottom dropping out of things. For me, then and there, I could feel a bottom dropping out of everything. Whatever hopes I had of living through the European campaign, hopes that I didn't want to look at too closely for fear they wouldn't come true, fell slowly away. There would be no end.

"My God!" We sat looking at the opposite wall in silence. After about an hour, somehow one accepted the thought, picked up, and went on living.

After supper that night, Phil and I put away our mess kits and went downstairs to see where the rest of the litter bearers were staying. They looked up as we opened the dining-room door, not friendly in their stare nor yet unfriendly, but withholding their greetings for a moment or two. That always happened. If the group became temporarily separated, a feeling of rivalry sprang up between the different units. Each set about "having things better" than the other, and all communication was cut off.

The priest was sitting on the sofa in the snug, brownish,

candlelit dining room, going ahead with his German lesson to Ted Jameson and a few others, but most of the men, accustomed to his presence, ignored him. He turned and smiled at Phil and me to include us in the lesson. I said to Phil, "Ask him to what extent the Nazis interfered with him as a priest."

As usual, Phil blinked behind his taped-up glasses, but after a little while he formed the sentence in German. The priest answered, puffing on his pipe. Phil nodded and said, "Yah, yah."

"What did he say?" I asked.

Phil always seemed distracted at such moments and appeared to have difficulty in translating. "Well, he—he said they didn't interfere with him *personally*. He was permitted to hold services, but he had to be careful of his sermons, and the Catholic school was shut down."

Ted claimed the priest's attention and continued his lesson, proving himself a quick but inexact pupil, and since some of the men wanted to go to sleep, Phil and I reluctantly went upstairs. It had started to rain.

Suddenly, an hour later, we were wakened by Lieutenant Serletis' voice: "Pack up! Fall out, everyone! Let's go, let's go, let's *go!* Hey, you guys up there, we're clearin' *outta* here!"

"Oh, what the hell is this?"

"What's he saying 'fall out' for?"

"Let's *go*, let's go up there! Let's *go!*"

We began hurriedly putting on our leggings and overshoes, rolling our equipment in the dark bedroom. Captain Stettner had gone ahead in the heated ambulance, leaving Lieutenant Serletis in charge, and the responsibility, the fear something would go wrong, made him shout "Let's go-o-o-!" every few seconds.

"Raincoats, everyone! Put on your raincoats!"

You could hear the rain dashing itself against the snug house. "All right, you guys, let's *go* there. Got to load up this truck!"

In the drenching rain we made repeated struggling trips out to the little truck, carrying the stacks of blankets and medical supplies. A gale was lashing the trees in the yard, blowing them down almost on top of us. There came a loud cracking sound from one of them, but nothing fell. The rain suddenly redoubled its fury.

Finally, with our full field packs buckled on, our gas masks, belts, canteens—all our equipment, and I with the carbine "slung"—we streamed out of the house, through the narrow cobbled alley and up to the main road at its top. The line companies were already marching past in double file, picking up speed as the officers shouted instructions. We fell in and set off with them.

The night was pitch-black, with a high, veering wind. The rain beat against us, noisy on helmets and raincoats. A constant spray bounced off the rim of the helmets, and in the back rivulets poured down inside one's collar. Where the raincoats ended or blew open, the legs of our pants became soaked. Trying to rush, the men slipped and skidded in the sucking ankle-deep mud. As the night progressed and the rain continued to smash down in sheets, the dirt roads grew softer and softer, deeper and deeper. Sometimes against the rainy sky and flailing trees you caught a dim silhouette of the men. It looked like a scene from the First World War, showing the doughboys slogging through the mud; still, as was often the case, one could not help feeling that this long, forced march would seem to an observer worse than it was. One was buoyed up by the thought that rain could not fall harder, and yet one was surviving, plunging on. I slipped from time to time but did not go down as others did repeatedly; I was not exhausted—in fact, felt rather well—and I did not have dysentery at the time. Except for one's hands and soaking wet gloves, and the wet scarf and shirt collar, it was not bitterly cold.

After hiking an hour or so, we came out into a stretch of open, hilly country, fairly treeless, where the visibility was better, and just ahead of me I could see Lieutenant Serletis tiredly lifting his little legs, trying to stagger through the deep mud. "Oh, Jesus, I can't," he was saying. He faltered, bent over, and was on the point of giving up completely when Sergeant Campbell, who wanted the lieutenant's job and might have been looking forward to this moment for months, suddenly put out his large hand, grabbed him by the arm and started to drag him along like a father with a child, forcing him to keep up. Occasionally when a shell went off somewhere, the sky would light up biliously for a few seconds, and in one of those moments I saw Sergeant Campbell's homely, big face. He was smiling, it seemed, at himself, at his ambition, his desire to order others about.

At one point there was congestion of the road. Vehicles were passing through a company, forcing the men to the edges of the road. The medics were ordered at the same time to get past the company and hurry ahead. It was so dark, however, you couldn't tell whether the man in front belonged to your group or the company through which you were passing, and, to make matters worse, the road forked at that point, splitting in two, with one road climbing up a hill. The confusion mounted, and though we had been warned to be silent, you heard cries, curses, men calling. "Where the f--- are we goin'? Who's this? Hey, Clayton! Clayton, where the hell are ya?" C Company.

"I'm up here," Clayton answered. "Who the f--- wants to know?"

"Well, goddamit, you're on the wrong road! Git down here. Hey, you guys!"

To make the bypass, the medics had to plunge down off the road into a wide, knee-deep pond on which the rain was beating noisily. One of our men lost his footing and went full length on his face, struggling up with a splash and an oath, only to fall down again. Sergeant Campbell dragged Lieutenant Serletis like a rag doll across that stretch by main force. I don't believe the lieutenant's feet ever once touched bottom there.

We climbed up on the road again and were stamping the mud off our overshoes when there came a roar, a terrific explosion in our midst. There had been a sudden, blinding flash of light—white, it seemed, with red in its center—and then very loud, very close by in the darkness, came the cry, "*Medics! Medics!*"

Everyone was shouting, scattering as if we had been exploded apart. Men hurled themselves past me down into the ditchful of water.

The screams continued: "Mother! *Mother!* My legs! Oh-h-h, my legs. My le-e-egs!" A second voice was crying, "Help! Help! I'm blind! God, I'm blind!"

"*Land* mine!" someone was shouting excitedly. "Set off a mine! The road is mined! Get off the road!"

"No, that was a *shell!* There'll be another in here in a minute!"

"Schaeffer!" called Sergeant Campbell. "Phil Schaeffer! Take your squad and go in there. See what the trouble is. Rest of you medics, keep right on."

"Phil, do you want me to stay with you?" I asked, flinching, expecting another explosion any second.

"No, no, you'd better go ahead. Ted? Ted Jameson, are you there? Cliff?"

I went ahead with the others, looking back over my shoulder, trying to see what the trouble was. A jeep that had been coming along the road stopped with a jam of brakes just as the explosion occurred and there seemed to be some trouble about it, as if it had run over someone in the excitement. Sergeant Campbell was now sending back stretchers with two of the squads.

The whole thing took place in a minute. After the first instinctive scattering, the C Company men regrouped and continued on slogging in the rain and mud, looking back to where the screams were coming from.

The rest of the long hike in the rain is gone, as is our arrival toward morning in a farmhouse at Cobshied, where the captain and the aid-station group were already sleeping. Memory picks up, not entirely clear, later in the morning. Preacher, Warren Troy, the captain, Lieutenant Serletis and I were sitting with Silly Willie and his assistant driver in the farmhouse kitchen. My clothes were drying on me. I was smoking a cigarette, flicking the ashes on the floor, looking out the window at the heavy fall of rain. The ambulance was just outside the windows. Beyond it, a wet green field stretched away and rose suddenly into a long, wide slope, its top crowned with pine trees. The litter bearers were still out, following the companies which, as a climax to last night's long hike, had continued on without a rest to make the assault on the Siegfried Line. The crash of shelling, the stutter of machine guns and the rattling of small-arms fire reached us clearly. German artillery sent heavy shells screaming over the slope, over our farmhouse, into the 18th Armored Division area somewhere behind us.

The captain paced up and down in silence, impatiently awaiting the word to move the station up farther. Attacking the Siegfried Line, I thought, and prayed suddenly: God, don't let this be a slaughter. Help them. *End* this. In imagination I saw them running, being hit, reeling back. But I couldn't pin my mind down. At almost the same time I was hearing the voices of the English men and women in the smoky little parlor of a pub in Stone, singing, "We'll 'ang our washing on the Siegfried Line, on the Siegfried Line—" and then trilling, "There'll be blue bairds ovah the white cliffs of Dovah—"

"Here's someone now."

Four of the litter bearers came down the steep hill in the rain almost on the run. I got up and opened the door and the sound of shelling, of small-arms fire, the smell of rain was immediately much clearer. Bob Russell, Don Stoddard, Phil and Ted Jameson came in, carrying Sergeant Betancourt of C Company on the litter.

"Where's he wounded?"

"In the thigh."

"How're the boys doin'?" Captain Stettner asked.

"Well, they're gettin' through a *little*. They knocked out some of the pillboxes."

"Phil, what happened last night on the road?" I asked. "When the explosion went off?"

"Oh! That! I couldn't see a *thing!*" he said. "The men kept moaning and screaming and the officer who came running along wouldn't let us put on a flashlight even for a second to see what we were doing."

"Were they very badly hurt?"

"I don't . . . think so, but I couldn't see. They were in the ditch full of water, and I knelt down, trying to hold them up, but we kept rolling over, sinking in the mud. My God, it was awful! I thought I was bandaging one man's head, and instead I had the bandages all over his neck and then his shoulder. He had to tell me. There wasn't anything I could do but give them a shot of morphine before they took them back."

"What hap', Phil?" Tubby was asking. "They step on a lan' mine?"

"I don't *know*, Jim! I know it wasn't a shell. Someone said one of the men fell and a grenade on his lapel went off, but that would have blown his chest away! One got it in the legs and the other in the head."

"*Ooh*, did they yell!" Ted Jameson added. "One kept begging for more morphine all the time. 'Put me out of this! Put me out of this! Gimme another shot.'"

"But listen, Phil," Tubby asked. "What happened up there with this jeep, and this Sergeant Danowski?"

Phil looked startled. I felt that I did too. "What?" Phil blinked. "I didn't hear anything about that."

Silly Willie took up the story. "You didn't? Well, Campbell sends two of the squads back with some litters to pick up the wounded guys, and you know how dark it was. Well, when they git there, they say, 'Where's the wounded guys?' And a guy, layin' right there on the road, groans an' says, 'Here. Right here.' So they lift him up and put him on the litter. It's this guy, Sergeant Danowski. He tells them he got run over by the jeep, and he's moaning about his leg. So they start totin' him back. It's a hell of a long haul all the way up here an' he weighs a good two hun' an' twenty. They finally git him in here, an' the captain says, 'What happened to you, Sergeant?' An' he says, 'I was run over by the jeep.' Well, Jeez, *then*, you know, it begins to sound fishy: he wasn't anywheres near where the explosion was! So the cap'm takes a look, an' there's just this little bitty red mark on Danowski's knee, like where he skinned it a little. Not even bleeding. See, here's what it was: when the jeep comes along and slams on the brakes, it hits Danowski and knocks him down. It don't hurt him but he figures what the hell, it's a way out, and he lets the guys carry him goddam near two miles." Yes, I thought, a way out, a way back to his wife. "Well, the cap'm gives a *yell* out of him, an' Danowski, by God, he scrambles up off that litter faster'n any wounded guy *I* ever saw. The cap'm tells me, he says if he ever sees him aroun' this station again, he's gonna have him court-martialed."

That, I realized, must have happened shortly before we reached the station at the end of our hike.

Preacher, down on his knees, had unbuckled and cut away Sergeant Betancourt's pants and underwear. There was a big, deep, jagged puncture in his thigh.

"Colder'n a bitch out there," Sergeant Betancourt said to me, trying to stop the chattering of his teeth.

"Want something that'll make you warm?" Captain Stettner asked, smiling, in good spirits, while Preacher worked on the wound.

"What you got?"

The captain returned a moment later with a generous shot of whisky or perhaps brandy.

"Where'd you ever get that, sir?" Sergeant Betancourt asked.

"Medical Supply," the captain said, smiling. "Medics have a special ration of liquor just for wounded men."

I was shocked. It was the first I had ever heard of it, and the last. Sergeant Betancourt was the only one I knew to get a drink of it.

In the afternoon the captain went up ahead in the jeep with Tubby and Charlie Heydt, and at around four o'clock he telephoned for the rest of us to move up at once. Silly Willie, of the greenish-yellow hair and sunken upper lip, drove us in the ambulance across the open slippery field. Howard Mason, in the truck with the little trailer behind it, had bogged down in the ooze, and he called out a warning to us, but Silly Willie only laughed, stepped on the gas and, with a furious spinning of the wheels, we started up the broad slope. Along its summit, between the pines, I saw infantrymen running, one brandishing his rifle. Artillery shells crashed loudly. The ambulance went part way up, paused and slipped back fast. Silly Willie started it up again. We reached the same point, slipped back and began to sink a little. With a laugh, Silly sent the ambulance forward once more, this time as if he intended to buck through the hill rather than ride up it; we rolled back, the wheels spun swiftly and sent out a slathering of mud. Silly Willie appeared to be enjoying himself immensely, but the ambulance sank down to the hub caps and now could go neither forward nor backward. The heavy mist turned into rain and swept across the windshield. Locked inside, we could hear the rat-tat-tat-tat-tat! Tat-tat-tat-tat-tat! Tat-tat-tat of machine guns up on the hill and the whine and ping of M1 rifles.

Preacher suddenly said, "Unlock this here goddam door and let us out!"

Choking with laughter, showing a froth of bubbles on his wet triangular mouth, Silly Willie said, "Oh, you boys want out, maybe?"

Preacher began to swear, which was uncharacteristic of him. "Listen, At—" he bobbed his head down and looked at me over his glasses—"you take one of 'em boxes of medicine; I'll take the other, and we'll try to git 'em up there to wherever the hell it is that we're agoin'."

The step clanged down and the back doors of the ambulance opened. Preacher handed the heavy box out to me. I had my rifle and equipment on and I was carrying a little oil lamp we had picked up. The other men took armsful of blankets and litters and we began to run up the steep, wet slope, with the sound of rifles cracking and machine guns stuttering insistently. The box, cutting into my bare wrists, grew heavy. If I could have uncurled my fingers, I would have let go the fancy little lamp. I could feel that I was smiling. Slithering

246

and clambering, scattered from each other, we continued to climb. Enemy shells ripped through the wet air over our heads. Near the top of the hill Charley Heydt materialized out of the pine trees, jumping up and down, waving us on impatiently.

Some one of the medics ran part way down and relieved me of the box of medicine. I paused, out of breath.

"We're in a pillbox up here," Ted Jameson said, running down excitedly. "You should see what they're like!" I started up with him. "Here's where we came with C Company in the attack this morning. Right along here." The place looked as I imagined the moors in Scotland. The thin rain blew and there was mist; and some tall sort of plant, like heather, blew all in one direction, saturated with dampness. From the pines a little farther up there came a sighing sound. We began to follow a winding footpath leading up that I hadn't noticed before. "Right there," Teddy said. "That's where Sergeant Janovic was killed. He had both his legs blown off. Ooh, I think he's still there! *Look!*" There was a crumpled, wet shelter-half in among the heather to one side of the path. "Yes, *he* was killed and Sergeant Stancliff too. You knew them, didn't you? Weren't you in C Company?"

"Yes." The memory of both came back. One had led the Second Platoon; the other, with Sergeant Danowski, had been one of the squad leaders.

"Don't you want to *see?*" Teddy asked. "*Look!*"

"No," I said. "For God's sake, leave them alone. Come on away."

I remembered a hot summer evening after Retreat in Fort Jackson. I was standing on the second floor of the barracks at the back screen door where the little balcony was, and down below, sitting in the shade on the coarse grass, were all the noncoms. An unpleasant lieutenant who had not come overseas with us was haranguing them because discipline in the company was growing lax. "I want you to treat these men like dogs!" he shouted. "Like *dogs!* And if you won't do it, we'll get other noncoms that will! Dismissed." The officer strode the short distance into the company office. The noncoms, most of whom were married and depending on their salaries, got to their feet in silence. And Sergeant Janovic, stocky, short, spunky and blue-eyed, walked into the company office after the lieutenant, ripped the stripes off his sleeves and tossed them down on the desk. "I don't treat anyone like a dog," he said in his tough, quiet voice. Later they had come around, apologized, and asked Sergeant Janovic to take back his stripes. He had never been particularly friendly with anyone.

Sergeant Stancliff was from Fayette, Alabama, thin, tense and serious, his young face pulled into a frown of sternness. High coloring like stain spread over his sunburned cheeks: he was a young man in brightest Technicolor. He too was married, and the responsibility of being a staff sergeant weighed on him; I had never seen him smile or laugh. In memory he does a one-step from man to man at Retreat. While staring straight into your face, he suddenly slapped the presented rifle out of your hands and inspected it. Later, he went about in the rear to see if the men needed haircuts. "Rossofsky, git a haircut. Atwell, git a haircut. Louden, git a haircut. Smathers, you don't need none. Hepp—" There was that, and then the picture of him walking out of his little squad room in his khaki underwear shorts to lay down the law, looking, with his skinny body and knobby thin legs, about fifteen years old. "Don't know how he can do it," the men used to say. "Built like a f---in' stringbean, but on a twenty-five-mile hike he keeps right on goin' when everyone else is draggin' ass." Yesterday in Aaw he had just received the news that his young wife had given birth to a son.

Ted Jameson and I moved away from where they had fallen, climbed to the top of the hill and came into the wet gloom under the pines. Though I knew the Siegfried Line was near, I was for some unaccountable reason surprised to find that it was an actual line: I walked between a row of stubby, heavy, cement posts driven into the earth and emerged onto a broad, wet dirt road strung with barbed wire. This was the first line of defense; the Siegfried Line in all, I knew, extended back for several miles.

"Come on," Ted was saying. "We're down here in one of the pillboxes. Wait till you see them inside!"

Bob Russell, Jimmy McDonough and Mike Nowak came walking along the road toward us. "Les," Bob Russell said, "they ain't room for us down there. You gotta come with us into one of these here pillboxes for the night."

Where we were it was quiet. The afternoon was almost gone. The pines, tall, with great, wet sweeping branches, intensified the gloom. Walking along the road, I saw my first pillbox; it was camouflaged and I was upon it before I realized it. In the indistinctness it looked like the curved stone top of a prehistoric ruin that had almost sunk into the earth. Bushes and bare young trees grew close about it, and then with a little shiver I saw the deep oblong slits in its blindness: gun positions. The ground sloped down toward the rear so that from the back the pillbox seemed high, large, bigger than most farmhouses. The wet concrete was a dirty grayish-yellow. A sagging plank over a deep, wide puddle led up to the entrance. We crossed it, halted in the doorway and broke into nervous laughter. The narrow opening in the cement was black, mysterious, and from out of it came a sour smell, faintly warm and smoky, a smell of foreign food and of unwashed bodies.

Our hands against the slimy cement wall, we felt our way forward in the dark and went down an unexpected step into a room. I fished out a stump of a candle, lighted it, and, after a moment, walked over and set it on a heavy wooden table. The blind room began to be revealed—a room perhaps nine by twelve. Cement floor and walls. The table and four straight chairs. Sleeping bunks, three on a side, with the gray German blankets dragged awry, as if the men had jumped out in haste.

The fear of booby traps held us motionless for a while. I lifted my head and struck my helmet a sharp blow against the cement ceiling. One had to stand perpetually stooped. What a sour stench! A stench of damp, unclean blankets, discarded socks, acrid smoke, fish—yes, there was an open plastic dish of herring on the table. No pin-up pictures of any kind. I brushed my damp hand on the front of my field jacket, and as I did so I noticed that my hand glowed with phosphorescence. A little of it came off on my field jacket. Like a ghostly, shimmering fungus, you could see it glimmering here and there on the walls, on the edges of the bunks. The smell of the place grew stronger. I kept trying to place it exactly. It was something like a firing range. The word "brimstone" came to my mind.

"Fer crissake, someone, *say* something!"

We laughed a little, but, remarking on the place, our voices remained muted, almost whispering. We put our blankets down, and, though hungry, delayed eating, took the candle and made a search of the place. There was a windowless cement corridor with sudden steps down into a small dungeon that contained a medieval-looking bench and two antiquated, dirty cooking stoves, in one of which a fire still smoldered and burned. A scorched pot of food had cooked on.

Back in the first room, the candle showed signs of going out at any moment. We prepared our beds, which resembled the bunks on the *Queen Elizabeth*, except that these had criss-crossed rope where the ship's had taut canvas. Gingerly we removed the smelly, damp gray blankets the Germans had used, holding them by one of the corners, giving them a yank and letting them drop to the ground.

Then we opened a ration, but by now there was less and less in each unit one felt like eating. The candle went out and the phosphorescence glimmered all over the walls, the table, the metal supports of the bunks. The rough cement wall at the back of my bunk trickled with moisture. A draft could be felt coming in along the floor. The room seemed to fill with mist.

I was chilled, lying rigid and uncomfortable, as far from the dripping wall as I could get without falling out of the bunk. As usual, I appeared to be the last to go to sleep. Faintly over the snores I could hear the wind sighing through the pine trees, and I lay watching the ghostly mist pour in. Echoes of German voices seemed to linger, giving commands, and the sad tune of "Lili Marlene" that they must have sung or hummed, writing homesick letters. All the German dreams that led them on to war, all the myths, all the hours of standing guard outside—the room held the echoes and re-membrance. I fell asleep hearing the pines toss and sigh sadly in the rain.

We were awakened the next morning by someone banging a mess kit against the concrete doorway. "Hey, wake up in there! We're moving out, and you guys are late!"

By the time we had breakfast and got back to where Ser-geant Campbell and the others were, they were packed and ready to leave. A plan had been made about which I knew nothing until the moment of hurried departure. The captain and the aid-station group were climbing into the ambulance. One litter team, made up of Sam Benton, Jr., Jimmy McDon-ough, Tom Lawlor and little Jenkins, were told to follow in Tubby's jeep. I had gone over to buckle my gas mask on the back of the little truck when it suddenly pulled away. Then the ambulance roared off, and when I looked around I was the only one left standing on the Siegfried Line Road.

"Hey!" Tubby shouted, about to drive off. "Better hop up

here on the hood." I ran over, jumped up, and we were off with a spurt almost before I was settled.

I was surprised that a jeep could go so fast. It seemed to me, looking about for something to hang onto, that we were traveling almost seventy miles an hour, squirting high fins of mud water in either direction. The big Red Cross flag was whipped taut, making a loud tutting sound in the wind an inch or two from my face. One slap from it, I thought, pulling my head back, would be enough to knock me from my insecure perch.

The road swerved and cut inland through a ragged pine belt. There was nothing else in sight but the speeding ambulance far ahead, and sometimes we lost it around bends and in hollows. We appeared to be participants in a wild chase that went on through a deserted country. Perhaps fifteen minutes later, still with no one in sight, we pulled up suddenly in the driveway of a lonely, cheap-looking, rain-soaked farmhouse and carried the equipment into the kitchen.

"Don't unpack everything," Captain Stettner said. "We might be pullin' right out."

I was completely lost. The captain had evidently explained the situation and no one referred to it again. If the captain was uneasy, no one spoke in the aid station. That was one of the unwritten laws. The telephone was not in, and until the connection was made, the captain was like a worried bear, pacing up and down, pausing now and then to listen, then pacing again, thinking. "God, I'd like to get up there," he said. "The boys will be movin' in."

But an hour or two later, as the wire men were putting in the telephone, the acting Regimental Surgeon drove up in a jeep. He came running up the path with his driver: a loud German artillery barrage had just broken out. He burst in the kitchen door, red-faced. "Good God!" he said.

"What's the matter, Bayl?" Captain Stettner laughed. "Didn't you know it was hot up here?"

"Not *that* hot!" Captain Baylor nodded to Preacher and the others he had known in the United States.

"Why, I'm just awaitin' to move farther up! We're gonna push right through."

"I don't think you'd better, Vic," Captain Baylor said with cool firmness. "I'd say you were far enough forward just where you are. Too far, for that matter."

"But the boys will be gettin' into town there, and I—"

"If I were you, I'd stay right here." The tone was smooth and friendly, but, underneath, the order was clear. "Phone me later in the day. Keep in touch with me. I don't mind telling you, I'm going to get the hell back out of here as fast as I can!" They parted with bursts of laughter, but the acting Regimental Surgeon had carried the scene and Captain Stettner could not move up against his orders. We were occupying the last house in a hamlet called Oldsheim; the coming attack was to center on a town two and a half kilometers farther on in a draw, called Olzheim. Looking out the kitchen windows down a long, gentle pine-covered slope, you could almost see that far.

The line companies, probing below us for an opening, could make no progress. Fierce German artillery held them up and tanks fired directly upon them. The situation was unchanged at three in the afternoon, but Captain Stettner hit upon a somewhat risky scheme. Trusting that the acting Regimental Surgeon would not again drive up to where it was so "hot," he left Phil Schaeffer's squad behind in the kitchen to answer the telephone should Regiment call; and, taking the rest of us, he told us to pack up and be ready to rush down into Olzheim to establish a forward aid station.

Once more I rode on the hood of Tubby's jeep, and there was the same wild chase after the speeding ambulance. We flew past a single smashed, grim farmhouse at a crossroads later to be known as "88 Corner," on into the country, made one sharp turn and came flying toward the town of Olzheim. On either side of the road, a rough plain ended in high hills which the Germans held. At the narrow entrance to the town, the hills grew closer together and the road through at that point was in the narrowest part of a V.

The ambulance jammed to a sudden halt outside the first building in town: a long, rambling *Gasthaus*. With a scream of brakes, Tubby halted the jeep. The whipping flag dropped down, and as I slid off the hood I heard sniper bullets zinging like swift, angry bees all about us. A chip of cement flew off the half-demolished building opposite. The captain jumped down from the ambulance and made a heavy-footed run for the door of the inn, calling back over his shoulder, "Unload all that stuff! Blankets, stove, and—" He rushed in and the door slammed behind him.

Ducking down, we ran to Howard Mason's little truck, dragged out the litter bearers' full field packs, the litters and blankets, and rushed for the inn too, kicking the painted green door shut behind us. "Phew!" "That was close."

There was a narrow hall with a rising staircase choked off with fallen beams, a cascade of bricks and plaster. The captain was walking quickly about, searching for the cellar. Underneath the stairs a short flight of steps did lead down to a sort of small dugout, but two unshaven, battered-looking artillerymen were wedged in it, one talking into a telephone.

"Any cellar in this place?" the captain asked with a smile. They looked up, their faces tough and tired and sour. "No," one said shortly, hardly bothering to answer at all; the other went on talking into the telephone. Snubbed, the captain turned around. Shells were crashing about the inn, great parts of which were already demolished.

From the hall a step went down into a long, empty taproom paneled halfway up with glossy, greenish-tan wood; there was a black wallpaper and a border of purple grapes above. The place was chill, drafty, unsubstantial-looking; the floor was unvarnished, and there was a light scattering of wooden chairs. Sergeant Campbell had run out to the truck with one of the men, and they hurried in, panting, carrying the round Army stove and some lengths of pipe. "Get this damned place blacked out right away," the captain ordered. "Hang a blanket over the front door out there and another over this doorway here. Close those shutters and lock 'em!" The men began to work, giving each other a stare in passing. This was most definitely not a good spot.

I stood with the others, watching Sergeant Campbell and Howard Mason finish setting up the stove.

"All right, you boys." The captain, pacing restlessly, came to a halt and smiled at our oversight, giving his head a shake. "We gotta get some wood for this fire." He snorted a little to clear his nasal passages. "We can't have a cold aid station. That's the first thing we gotta have's a warm place. Each of you better go out and scout around these farmhouses an' bring in an armful of wood."

I was stunned. Go *out*? We stood staring at him in disbelief.

"You better go one at a time," he added, "an' leave about ten yards between you. Better go now before it gets dark."

We moved out toward the front door. "What's the matter with all this wood around here?" I asked the others. "Couldn't we chop it up?"

Mike Nowak said, "Aah, he's got a bug up his ass. He says it's too big, it's too wet."

We stood in a group, smiling at each other nervously. Tom Lawlor settled his helmet on his head with a football player's gesture, opened the wooden door and started swiftly down along the road. I gave him a little time and then started out after him. Walking fast, he looked back over his shoulder and laughed. We both broke into a trot. I looked back and saw Sam Benton, Jr., coming out the door.

From the hills above us to our right there began the insistent br-up, bup-bup-bup-bup-bup of German burp guns opening up. I started to run, hearing bullets whizz just over my head. In a long open stretch within clear observation of the hills we had to cross a wooden bridge. While I was running along it, part of my mind noted the clear, swift stream for washing water. On the other side, Tom Lawlor hung back until I caught up to him and the two of us, slightly out of breath, hustled along, talking and laughing.

"I don't *like* this damned place!"

"Me neither!"

"And I don't see any woodpiles. What's more, we're the only ones out. Sam Benton started but I don't see him now."

"I'll feel better when this bank up here hides us a little."

We came to our first house, set in a small farmyard, walked up the inclined driveway and, around in the back, came upon a large woodpile. We had recently been lectured again about booby traps and mines. "One of the first places they pick out is a woodpile, so you want to watch out for them." In the fading light we stood a long while looking at it silently.

"Well?" Tom Lawlor asked. We laughed and looked at the woodpile again, unwilling to touch it.

Sam Benton, Jr., came quietly up behind us. There was no need for him to ask what we were deliberating about. After surveying it a moment or two, he said, "Well, should we trah it, men?"

"I guess so," I heard myself saying, and stiffly the two of us bent, watching each other's eyes, synchronizing our movements. The both of us reached out one hand, removed the first block of wood, expecting to be blown to bits at any second. Each succeeding piece came away a little more easily. "Get the underneath pieces—the dry ones." I had learned to stretch out one arm and lay the pieces along in a neat row, then to place on it a second layer and a third, taking as much as I thought I could carry back.

On the return trip we separated and allowed a ten- or fif-teen-yard interval between us. Coming out into the open near the bridge, we hurried, and immediately on the hills the German machine guns took up their stuttering. Interspersed with it there was the crack, whing and ping of rifle fire. Running, saying an Act of Contrition, I began to drop some of the chunks of wood. "Met his death carrying a load of fire-wood—"

As I burst into the dark hall, breathless, Jimmy Mc-Donough was loitering there. "You guys are crazy," he said. "I wouldn't go out in that for anyone. I told him so."

I stared at him. "What'd he say?"

"What could he say? I told him I wouldn't go, that's all. He has no right to send you, so what could he say?"

I went down into the room and let the wood drop to the floor beside the stove. The captain seemed to have lost all interest in it. Other wood had been found in the back, had been chopped up, and the fire was already started.

The telephone line was put in, and when the captain called the "rear station," Phil Schaeffer told him Captain Baylor had not rung. Most of the men wished that he would and that he would order us back. Their nervousness made me nervous. And after getting us there, the captain began to grow increasingly tense, listening at any sound, swinging his head sharply toward the door as if he expected the Germans to pour in upon us at any moment.

It was here that I began to notice how really afraid Preacher was. He had made a joke of it and up till now I had assumed he was as brave as the next one. He always slept under the table on which he had piled the medicine chests, and I thought he did this to be close to his wares. Now I saw that it was because he felt safer with the added protection and weight above him. He admitted that he left the station only to go to the latrine and get his meals; for the latter, he always made use of his rank to cut in ahead of the long line; and as if to convince himself the trip would be a brief one, he never bothered to wear his field jacket and he left his overshoes un-buckled and flapping. If the situation outside appeared at all perilous, he again made use of his staff sergeant's rank to dip into the medics' supply of C rations and remained indoors.

A farmer in civilian life, he still kept early hours and was always the first to retire at night. He had no curiosity about

Europe whatsoever. Arriving in a town, he jumped out of the ambulance, ran for the aid station and stayed inside it away from the windows. His mind was closed; it rejected any new ideas, seemingly for fear that while acquiring them, his old ones would scatter from him and be proven false. "Ah don't know nothin' about that," he said shortly, and you could see his round face with the full pink cheeks and round blue eyes become stiff, set and on guard. He was inordinately cheap, even to the point of abstaining from air-mail stamps for his letters home. Nor would he permit his wife to send him any packages; consequently when ours came he never felt free to share them. His wife had a fairly good job and she was saving every penny. I have never seen Army food so poor that he could not eat it with relish. Despite these failings, I liked him.

"How'd you come to be picked for the medics?" I asked.

"Well, Ah was in the Three Cs like Jenkins here, 'fore the war broke out, an' when Ah was only in it a little while, they tol' me Ah was to work on first aid. Ah went in the Cs 'cause my parents died. Ah have a brother, but mah home sorta broke up. Ah didn't mind the Three Cs at all."

"I thought it was lousy," little sharp-faced Jenkins said. "They treated us lousy, worse'n the Army. Or almost worse. I was out in Oregon, and jeez, I didn't like it nohow. They treated us so lousy a bunch of us won' on strike. Then they said they were gonna treat us better an' they din', and then I went over the hill. I was over the hill t'ree months."

"Were you, Jenkins?" I took another look at him. He was younger than I had first thought, and some of the pinched Cockney miserableness that had shown on his arrival that snowy day was leaving him. "Where'd you go when you went over the hill?"

"I come home. I tol' Mom how they was usin' us, tol' the girl friend, and Mom says, 'Well, then, stay home.' So I did. I din' go out much. I just hung aroun'. Then one night—it was the night before Thanksgivin', I remember—I was takin' the girl frien' home from the movies an' just as I got to the door, they grabbed me."

"And what happened?" It sounded like the Gestapo.

"I had to go back an' finish out my stretch. Then I finey got out, an' along comes the Army. Jus' when I'm learnin' how to be a cabinetmaker. When this is over, I swear to God, I swear I'll never sign up for nothin'. Nothin'! I don't care

256

what it is! I won't write my name on nothin'!"

"Well, Ah'll say good night, fellas; I'm gonna turn in." Preacher rolled under the table.

The rest of us spread our blankets on the floor. Every now and then a fierce artillery barrage broke out with German 88s screaming and banging in the dark. In the midst of their attack, our artillery would open up in reply. The explosions roared back and forth over the taproom; we could not help feeling we were caught somewhere between the two, too far forward. Where the line companies were we did not know. In dread I supposed they were out trying to capture the hills surrounding the town, but hours had passed since we had shot into the empty-looking town, and there had been no wounded men brought in. Outside on the high ground, German burp guns stuttered, chattered and then were still, as if they had opened up on a patrol.

Previously we had been told by the captain that Olzheim, though insignificant to look at, was the center of important communications to Prum and Stadkill, and I understood these communications were buried somewhere in the hills that ringed the town.

Despite the heavy barrages that made me reach out my hand in the dark to make sure where my steel helmet was—and once the explosions were so close that I dumped everything out and clamped the helmet on—I fell asleep and slept fitfully through the night.

By the next morning, after God knows what sort of a night, two of the line companies had arrived in the town. Jeeps now and then flew by at top speed; from our windows you saw an occasional infantryman duck and run swiftly across the road to get into a cellar. Sergeant Concannon drove up beside the inn and, without dismounting, shoved the round, flat cans of food in through the window and drove on up the road as fast as possible. First Battalion Headquarters was stationed in a stone schoolhouse in the center of town that was under almost constant enemy fire. The Germans still held much of the high ground, and the attack continued bitterly for the next two days.

Captain Liebert, C Company's commander, whom I had seen in the kitchen at Schonberg staring into the candlelight, was killed, and Lieutenant MacKenzie temporarily took his place. It seemed a particularly unlucky position, for he made the fourth commander C Company had had within the space of two months.

A strong enemy counterattack was expected momentarily. The Germans were said to have amassed five thousand men, supported by tanks, ready to pour down into Olzheim. In the meanwhile, there was the constant Rat-tat-tat-tat! Tat-tat-tat-tat-tat-tat! *Br-r-up-bup-bup-bup-bup!* from the machine guns on the hills, the steady ring of the telephone with reports of casualties here and casualties there. The litter squads ran out, sometimes to go high into the hills to bring down the wounded. Infantrymen showed up acting as litter bearers, and the walking wounded began to make their own way in, hobbling, bandaged around the head, an arm or a leg. The crowded ambulance made quick trips back to Collecting, back to us, back to Collecting. The salvage rifles and equipment piled up. I kept them in the one dry corner of the flooded, smashed-up kitchen.

Awaiting the counterattack was a nerve-wracking experience. Would it be beaten back before the enemy poured into the town? Would we be ordered to hold at all cost, with street fighting and a massacre, and only a few able to make an escape? In the midst of a heavy German barrage, a well-educated line-company boy walked into the hall and called down into the taproom, "Say, Doc, do you think you, or one of your men, could come up to a house here in town? There are two sick old women there, bedridden, and they need attention."

Shaking his head no, the captain asked, "What's the matter with them?"

"Well . . ." The boy smiled a little. "They're frightened and they're badly constipated."

"Anyone who's badly constipated durin' an attack like this is lucky!" the captain said, and mentally I agreed.

"I know, Doc, but hell! It's two old *women.*"

"Nope." The captain, smiling, continued to shake his head and the man walked out.

By Sunday, the third day in Olzheim, there had been no counterattack and things were somewhat quieter, though the enemy still tenaciously held large portions of the high ground and kept firing down on the town. The telephone rang, announcing that the Catholic chaplain had driven up in his jeep and would say Mass in one hour at the stone schoolhouse. I was dirty and unshaven and went out with Tom

Lawlor to get some washing water. Each carrying a pail and a pot, we walked quickly up to the bridge, hung from it for a moment and then dropped down onto the steep banks between which the icy water rushed. We had a hard job getting up with the water, and once on the road, to an accompaniment of sniper bullets, we started to run, slopping the water in our haste.

I washed, shaved, brushed my teeth. Jimmy McDonough, Tom Lawlor and I were the only Catholics of our group starting for Mass.

"Listen," we were told, "when you get up near the school-house, duck down low and get around the back as fast as you can. The Jerries keep firing at the front door all the time."

We went past the stream, up the hilly main street of the town. Tom Lawlor was saying, "Gosh, I sure hope I get home for my brother's ordination next year."

Jimmy McDonough rolled along, one eye on the nearby hills, the tips of his fingers in his trouser pockets. "I just hope I git *home*," he said.

The sky was gray; the only men out and about at that time were Catholics, converging from lanes and the cellars of houses toward the high-up schoolhouse. Shells fell not too close and small-arms fire and burp guns rattled on the hills, but at the moment the Germans weren't firing on the schoolhouse. We went down a side path that was cut into a hill and descended into the cold cement cellar where Mass had just started. Rifles leaned against the back wall and the men were kneeling amid broken windowpanes on the cement floor, most with their eyes closed and hands clasped, their tired faces wiped clean of expression.

When we returned to the *Gasthaus*, Captain Stettner was walking about, shaving, using Lieutenant Serletis' toilet articles and towel. A jeep drove up and came to a swift halt outside; a tall figure of surprising freshness, cleanliness and verve jumped out and came into the hall. It was the new Protestant chaplain, arrived to take the place of the one who had been evacuated at the close of December outside Rheims. He was about twenty-four, dark-haired, high-complexioned and handsome, dressed in a green trench coat that looked brand-new. His steel helmet with its small white cross was new, his combat boots were polished, his trousers were even creased. He looked like an advertisement for Abercrombie and Fitch, Officers' Uniforms. He was friendly, eager, and nervous. "This where I belong?" he asked, smiling. "We ready to hold services here?" Gibbons, his driver and assistant, a friend of Warren Troy's and Phil Schaeffer's, had followed him in.

We told him no, he belonged farther up the road at the schoolhouse. He seemed rather shocked, as if he had just been congratulating himself on having landed safely, but he smiled again, very widely. "Just a little further ahead? Straight up the road? The schoolhouse?" He thanked us for the information. We warned him twice about ducking down, wished him good luck in his job. He went out with Gibbons and they drove off, fast.

Just as they left, Lieutenant Serletis, who had been sent up to the schoolhouse on an errand in the jeep with Tubby, burst through the door, gray-faced, his jaws chattering. "Holy Christ! Look at this!" To duck an incoming shell, he had flung himself out of the jeep and down the road into a ravine with such force that he had cut his wrist and had to have it bandaged.

The captain watched him, smiling with a mixture of fondness and something close to contempt. Lieutenant Serletis, while being bandaged, went on jabbering about the closeness of his escape.

"That's five points for you, Nick," the captain said.

"Whaddya mean?"

The captain gave his head a shake and smiled. "You get a Purple Heart."

We were all too surprised to speak. Captain Stettner, of course, had full power to decide in the matter, but there was not always logic or even consistency in his judgments. It depended almost entirely on whim. Sometimes men had received shrapnel wounds during combat, had had them bound up by their aid man and had continued on with the attack. Even when, a few days later, the wounded man appeared to claim his Purple Heart, accompanied by the aid man as witness, as often as not the captain decided the man was not deserving of the award. Howard Mason, our truck driver, came in one night from the parking space with a scratched ear that bled two drops. He claimed a piece of shrapnel had caused it, and he was given a Purple Heart. "As long as it's the direct result of enemy action," the captain quoted. Yet when Sergeant Campbell came in a few days later with a small cut similarly incurred and requested the Purple Heart, the captain shook his head and said, "Nope." Now he decided the enemy had caused Lieutenant Serletis to fall and cut his wrist, and the lieutenant was therefore entitled to the ribbon and the five points.

Lieutenant Serletis was so completely miserable, so sick-looking, and had such a heavy cold that at the moment no one begrudged him his Purple Heart. His little combat boots were still, as always, wet; I had never seen him take them off. Shortly after Warren Troy, with frigid imperturbability, made out the Purple Heart notation, the captain took Lieutenant Serletis to one side and talked to him in a low voice. The lieutenant, shivering, kept making an abrupt little gesture as if trying to brush something away. In the end, however, he gave in and the captain turned around.

"Warren," he said, "put an evacuation tag on Lieutenant Serletis. He's goin' back to the hospital for a few days to see if he can't lose that cold."

"Jee-ze, I feel terrible about this," Lieutenant Serletis said. I believe he did. We tried to soften it for him, running around to find his toilet articles, writing paper, his tiny overcoat and gas mask. And now that he knew he was about to go back, relief flooded him. He went slack, sitting there in his coat with the collar turned up, waiting for the ambulance to drive him to Collecting, his head sagging forward, his eyes closed.

Just as he left, a jeep raced up to the door. The driver jumped out and ran in to us, white-faced. It was Gibbons, the new chaplain's assistant.

"Hey!" he cried. "Some guys! Come out! The chaplain—"
Four men ran out with him, lifted the unconscious new chaplain out of the jeep and carried him into the taproom. The driver followed, shaking and crying. "R-right as we came out! Just as we came out, they opened up. He didn't know how to—he wasn't quick enough—"

"Is he hurt badly?" asked one of the men who had carried him in.

"A goner. All shot to pieces. Machine-gun bullets. He must have stopped every goddam one of them. He's bleedin' like a sieve."

It took Preacher and the captain a long while to bandage all the wounds, and then the chaplain, who looked like gray marble, was covered with his new but bloody trench coat and two blankets and carried out into the ambulance. The

261

captain instructed Gibbons, whose face still showed signs of twisting all awry, to stay with us until he felt better.

A large shell whistled in with its long, familiar, terrifying scream and crashed just across the road, exploding away a huge corner of the building. When I went out to the doorway to look, everything was quiet once again. A moment or two later the road became crowded with vehicles and double lines of men moving into town.

"Hey!" I heard behind me. "We're being *relieved!* Twelfth Division's taking over!" The litter bearers crowded around the doorway to watch. It was about four o'clock.

"Tubby!" The captain came out.

"Yes, sir?"

"I want you, and one squad, and you, Atwell, to get goin' right away. Fast as you can. Get back to that farmhouse where Schaeffer is, and hold the place for us as a station. We'll be right along in back of you. Don't let anyone get it ahead of you. Quick now!"

We rushed to do up our equipment and buckle it on. Flakes of snow had started to fall. Once more I had to ride on the hood of the jeep. We started off almost with a leap, and just as we flew out of town the enemy sent in a tremendous artillery barrage.

The kitchen of the farmhouse was being held by the Second Battalion medics, and Phil Schaeffer and his squad were present rather by sufferance. As time went on, however, more and more newly arrived men from First Battalion Headquarters came in to warm themselves at the stove. The air became thick with cigarette smoke. Men ate, threw ration cans and boxes anywhere and slumped down on the floor. Then the room grew badly overcrowded. Even the narrow, dark hall became packed. The Second Battalion medical captain rose up and shouted to the men in the hall, crowded like rush-hour passengers in the subway, that they must leave a space open in case wounded men were to be brought in. But the crowd grew thicker and thicker and finally he gave up; his men folded his cot and carried it out along with their medicine and records. Shells screamed and exploded almost constantly.

We had expected the rest of our men to come immediately after us, but several hours passed and, when finally they did arrive, they were red-faced, startled-looking, and their uniforms were covered with snow. The captain and the aid-station complement came first. "God, what a time! Jeez, you missed it! You guys no sooner got out of there than things *really* got hot, didn't they?"

"A Company got the s--- kicked out of them. Boy, they were out on the road, lining up for chow, and the Twelfth Division was moving in. You talk about no bunching up! There were vehicles all the hell over the place, some coming in, some trying to pull out, and the guys all jammed together on the chow line when the Jerries drop one right in the middle of the whole f---ing mess. We were all ready to pull out when suddenly we get the word. Hey, Preach, how many casualties we get all at once? Six? Eight?"

I caught the end of the captain's conversation: "So shaky I made him go and get his organ off the jeep, set it up inside and play the damned thing. We had a couple of hours of classical music right there." He was smiling, referring to the wounded chaplain's assistant. "Calmed him down after a while. But havin' organ music in the middle of a big attack . . . It's some war, I'm tellin' you."

There were so many conversations going on in the kitchen that I did not understand what happened next. I saw the rest of our men come in, scarlet-faced and snowy, with some story I couldn't hear above the din. Silly Willie appeared to be making an explanation to the captain, who looked suddenly shocked. From across the room, I was wondering why the newest arrivals, coming in with Silly Willie, should be so covered with snow.

A few minutes later I heard the captain say, "Well, someone's got to go out there to the ambulance. Anyone feel like volunteering?"

No one answered. "Let's see . . . Phil? Phil Schaeffer? Do you want to go?"

"Oh. Oh! Yes, sir."

"Better take Jameson with you."

I understood that three wounded men were still in the ambulance and that the captain was asking someone to lift them out and bring them in.

"I'll go with you, Phil," I said.

"Do you want to?" The captain asked in marked surprise. The thing began to seem very strange.

"Yes, I don't mind," I said. I put on my helmet and started for the door. Surreptitiously, Jimmy McDonough took hold of the back of my field jacket to detain me.

263

"Les, don't be a damned fool! Don't you go!" he warned in a low voice, hardly moving his lips. He was not looking at me.

"Why not?" I heard the artillery shells crashing and whining, but we had often gone out to load up the ambulance under similar circumstances.

"Don't be a fool!" He did not want the captain to hear or to notice. "Take my advice. Don't go."

A slight feeling of nightmare came over me, but Phil and Ted were waiting at the door, and I went down the narrow black hall with them, out into the wind and the wet blowing snow. Two men walked ahead of us.

"Yes, he has a winch," Phil said to Ted, and after a moment it dawned on me that we were following the two men.

"Who are they?" I asked, and Phil, preoccupied, said, "Oh, they're—well, they're drivers. Yes."

"But where's the ambulance?" I knew that whenever possible it was parked in a place that might afford natural camouflage, but we had already gone some distance down the snowy road and there was nothing in sight but a small truck.

"It's not here, didn't you know that?" Ted asked.

"Wait a minute," I said. "Aren't we going to unload three wounded men from the ambulance?"

"No!" Ted squealed with laughter. "Is that what you thought? We're going to *get* the ambulance."

"*How* are we going to get it?" I asked, dazed.

"Well, the truck driver has a winch." We had come to the little truck. I was still struggling under the impression the ambulance was close by; I thought we were pausing to get a rope from the truck. "The captain," Teddy was explaining carefully as the shells kept up their wild crashing and exploding, "wants *us* to get the medicine boxes if we can't do anything else."

"You boys wanna hop in the back?" the truck driver asked in a heavy Kentucky accent.

"How far are we going?" I seldom remember being so confused.

"Oh, jes a mile, two down the road. Down by that turn."

"As *I* understand it," Phil said, climbing stiffly up over the tailboard, "Silly Willie let the ambulance go off the road into a ditch right outside of town there."

"I did not foresee this," I said, climbing in after him.

Ted got in and the little truck started down the road to-

264

ward Olzheim. It was very cold; we were riding down toward where most of the artillery shells were exploding.

"If we can't get the ambulance out of the ditch, we're to
take the medicine and stuff and bring it back, is that it?"

"Yes. The boys had to jump out and make a run for it, so
they left all their packs and equipment. We won't have to
bother with that, though. The captain is only worried that if
we got any casualties during the night, we wouldn't have a
bandage or a damned thing to put on them."

I felt relieved to know at last the full situation.

The road seemed to have narrowed suddenly—either that
or the little truck slowed down as if the driver were unsure
of his way in the dark. A shell screamed in before us with
such a blasting roar that, bent over, we jumped to our feet.
The driver jammed on the brakes. Another shell exploded
even nearer with a huge blinding flash in the bank beside us.
A tide of excitement rose up in a split second: without
words, all five of us leaped out of the truck and flung ourselves down into the slushy snow. My head was pounding
and my mouth had gone dry. The third shell came in with a
fearful jolting crash and was immediately followed by a
fourth. I thought the last one had blown the truck to pieces,
but when I glanced around, it was there. From the first momentary feeling of relief that we were not still inside the
truck, we were all seized with the violent desire to be under
cover. We lay panting.

"Let's get the hell out of here fast," I said. "Driver, let's
go!"

"Should we go?" he called.

"Yes! *Go!*"

We jumped up and got into the truck again. Now, my
God, if shrapnel's pierced the engine . . . No, the truck
started forward, and a hail of big artillery shells roared in,
some landing just behind us, some ahead. They all came
across the dim white plain from the low rolling hills to our
right. We reached the first of a long line of tanks. Stalled,
spread out at intervals along the narrow road, it was they
that were drawing the enemy fire. Some were in clear sight,
their turrets slammed down; others were in the shadow of a
bank to the immediate left of the road. With scarcely any
space, we began to drive in and out to get around them.

We passed two when the intense barrage opened up again.
It was odd how something in one's blood seemed to know

from the second the long piercing shriek began whether the shell was hurtling straight for you or not. These most definitely were. The truck again stopped, and without consultation or delay we sailed out into the snow. The first shell exploded with a tremendous flash and a crash, and when no shrapnel hit me I scrambled up as the second scream started and sought refuge to the left side of the truck, close to the rear tire. Phil and Ted were lying there, spread flat out. The explosion went off and my face banged into the slush. Behind the front left tire, the driver and his assistant had got up to a nervous crouch, not knowing whether to stay there or to run, and now from all of us there began a wild, incoherent shouting:

"Away from the truck! Away from the tanks! Zeroing in! No, get down, stay! Get in the open! Get under the truck! Crawl under! No! Here's another com—" The blinding, ear-splitting crash. One's body furiously jolting against the ground. "God! L-let's get out of here! Get *out!* No! There's no place to *go!* It's the *tanks!* They're after the goddam tanks! Let's go, back there! You ready?"

Shivering, weak with nervous haste, we pulled on the strap and climbed up over the tailboard. "Don't sit on the bench! Phil! Ted, get down on the floor." But why bother? We were caught this time, and this was the end of everything. I was intensely keyed up and shaking from head to foot, but even with the conviction that my end would come in the next few seconds, there was nothing I wanted to say; I felt I didn't know Phil and Ted that well.

Some of the tanks were in motion now, clanking ahead for a short space. We raced past a few of these, and while the shelling remained heavy, it no longer seemed personal; the tension inside me started to relax. We started to exclaim, to laugh with nervousness. I wanted a drink of water badly, but none of us had taken along our canteens. This, I told myself, was a single action such as any line company went through daily, and it would be over in perhaps fifteen more minutes. By then I would be back safe in the farmhouse kitchen. I brushed the heavy slush off my clothes; the wet had come through my pants, particularly at the knees. I sat up on the floor, gripping the edge of the seat, staring out through the windshield where the wipers clicked back and forth, clearing away the snow.

"Okay, boys, this is it."

266

We jumped down out of the back and, feeling thin and shaky, I started to walk down the road with Phil and Ted. The drivers were a few steps ahead of us, one carrying the coil of rope. Tracer bullets and artillery shells were crashing into Olzheim.

"There she is, down there."

At the widest part of the curve in the road, just outside the town, the ambulance had run off and down the incline. It was in a lurched, slanting position. We were near enough to see it clearly, with its broad red crosses standing out dark against its own whiteness and the dimmer whiteness of the snow.

"Come on. I'll bring the truck up closer to it," the driver said to his assistant. Hands in pockets, the three of us waited while they backed the truck up to the rear of the ambulance. Then we began to walk toward them. The driver got down and started to unwind the rope.

"I think we'd better get the medicine boxes out first, just to play safe," I said. "Come on, before they attach the—"

Before I could finish, with shocking loudness a German burp gun opened fire on us from directly in front of the ambulance. There was an instant of frozen surprise, then we fell flat. The bullets sprayed with orange-red flashes just over our heads. There came a brief and ominous pause. Before the shock had time to register, I realized I had seen a German in a white winter uniform step from in front of the ambulance to open fire.

"Get out of here!" I shouted to Phil. "My God, quick! Take cover!" In confusion, I looked around. The only cover was the little ravine to the far side of the road, and I was afraid to crouch up and make the few steps' dash for it. Phil, obeying me, got up stooped to run, and again came the loud chattering burst of the machine gun. The German was coming after the three of us on the road, momentarily leaving the two drivers lying in back of the ambulance. "Down! Phil, get down!" I cried so loudly my throat went hoarse. "He can *see* you!" Phil dropped flat. My head was pounding. None of us was armed. The burp gun was moving, coming between the drivers and ourselves.

"There are *two* of them!" Phil shouted back across his shoulder to me.

"Crawl!" I yelled. "Up the road! Away!" As quickly as I could, using my elbows and one knee, I began to squirm and crawl up the slushy road. The machine gun kept firing, its bullets flaming about a foot over our heads.

"Les! Down *here!*" Ted was urging. "Down in the *ditch!*" He was on the far side, on all fours like a bear, making a short rush, but the tracer bullets were barely missing his large behind.

"*Down!*" Phil and I bawled almost in unison. "Get your ass down! Get down! You're not safe!"

I saw Phil, up on his hands and knees like a baby, swiftly paddling forward, and to my horror he lost his sense of direction and began to crawl off the road straight toward where the burp gun kept up its firing. "Phil!" I shouted, aware that we shouldn't be shouting. "Phil, come *back!* You're going right *into* it! The *other* way!"

The three of us started up the road. But even so, we could not hope to crawl as fast as the German could walk. At any second he would understand that we did not fire back because we could not; and that, I felt, was the only thing that kept him from rushing up and spraying us.

Along came another stream of scarlet flashes, firing now not from behind us or beside us, but from a little ahead, as if to drive us back toward the ambulance. They let up when a flare suddenly burst overhead, bathing us and the road for a wide circle in brilliant, chalky-pink light. I was stunned and blinded momentarily; then I saw the shadow of the tree near where Phil was lying, sharp-edged, with every twig distinct on the snow. We lay still, panting. My mouth tasted like copper. Four close shells landed in beside us with an enormous explosion, a sudden violent crash and whistle of wind; two ripped into the bank just beyond us. "Mortars!" Phil cried. "They're firing in mortars!"

There was a sound on the road behind us. I looked back over my shoulder and saw that the two drivers had run from the ambulance to their truck. They had jumped aboard and started it up. The burp gun began to fire again, spraying fast just over my head and around toward the truck.

"They got it going!" But to my disbelief, they rode not toward us but away, toward Olzheim itself. I could feel myself cave in, lying on the road; then the driver made a sudden screaming turn, brought the truck around and started back. To keep from being run over, I had to scramble to one side of the road on my stomach. As the truck came near, it slowed down and Ted Jameson, despite his weight, made a soaring spectacular leap and was over the back and inside. I had got up from a crouch and was making a run for it.

"Are you all in?" the driver called.

"Yes! Go on!" Ted was crying, hammering on the tail-board. "Go on! Go on!"

"*No!*" I shouted as I hauled myself over. "And Phil's not in yet." I turned around to give him a hand up. The mortars smashed in again. I don't know whether my frantic clawing and clutching at Phil's arm was a help or not. The truck kept rolling and he was running behind it, trying to make the jump up. With nerves ready to snap, it seemed to me that he'd never get in. When he was halfway over the raised tail-board, I pulled and hauled him in and with Ted set up a loud clamoring to the driver, telling him to get going.

All three of us were lying on the floor. Ted had burrowed his head under my shoulder. I looked up for a second as we gained speed and saw out the square back opening of the truck the black sky pierced by the flamelike streaks of the tracer bullets. A mortar's scarlet explosion filled the opening and I banged my head down.

The little truck was racing through the slush, but not half fast enough to suit me. For a while we seemed to be in the clear, and the shells that crashed and fell, fell impersonally, not aimed specifically at us. I found I was lying in something sticky, like paste, that had spilled on the floor of the truck. The chained tires kept up a steady hiss just below me in the slush. I was about to let go, to give in to relief, when we ran into trouble again. We had come back to the tanks crowding the narrow road. They were still under fire.

The first few were stationary and we managed to get past them, dark, hunched, brooding monsters drawn up in the shadow of a slight hill beside the road. There was a short, empty stretch of road and then another tank, clanking slowly along, its engine making a great roar. Our driver tried to by-pass it, but the tank was in the center of the narrow road and there was a short but steep drop on the side. We fell back and crawled along. The driver made several attempts to get by, shouting impotently, swinging out only to be forced back again. To add to his trouble, the snow blew thick against the windshield faster than the wiper could clean it; he had to rise up from his seat every now and then and lean his head out to judge the distance. The enemy continued to fire. At last, making use of a slight outcurve of the road, the driver skinned the truck past; in doing so, the edge of the road gave way and we almost crashed down into the gully. There were about eight more tanks to pass. My teeth ached from gritting them.

The driver, I noticed, was sitting on two or three folded Army blankets. In trying to jockey past one of the remaining tanks, he rose up, leaned out, and had just sat down again when Ted Jameson said, "D'you mind getting up a second?" The man raised himself up a little and Ted sneaked one of the blankets off and wrapped it, doubled many times as it was, about his head.

I was chilled now, shivering in a cold sweat, and coated down the front with that thick, slippery, white paste. It occurred to me that it might be powdered milk sticking to my wet clothes. "What in God's name is he wrapping his head up for?" I asked Phil.

Ted heard me, lifted his head and spoke from between the blanket. "Well," he said, "I've always heard that sometimes even the thickness of an overcoat is some protection. It stops a shell a little. So . . ." He covered his head again and buried it.

A few minutes of fast driving after getting past the last tank brought us back to the farmhouse, our mission unsuccessful. The house was so overcrowded that now we could scarcely force our way down the dark hall. Message Center was set up in the front room; a dim light came from the switchboard; and fanning and fading, there was the firefly glow of countless cigarettes all over the dark room. Somewhere in the hall an officer's voice was crying, "No smoking! No smoking in here. Keep this hallway *open!* Some of you men will have to go outside." But no one went out and no cigarettes went out either.

In the kitchen the two drivers made their way over to the captain to explain what had happened, while Phil, Ted and I, going into bursts of overexhilarated laughter, started to tell our story to the litter bearers. I found it impossible to stop talking, though I could see that no one was particularly interested. "They had us pinned down with burp guns. Was there one, Phil? Or two? And then flares came, and mortar shells—" It was the same story one heard day in and day out; it mattered only to the ones to whom it happened. Now, even in the light, I could not tell what the thick white paste was that covered me from shoulders to knees. I scraped most

270

of it off, using my mess-kit knife.

Almost before we had finished impressing our excited story on an uninterested audience, a new distraction came along. Two drenched and shivering infantrymen walked straddle-legged into the room, one holding his wet rifle out from him stiffly. In an attack, they had both fallen into a swollen stream and had been tumbled over in it many times. One of the men had nearly drowned. Water oozed from them and formed a puddle around their feet. With chattering teeth and a smile, one man said, "Got any d-d-dry clothes, Cap'm?"

"Haven't got a thing," the captain replied, also with a smile. "Not a thing." I don't believe he found their condition amusing, but he had assumed his pose of patronizing detachment, as if the GIs were a breed apart, unfailingly funny no matter what their predicament. "What battalion are you from?"

"Second."

He shook his head, still with the half-smile. "Can't do a thing for you, boys."

"Can't we even—?" Couldn't *anything* be done, the man's face asked. "Couldn't we git these here wet clo'es off and git some *blankets?*" Their teeth chattered. The other man, a silent scarecrow, continued to hold his wet rifle out from him.

"Sorry, but you boys are gonna have to go down to your own aid station."

The more voluble of the two was astounded. His voice squawked. "You mean we can't even— *I'm* 67th," he cried. "I'm from the 67th—" He stared, incredulous.

The captain, with the smile that inferred "There's no use; I couldn't explain because you'd never understand," repeated, "Sorry. You have to go to your own station."

"You mean out? We got to go *out* again? Like *this?*"

"It's not far," Captain Stettner said, relenting somewhat. "It's only a little way down. It's a law. I can't do anything for you. It's tough, I know."

"He-*heez*us H. Christ, *how* d'you like that!" The dripping man looked at the captain, then drew his eyes away, turned to his companion and said roughly, but as to a friend, "Come on, let's get out of here."

The kitchen had become silent; the two men walked out in their dripping clothes. The half-smile had come back on the captain's face. He shook his head. "It's a new law. Nothin' I could do for 'em."

The crowd in the kitchen did not look with admiration on him for expelling the two drenched men, and suddenly he called, "Everyone who doesn't belong here, outside. I want *all* of you men outside. Litter bearers an' everyone. Only the ones working in the station can remain. We gotta keep this place clear!"

"Yeah, sure," Mike Nowak said as we pushed our way out. "Now he wants to go to sleep. I can read him like a book."

With Jimmy McDonough and Mike Nowak, I managed not only to squeeze into the room where Message Center was but I even succeeded in sitting on the floor. No one was allowed to speak because the operators were listening in. Some men were called out after a half hour, and then I could stretch out my cramped legs. I was prepared to sit up all night when suddenly we too were called to put on our equipment and get out. It was sometime after midnight.

We stumbled out tiredly and lined up in twos before the farmhouse. The snow was turning to rain and a high wind had sprung up. Unprotesting, taking it as a matter of course, we started off on foot, walked to a nearby crossroad, and snapped awake. A line of two-and-a-half-ton trucks was drawn up there and men were beginning to climb onto them. No matter that they were open to the sleet; it would be better than walking, and, the best part of all, they stretched down a dark lane pointing away from Olzheim, not toward it. All at once a buzzing began: "We're going back! Back for a ten-day rest!" "To Rheims!" "To *Paris!*" "Hey, driver, how far we goin'?"

"Not far. Just a little ways back. Nex' town or the one behind it."

But it *was* for a ten-day rest.

The Kentucky driver and his assistant who had gone down with us to get the ambulance now made a second trip, this time by themselves, and they succeeded in hauling the ambulance up onto the road and driving it back. For this, one later was awarded the Silver Star and the other a Bronze Star.

I did not know for the first two or three days that we had come back to Aaw, "where the priest's house was." The small, half-ruined German towns looked almost indistinguishable and we had arrived at night in the rain. We awoke late, perhaps at eight or eight-thirty, with our clothing still wet. There were far too many of us for the small, narrow bedroom that was intact except for a few wide cracks through which a draft blew. It was a cream-colored, water-painted room with a tiled stove in one corner, set up on a curving cement step which gave the place a Mexican air. The floor and the cracked green door slanted badly. In the hall outside, the staircase going down was so steep that one almost tumbled out of the room and down the stairs. Edging across the top step, you passed the broad chimney and came into the unfinished part of the attic. Here were broken chairs and washstands, bags of grain, trunks, a wurst or two, and cartons of junk. There was a huge hole in the shingled roof made by a large unexploded artillery shell that still hung halfway through, silvery and menacing at first, but in time we grew accustomed to it and even forgot to see it.

The stairs ended below in a murky foyer with a ceiling-high wardrobe and a massive ugly sofa upholstered in cut velvet. Most of the floor was flooded ankle-deep with blackish water. The aid station was in the main room of the house, up one step, and facing the back garden and the soggy fields stretching away from it. The windows were small-paned and recessed, the furniture dark, nondescript, with several Windsor chairs and mission tables. There were terrariums and hanging plants, the green very fresh and strong-looking. The Army stove had just been set up and was burning cheerfully.

Each morning the sick call was very long. When I came down the stairs, I'd find forty or fifty men all from one company crowded into the wet foyer, on planks laid over the puddle. They still came with very heavy colds, the ever-present dysentery, with laryngitis, cuts, infections, boils, burns, sick headaches. I gave out the numbered cardboard checks I had made, hung the corresponding number over the sights of the weapons, stacked them against the sofa or wardrobe, and put the pistols in my pockets, saying, "Remind me: yours is in the left-hand pocket of my jacket." "Yours is in my right-hand hip pocket." "Yours is in my belt." Then, loaded down with pistols—I was a little afraid of them—I carried in the company sickbook and sent in "the first four guys." There would be idle talk and an exchange of rumors with the men waiting on the line. "Hey, At," Preacher would call, "send in the next four. No, line up all the ones that's got the GIs and I'll take them first." As the men left, I returned the pistols, rifles and grease guns, and used the same worn checks for the next company crowding into the foyer. Going into the aid station, I'd announce, "C Company coming up. There's one man left over from A Company who didn't sign the sickbook. Do you want to take him? He has the GIs."

"Yeah, send him in." With a ripping sound that sent chills through me, Preacher swiftly pulled a broad band of adhesive tape from around a man's hairy chest and ribs.

By now C Company was composed mainly of replacements, but here and there there'd be a familiar face: Atanasio, grown gaunt, still with dysentery; the effete Everett Telford, explaining in a laryngitis whisper that the medics were not doing a thing for him and bearing a special note from his company commander; the indomitable Sergeant Brauer, taking me aside to ask, "Atwell, vot the hell am I to do? You see that man there?" He pointed out an unmilitary figure somewhere in his thirties. "He iss a replacement and no goddam good as a soldier. Good in other ways, a good man, intelligent, a designer in civilian life, married, very good, does anything you say—but he does not belong here! I beg that goddam captain of yours, 'Let me send this man back so I can get a young man for my platoon. This man is always sick, always passing out.' He will not *do* it. Will not listen to me!"

The man turned around on the line, looking to Sergeant Brauer for guidance. There was nothing I could suggest except getting a letter from Lieutenant MacKenzie. Sergeant Brauer had been coming down with the man almost daily. About ten days later, Sergeant Brauer told me the man dropped dead of shock in the midst of an artillery attack.

Little Louden, the ammunition bearer for the B.A.R. team and the first C Company man to have been wounded, had just been released from the hospital and he showed up on sick call several times at Aaw with a heavy cough. The first time he came in Preacher remembered him and asked to see the wound in his thigh. I walked into the room as Louden rolled down his pants leg and went out.

"Mm-mh," Preacher said when the door closed. "*Thought* he was back purty quick. They never removed the shrapnel at all! That leg's gonna bother that kid; he's gonna have to have that shrapnel taken out some day."

"They've sent him back like that into combat?" I asked.

The captain looked at me a moment and said, "Whatever

274

you overhear inside this station isn't to go any further, you understand that."

"Yes, sir," I said, but the next day I saw little Louden standing on line in the foyer, coughing and shifting from one leg to the other, and I said, "Louden, does your leg ever bother you?"

"Yeah, it bodders me sometimes." He grinned, showing dirty little teeth.

"Well, why don't you come in each time it does and report it?"

"D'hell wit 'em."

I couldn't say any more at the time, but the next day when he left the house with his handful of sulfa pills, limping and hopping a little, I took a chance and ducked out after him. It was a windy day, with rain spitting, and at first when I called to him he was not going to come back. Finally he did, and I said, "Look, Louden, every time your leg hurts you, come in here and tell them so. If you'll make enough of a complaint, they'll have to do something for you. I'm not supposed to tell you this, so don't say I told you. Do you understand?"

He looked at me, uncomfortable, suspicious. His sallow, immature little face, with its soft adolescent mustache, twisted into an embarrassed grimace. "They won't do nuttin for me," he said.

"Look. Take my word for it. They will. They'll have to. But only if you'll put in a complaint."

He never came back again, and at the start of the next attack he and Braaf, the former Tiger Patrol man, joined forces, ran away together and deserted.

On the first four or five rainy days, and then on days that were fair, Sam Benton, Jr., offered for a small sum to take the mess kits back down the street after each meal and wash them. He charged about ten or twenty cents per mess kit— whatever our smallest piece of paper currency was. "Ah'm not proud, no sirree," he said, feeling shrewd and business-like. About six of us turned over the mess kits to him, and each time he brought them back, he collected one of the little red, white and blue bills. Some of the six began to count up how much he made each day and they discontinued the service. I was his steadiest and finally his only customer, and he thought me a fool. Toward the end of our ten days there, he announced publicly he was no longer in the business of washing mess kits. "Ah got what Ah was savin' up for," he said. "Ah'm sending that money home to mah minister. He can use it more'n Ah can."

"—Admirable," Phil Schaeffer said uncertainly to me.

"Yes, and it would have been more so if he hadn't said anything about it."

War and travel had done little to widen Sam Benton's horizons. By determination, it seemed, he remained the same. "Every time," he said, "Ah drive past mah girl's house, it makes m' heart go pit-a-pat." We could all have said it with him, but none of us could have laughed with quite the same freshness. "Yes, sirree," he reminisced, "m' brother courted Miss Martha Lee, and Ah courted Miss Lucy Lee. An' every time you take those two girls out on a date, you have to go with 'em firs' to church."

"What the hell would you have to do that for?" asked Warren Troy, the clerk. Tired of Preacher's closed mind, he had come upstairs to talk to us, and now his whole face tightened with annoyance.

"Waal, tha's the way they wanted it, an' that's the way it was. Bes' way."

"I don't agree. I think it was damned silly and narrow-minded of them," Warren Troy said, but Sam did not like to argue, ever. He brought forward his views and, smilingly, pityingly, refused to defend or change them.

" 'Lips that touch liquor will never touch mine,' " he now quoted. "No, sir. Never go out with a girl who'd drink or smoke. Good girls don't do those things."

Trying to control his temper, Warren Troy said, "My sister smokes and she drinks too, in moderation. What have you got to say about that?"

Sam smiled in an angelic way, shook his head and was silent.

He had gained the confidence of Bob Russell, and sometimes when I returned from the aid station downstairs I heard the tail end of their discussions. I gathered that Sam was trying to lead the swarthy twenty-three-year-old Bob Russell back to the path of righteousness and that there had been a confession wherein Bob Russell told Sam all the sins of his past life and gave the details of his marriage that led up to his divorce. For a while Sam Benton seemed to be trying to effect a reconciliation between Bob Russell and his wife, but further confidences turned him against this course and he agreed that the two should remain apart.

I didn't know what caused the divorce, and didn't ask, though several times Bob Russell appeared anxious to tell me. It was as if he were not sure Sam was the best confessor he could have found. "She jes give me a bad deal!" he exclaimed, rolling his dark eyes around to me and looking extremely serious and regretful. "An' now she's always writin' to ask me to come back to her. Ah'm not goin' back, though." He had been eighteen when he married, and the girl sixteen or seventeen. He had brought her to a small, isolated, rocky tenant farm where he had "worked like a horse."

"She got custody of mah three boys, 'cause Ah don't think a chile should be separated from the mother no matter what she done. She wants to do the right thing now. Why, you know somethin'? She even sent me ten bucks in a letter when Ah was in Fort Jackson jes so's Ah'd have some spendin' money in mah pockets. But there's some things a man can't forget."

"Do you ever write to the boys?" I asked.

"You can't. They're too young. One is—" His eyes squinted. "One is five, and one' jes four, I think, and one's about three. Yes, three years ole."

"Haven't you seen them since?"

"Oh, yes! When Ah went home on furlough. She's doin' a good job on bringin' 'em up."

"Is she a pretty girl?"

"Yes . . ." He deliberated a moment. "Ah'd say she was a right pretty girl all right. Blonde."

It struck me he couldn't talk of her so frequently and not be still in love with her, and yet since he had gone to Sam Benton, Jr., with his trouble and they were of the same faith, I didn't like to interfere. He brought the subject up several times, however, indirectly asking my opinion, and finally one night in Sam's presence I said, "Well, she was very young when you married her, and from what you say it was a lonely, hard life for her on the farm. If she's made mistakes, she's most likely over them now. She's grown up, and asks you for another chance. I don't see why you don't try it. You can't lose by it and you have everything to gain."

"But not after what she done. A man can't forget that," he said, wanting to be convinced that a man could.

"No use," Sam Benton, Jr., said shortly, holding up his hand, three fingers of which had been injured in an accident and were left powerless. He had already decided. "If you knew, you'd see it's no use. Come on, Russ." He led Bob Russell off to their bedroom for another long religious talk.

Russell had become his disciple, but one who every now and then showed signs of lapsing from his new high resolve. When the conversation in the room took an indecent turn and became anatomical, Bob Russell would usually lead off, and Sam would say sharply, "Le's change the subjec', men. Not fit subjec' talk about." A little silence would fall and for a while they'd sit still and wide-eyed, rebuked.

On one of these mornings, after breakfast, Ted Jameson, oddly smug and silent, heated water and began to wash and shave with extra thoroughness, getting Cliff to hold up a little hand mirror for him. It seemed unusual but I didn't remark on it. "Do you mind," he asked, "if I borrow your scarf? I think it looks better than mine."

"Why?" I asked. "Are you going off to get married?"

Cliff guffawed.

"No," Teddy said, "but I'm . . . Well, it's just that I have to look my best. Cliff, I think I'll wear your field jacket."

"All right." Cliff played it straight. "Just see you return it."

Teddy began to comb his heavy, wet hair, giving little shoves and finger waves to the front till he had secured the most artistic arrangement. Then he put on his glasses. "How do I look?" he asked.

"Smashing." But no one asked the most important thing. No one said, "Where are you going?"

He was going out to a nearby field to receive the Bronze Star for sitting up all night, giving comfort to the wounded lying out in the woods in the Saar Valley at the opening of the Battle of the Bulge. Several of the wounded men had written back from the hospital to their officers, commending Teddy for his help and bravery that night, and the medal was the outgrowth of the letters.

He was gone most of the day, and when he came back with the medal, he showed it to us with the proper amount of modesty, mailed it back to his young sister and wore the colorful ribbon on his field jacket for only a day or two when he noticed that it was beginning to get soiled. The other litter bearers were a trifle jealous and had very little to say to Ted about his Bronze Star, but Tubby summed up their feelings when he exploded, "Jesus, what an outfit! It takes Mabel to git the on'y medal in the place!"

The weather broke and the sun came out, glaring on the wet surface of the mud, shining on puddles, reflecting off pale plaster walls, off briars beaded with raindrops. Jeeps went by on the thick roads, splashed pale tan with drying mud. The air was heavy, moist and warm. Fields and manure piles began to steam.

On the first fine afternoon, with sick call over and nothing to do for the rest of the day, I grew tired of the crowded little upstairs room and went for a long walk with Jimmy McDonough. He was an easy companion, and we followed the muddy road in a far semicircle outside the town. Except for the distant booming of artillery from Olzheim, where the Twelfth Division was, there was no reminder of war. We had grown too used to our uniforms to be aware of them. Leaning our elbows on a stone wall that overlooked a long valley, we let the sun beat on our faces.

Jimmy McDonough was thirty-two, somewhat stout and good-natured-looking. Upon arriving to join us, he had become friendly at once with Mike Nowak; they found they had similar backgrounds, friends, and even distant relatives in common. Almost everything Jimmy said sent Mike into laughter. "Jeez, what a guy! Hey, Jimmy, come on back. Come mere."

"No, listen, I ain't kiddin'."

Even that was enough to make Mike laugh.

Before the war, Jimmy worked for Bendix Aviation. He left the country on the *Ile de France*, bound for England, when "my kid" was nine months old. That was in the winter of 1943, and he was sent on detached service to the marshaling area around Weymouth and Dorchester to train for the invasion.

"Gee, I hated England: I was so *homesick*. The first few months I was eatin' my heart out. I wanted to be home and see my kid. They didn't have nothin' in England, nothin'! I was there through the bombings. I used to like eatin' in the Red Cross, but that was all. You know how it is for a married man—what the hell, *I* didn't want to go to dances or fool aroun' with the girls. I was by myself all the time. And, Jeez, the weather! All that rain. You know we wore our regular woolen uniforms all summer long? It never gits hot! And at night it stays light—well, all night long!"

I looked at him. "Stays light?"

"Ya don't believe me? Honest! Stays light till about eleven o'clock. Boy, you can have that place. And the trainin' we had! All through the cold weather climbin' in and out of assault boats down in the water. We'd be drenched for hours, doin' it over and over; and in the cold weather that brine, you know, would sting the hell outta you. Then at night— we trained at night too—there were gliders dropping and planes dronin', flares goin' off. One thing, they fed us pretty good. We didn' know from one day to another when D-Day was going to be, but then this night we had a big roast-chicken dinner, all you wanted, and that's how the guys knew.

"Oh, Jeez, the guys looked wonderful leavin' for the invasion. They all had invasion money, all new weapons, brand-new uniforms—that impregnated clothing—life preservers on—"

"Why didn't you go with them?" I asked.

"Oh. I was overstrength. Me and about one or two other guys. We were there in case someone got sick, and boy, did we sweat *that* out! Everyone else went and we were upstairs at a window, lookin' down on 'em. Honest, I never saw guys look so swell. They were all laughin' and shakin' hands in the sunlight. They were sick of trainin'. They wanted to git it *over* with. And they were told the only resistance they were gonna meet was the *Volksturm*, just an army of old men; the planes had everything else knocked out. It was gonna be a breeze. That's what they told them. And I'll never forget the general makin' them like a farewell speech. He says, 'Maybe one of you men—*one* of you men—will win this war.' So the bands strike up and the guys march out, everything brand-new on them. And then the camp is empty. The guys had all kinds of oversupplies they left behind them: clothes, toothpaste, socks never worn, shoes. We waited around and waited, and then we see all the planes comin' back real low with the wounded."

In telling it, he relived it so it was impossible to break in and ask him questions. Looking out across the valley that was hazy in the sunlight, with puffs of smoke bursting where the German artillery shells exploded, he didn't see it at all; he saw the planes returning over the English Channel.

Leaving the sun-warmed wall, we started back for Aaw. "What are you going to do when you go back to civilian life?"

"Aah, I don't know," he said. "I'm not worryin' much. I'd like to have a bigger family for one thing."

"Don't you think we'll be sent to the CBI?"

"Aah, I don't think so. D'you? I think they'll say guys over thirty don't have to go, or somethin' like that. Aah, they'll never send us."

On another sunny day, a group of us went for a walk outside town in the opposite direction. We jumped across a stream that ran flashing through a farmer's fields, and climbed a hill to a country churchyard. It was a Protestant church made of stone and securely locked. We moved through the small graveyard looking at the names and dates on the headstones, some of which went back to the seventeenth century. Here and there were the graves of German soldiers from the First World War. Phil stood translating the epitaph of a captain.

"He even gets a better tomb than the privates," Don Stoddard said. "It's the same in every army." But it was not a question of rank; these soldiers were buried in their family plots.

"—died of his wounds in his twenty-seventh year," Phil was reading. Then, with a little shock, we came upon fresher graves of German soldiers from this war—1942 . . . 1943 . . . 1942 . . .

We left the graveyard, which had been shady and chill, and sat on the steep bank in the sunlight. The earth was damp; we took off our field jackets and put them under us. "No, but if you had your choice," someone was saying, "of staying here in the Army of Occupation or going to the CBI, which would you take? I'd take staying here."

"Oh, hell, so would *I!*" Don Stoddard said. "I'd stay here— let's see—I'd sign up for three years. Three more years out of my life if I didn't have to go to that f---ing CBI."

"Well, I'm *in* almost three years now," Phil said, "but I'd sign up too if they'd let me."

"I'd stay here *five* years," Ted said suddenly, "rather than go to the CBI. Ooh, I dread the thought of it."

Down below, the little stream sparkled. A few ducks, very white, sailed along. One began to take a bath, making a great splash. Don picked up a stone and, with sudden force, shied it at the duck, narrowly missing it. He picked up another.

"Don't," I said, "for God's sake. Let everything alone.

There's been enough."

All of us laughed, and Phil accepted a cigarette, which, because of his asthma, was rare for him. That morning, waking up, I saw him kneeling with his head bent over, almost touching the floor. Prayers? I wondered. His face was scarlet. "Phil, what on earth are you doing?" Ted had asked.

"Trying to—trying to get my breath!" he had gasped.

A sturdy farm girl in a blue dress and a blowing white apron, her sleeves rolled up, came walking along the bank of the stream, carrying a wide basket on one hip. "My grandfather has a farm," Don was saying, "and we used to go out there in the summers. And once one of the ducks cut itself on something—it was bleeding to death, and my mother ran inside, got a needle and thread, sewed the damn thing up and it was perfectly all right after that. Just sewed it up with white thread."

"Then you come by the medics naturally?"

He laughed. "Hell, they just pick a couple of hundred guys inducted together, and you're all medics." He was twenty-one now, had had a year at the University of Nebraska, where he played baseball and basketball; he hoped to finish up at law school. After a thirteen weeks' medical basic, he went to A.S.T.P. in New Hampshire, where he met and became engaged to the girl he wrote to, then he applied for the Air Force, passed the exam, trained in Greensboro, North Carolina, but was shifted back to the Infantry at Fort Jackson. Of average height, he had a perfect physique and an even, short-nosed American face. His I.Q. was the highest in the division, but in general conversation there were no signs of it, for, like many other boys of good background, he submerged himself and became indistinguishable from whatever group he happened to be with at the moment.

Farron, the young aid man at C Company, had come from the Air Corps with Don and had been his best friend. Phil had told me Don felt the boy's death very deeply. In speaking of our first big attack in the Saar Valley—talk went back to that continually—Don said he hadn't been in the least afraid of the landing 88s, and had got down only on one knee until the shells came so close the companies began to shift from one side of the road to the other. "I think it took me about fifteen minutes to see that everything was in a mess and I didn't see anything but confusion from that point on."

"Did you see any deer running around? Or any cows?" I

had begun to wonder whether I had actually seen them or only imagined it.

"*I* saw the deer," Cliff said in surprise. "D'you see 'em too?" He looked relieved. "Thought I was the only one."

The sun started to go down. Chilliness came quickly; we had stayed on the hillside too long. We jumped over the stream and, hearing the distant clinking of mess gear on the still evening air, we began to run.

That night, for the first time since we had been in combat, there were to be moving pictures in a barn in town. At the thought, one's spirits took a sudden lift. Racing up through the muddy fields to get our mess kits, we agreed to go to the movies together. There was something about the dusk, the first stars, the feeling of being without responsibility, among close friends, coupled with the raw smell of impending spring, that took me back many years to similar moments in college. As soon as I realized it, I felt like an outsider again, almost a generation removed from them.

Anticipation of the movies made even the stew and dry ration crackers taste passable. The blow fell immediately after: the movies were not for us until a later night. Deciding to go anyway, we went out into the street. Darkness had fallen and the moon shone down on crowds of men moving up the narrow cobbled street, many smoking cigarettes they held cupped in their hands. You heard the deep murmur of voices, the tramp of feet, men coughing and spitting; above all a generator chugged away with the sound of a motorboat. At the top of the clogged street an officer began to shout that this showing was *not* for First Battalion men. "All First Battalion men, go back!"

No one obeyed. You caught the glint of their grins, of their eyeballs in the moonlight. "Come on!" the crowd began shouting. "Let's in, let's get this goddam thing going." "Get the men out of the hot sun!" "*Aah-h*-ha, Sa-a-n Antone!" "*Hubba*, hubba, hubba!" There began a push forward.

We skinned up past the officer on the steep, dim staircase and entered the second story of the building, a sort of loft, its ceiling supported by rough beams. There were only a few rows of wooden benches, already occupied; the floor was covered thickly with straw. The picture had started. We ducked down, stepping in the dark on and over legs, feet and rifles, sank down in the rustling cold straw, craned our necks up. The picture was *Up in Mabel's Room* but there was something wrong. It took some time to adjust oneself to the innovation. The silver screen was missing and a pair of cretonne draperies had been tacked flat against the front wall, so that the actors looked transparent, projected against a static pattern of bleached flowers, parakeets and curving leaves.

The picture itself was poor, but it was novel seeing pretty, well-dressed girls and men in civilian clothes against undamaged interior-decorators' backgrounds. I could not sit up high enough to see in comfort, and the straw was icy cold. We watched the figures running in and out of brand-new bedrooms; husbands and wives having spats and absurd misunderstandings; Charlotte Greenwood clumping about the halls in overshoes and a negligee, with a shotgun in her hand. The men roared with laughter. As soon as it was over we filed down the stairs in a crush. Outside, seemingly our same crowd was waiting to go in for the next show. I was chilled through and, as always after a movie, slightly dazed, not wholly aware of where I was or what I was doing.

On one of the last nights of the rest period we went to the same loft and saw Rita Hayworth in *Cover Girl*, which, by comparison with the earlier picture, was a wonderful treat. The music, dancing, chorus girls, the flow of color ended much too soon. There was a memorable song, "Long Ago," with Rita Hayworth moving between stacked-up café tables in an evening dress that had yellow roses across her breast and a skirt that swung back and forth like a bell.

From Aaw, we went a few miles on to Roth, into a defensive position, and lived for several days in a small rural Catholic church. Some of the litter squads had been transported up to the new town ahead of us; I arrived toward evening, and the men were hanging double Army blankets up over the tall windows. The pews had all been pushed in a heap up near one of the side altars.

Ted Jameson came out of the sacristy to greet us. "It's wonderful! There's an organ—I've been playing it—and there's lots of room. Come on, I'll show you." On entering, I felt as though I should have removed my helmet, and, following him down the aisle, I realized with a little shock that I was smoking a cigarette. The altar rail was open and I stepped up. "Look what's still here," Ted said. "Isn't it nice?" He straightened up the toppled figure of one of the Wise

· Men outside the Christmas crib.

The altar was bare and the tabernacle door stood open. A short passageway led into the stone sacristy, a room empty save for the presses that held cassocks and vestments and a few long wooden benches.

We had moved so frequently that new surroundings had no meaning for most of the men. They merely came in, threw their equipment down. In two or three minutes they were thoroughly accustomed to the place, were tired of looking at it, and the usual aimless discussions and arguments were resumed. Since the rest period at Aaw, a terrible boredom had set in on all of them. You could see it in the way they sprawled on the two benches, on the floor, in the dull repetitiousness of their talk and the endless halfhearted ragging.

I moved my belongings up into the choir loft beside those of Phil, Cliff and Ted. The mere fact of being quartered in a church made me feel peaceful and almost happy; also there was an air of spaciousness, a little echo to voices and to sounds.

We were there for perhaps five days of idleness, of waiting. There was talk of a big push impending, but our life was no different than it had been during the ten-day rest. Captain Stettner left us for several days to examine the hospitals in the rear areas, and during that time we had about six casualties, most all of whom had their right foot blown off by mines while out on patrols.

The organ was an old-fashioned oak affair that had to be pumped by hand. On Ted Jameson, it acted like catnip to a cat; he could not let it alone. He played very badly, by ear, and he would have played by the hour with Cliff pumping faithfully had not Phil and I told him it was annoying to the others. The acting Regimental Surgeon did not approve of the litter bearers living in the station and was all for farming them out permanently with the line companies. He drove up daily in the captain's absence, and the litter bearers tried to make themselves scarce or busy during his visitations. It was invariably then that, with great inaccuracies, Teddy would be mournfully playing "Mighty Lak a Rose" up in the organ loft.

On the second day of our stay, Special Services set up the generator outside, hung a silver screen before the altar, and line-company men started arriving from all directions by

285

platoons to see *Cover Girl* again, and then on the next day to see Abbott and Costello in *Lost in a Harem*. *Cover Girl* was shown three or four times the first day. The church was blacked out, and the film broke seven or eight times during each showing. At first the men booed, clapped and shouted, "Lights! Lights!" but afterward they grew accustomed to seeing the film in installments and merely talked quietly during the dark intermissions. I sat up in the organ loft and watched *Cover Girl* twice again.

As for *Lost in a Harem*, one repeated line—"Slow-w-w-ly I turn"—became a battalion classic, and took its place with "Hey, Roy, I'm dan-n-cin'!" In our group, Paul Clifford, the last one would suspect, turned out to give the best imitation, remembering every inflection and gesture of the original. We saw *Lost in a Harem* possibly six times. Living in the church, there was no way of avoiding it. At times I found myself unable to stop laughing because the whole situation— the war, the rural church, the two low comedians—seemed such a completely unreal combination.

The Catholic chaplain, hearing that movies were being shown in a consecrated place, raised an objection, and they ceased. Some of the men complained, but no one cared particularly. At the time, no one seemed to care about anything. Sentences went unfinished; listening faces were loose and vacant; everyone yawned, sprawled, wrote letters in a desultory way, waiting for one tiresome, not quite sufficient meal to follow the other. The men hung around the sacristy, crawling over each other like puppies. "Go wan, ya f---." "Aah, ya f---." "Git ya feet off me, ya greasy bastard." "Ah'm telling you, boy, if Ah ever gits back home for a furlough, they're gonna have to burn the woods and sif' the ashes to find *me* again."

That particular afternoon was unseasonably warm; the sacristy door stood open and some of the litter bearers, out on the back steps, shielded from the wind, lifted their faces to the sunlight and watched the planes buzzing and droning in the sky. A few vehicles went along through the sticky muck of the roads. "Come on, sit down," Jimmy McDonough said lazily. "Here's room. Come on, it's swell here in the sun." But I was afraid to relax lest some huge, waiting, inward exhaustion gathered over the past few months would roll up and hit me with such force that I wouldn't be able to pull myself together afterward.

Captain Stettner returned to us, very brisk, very glad to be back at first, filled with stories of life in one of the big hospitals in the rear. There was no real audience, however, for him; the men were too bored and apathetic to listen beyond his first few sentences, and soon he reverted to his usual self and boredom overtook him too.

Now it was the captain who played the organ. He was a little out of practice, but you could tell that he once had been fairly good. He would no sooner finish playing—and his finishing meant that he had heard enough music for the day—than Ted Jameson would ask, "D'you think anyone would mind if I played a little? Just quiet?"

"I wouldn't if I were you."

But Ted was not strong enough to resist. He played with hesitant trial notes, quivering, mistaken chords, sudden groans, while Cliff pumped away, half in pride, half in embarrassment.

"Now I want to try 'Pale Hands I Love Beside the Shalimar.' Keep on pumping, Cliff. I don't know how the middle part goes, but here: 'Pal—' No. 'Pale hands I—I—love be-beside the Shali-ma-ha . . .'" He had quickly picked up the mannerisms of a small-town church organist: the little hushed cough, the eyes heavenward while he played, the glance in the tiny candlelit mirror, the sudden turning around on the bench, head lifted inquiringly when someone downstairs in the church shouted up to him to be quiet, for *crissake*—give it a rest!

The captain, disliking the solitude of the loft, had some of the men haul the organ down the narrow stairs for him so he could play in public. And downstairs, the organ was more of a temptation than ever to Ted.

German civilians came daily to the aid station for treatment—silent, expressionless farm women for the most part, bringing in glum children with sore throats, heavy colds and bad tonsils. There was a quiet, depressed unwrapping of woolen scarves; overcoats and sweaters came off. Heavy shoes and boots clumped about. This had become part of their lives and ours. The women explained that their own doctor had been commandeered by their retreating Army. Some claimed to prefer the American doctors and said they had been treated by them the previous autumn, before the Battle of the Bulge. This surprised me because I hadn't real-

ized American troops had penetrated Germany so long before, and it seemed to minimize greatly our own break-
through on the Siegfried Line.

One afternoon the captain was driven with Preacher on a
sick call to some bedridden Germans. He returned in an hour
or so and told me the civilians were crowded up as many as
thirty or forty in a house. For food they had cheese, potatoes,
cabbage, flour and unpasteurized milk; occasionally they
slaughtered some of their livestock.

"Are you interested in seeing them?" he asked.

"Yes, very much so."

"I'll bring you along with me tomorrow when I go back."

"Thanks. I'd love to go." I turned away, happy, with something to look forward to.

A homemade shower had been set up by Battalion Headquarters in a barn at the far side of the churchyard. We went
in rotation, two men at a time, taking a towel, soap and a set
of clean khaki underwear, leaving off our field jackets, helmets and leggings. The absence of leggings was the strangest
sensation of all; I felt as if I were wearing floppy sailor pants.
A catwalk of planks had been laid down over the mud and
soaking brownish grass of the churchyard. It was raining as
I started over with one of the litter bearers.

Inside, the barn was rough, with a dirt floor. It was to have
been a four-minute shower, but we came in at the end of the
day and Chris Taylor was running it. He sat up in the loft
to turn on and off the hot water that came through a huge
tank he had converted from some other purpose; I think he
said it had been a gasoline drum. Drafts of cold air blew into
the flimsy barn, but there was an Army stove blazing away.
The dirt underfoot was wet and slippery; you had to stand
on short sections of board, and there was a kitchen chair to
put one's belongings on. I peeled my clothes off in a rush and
stood under the shower, discouraged to see how thin I had
become and how dirty. The water gushed down, hot and
plentiful. I lathered quickly and my skin felt as though it
could soak up the water. My eyes stung with soap, but even
that was rather welcome. I washed and washed again, trying
to make out what Chris was saying through the beating and
splash of the water.

"More?"

"Yes."

"You can have all you want."

Thoroughly washed, I felt even lighter in weight and strangely tired. In the clean underwear, I stood near the stove, smoking a cigarette, unwilling to put on my dirty uniform.

"Are you going to be in business tomorrow?"

"I think we're moving," Chris said.

"Where?"

"Back to that lousy Olzheim again. The Germans are still fighting like hell for it; they're still holding the high ground."

There would be no visit to the German civilians.

We went back with our pores open through the raw, damp evening, swinging the wet khaki towels, and came into the lantern-lighted church to the tremulous sound of Ted Jameson's organ playing. During my absence there had been a casualty brought in, another man with his right foot blown off by a mine, but as soon as he had been bandaged and carried out to the ambulance, he was forgotten. To wear a metal foot for the rest of his life, to limp, to have pain particularly on rainy days, so that even years and years from now he would remember the thawing fields around Roth, the aid station in a church where, while the morphine was taking effect, someone had been playing the organ . . .

Back in the stone-floored sacristy, Charley Heydt lay ill. Small, flat-nosed, eyeglassed and wiry, with a black crew cut and the look of having just escaped being hare-lipped, he lay on a litter with a large brass pan pulled close by. He had been sick for several days without complaint, prey to nausea, fever and migraine headaches of intensity. The men sprawled and climbed aimlessly over him, knocking against the litter. A few times, blind with pain, he had asked them not to make so much noise and they complied for perhaps a minute or two. It was not that he was not well liked, but as a group they lacked consideration, self-discipline and sympathy. Sick, he was not interesting to them. Occasionally he turned his head and vomited into the brass pan, and after an hour or so, when the sour odor became acutely revolting, someone took it outside and emptied it.

During one of the last afternoons when I do not know whether he felt better for a moment, or knew he was so sick that he'd have to be sent to the hospital, he told an astonishing story. The talk in the sacristy was shiftless, part jeering back and forth, part the eternal reminiscing of various war episodes.

289

"—and the Jerries opened up on us with a trail of tracer bullets, layin' 'em right down—" "Never forget the time ole Burrell's helmet dropped off—ha-ha-ha—an' he thought he got his whole head blown off." "And these two C Company guys shot themselves through the foot, see, and they're sent to the hospital, where I hear they use all the S.I.W.s lousy. And then the day they come back to the company, they're standin' there, just back about ten minutes, when along comes an eighty-eight and kills 'em both." "Hey, remember when we stayed in the chateau some guy took a leak in Steve Brudzinski's helmet, and Steve didn't know it and he slapped it on?" As usual someone mentioned the Saar Valley and then Charley Heydt, getting up on one elbow, feverish-looking, launched into the story about which, up until now, there had never been the slightest allusion.

"Hey, you guys, 'member that time, that Sunday in the Saar?" His small face puckered when he smiled, and in talking he sounded as if someone were lightly pinching his nostrils. He turned to me. "We had about—I don't know *how* many wounded guys in the station. In the tent, and layin' around outside, waitin' to be carried in. Guys all shot to pieces, woun's all over 'em. Preacher and me and the cap'm workin' over 'em, see, patchin' 'em up, and more guys keep comin' in all the time, walkin' wounded and all kinds, and then *one* guy comes tearin' in and he starts yellin', 'Run! *Run!* The Germans are comin'! Run, here they *come!*' With that he takes off like a big-assed bird, an' the first thing I know ole Preach lights out, an' then the cap'm runs, and there's hell to pay. Wounded guys cryin' and yellin' at us not to leave them, and some of the poor bastards on broken legs get up and start hobblin' off into the woods, and other guys, dyin', begin crawlin' off their litters, scared the Jerries'll get 'em an' torture them. Soon, the *on'y* ones left in charge is Joe Mortara an' me. We rush outside the tent and grab up a pair of M1s. Hell, we're gonna fight it out. An' we wait an' wait an' wait—and no Jerries. There *was* none!"

He went into a roar of laughter. "See, it was just this shell-shock guy. But everyone run off an' lef' all the wounded guys there on the ground. So then, after a while, they all come creepin' back." This was the part of it he enjoyed. The sacristy had become dead-still except for his nasal voice. It was impossible for me to know or ask who of those present had been there to run off. Heydt's eyes swept over all of them. I

290

kept my glance fixed on him. "An' the las' one in is the cap'm. By this time everything was to rights; we're bandagin' guys again and quietin' them down. So Stettner says—you know, puttin' on a big front—he says, 'Where the hell did you guys *go* to that time?' I says, 'Everybody run off but Joe Mortara an' me.' An' he says, '*I* went out to load up the truck!'— which was a crock of s---, you know. He just tear-assed outta there as fast he could go. See, he was always worried because the place looked like a f---in' arsenal, with guns an' rifles an' everything else all piled up there from the wounded guys. He was afraid if the Jerries ever broke through on us, they'd claim we were armed and shoot the whole bunch of us. That's why he got you, an infantryman, so he could say you were in charge of all the weapons in case the Jerries come along."

"You mean I'll be the baby they throw out of the sleigh to the wolves?"

He didn't know the allusion, and soon after telling the story his fever went up, he became delirious and was sent to the hospital that night.

His story did not jibe with the fact that the captain now went everywhere with a pistol in an underarm holster; still, no one had denied any part of it, or seemed the slightest bit surprised. Throughout the telling, they had sat staring squarely before them.

His illness left us short one technician, and since Phil Schaeffer was behaving in a more absent-minded manner than ever, talking and arguing with himself, the captain decided to keep him indoors and ease up on him by putting him in Charley Heydt's place during the coming attack on Olzheim again.

The next afternoon, in the rain, we left the church to go forward to Olzheim by ambulance, jeep and truck. Phil seemed a little more comfortable in mind, and I asked him if he had had all the necessary training. "Oh! Oh, yes, yes," he said. "I . . . uh . . . yes! We all had it in the States. Everyone here but Sergeant Campbell is a medical technician, or at least was trained as one."

The place we rode up to, called 88 Corner, or, more often, just the Crossroads, looked familiar, as if I had passed it swiftly once before while riding on the hood of the jeep. At the crossing itself there stood the one half-demolished, gloomy-looking little house. Its front steps, made of stone, had been partly blown up; most of the roof and all of its windows were gone. Attached to the far side, a garage or barn was hanging in half ruin. The doors were missing from this extension and may have been buried under the heap of rubble that spewed forth into the yard. There was a long, ominous stretch of cracked-off, bare trees behind the house and again directly before it across the road. A swath of such jagged, shorn, dead trees is often seen before and behind the targets of firing ranges. Close beside the garage and everywhere else the trees grew up whole, very tall, many of them pines sighing now in the rain.

As we clicked open the low gate and started up the path, we saw two dead American soldiers lying in the front yard; near them were two wounded Germans on litters. With a glance for the dead and the wounded, we went heavily burdened up the broken steps into a shaky hall, past a ruined living room with wet orange-red walls and fallen beams, along to the back of the house where a flight of steps led down into the cellar. At the bottom one almost met the other cellar staircase that went out into the back yard. A hall, lined along one side with deep storage shelves, led into the one room of the cellar itself. It was not large. There were two oblong windows high up near the ceiling, similar to the one in the hall. The floor was of dirt with here and there a plank laid down from upstairs; a door, still with both knobs, had been used as further but tippy flooring. Again, against the back wall and part of one side, two long storage shelves, possibly five feet deep, had been constructed of rough-hewn logs with slight spaces in between them. We piled our belongings on them. The rear seat of a car and a kitchen table and chair were the only furnishings.

The litter bearers had all come up with us, but Sergeant Campbell had made an arrangement with Captain Reddy to send them out with the line companies as soon as these would come past. They were depressed with the arrangement, and also by the fact that Captain Stettner no longer seemed to care whether they stayed with the station or not.

"I want someone to go up and carry those two dead boys out of the yard," the captain said. "Put them some place out of sight so the line-company boys won't see 'em comin' past. Phil?"

"Oh! Yes, sir!"

"Get someone to go up with you."

"Cap'm, how about the two wounded Jerries?" Sam Benton, Jr., inquired. "Should we bring 'em in? Pretty bad wounded, looks to me."

"The hell with them. I don't want them in here."

Glances exchanged behind his back, and he became aware of it.

"Would you mahnd, sir, if I treated 'em?" Sam asked. "Or if Preacher came up?"

"I won't have 'em in here! We won't treat 'em! I'm not gonna send the ambulance back with two lousy Krauts." After a moment he turned to Sam. "If you want, go up and stop some jeep, put 'em on it and send them back to Collecting. But I won't have 'em in here." It was inconsistent after treating them all along, even going to their houses.

"Yes, sir. Thank sir." Sam Benton looked around. "Anyone come up with me?"

No one answered, so I said I would. Together we went up into the yard. The rain came down steady and cold. The line companies were already late in arriving.

The two Germans—one thin, gray-faced, almost unconscious; the other dark, with a short brown beard—were lying covered each by a wet muddy blanket, with the rain falling on their faces. The darker man, seeing us, cried out in a groaning voice for something, perhaps to beg that we would not kill them. I said to him, "Ich bin ein Sanitater. Gehen tsoo ein lazarett. Lazarett. Krankenhaus." He understood about the hospital but groaned deeply and tried, with eyes closed, to tell me, I think, about his wound. I had to say, "Ich verstehe nicht."

A truck crashed past at highest speed, then two jeeps raced by, the drivers ducking down low at the open crossroad. Sam and I stood at the edge of the side road, near the corner, and waved to flag down each vehicle that came by. One finally did slow up though most of the drivers shook their heads and tore past: the speed as well as the cracked-off trees made me realize the place was dangerous. To the driver who slowed, we shouted up the name of the town where Collecting was and asked if he were going there or anywhere near it. "No! No, for God's sake!" he shouted back, overwrought, then threw in his clutch and tore along. The first of a series of German artillery shells came in, whizzing close over the house and the splintered treetops.

293

"Let's go back and move the men over here in case anyone stops again," I said to Sam. "It'll save time." The day was getting darker and wetter. Neither of us had our raincoats on—just our field jackets; we had been standing then about ten minutes beside the road.

The two Germans were lying silent in the rain, thinking we had abandoned them. Puddles had formed in the hollows of their blankets and their faces were beaded with raindrops; the brown beard was almost silvery with rain. The gray-faced man looked like a corpse, but his eyelids fluttered when he heard us approach. Again I said, "Lazarett . . . Krankenwagon . . . Deutscher soldaten gehen tsoo Amerikanishe Krankenhaus"—though I had practically given up hope. The shells were coming in, dangerously close, some exploding in the jagged swath behind the house, some landing before it across the road. My eye kept measuring the distance to the cellar door.

We picked up the thin, gray-faced man first and carried his litter out of the yard, setting it down close to the side of the road. His blanket's edge floated out on the curve of soft mud. Then we went back and carried out the other man, who groaned with each step we took. His eyes opened in surprise when we set him down so soon, still outdoors in the rain.

A truck came by a minute or so later, refusing to stop, the drivers shaking their heads in advance. Its tires sent up an enormous spray of mud and water into the air that landed all over the wounded men. The dark man opened his eyes, seemingly in disbelief. When a few more shells screamed in and exploded very nearby, I became jittery.

"Listen," Sam said. "No use two of us standin' here. Two can't do no better'n one. You go on in. I volunteered for this. I'll trah 'em a while longer."

"Well, all right," I heard myself agreeing in a weak voice. "As long as I can't help—" I went back into the cellar, wondering what was the matter with me: in the Saar I hadn't been nervous during barrages much worse than this.

The litter bearers were checking their gear, putting it on over their raincoats. An air of gloom prevailed. About ten minutes later Sam Benton came down; he had stopped a truck driver, who had taken the two wounded Germans part way to their destination.

A man posted in the front doorway ran down to say the

line companies were coming along, and the first litter squad went out. I went up and stood at the gate to watch. With the tall, furled litters across their shoulders, giving them at first the appearance of skiers, they fell in onto the end of A Company's line. The infantrymen jeered and laughed ruefully, seeing the litters coming toward them.

Wet and dejected, the companies went by, a double file of weary men looking neither left nor right, the collars of their field jackets turned up against the rain. Here and there you saw someone limping. The officers walked along at the side, speaking now and then quietly and briefly. It was an almost silent procession. C Company went by and I did not know whether to call out or not. No, I thought, and remained silent behind the low gate. None of them looked over in my direction. A little beyond the house, trees grew close on either side of the road; some trailed their dripping branches down on top of the men. Everything in the wet half-light looked mournful and discouraging.

The only sign of military snap came toward the end, as the last of our battalion was going by. In the indistinctness I saw Captain Hillier, who had been relieved of the command of C Company when he had left Metz, now leading up his new outfit. He had been sent down once more from Division Headquarters to command a rifle company. He was ordering his men to bypass the last platoon of our battalion, giving the orders in his deep, resonant voice, swinging his fists, trying, it seemed, to encourage his men, to impress them with his decisiveness and instill in them some of his own military bearing. And yet as he stood facing me across the road, his pants unbloused at the knee, and unconsciously marking time—to nothing, since no one was marching at attention— he gave the effect of someone without hope, determined to make what he could of a very bad bargain. If he had no talent for commanding men, at least he had unswerving obedience to his superior officers. He had been told once more to lead a line company, and lead it he would. The only trouble was, we heard a few days later, he led the company up the wrong side of a hill, in full sight and range of the enemy, and lost so many of his men through the mistake that once more he had to be relieved of his command and be sent out to one of the other regiments under a decided cloud.

Depressed by this preview of a big attack, I went inside and down into the cellar room.

"A Company's supposed to take the high ground," I heard someone saying.

"Yes, but they're late," someone else replied in a worried tone. "They're all late hopping off."

There were now only a few of us there: Captain Stettner, Preacher and Phil, Sergeant Campbell, Warren Troy and the two ambulance drivers, Silly Willie and his assistant. Preacher was coaching Phil, showing him where the various things were in the medicine chests. Phil kept saying, "Yes, yes, I see. Yes." He was blinking and appeared distracted— just slightly so—and rather clumsy in moving about, as if he weren't co-ordinating perfectly. He was constantly losing things, putting them down and forgetting them a moment later, and he had developed a habit of seeming to listen alertly when there was no sound at all from outside. Preacher tied the medical scissors to Phil's belt for him on a long piece of tape.

"Listen, At." Preacher came over to me, drawing in his chin, speaking confidentially. "Phil here is supposed to break in an' help me, but if you wouldn't mind, Ah'd appreciate it if you'd sort of stand by. Just in case."

I said of course. Up till then I had helped him once in a while, holding the foot of a leg that had been broken, or supporting a man while he bandaged him.

Word came to us by telephone at around six or seven o'clock that A Company, leading off the attack, had run into trouble less than one kilometer from us and had failed to take the high ground; and shortly after that the casualties started to swamp the station. Someone previously had kicked the sash out of the narrow, high-up window in the hall, and an Army blanket hung over it to shield the light that poured out of our room. It was through this hall window that the litter cases passed in and out, since the stairs leading down from the yard were too narrow and the turn too abrupt to get a stretcher through.

In the cellar you'd become aware, over the smash and shriek of shells, of muffled voices talking and calling just outside; the Army blanket would twitch aside and a voice, suddenly clear, would call down out of the rainy darkness, "Another one! Someone grab a hold there."

Two of us who were tall would go out.

"Hey! Hurry up," you'd hear from outside, and when we lifted a corner of the blanket: "Hey, watch that goddam light! You ready?"

Rain beating down, and shells exploding, and the two wet front poles of the litter coming through the window, followed by a pair of soaking mud-caked overshoes. By reaching straight overhead, I could just catch onto the poles. Then it was a matter of sliding the litter through until Warren Troy or Sergeant Campbell—whoever was with me—could grasp the back poles. There, badly cramped for space, we had to execute an overhead turn and lower the stretcher. Each time I was forced to scrape the knuckles of my left hand against the rough stone wall in order to make the turn. Before the night was half over, the back of my hand was raw and bleeding.

It took very little time to realize that this was, at least for our battalion, a disaster. The wounded came through the window in an almost endless stream. There was hardly a moment when three or four men were not lying inside on the dirt-and-board floor, crowding the place so that one could step about only with extreme difficulty, while out in the hall, in the dark, the walking wounded waited in a long line, some half conscious, lying on the deep log shelves, all soaked with rain and blood.

Like the others working in the aid station, I became suddenly rushed, trying to do several things at once. Get the unworn overshoes, shoes and dry socks from the wounded, and keep them in one pile ready for redistribution; gather up the weapons, the bandoleers of ammunition, often sticky with blood, the steel helmets and helmet liners, the light packs, the muddy gas masks and raincoats. Here was a pistol. That went into my pocket, and I must remember the sergeant's company: pistols, watches, compasses and binoculars had to be returned as soon as possible. Another litter coming in. Reach up, turn, scrape of knuckles, lower and carry the man in, set him down.

"At, Ah'm finished with this one. You mind takin' the litter out with me? The ambulance is goin' back." To the new arrival: "Be right with you, son."

Out into the hall, lift high, turn, scrape of knuckles; one end of the litter going out the window.

"You got it, Silly?"

"Yeah. Can't take no more litters this time. Got any walkin' wounded?" Silly Willie and his assistant were here doing yeoman service, dragging the litters out under shellfire, running with them to the ambulance over the heaps of rubble. I must remember, I thought, to lock those rifles in the salvage pile in case anyone falls over them in the dark hall. But before I could get to it, Preacher said, "At, you wanna take these five walkin' wounded up an' see they git to the ambulance?"

"All right, boys." Shuffling, hopping, some with one bare foot bandaged, some with arms in splints, heads bandaged, some frightened now and shuddering—out into the short black hall and up the stairs. I kept talking to them, leading the way, one arm around the worst case. "Hang onto the man in front of you. The steps go straight up." At any other time the man I was helping and many of the others would have been stretcher cases, but that would take up too much room in the ambulance, and this way the five could slide in between those already lying down. Now along the dark hall on the first floor. "Watch out, boys, and stay close to the right. There's a plank missing here and there on the left. Stay close to the wall." I strained my eyes to see the dim oblong of rainy night at the end of the passageway.

Outside onto the broken stone steps. *Whizz! Whizz! Crash!* Scarlet streaks through the rain. Shells exploding with a blinding red-and-white flash, small-arms fire, and Screaming Meemies filling the night with their hysterical banshee wailing. Some of the wounded balked and wanted to turn back.

"No, come on, it's all right, boys. They're falling 'way off. It's only across the yard, down to those trees. Come on. It's all right now. Watch the steps here. If you can't make it, wait, and I'll come back and get you. Hey, Willie! Willie! Where the hell are you?" In the dark, under the tossing dripping trees, I couldn't always see the ambulance. *Whizz! Whizz! Rat-tat-tat-tat-tat! Tat-tat-tat-tat!* "Willie!"

"Here! Hurry up! How many you got there?"

"Five. Can you manage?"

"Yeah. I'll get 'em in. Go on back."

"All right. Good luck."

Back across the yard, and in, with a slight shudder. Down the stairs. More wounded to come through the hall window. More dark, murmuring walking wounded in the hall, waiting, their eyes glinting in the flash of light. "Hey, fella, got any cigarettes?" "Hey, got any water?" Toward ten o'clock I discovered I was soaked with sweat. It was streaming down my face. I took off my helmet and field jacket. The same

298

sentences were used over and over again: "Next man, come in. Where ya wounded?" "Name? Rank? Serial number?" "Take your wound tablets?" "Where were you wounded, do you know?" This was a new question Warren Troy had to ask, and it related not to the body but to the name of the town or locality. The answer usually came back, "Down by the creek there," or "Down that little farmhouse"; more often: "Beats the s--- outta me." Warren, without a flicker, usually wrote down Nuenstein or Olzheim. "At, will you hol' this man? I want to pull his leg out straight. Now this is gonna hurt fer a minute, fella, an' then—" The captain's voice behind me giving a diagnosis: "Compound comminuted fracture of the tibia and fibula; fractured pelvis and—" something or other which Warren Troy wrote down on the tag. "Phil, see if you kin git over the other side here an' when I pull—" Phil, startled-looking, awkwardly crawling over, dropping his scissors on the way. The captain, confined to a space between two litters, managing to take a few steps, turn, take a few steps, turn. The wounded man braced against me, suddenly crying out in a loud shout as Preacher straightened his broken leg. "It's all right now, it's all right. That's all."

Now in close-up, I saw bloody stumps where feet had been blown off, caved-in ribs, shattered heads, arms and backs ripped open as if by giant can openers. Quick, carry this man out. Turn, hoist, scrape. And another. And there was one waiting up there in the rain to be poked in. The window opening was maddeningly small and someone outside tried to kick away the dirt heaped up before it. The man coming through had a wounded arm lying helpless across his chest; it received a nasty bang against the top of the window frame and the man cried out in sudden pain. "Sorry. Sorry. We couldn't help it, Bud." And there was tough little Chipman from C Company, crying and shivering among the walking wounded, saying, "Atwell, come mere. Help me."

"Are you badly hurt, Chipman?"

"No. I'm not wounded. But I can't take no more."

"Wait then. Wait."

The sense of time disappeared. Turn, hoist, scrape. Up the stairs with the walking wounded. More slavage to be thrown into the heap that grew rapidly higher than my head. This time in the dark, I unloaded the accumulation of carbines and M1s, but the B.A.R.s and grease guns I did not know

299

how to deal with, and had to leave them alone. The cold damp air coming in at the foot of the back stairs struck my perspiring body. I'd love a drink of water. Back to the blazing light. "Hey, Doc!" The walking wounded reached out to detain me. "When are they gonna look at us? I'm shot up here. My knee—" "Hey, Doc, I'm bleedin' here." "Hey, this guy passed out."

"The first chance they get. In a minute. As soon as they get rid of these three men on litters."

"Doc, wait a second. Where can I take a s---?"

"Upstairs. Near the barn. Can you get up by yourself?"

"I'll take him," said another of the walking wounded,

"Kin we smoke here?"

"Yes. Cup them."

"Hey, how about some water? How about some food?" Inside again. "Name? Rank? Serial Number? D'you take your wound tablets? D'you have a shot of morphine?" "Listen, Deac, I'm gonna have to hurt you, jes a li'l while." "Look and get his name from his dog tags." The jingle of metal tags, and Sergeant Campbell starting to read out the name laboriously. The captain saying. "Wait a minute. Never mind. Someone take this man out. He's dead." "D'you take your wound tablets?" "Where were you wounded, d'you know? Name? Rank? Serial number?" "At, will you git this man a drink of water? Here's his overshoes and socks. An', listen, that guy over there wants a cigarette. You got one to spare for him?"

"In a second."

Lifting the man's head, holding the stein of water to his lips. Lighting two cigarettes, one for myself, one for the other man. His eyes had closed. Touching him lightly, "D'you want a cigarette?"

"Oh. Yeah. Thanks." An older man, large, sturdy, his head bandaged and one wounded arm lying on the blanket. "Boy, that tastes swell." Another drag. "Listen, is there any way I can send a letter to my wife?" God! "I got it all written; I didn't have time to hand it in."

"Oh. Yes. Give it to me and I'll have it censored for you. I'll mail it."

"Kin you get it? It's in my pocket here. In my shirt." A crumpled V-mail form, faintly warm. "Will they notify her I'm wounded?"

"Yes." My jaws were tired from talking. "I'll tell you what

to do. As soon as you get in the hospital, ask the nurse or the ward boy—anyone—to send a telegram at once. Sometimes they'll do it. Pay them, bribe them. Just tell them to say you're not badly hurt, don't worry, that you'll write in a day or two, and to sign your first name to it. It'll get home before the War Dapartment notice."

"Will they do it?"

"I *hear* they'll do it. It's worth trying."

"Thanks. I hate to bother you, but you got anything to eat around here?"

"There's a half of someone's supper ration here. Could you eat it?"

"Could I!"

"Can you manage with one hand? Here. I'll feed you this and you can eat the crackers yourself." Three mouthfuls and the canned meat was gone. I gave him the crackers and stood up.

"Thanks. Look . . ." The uninjured hand reached into his belt and produced a small German revolver. "Here's a present for you."

Confusion. "Oh, thanks! Sure you don't want it yourself? To keep?"

"No, you take it. Go ahead. What the hell, I'm gettin' out of this."

"Good luck."

The captain had stood looking on. The man was carried out and lifted up through the window. "Presents yet," I said.

He smiled. "Don't you want it?"

"I don't want any part of it."

"I'd like all my litter bearers to have a pistol."

"Here's one to begin with then." I handed it over.

"D'you pick up any more tonight?"

"Yes, two. From C Company. I have to return them to Sergeant Hill."

"I'll take them," he said. Glad to be rid of them, I got them from my field jacket and gave them to him. "Just forget you ever saw them."

"Yes, sir."

Momentarily we had no litter cases in the station. Preacher and Phil were working on the walking wounded. I started to sweep up the bloody bandages, the swabs, the bandage boxes and pieces of uniform.

"At . . ." Preacher led me over a foot or two into a corner. "Ah'm gonna have to depend on you. Phil's sort of rattled here an' he gits *me* all fussed and rattled. Ah think Ah could work better with you."

Phil, as far as I could see, had been working feverishly, and now, stripped down to the waist, was streaming with sweat. "I don't know anything about wounds or bandaging," I said to Preacher.

"Well, tha's all right, but just—if you can—if you can jes stand by me an' keep handin' me Carlyle bandages. See if you kin keep about twelve of 'em open an' allers ready. Keep ahead of me. An' nen, if you kin git the time, cut off some strips of this no-good f---in' adhesive tape we got here, an' heat it over the lantern. Unless you heat it, that stuff wouldn't stick to s---."

"All right."

I began at once to open the Carlyle bandages. They came in a gray cardboard box, firmly packed, more firmly packaged in cellophane. My hands were shaking so from the lifting up and down of heavy litters that I couldn't undo the cellophane until I had got a start by tearing it with my teeth.

The rush was greater now. In between hoisting the wounded in and out the hall window, unloading salvage rifles and flinging the muddy equipment onto the pile in the hall, leading the walking wounded out to the ambulance through the rain, I stood over Preacher, giving him a bandage every time his hand came up. Gauging how long it would be before he'd want another, I heated assorted lengths of adhesive tape over the lantern and hung the strips from my sleeve, where he could grab for them. I was hemmed in between two litters, and here again were glaring, unavoidable closeups of puckered, mangled, brilliantly lighted flesh, silvery-white bones splintered and gleaming through blood and sticking out, entrails spilling out of a belly, a flap of skull hanging loose, a horribly shattered hip, a foot in an overshoe hanging by a thread, a face that was nothing but a pulp with eyes looking out of it at me.

"Atwell! Gimme one of those bandages, quick!" The captain. "Phil, get some tape!"

"I have some here heated, on my sleeve," I said.

"Fine. Keep a supply ready."

Tearing open more bandages, heating more tape, I worked with Preacher on one side and the captain and Phil on the other. Warren Troy, former clerk for the YMCA, big, sandy-haired, severe-looking and eyeglassed, maintaining an admirable air of calm and efficiency, squatted down on his haunches between the two ever-present litters, asking in his firm voice, "Your name please? And what's your rank, Bill? What company? And where were you hit?"

"In the back."

"No, I mean what town, or near what town?"

It was then possibly eleven-thirty at night, still raining, with shells roaring and crashing in our immediate vicinity, but not on the house itself. Twice the ambulance had no sooner returned from a trip to Collecting than shrapnel blew out a tire, and when the barrage lifted somewhat, Silly Willie and his assistant rushed out to change it. At once then they loaded up and started off again on a constant, dangerous shuttling back and forth. Irritating fools in ordinary circumstances, in this pinch they were wonderful.

Now and then for brief moments I'd see some of our litter bearers, who, upon completing a haul, would come down into the cellar for fresh supplies or to apprise the captain of the situation. Red-faced with the exertion of carrying through wind and rain, their trousers soaking wet where the raincoats ended, they stayed only for a few minutes and went back to rejoin their companies.

"How much longer can you hold out?" the captain asked Paul Clifford, who was taking Phil Schaeffer's place as squad leader.

Cliff, standing with his legs wide-spread, rain glistening on his face, said, "Don't know, sir. Guess long as you want."

"All right. Go on back. I'll call up for some 210th boys to relieve you."

When he did so, he requested them not to bring every last thing they owned with them. Usually for a twenty-four-hour stay they came with a case of ten-in-one rations, officer-like bedrolls and barracks bags. The men, when they did arrive from Collecting, had not been told and they came into the cellar room weighed down like beasts of burden, eight of them.

On and off there was something like that to laugh about. One wounded man was carried in, set down on the floor, and when Preacher began to rip through his field jacket with the scissors, the man was discovered to be wearing, of all things, a black silk dress tie. "What the hell, it was a Christmas present," he said. "The package just came this morning and I
303

thought I might as well put the goddam thing on and wear it. My mother-in-law sent it to me."

During a momentary lull, our mail was dumped in the hall window. I too had a package from home and there was the chance to open it. I saw that it contained a can of chicken, a homemade loaf of nut-and-date bread, a jar of guava jelly, a knife, and a box of Rosemarie de Paris chocolates. I had time to look but not to taste; more wounded arrived and for an hour or so I forgot about the package.

When the next breathing spell came, I went back to it, and, resting the loaf of nut bread on one of the logs of the shelf, whittled through it hastily with the knife, keeping one eye on the hall window. No one coming in. Quickly I spread the guava jelly and distributed the slices around. I noticed the tips of my fingers were extremely sore and covered with blackish-yellow blisters; it took me a minute or two to realize why. I had been heating the strips of adhesive tape too close to the top of the scorching gasoline lanterns. The nut bread and guava jelly tasted delicious. I had the only second slice, a large end piece. There was just time to bolt it down when the muffled voices from outside announced that more wounded men were coming in.

At the end of a prolonged artillery barrage, little Jenkins and equally little Burrell, the boy who was always falling asleep, were brought in, drenched, crying, shaking with combat fatigue. They arrived almost together, staring wildly, looking around them in fright, and each time a shell exploded outside they jumped uncontrolledly and went into fits of crying and shivering. I was busy when they arrived, and when I next saw them they were lying on one of the log shelves, on top of the jumbled equipment, still in their muddy raincoats, asleep but twitching and crying now and then. No one bothered with them for hours; no one had time to. They were out of the way.

In a fragmentary manner I realized that other things were going on in the small, busy cellar room. I looked up once from heating adhesive strips and saw Big Steve Brudzinski run in and say, panting, to the captain, "We got pinned down! There was nothin' we could do. We couldn't get out there to the guys. We couldn't get them." I could sense from the looks of the rest of his squad—Bob Russell, Don Stoddard, and Pancho—that something was wrong, that Steve had prevailed upon them to return to the station.

"Well, try again, Steve," the captain was saying. "That's all you can do. I know you're doing your best."

Out Big Steve stalked with his three partners. That I saw in a small flash, and realized that outside in the hall among the walking wounded, bitter grumbling had started up against some of the aid men and litter bearers for shirking at the height of the attack, letting the wounded lie there and bleed. Then an hour or so later, just a minute or two after a particularly heavy barrage lifted, Steve Brudzinski broke into the room, crying, with a bloody nose, holding his ears. "I'm—I'm *deef!*" he shouted, dancing about. "I'm deef! I can't hear!"

"Concussion," said the captain. "Warren, put a tag on Big Steve. Steve, you're goin' back." And Big Steve wept, I could not help thinking, with relief.

The night seemed to reach a wild, sustained climax. "It's hell!" you'd hear the walking wounded say. "It's hell out there! They're *murdering* us!" While I was leading them out to the ambulance, shells whizzed and screamed and crashed constantly. There were flashes of rifle fire and men were shouting in confusion to each other in the woods that grew up close to the house. In the sagging barn or garage attached to it, the dark figures of deserters picked their way among the fallen beams. There were men inside the house, too, hiding in the dark living room on the first floor, whispering, scuttling when I came along the hall with the walking wounded. "It's hell! It's hell out there."

The Command Post at C Company suffered a direct hit from a German 88. Two men were killed instantly; there were nine litter cases and what appeared to be countless walking wounded. For the space of a hurried hour or so, I seemed to know personally almost everyone who came in. "C Company—" "C Company—" "C Company—" "C Company—" Five or six men in a row had shattered forearms. Ahlhauser, who had joined up because his young brother had been killed in the Marines; Gramling, my former assistant squad leader, who had always had such an exhausting time getting his boys off to town on a Saturday night in camp; Everett Telford, with the light, girlish voice; the man called Lucky; and any number of replacements who had just arrived at the front lines that afternoon.

In the midst of the crowd from C Company, several wounded aid men came in, among them O'Rourke, still with

305

a chip on his shoulder, still bitter and argumentative, jeering now that we were all stuck and he was going home. These sights and events sometimes followed each other swiftly or happened simultaneously. Working steadily, carrying men in and out, one saw them with but part of one's mind.

I went over and sat down for the first time that night on the log shelf to hold a cigarette to a wounded man's mouth, and suddenly someone badly hurt was carried in from the hall.

"Cap'm!" Preacher cried—the signal that he was beyond his depth. Four infantrymen had carried their companion in on an improvised litter—a long shutter that they had ripped from the window of a farmhouse. They had lashed the man to it in order to make the haul. It was a large, very bad, sucking chest wound. Preacher and the captain were bent down, trying to get the man's clothes off, but he had been tied in some strange way to the slats of the shutter. The four who had carried him stood looking on. "The goddam shutter *broke* when we were halfway here," one of the men said. "I think we near killed him getting him down here."

"One hell of a chest wound," the captain said.

"It's his back," the man said, wiping his sleeve over his wet face. "His back's worse then his front. He's all shot to hell."

"If Ah could only git this stuff *off* him!" Preacher cried impatiently, and his scissors began to rip through cloth. The man groaned, and there came the clear sound of his breath gasping in and out the hole in his chest.

"Quick, Preacher! Quick!" the captain said. "How the hell have you got him on this? We'll have to lift him up and tear it from under him. *Pull* the goddam thing apart!"

The man's clothes had been cut away down past his waist, and still he was not free of the broken shutter. The gasoline lantern blazed on his flesh, which was the only white thing in the room. The large wet wound was scarlet. All about were bent dark figures, staring, intent faces, shadows, silence.

"All right now, *up* with it, and you grab it."

They lifted the shutter up and the man's body, young, slender, torn open, rose up with it, arched itself in pain while the head fell back. For the first time I recognized him: a boy, well educated, of a good family, named Sefton, from C Company. He cried out in agony as the shutter was wrenched and ripped away from under him. While he hung up there, the scene took on the aspect of a painting, a Descent from the Cross. A moment later they were lowering him onto a litter.

As soon as he was bandaged, he was rushed out, and almost at once there was another scene, similar in its shattering effect. Another boy was carried in, set down with a jolt, and once more Preacher called, "Cap'm! This man—shot through the throat—" The rest was a jumble. At the base of the man's neck I saw a jagged hole spurting blood, big enough to sink one's hand in.

"Quick! Christ! Blood plasma! Warren, quick! Phil, get out an' let me in there! Preacher, get hold of that tube in his throat so he won't choke to death."

"God!" Preacher made a grab for it. "I can't—the blood—"

"Let me!" the captain moved in, knelt over the boy and rammed his hand into the hole, began to feel around. My nerves were stretching, tightening. Warren Troy and Sergeant Campbell were quickly unwinding the blood-plasma apparatus. "God *damn* it!" the captain cried out. "I've lost it! It's slipped! This blood—God, he's gone!" A chill shot through me. Then suddenly: "No! *Have* it! I *have* it! Quick now while I'm holdin' on. Gimme the clamp! Get that goddam plasma *working!*"

Minutes of tense waiting while the blood plasma was administered. The room was silent except for the explosion of shells outside. At last the captain got heavily to his feet.

"Is he all right?" someone asked.

"Yeah." The answer came in a tired voice. "They'll fix him up at the hospital—if he lives till he gets there." His voice picked up. "Where's Willie? Is Willie back? Someone run up and see. Willie, rush this man through!"

But Silly Willie told us later that the man died in the ambulance on the way.

Now out of the steady rush again of tearing open bandages, heating strips of adhesive, running out when there was a chance with the salvage equipment, there was the sight of Bill Woods of C Company, with blood from a scalp wound pouring down all over his face and GI glasses. He was holding his steel helmet that had been ripped open up the front as if it had been made of cardboard. "Hello, At!" he called in his clear voice, with a laugh. "I've been having a wild time." He sank down exhausted, but not daunted, on the pile of equipment the 210th medics had brought up.

"Don't you want to take your glasses off?"

"What for?" Between the rivulets of blood there was hardly a space for him to look through. "What's going on here?" he cried as I started to take off his overshoes to put into the salvage.

I was tired of explaining the same thing to one after another. "Got any dry socks on you? I'll have to take them. You'll get all new stuff in the hospital. I'll take your carbine and all your ammunition too. You can't carry any of it in the ambulance. It's against the Geneva Convention rules."

"That right? Well, here. Who the hell ever wanted it anyway?" He broke into a laugh. "My shoes too? Hey, can I get to hold onto this helmet? I want to keep it for a souvenir."

Now, bursting in with a suddenness that surprised everyone, were the breathless, wet figures of aid men Eugene Webster and his co-worker, Cataletto. Webster, a tall, lanky, black-haired backwoodsman, had for a long while done an outstanding job at his company, but recently word had begun to trickle back that he and Cataletto were frequently missing in attacks. The rain dripped from their helmets and glistened on their olive-green raincoats. A silence fell. One could tell a scene was impending.

"Why aren't you men with your company?" the captain asked swiftly.

"Cap'm—" Webster took off his helmet and hurled it to the floor—"I'm finished! I had enough!" His voice cracked and went high. "I cain't *take* no more. Cain't do it! Let someone else go out there!"

Cataletto, who was shorter, broader, stood silent, round-eyed, yet you would gather that he was the brains of the team.

"What the hell is this, Webster? Get back there where you belong!"

"I ain't gonna! I ain't, I tell you! Goddamit, you can *shoot* me!"

"You're gonna go or you'll be court-martialed!"

"But, Cap'm!" Tears suddenly burst from Webster's greenish eyes. "I'm—I'm all through!" His voice shook with crying. "I stood enough! What the goddam hell you think I'm *made* of? I *done* my part and I'm *through!*" He was about to sink down to his knees, but the captain grabbed him by the front of the raincoat and held him up.

308

"Listen, Webster, cut out this cry-baby act and get back there where you belong. As soon as I can, I'll replace you, but right now you're needed. Go on now! If I catch you around here again, by God, you'll face a firing squad!" He turned on Cataletto. "You too, goddam you! I've heard enough about you to fix you for life. I'm giving you this chance to get out of here and back to your company, and don't let me see either of you around here again."

"*Please!*" Webster cried hoarsely. "For *Christ's* sake, have mercy!" He shuddered, broke down and wept without control. "Have mercy! I cain't—"

"Get out! *Out!* Get out of here!"

Cataletto, who had not moved or spoken, now fell back a step. Webster choked off his sobs. His eyes glittered dangerously. He was panting. Violence gathered itself, seemed ready to explode behind his tightening white face. Staring venomously at the captain, he reached out his long, thin arm, scooped his helmet up from the floor and in silence rushed out of the room. Cataletto ran out after him.

None of us moved or spoke for a moment.

"*Had* to do that," the captain said. "Webster would have stayed with his men. It's that goddam Cataletto."

Fifteen or twenty minutes later, when I had forgotten the scene and was leading the walking wounded out the back way through the debris of the barn, I caught a glimpse of Cataletto's face turned over his shoulder as he plunged away into the deeper shadows. We heard in the morning that he had deserted, but Webster had gone back to his company.

About an hour after that, I was lifting a wounded man in through the hall window, and as I carried him toward the lighted room I saw Sergeant Danowski from C Company in the dim passageway looking strained and tense, his eyes darting about. I carried the man past him, set the litter on the floor, returned immediately to Sergeant Danowski and said, "Are you wounded, Sergeant?"

"N-no! No, but I—I got to see the medics. I—I'm—" He started to go by me, to get into the room.

I said, "Wait. Not now. They're too busy with stretcher cases." At the last minute I didn't have enough nerve to tell him to go away.

I hurried in, made my way between the litters and started handing down the bandages and ripping off strips of tape to heat. Sergeant Danowski advanced a few steps past the doorway, took a look, saw a man dying on the litter at his feet, and he retreated in confusion.

"Who was that?" the captain demanded. "Was that Sergeant Danowski from C Company just came in? Does anyone know? Atwell?"

"What was that, sir?"

"If that's Danowski out there and he's not wounded, I'll see to it that he's court-martialed in the morning. I'm just *waiting* for that guy."

As soon as I could, I gathered up some salvage equipment, went out into the hall again and, afraid the captain would hear me, dragged Sergeant Danowski by the sleeve out to the narrow stone steps that went up to the yard. The fact that he came so willingly and put himself so completely in my hands made the thing awkward. I kept thinking of him shouting at Dave Rossofsky about the B.A.R.'s malfunction and seeing him as he had stood alone, looking so homesick that damp morning in the courtyard of the villa at Metz. I remembered what Ahlhauser had told me of his wife having the bad fall and then not writing again, and I had an idea of what must have been going through his mind: Ahlhauser gone, Gramling gone, Rossofsky gone, Louden, Stancliff, Janovic, Lieutenant McGrath—almost everyone who had started out with him.

"Sergeant, look, if you're not wounded, for God's sake, don't stay around here. Go some place else. Try one of the other aid stations." The light that streamed out struck his broad face dimly; it was turned away from me, his eyes wide with listening. "The captain's out gunning for you; he's been sore since the night you said the jeep ran over you and the boys carried you in. He saw you just now and said if he catches you around here he'll have you court-martialed. Go some place else."

"Yes," he whispered. "Yeah." He was panting, still not looking at me.

"He might come out here any minute. You'd better hurry up. I mean it. Any place is better than here." The sound of a prolonged barrage, the long flying shriek and explosion of shells were very loud and near.

"Yeah. All right." He had a heavy hand on my arm and with it he gave me a sudden shove backward that started himself up the stairs.

I worked on mechanically for another hour or two, remembering nothing, but aware that it was at last beginning to grow light out. We had worked through the night. Jenkins and Burrell had been sent off in the ambulance, and two or three of our regular litter squads had come in, too exhausted to talk. Most of the men, with their raincoats and equipment still on them, had crawled in on one of the deep log shelves and were asleep in an exhausted, sodden mass.

The wounded continued to come in. A German Lüger was taken from one man while he was being bandaged, and it was given to me. I put it in my hip pocket and forgot it. Shortly after, I started to lead out a group of five or six walking wounded, having difficulty this time supporting a man with a badly injured foot while with the other arm I was holding a shivering combat-exhaustion case, the worse of two. The second was just behind us. "All right, boys, up the stairs. Not too fast. This first man has to go slowly." Holding onto me, he hopped up each step, bringing back memories of Sergeant Weems. "All right, now, along the hall here. The hall goes straight through to the front door. Stay over on your right. On the right. There are floorboards missing on the left." I had to let go the combat-exhaustion case as we shuffled down the narrow, black hall. "Follow along. That's right, keep right on coming. Hold onto the man in front."

The sky was between night and morning; everything in the dark light looked unreal. The rain had practically stopped. As I was halfway down the steps with the first man, again holding onto the flinching, weeping combat-exhaustion case, a series of German 88s began to scream and crash in. Confusion broke out. The first man jumped by mistake on his smashed-up foot; the shell-shocked case broke away from me and ran with his hands up over his head, off across the yard in the wrong direction. The others had turned back and were trying to cram themselves in the narrow door. I had to leave the man with the badly wounded foot on the path, chase after the hysterical one and bring him back before he got into the woods.

"Come on out! Come on! It's not bad. They're not falling near. Come on, the ambulance is waiting for you. Are you all there? Where's that other?" Yes, the other whimpering, shuddering one was beginning to come out, another man with a wounded foot and bandaged head holding onto him. "Here you are, Willie; can you fit them in? You'll have to go easy with this first man. Slide him in; I'll hold his foot."

311

A light-haired man on a litter inside the ambulance, lying on his stomach, stared out at me sourly. When I looked at him again he had put his head down in his arms in complete disgust. Suddenly remembering him down in the cellar, I reached into my hip pocket and gave him back his German pistol, telling him to hide it inside his shirt. With a shock he came to life and kept calling back his thanks till the ambulance doors closed and I was almost back inside the house. Brooding about a pistol, I thought. What had it meant to him? A souvenir of the scene wherein he had disarmed a German soldier? Or just the thought of the hundred dollars it would bring in Paris?

When I returned, there was no one but ourselves in the cellar. I stood on the wooden door, looking through the stale drifts of cigarette smoke from Phil to Preacher, to Warren Troy, then I said, "I'm going to lie down right here." Dimly I heard someone reply, "Me too." I don't remember lying down on the paneled door; I think I was asleep before I stretched out. It seemed only a moment later that I awoke, but an hour and a half had passed. Preacher, Warren Troy, the captain and Sergeant Campbell were still on their feet, moving around. During the time I had been asleep, more wounded men had been brought in, had been bandaged, and had been hoisted out the window. As I stood up, the door rocking under me on its knob, Warren Troy was competently tying an evacuation tag onto a man's field jacket.

It was Sergeant Campbell who had awakened me. Still more wounded men were about to be carried in, and the space I had occupied was needed. The litter bearers were sleeping exactly as I had last seen them, a jumble of muddy wet legs, arms and exhausted faces. They looked as though it would take an explosion to awaken or untangle them. I helped lift in the new casualties and then went upstairs to relieve myself. Gray daylight had come. The men who had taken shelter in the house itself or in the barn were all gone again. A thin, cold rain was falling. Shells still crashed, but now less frequently, and there was no one in sight.

Straub, from C Company, came down the stairs from the yard, leading a walking wounded, and he remained in the doorway, talking to me for a few minutes while I unwrapped bandages and heated tape again. "The company took a hell of a poundin'," he said in his mournful voice that had a broad New York accent. "I think it was the worst night I remember. Lieutenant MacKenzie is in tough shape."

"How?"

"He's all—he's like out of his mind a little. He don't know what's goin' on. They're bringin' him down here now, a couple of the guys. They were in a farmhouse an' a tank opened up on them. Fired right into the room where they were. MacKenzie got knocked down a flight of stairs. You remember Ciani. He died down the cellar there. And Rodriguez." I found myself wincing as I handed down the bandages. Ciani was a quiet man, a cabinetmaker who had worked in Altman's. He used to ask me sometimes why we had to be fighting: "*I* was gettin' along all right; no one was botherin' me. Why can't we all be peaceful?" And Rodriguez was the medical student with the year at the University of Rome whom Captain Reddy had wanted to put in my place here at the aid station. Straub went on naming those who had been killed. Back in camp, he had worked in Sergeant Hill's supply room with a Franciscan rosary around his neck and a bunch of religious medals on a safety pin pulling a hole in every undershirt he owned. He had a sober, dark-eyed monk's face such as one saw in Cranach's paintings. "An' you remember Harry Nordstrom? He got it too; he was killed." Nordstrom and Straub had been fast friends. "One of the guys said the first shell from a tank blinded him, but he come right out, crawlin' on his knees, to put up a fight. Blind. The kid was game all the way through. Somewhere, they said, he picked up a B.A.R. an' he had that with him when they got him."

Straub told the story simply, in a monotone, as if the same story would soon be told about him. I felt like crying and couldn't think of anything to say. Straub lingered for a moment or two, then turned and went back to the depleted company.

A few minutes later Lieutenant MacKenzie came half falling down the cellar stairs with two of his men holding him by the arms. He shook off their help and flung himself down on the one kitchen chair. His head fell back against the wall. "I'm ohll *right!*" he kept insisting, with his marked Georgia accent. "I'm really ohll right! I don't want to be sent to the hospital. I have to get back to the company—but, my God, my God!" His face had been blackened by gunpowder and then whitened by falling plaster dust. He had been crying and you could see the tear streaks down that thick caked surface. Now, one could not be sure whether he was crying or laughing. His head rolled with exhaustion, but his voice came out suddenly loud: "Ah lost thirty of mah men! Thirty men killed! They bunched up there at the fence. I told them not to! I told them to get over it, but they bunched up. My God! Someone give me a cigarette."

"Ward!" the captain called, shaking him by the shoulders. "Ward! Ward MacKenzie!"

"No, I'm ohll right. Really I am. I'm just so tired, so god-damned tired." His face smiled but tears poured out of his eyes. "Even when some of us did get in the house, a German tank came up and opened fire. I yelled, 'Down! Down the stairs!' And before I could get to the doorway the tank opened up again, and the first thing I knew I was lyin' at the bottom of the stairs and one of mah men, Ciani, was lying on top of me with half of his back and one arm blown off. We got him downstairs an'—an' someone—" He began to cry. The tears washed down over the black and white layers on his face.

"I think we'd better give you a rest, Ward."

"No! No, I'm ohll right! But fo' God's sake just let me lie down here some place for a little while."

He was taken to wherever First Battalion Headquarters was located and put to sleep there.

A little later Sergeant Concannon lowered in through the hall window the flat, aluminum cylinders containing breakfast, and after a short discussion Sergeant Campbell went over and woke the litter bearers, shaking them repeatedly. Stiffly, dazed and unsteady, they crawled down from the shelf, made faces, stumbled against each other and began in slow motion to get out their mess kits. While eating their breakfast, drinking the lukewarm coffee that tasted like ether, they stared haggardly before them in silence. Upon finishing, still in their wet clothes, they climbed back onto the shelf again and in no time were asleep, their dirty mess gear left on the floor.

The blankets came down from the two high windows; gray light fell down into the room. The air was stale and heavy with the smell of men sleeping, wet shoes, wet uniforms, stale cigarette smoke and dirty mess kits.

We stayed in the cellar for three days while the stubborn attack continued. There was scarcely a minute when someone

314

wasn't being hoisted in or waiting on a litter to be hoisted out again. The litter bearers slept through most of the first day, being roused every now and then to go out and bring in another wounded man. There was very little talk out of them and no post-mortems about the attack; they were too tired for that. The 210th medics came in exhausted, and another group was sent up to take their place.

"I don't like the looks of those windows up there," the captain said, halfway through the first morning. "Don't like them nohow. I think someone should go up and pile a nice thick layer of stone an' dirt an' sod up against them. Cover 'em all up."

No one moved. At the moment, shells whipped low over the house, some exploding so close that the foundation shook. The captain kept worrying about the windows until Silly Willie and his assistant, going up to see if the ambulance was all right—twice more shrapnel had flattened a tire—began to place some rocks against the panes, and then they crushed earth around them with their feet. Two German 88s screamed in, exploding with a terrible roar in the back yard.

Everyone in the cellar fell to the floor. Just as the third shell came in, Silly's assistant dived head first through the hall window and landed on all fours with a crash. He was gray-white, with huge round eyes, and a second later Silly Willie came clattering down the stairs screaming with laughter, and he continued to laugh and stamp about until tiny tears trembled on his albino eyelashes.

"That's fine," the captain said, looking up at the windows a little later. "Only that's not enough!" He was smiling. "We want that good and thick there. Twice, three times that much."

"I couldn't stay any longer up there, sir," Silly Willie replied. "Them sonsabitches come whizzin' in faster'n hell!"

"I know, I know," the captain said with a smile and a shake of his head, "but we gotta get those windows fixed." He worried and cajoled about them on and off for the rest of the day, but he did not give a direct order and the windows were left as they were.

Rather late in the afternoon when food was again lowered through the hall window, the tired litter bearers got up and ate, and afterward Phil, Ted and I gathered all the dirty mess kits and made an uneasy trip to wash them down at C Company's kitchen trucks about a half mile away. The day was

315

closing in when we returned. In the sagging, drafty rooms on the first floor there was the creak, the whisper and quiet rustling of men who had sneaked off from their companies for the night. Downstairs a line of walking wounded waited in the hall; three looters were beginning to go through the packs in the salvage equipment; and two wounded men were being lowered in through the hall window.

Within a few minutes the fearful racket of a heavy enemy barrage opened up, with 88s blasting their way nearer and nearer the house. Everyone in the room paused, listened. Then the first of six or eight shells exploded with a shattering roar so close in the back yard that someone shouted, "This is *it!*" and everyone fell to the floor. I was sitting on the automobile seat and, suddenly frightened, with my knees jackknifed high, I found I was unable to give the necessary push to get up off the low seat. I saw one of the wounded men, lying directly at my feet, grip with all his might the edge of the Army blanket that had been drawn up over him. His eyes stared with terror at the ceiling. Another deafening smash. Another. The house, the cellar walls were shaking crazily. And now came one mighty crash that broke the cellar windows and blew into the room an explosion of splintering glass, dirt, rocks and shrapnel that bounced and ricocheted all over the place. I buried my head on my chest and heard the next shell roar out. Dirt again came flying in the broken windows.

To my disbelief and horror—I first thought he had gone out of his mind—Warren Troy, on the floor, in a loud voice he tried to keep firm, had begun to sing "Onward Christian Soldiers." "—so-o-o-ldiers, marching as to war . . ." The next words were drowned out by a tremendous thundering crash that brought a huge part of the house down above us. Hemmed in by the litters, I tried again to scramble off the automobile seat but could not get the proper leverage. ". . . forward into ba-a-t-t-le . . ." The voice shook, quavered badly and sent chills down my spine. The room was clouding with plaster dust. Mentally, at top speed, I began to say the Act of Contrition, convinced that the next explosion would kill us all. There came another hideous blast that jumbled the figures on the floor; I rose up and flung myself forward over the man on the litter. That explosion crashed off inside the house. One's eardrums nearly burst, and walls and beams came down with a roaring sound and the screeching of nails ripping loose. Something like a ton of coal seemed to crash violently into the hall just outside. There was an instant of stunned silence, then through the clouds of choking plaster dust came the mingled cries, "Medics! Medics! My God! Medics! Mother! *Oh*-h-h-h!" And from upstairs among the wreckage: "Wounded! I'm wounded! Get me *out!* Help! Help! Medics!" Voices from everywhere seemed to be crying, "Medics! Medics! *Oh*-h-h! *Oh*-h-h."

I managed to get up, shivering without control, and for the moment I couldn't speak or take a step forward. Then the other figures started getting up one by one. "Anyone hurt in here? Anyone killed?" No. The last man picked himself up, leaving only the two wounded men on the litters. There was a rush to get out to the wounded in the hall. Those nearest the door said later all they had to do was reach out and pull them in. Everyone out there—all the walking wounded—had been wounded again.

For the three evenings that we were in the cellar there was the same performance: the house itself was shelled, though not again hit, sometime between four and six, and, once that was over, there was a sense of relief. We slept badly, heavily crowded, on our sides, in rows on those deep, rough log storage shelves. The wounded still came in drifts, and once I was holding a man up while Preacher bandaged him, and behind me I heard Warren Troy's voice, calm and officious, asking, "Your name please?"

"Stanley Danowski."

"Rank?"

"Staff Sergeant."

"Company, Sergeant?"

"C Company."

When I could, I looked around. He was lying on a litter, pale, his eyes closed peacefully, having an evacuation tag tied through the buttonhole of his field jacket. Out of it, I thought with a feeling of relief, and turned back to the man I was holding.

The night before we left, while we were eating supper out of our mess kits, two wounded men were carried in and set down. The room was crowded with all the litter bearers milling about, dipping into pans of food. With those who were not working on the wounded, I sat hunched over on the edge of the low shelf, eating. Directly in front of me, sitting up on a litter, was a man whose shirt and undershirt had been cut away from the wound on the top of his shoulder and neck. I stared down at the deep scarlet triangular wound, seeing the heavy web of muscles and the oozing blood in the bright lantern light. At first I thought a whole bandage had been sunk into the wound and that it was soaking up the blood; then I saw the fiber was not that of a blood-soaked bandage but of heavy torn flesh. I was looking directly into the shattered deltoid and neck. For a split second, in the act of lifting the spoon to my mouth, I became dizzy and sick, then the feeling passed off and my hand brought the spoon to my mouth. Beginning to grow interested in what I was looking at, I went on chewing and swallowing the food.

Teddy Jameson was sitting beside me eating comfortably.

"A few months ago," I said, "I wouldn't have been able to look at that and go on eating." Once, I remembered, during a summer storm that came up in the evening, I ran upstairs to close the windows in my bedroom and somehow or other rammed both my hands through the glass. There was not much pain, but when my brother came running up and put on the lights and I saw the blood and splinters of glass in my wrists, I had to look away in a sudden sweat and weakness.

Ted Jameson was laughing. "Oh, sure," he said. "Me either. Now it doesn't matter at all." He scraped at the bottom of his mess kit and then licked the spoon, watching Preacher shake the tiny envelope of sulfa powder into the wound and cover it with a Carlyle bandage, which he fastened down generously with adhesive tape.

There was no use in thinking about the bad air, the ever-present smell of stale smoke, sweat, mud, damp wool, wet shoes and socks; there was no thought of washing or shaving. Toward the end, when the whole attack was over and we knew we were about to leave, I tried with the others to write a V-mail letter, but I could not finish it, could not even pin my mind down to say the usual blank things I said in my letters home. To remain any longer in that cramped cellar room with the rocking door on the floor had become an agony. I pitied myself, forgetting how gladly anyone from the line companies would have changed places with me.

The attack came to an indecisive close. The captain rode down into Olzheim and an hour later telephoned for the rest of us to join him there. Dully, without hope, without caring about anything, aware only of a burning anger underneath—

so that, I thought, I could pick up a machine gun, walk over to the German lines and riddle every German soldier in sight and do it gladly—I packed up and went down the short distance with the others once more into Olzheim itself.

March

The inn was slightly more battered than it had been before. Its green door was peppered with a spray of fresh bullet holes, and the greater part of the building across the road had crashed down in ruins. As yet, not all the hills surrounding the town had been taken; the Germans put up sporadic bursts of machine-gun and small-arms fire, the echo of which floated back lazily from the high ground opposite. An attack was in progress not far ahead.

I still carried the partly written V-mail letter, and though there were times when I sat idle in the taproom for a half hour at a stretch, it did not seem worth while to add a final paragraph and sign it. Writing letters just then seemed like talking into a dead telephone: one felt entirely cut off from civilian life.

On a Sunday, our third and last day there, the sun made scattered appearances, coming out with sudden bright warmth through fast-blowing, low white clouds which parted like a stage curtain to disclose a shining June-blue sky. The stream flashed, the grass on its banks turned vivid green, and despite the stutter of machine-gun fire from the hills, birds sang and flew up in garlands against the sky.

After lunch an infantryman came in to report that there were some wounded Germans in the hill just above the inn and to ask if we wanted to treat them. On this particular day the captain was indifferent; he shrugged and left it up to the litter bearers. They had been rushed all morning, carrying in our own wounded, but after talking it over briefly, several of them took litters and went up to collect the Germans.

There were four in all. Trucks and the ambulance blocked our door at the moment and the litters were shoved in through one of the wide windows. I held aside the blackout blankets, and such a soft, warm smell of spring floated in

319

past my face that for the first few seconds I became dizzy.

The Germans, in their long, wet, muddy coats, were put down on the floor. Two of them were weak and barely conscious; the other pair lay with their hands clasped up in back of their heads. From the four there arose a heavy stench of vomit, mud and excrement. One bony-faced, reddish man was gasping, his mouth stretched in an agonized smile. He had oversized buck teeth and his lips could not close over them. His hair hung down in a long blond sweep onto the collar of his overcoat and ended on the litter. It seemed only in America that men wore the Prussian crew cut.

"Schnapps," he begged.

"Schnapps!" the captain shouted. "I'll give you schnapps, you sonofabitch! Nicht schnapps! Deutscher soldaten—" In anger he lashed out at the man, either telling him the German soldiers could have no liquor, or that they had taken all of it with them.

"Wasser," the man begged a minute later.

"Goddam him, give him some water!" Wrathful, he walked away.

I went over to the water can, filled a paper cup and brought it back, but when I bent down beside the man, the stench from him was so strong that my stomach turned over. He was almost too weak to raise his head, and I started to put my hand beneath it to support it, but I found myself flinching, unwilling to touch all that greasy and, doubtless, lousy blond hair. The man, trembling, took the paper cup from me and he managed to drink some of the water, but most of it spilled and ran down his neck. He lay still for a moment and then grunted, "Danke." I rose and stepped away.

Preacher began to examine their wounds and one of the Germans set up a loud, labored groaning until the captain shouted to him to be quiet. After Preacher had cut the pants off one man, he knelt back and drew a breath. "Anyone volunteer to bandage a couple of these babies?" he asked.

No one answered at first. All the wounds looked serious. There was a shattered knee, with the rest of the leg badly swollen and discolored; a shoulder caved in and blown open; a large intestinal wound—that man seemed to be dying—and a fourth wound high up between the legs. Thinking, maybe the knee, I was about to speak when Joe Mortara, the short, sturdy Supply Sergeant, said, "All right; Christ, I'll do one." He spoke in a slurred monotone as if he didn't expect anyone ever to take an interest in anything he said.

He began with the man who was wounded between the legs, the job made acutely disagreeable by the fact that the man had a bad case of dysentery. This was the one with the buck teeth to whom I had given water. As he started to clean him off, Joe Mortara had to turn his face away and grit his teeth.

The four had lain out in the hills all night long. Their own aid man had done what he could for them and then had left them in a foxhole when the rest of the Germans retreated to another hill.

Warren Troy, in the meanwhile, was having his usual difficulty in making out their hospital tags.

"Wie heissen sie?" the captain asked, and the answer came back in a swift guttural. Sometimes the captain caught it the first time; at other times he gave Warren an approximation of the man's name. The soldier's identification booklet was seldom a help, because the Germans printed in Gothic-style characters that were unfamiliar to us. "Wie alt? Achtundzwanzig. Twenty-eight." The next question asked the man's rank, and most often the Germans either didn't understand or pretended not to. "Soldat?" the captain asked a second time. "S.S.? No?. No S.S. Hell, make him a corporal."

They were to be driven back in the jeep, stretched out across the back seat, and when it came time to cover them, the captain would not have our blankets placed over them. Two of the men were naked from the waist down and shivering badly, but he gave instructions to cover them with their wet and bloody overcoats, and on top of that went their wetter, muddy blanket. I was relieved when the four were carried out.

We were waiting in the meanwhile for one of our litter squads to come back. After sweeping up the floor and burning the used German bandages, I went over and held back the blanket that covered the open casement window. Shafts of sunlight fell into the taproom; the air was mild and warm, borne in on a puff of soft breeze. At the same time, a draft of cold air from the shadows came in too.

"Hey, At," Preacher called, "Ah'd feel a whole lot better with 'at blanket down and the winder closed!" He smiled, but he meant it, and regretfully I let the covering drop across the window.

Howard Mason, returning from an errand to his truck, said

he could see Sam Benton's squad coming in with a litter. He could just make them out, he said, " 'way far up the hill," and the captain suggested someone go out and give them a hand.

I went out with Mike Nowak. We waved and started to run up the road. On the far side of the bridge, we met the four men coming hurriedly, straining under their load. "One *damn* long haul!" one of them said as I went to the back and relieved Sam Benton. "Thank'!" he said shortly, transferring the pole to my hand, and without stopping he went swiftly past down toward the inn. The man on the litter was entirely covered with an Army blanket. After a short while I said, "God, this is heavy!"

Tom Lawlor, ahead of me, beginning to laugh, turned his head and said, "It's Colonel Hessig."

"No wonder!" I laughed too. "Is he badly hurt?"

"I don't know. The aid man had him bandaged up when we got there."

Sagging under the weight, we carried him across the bridge, down into the inn, and set him on the floor of the taproom. The blanket was removed. His wound, in the back or the side, was not a particularly serious one, but his face had gone gray, his eyes were frightened and he would not trust himself to speak above a whisper.

As opposed to his manner with enlisted men, the captain was all attention. Up from some depths, Colonel Hessig whispered, "Tell me the truth: am I . . . finished?"

"No, sir! No-o-o! You're gonna be all right, sir. We're gonna fix you up fine, sir." Very carefully and tenderly, Captain Stettner changed the bandages, keeping Preacher on hand as his assistant.

"What are the boys going to say about me?" whispered the foggy voice. "They're going to say, 'What a f--- up!' "

They'll say worse than that, sir, I thought, and yet I felt sorry for him because he was old and frightened and didn't believe that his wound wasn't fatal. The evacuation tag was filled out and Warren Troy tied it through the colonel's buttonhole. Then as a mark of special favor, two blankets instead of one were drawn up over him and folded back neatly. Just as he was about to be carried out to the ambulance, the old man raised a trembling, veined hand.

"Yes, sir!" The captain hurried over to catch the parting words and bent down close to the litter. The whisper came so faintly I couldn't hear it. It was an intensely dramatic moment. The captain was silent for quite a long time, then he straightened up with an embarrassed smile. We stood in awed silence.

"Would someone get a can or something?" he asked. "The —the colonel wants to take a leak."

At the unexpectedness of it, I nearly laughed aloud. No one moved at first, and then Tubby, who talked big but who was a notoriously easy mark, made a search and returned with an empty tin can. In a manner that disclaimed any part of the proceedings, he twiddled it for a moment and then gave it to the captain. At that I had to turn away and grin at the empty black wall. After a while I heard the captain saying, "Perhaps I'd better help you, sir?"

As soon as the colonel was driven away, attention became centered on Dick Gann. Always blank, mumbling, dirty and uncared-for, with his nose running and his glasses smoky, he had recently developed a bad cough and a spastic twitch that shot through his entire body. He sat sprawled on a kitchen chair near the stove, smiling vacantly and slowly wetting his loose lips. One hand hung limp, almost touching the floor. The warty, spatulate fingers crawled and twisted one over the other, then the spasm stiffened him, receded, and slowly the foolish smile returned.

"Just look at him!" Warren Troy said in anger. "It's a damned crime!"

"Make out a tag for him too," the captain said.

Learning that he was to be sent to the hospital, Dick put up a squawk of protest. The captain spoke to him kindly and reasoningly, and at last, assured that it was to be for a few days only, Dick gave in, gathered up the toilet articles he so seldom used, searched for his writing paper—to the best of my knowledge he had written one V-mail letter since I had been with the group—handed in his morphine and syringe, and put on his overcoat and steel helmet.

"And what is the diagnosis to be?" Warren Troy inquired in his most unbending manner.

The captain thought for some time. He gave the Latin words for "muscle-bound, inter auribus. Is that right, does anyone know? Is it 'inter' or 'intra' for between the ears? I want it so he won't be able to read if he looks on the tag."

"So wong, everybody; see ya inna—inna few days," said Dick, going out to climb into the ambulance. Everyone called out goodbye. We never expected or wanted to see him again.

"When the doctors get a look at that tag," the captain predicted, "they'll keep sendin' him back and back till he winds up workin' in a kitchen somewhere. Hell, he never belonged up here in the first place."

"'Here?' A man like that should never have been taken overseas," Warren Troy corrected. "Pure case of Army stupidity ever to make him a medic—or even induct him. There's where the mistake was to begin with." Warren Troy often stated his opinions with a sweeping disregard for the captain's feelings.

"If he doesn't like it," he remarked in private, "the hell with him. Let him send me out as an aid man. I wouldn't mind it in the least. I'd mind it, but I'm perfectly willing to go any time he feels like sending me, and he knows it."

After fighting for every inch of the ground around Olzheim, the Germans fell back suddenly in retreat. We streamed after them in a convoy, passing the first white surrender flags—sheets, tablecloths or pillow cases—hung from the upper windows of farmhouses. The sensation of rolling through Germany without a halt was strange after the past month, when gains were measured in yards.

The Germans were forced to abandon many of their vehicles when the gasoline ran out, and these we saw all along the road. There had evidently been no time to destroy them, for our men filled them up with gas and drove them along in the convoy. There were even civilian touring cars, which the German Army had seized and run as far as possible. American soldiers rode along in these, bowing and laughing, elegantly tapping their cigar ashes over the side. The new additions made the convoy enormously long. We ourselves had picked up a small truck and a handsome white ambulance equipped with a refrigerator, an electric grill, both unfortunately broken, a padded couch and well-designed storage cabinets. It was practically a trailer and it became the captain's personal property, the repository for his loot.

Riding in open trucks through the chill March air, we alighted around noon in the outskirts of Lissendorf, a fair-sized, commonplace town with higgledy-piggledy alleys on the outer edges, then cheap little suburban houses in rows, and, in the center, a long, busy main street like many in the United States, with trolley tracks, shops, department stores and small office buildings. At the east end of the town there was a bridge across the Kyll River which the Germans had blown up only an hour or so before, but a smaller bridge, just below, had been captured intact.

Our group of litter bearers was instructed to head for the main street of the town; and, taking a zigzag course, running in single file, we started down an alley only to be blocked off at one intersection by the crush of fleeing civilians turning down ahead of us. We had to push our way through them.

"Let's through! Let's through here!" At the sound of American voices in their midst, the people ahead turned around in wild panic, but seeing the Red Cross armbands, they tried to make a path for us.

Seen in close-up, the civilians were a different type than we had been encountering. Most of them were dumpy, pasty and thick-featured. From all, I would have expected more terror. Though they went in a drove, crowding down the same alleys, there seemed merely to be haste; they looked preoccupied, stern, like people rushing to work, knowing they're already a little late.

There was one blond girl who was richly curved, with fat pallid cheeks, chapped lips and yellowish teeth. She wore a silk scarf wrapped around her head, a tightly fitted winter coat with a fur collar, and boots that showed a few inches of plump silk legs. While we were trying to force our way through, she brushed up against one after another of us, smiling with her thick, unpainted lips, showing her yellowish teeth. All about her, badly in need of help, were old men on crutches; old women trying to manage two or three crying children and a toppling wagon of provisions and bedclothes at the same time; pregnant women carrying heavy children in their arms to keep them from being trampled underfoot.

We worked our way through that particular alley, criss-crossed down a few more, and, coming out onto the main street, bumped into the same cowardly stout girl, who greeted us again by putting her face up close and leering. Many of the people now were running, some down along the curb, while tanks clanged and crashed past almost on top of them. Up the deserted side streets, in the yards of small houses, American soldiers were stepping over fences, breaking into empty houses, working in teams, looting and searching for eggs, which had become a sudden craze.

We had to wait our chance and make single dashes to get

across through the traffic to the other side of the street. There, with no sense of surprise, we followed Mike Nowak into a doorway between two shops, up a flight of stairs and into a long office that had big plate-glass windows opening out above the street. The office—perhaps the Ration Board—had a counter running its entire length. The captain, Sergeant Campbell and the aid-station group had arrived by ambulance and were waiting for us.

Putting our equipment down behind the counter, we asked how long we were staying. No one bothered to answer. We joined them at the swung-out windows and looked down at the activity below. Directly across the way, in a fenced-in lumberyard, a temporary prisoner-of-war pen had been established, and German soldiers stood in it with their hands over their heads while being searched.

Loudly clanking and banging, another long line of tanks began to go by with infantrymen riding on them.

"Yay!" our men called from the window. "Give 'em hell, boys!" The boys laughed jeeringly, some holding onto their bumping helmets. "That's E Company going by now. There's Jack Parrish. Hey, Jack! *Jack*—up here!" The handsome, bareheaded, black-haired aid man, adjusting the strap of his helmet, looked all around, then spotted the medics and waved and laughed as he rolled by. More and more tanks went past with infantrymen hanging on.

A few minutes later there was a commotion on the busy street. Someone came rushing back with news which was called up to us above the clanging: Jack Parrish had just been shot through the head by a sniper and killed.

Shortly after, from the same direction, came a little knot of excited soldiers and officers, and in their midst, walking hurriedly, with one arm bent up behind his back, was a German soldier. A fast-growing, shouting crowd of soldiers was gathered behind.

"They got him!" we heard. "They got the sniper who killed the guy."

The wooden door of the pen was opened, the sniper was hurled inside. Our informant, cupping his hands beside his mouth, shouted up to us that the German had denied he was the sniper. The soldiers, milling about, suddenly fell back. An aisle opened along the street and General Purvis, last seen by me at Rheims shouting, "*Out* of those houses! Get out! Get out!" came striding along to the pen, accompanied by

Lieutenant Stuart Martindale of First Battalion Headquarters, young, broad and slightly bowlegged, wearing the only heavy-canvas combat jumper in our outfit.

He followed the general in and, on the general's orders, administered to the unresisting prisoner a sound beating with his large, solid fists, after which the narrow door was opened and the prisoner was dragged out. Hands over his head, stumbling, he was marched off by an armed delegation. About a half hour later we heard the German had been taken outside the town, ordered by General Purvis to dig his own grave, and, once he had done so, he was shot down into it.

The reaction to snipers was both understandable and a puzzle. We had snipers of our own, skilled soldiers, picked for their intelligence and keen eyesight. When I worked in the Art Shop in Fort Jackson, I made for the same Lieutenant Martindale five or six large charts of a new rifle sight that was then being issued especially for snipers. Lieutenant Martindale gave lectures throughout the battalion, using the four-foot-by-six-foot drawings, and he thought so highly of them that he had taken them over to Europe with him: I saw them blowing about a field one day in France. It always struck me as odd: the enemy snipers were unspeakable villains; our own were heroes.

In connection with this, a story sprang up somewhere and made a special appeal to Silly Willie, who told it many times in careful detail. In one of the other battalions—everyone was vague as to which battalion—a platoon was going along a flat road near a tall country church when suddenly one man was shot down and killed. There was no enemy in sight. The church was locked and deserted, but the company commander, acting on a hunch, forced his way inside and climbed up into the tower. There he found a beautiful, blond German girl. "Jeez, she was gorgeous," Silly always said. "So the cap'm takes a look at her an' he says, 'Let's have the gun. Where's the gun?' She don't say anything; just looks at him. So he goes over to her—" Silly's face, eyes narrowed, acted out the captain's part. "He says, 'Gimme the gun!' She shows her hands, empty. So the cap'm reaches out, grabs her dress by the front and *rips* it down." Silly tore the imaginary dress. "And there she stands with the most beautiful pair of tits he ever seen." Here Silly always had to break down and laugh for some time; then, straightening his face and getting back into character, he continued: "An' right there between them, there's this little German pistola. Well, he don't care how beautiful she is. He grabs the pistol and shoves it right against her heart, right against it, an' he says, 'You lousy sonofabitch!' an' he lets her have it. One shot an' she falls over dead. He walks down the stairs and out. Now that's the truth!"

We had been told to expect continuous sniping on the part of the German civilians. Old men, women, and even children, were said to have received both orders and practice to shoot us down, but aside from the beautiful blonde in the belfry, I never heard of a civilian taking up arms, though I don't doubt some must have done so.

After eating a K ration for lunch—the cheese by now had begun to give me canker sores—we were told to gather our equipment, get into the ambulance, and set off for a house in a different part of the town, nearer the bridge that spanned the Kyll River, there to establish an aid station. Neither the captain nor Sergeant Campbell came with us. Often I think the captain went to the battalion C.P. to hang around and talk to the other officers.

We crowded into the ambulance, heard Silly Willie slam the door and kick up the back step, which automatically locked us in. We sat with our gas masks and full field packs, facing each other in two rows. The town had long since been empty of civilians. We had driven only a few blocks when artillery shells began to slam and explode in the streets.

"Hey! I don't like the sound of that," so.neone said. "Those are coming in! They're not ours!"

"The bastards are shelling the railroad bridge."

As long as it's just the railroad bridge and we stay away from it, I thought. There came a deafening explosion in the street next to the one we were riding through. Out the back windows of the ambulance you could see a few American soldiers racing long-legged for shelter. We turned a corner and saw a jeep blown upside down.

"Hey, Sill," Preacher called, "supposin' you let us out of this goddam wagon!"

Silly broke into his croupy laugh. "You boys gittin' nervous back there?"

"You crazy bastard. Let us out! Come on!"

But Silly laughed and kept on driving. Then the raking sweep of the German artillery grew closer to us. Silly put on a burst of speed, driving the ambulance through the barrage in the hope of reaching the house we were to occupy. Racing up a street of small houses, he swung the wheel around and we flew up a narrow driveway. One shell exploded so close that he jammed on the brakes, and he and his assistant hurled themselves out on either side of the driveway.

Within the ambulance there was instant pandemonium, a wild bent-over rush, confused loud shouting, cursing, and pounding on the stoutly locked doors that could not be opened from our side. While two men rushed to the front and started to climb over the driver's seat, Silly ran around to the back and unlocked the doors. Everyone rushed for them at once, became wedged, and no one could get out. In the midst of that, another shell came screaming down. Some of the terrified men fell back, while four or five dived out in a heap on the driveway.

"Don't rush! We'll be killed in the rush!" I started to say, but a long string of smooth idiot sounds emerged. I jumped down on someone's back and tried to scramble into the narrow space between the green stucco house and the rear wheel of the ambulance. Crushing in on top of Phil Schaeffer, I attempted to say, "Maybe we'd be safer in back of the house!" only to hear again that same stream of smooth gibberish pour out. It flashed through my mind that I was beginning to crack up. A roaring blast shook the driveway, followed by an echoing stillness in which shrapnel could be heard striking and falling.

With one accord everyone got up, made a dash down the driveway, around to the front of the house and up the steps. The last one in gave the door a slam. We ran into the semidark interior of the house when there came another tremendous explosion, the concussion of which blew the front door off its hinges, and a rug on the enclosed porch rose high and quivered in the air. A great wind rushed up through the house, leaving a vacuum. After that there was complete silence for a while.

Everyone started to sweat with relief, to gasp, laugh, exclaim all at once. Preacher and some of the more cautious began an immediate search for the cellar and located the door leading to it in the dark central hall under the staircase. The rest of us dropped our equipment and started an investigation of the house.

It was a small, commonplace house and its enclosed porch

had been converted into a furniture store. No sign proclaimed it, but an assortment of inexpensive new furniture was stacked up there: sofas, upholstered chairs, most of them still in light crates, and spindly gumwood end tables wrapped in brown paper. As could be expected, I suppose, of someone in the furniture business, the dark living room, which had a linoleum rug on the floor, was virtually empty.

"The kitchen," Ted Jameson reported, "is neat as a pin, and I think I'll be able to cook on the stove. Come on out and see." It was a small white kitchen like thousands through the United States, where the only discordant note would have been the blue cross-stitched motto in German on the roller towel over the sink.

We went up the dark, bare staircase that cut through the center of the house and came out in a small bedroom on the attic floor with sloping eaves and windows overlooking the treetops. Silly Willie and his assistant got busy with their looting, though one glance would have shown anyone there was nothing of value in the whole house. The rest of us settled down on the beds, the chairs and the floor, beginning to smoke and talk. Preacher, however, was nervous; he did not like the flimsiness of the walls or of the roof so close over our heads, nor did he like the idea of tarrying on the attic floor.

I was lying stretched out with some others across one of the unmade beds when, with a splitting rush and shriek, the first of four shells came crashing in. There was an immediate shout, a scrambling up, a wild dash for the door and the staircase. "The cellar!" they were shouting. "Quick! Down the cellar! The cellar!"

I had sat up abruptly and saw Phil Schaeffer, in a low rocking chair, staring at me through his patched glasses. Somehow I could not wrench up out of myself enough energy or terror to run. The first explosion roared off in the street.

"The hell with it," I said. "I'm sick of flopping down each time they send over a shell." It was a degrading sensation, both getting down and picking oneself up afterward.

"If you stay, then I will too," he said. "Fine. We'll ignore it."

I regretted my rashness at once. Two other shells screamed into a deafening bang as he spoke, and the windows rattled as if in an earthquake. There was a rushing, a pounding of feet along the second-floor hall, the sound of someone falling noisily down the stairs.

After a long stillness both inside and out, we heard laughter below us.

"Phew! D'you see that?" someone asked.

Howard Mason's high Southern voice spoke amid his own cackling laughter. "All Ah saw was this streak of s--- goin' past me, an' it was Preacher!"

"You know dam well it'd be ole Preach."

"Ah didn' stop fer nothin', Ah'm a-tellin' you!" Preacher said, emerging from the cellar. "Whut'd Ah do? Fall on someone comin' down?"

"You come down there, boy, like s--- through a tin horn!"

We were suddenly ordered to pack up and leave the house, to get going in the ambulance, and head back for the center of the town, to wait beneath the railroad bridge. We hadn't unpacked anything, so we were out and crammed into the ambulance within a few minutes. Silly Willie drove off. The streets were all empty, with here and there large craters made by the recent shells. Houses had been hit and had come down, and another jeep had been blown up.

Near the railroad bridge, Silly stopped and let us out. To avoid an incoming barrage, a few soldiers were dashing for the flights of cement stairs that led down to the train platform, and we ran after them to the bottom. No one knew why we had been told to come here. If it were true that the Germans were trying to blow up the railroad bridge, it was the worst possible place for us to wait. I rather doubted the rumor, and thought the captain, wherever he was, felt the underground station would be safer for us than the house. The one big difficulty was that there was no covering over our heads: the long platform faced its duplicate across a wide space of tracks, entirely open to the sky. For a while we stood under the shelter of the bridge that spanned the tracks, but when another German barrage started up, we left it and went to the far end, waiting in the open. Long patches of damp could be seen on the cement siding. The day was raw and chill. After we were there perhaps a half hour, a messenger ran down the stairs, calling to us to leave again and return to the house.

Silly Willie's ambulance was nowhere in sight, and, since shells flew in every now and then, we started off on a run, zigzagging up through the empty, damaged streets, the handles of our entrenching tools banging against our legs, the canteens joggling. If anyone had said to me a few years ago,

"You'll be running with a full field pack on your back through a German town," my mind would not have been able to envision any part of it. Doing the thing seemed perfectly natural; there was even a feeling of exhilaration in running with the group. Winded, we came up the path of the same house where we were to remain for the night, and set about at once hammering blankets over the windows of the living room and kitchen.

Loud shelling woke everyone up many times through the night, but, sitting up, listening to it each time, half asleep, we decided it wasn't necessary to go down to the cellar. In the morning, we washed in icy cold water at the kitchen sink. There were K rations again for breakfast. Spluttering-hot, bubbling out the side of the little can that now smelled of burned paint, the chopped pork and egg yolk was not bad, particularly with hot black coffee to wash it down; and the dark citrus fruit bar was always a treat. The directions on that told you how you could boil it up with water to make a jam, but I never saw anyone try it.

Ted Jameson cleaned the kitchen, working diligently, cheered by the thought of pancakes. "I just have the feeling we're going to be here a good long while," he said, "and Cliff and I are going to keep the kitchen spotless." Wherever we went, he tried to put down roots.

Behind the house there was a neat back yard showing sprouts and pencils of green coming up, and a shed with garden tools and a bicycle which we rode up and down the driveway. I opened the door to another shed and discovered a clean toilet with running water, the first I had seen and used in months.

Ted Jameson appeared in the kitchen doorway.

"Want a ride?" I asked, pausing on the bicycle.

"We're leaving," he said regretfully.

We climbed onto the trucks and rode at a moderate speed through farming towns that grew consecutively duller-looking, dirtier and more dun-colored, each with large, squarish manure piles, steaming in the March air, in front of the houses. White surrender flags hung from the upper windows of almost every house. At Wiesbaum, by far the dirtiest, dullest town of the lot, with the highest and most numerous manure piles of all, we came to a full stop and were told to "detruck." Another division had pinched us out and we were to settle down for a four- or five-day rest.

In Wiesbaum the stench of manure was everywhere; the roads running down were mires of filth. The houses were low, set bare in their soggy yards, and they gave a hooded impression. Tan, mud, mustard-colored, spinach, brownish-green, cinder-gray, dirty oyster—there were rows of them lining the main, treeless, hilly street. One imagined that the inhabitants would be broad, potbellied, with dull pig eyes.

"Sure! That's how they tell how rich you are over here," I heard someone explaining as we jumped off the trucks. "By how much horse s--- you have in your front yard."

We were evidently in a millionaires' colony.

Perhaps through thoughtfulness on the captain's part, perhaps because he was tired of looking at us, the aid-station group moved with the officers of First Battalion Headquarters into a small, dirty house near the top of the hill, while the litter bearers were given three rooms in a corner house at the bottom. C Company's cooks and kitchen were on the ground floor, and we went past them, up a flight of creaking stairs, to get to our rooms. A part of the roof had been blown in and you had to step around a heap of rubble in the hall.

One of the bedrooms, separate from the others, had no stove in it and so was not sought for, but Phil and I, Cliff and Ted were glad to move into it since none of us liked sleeping in heated rooms with the windows shut. It had walls the color of bluing, dark carved furniture, a lace curtain, and two short double beds with red mattresses and pillows.

The first of the other rooms around the corner was used by day as a sitting room. The walls here were painted orange streaked with blood-color and gold. There was a broken love seat minus one caster, a green lamp table and a green tiled stove; the windows looked down over the street. The room beyond had three double beds in it and a tiled stove that Sam Benton stoked up high just before the men retired at night. The windows there were never opened.

After a long spell of sharing everything equally, having no secrets or privacy, a sudden barrier went up and "outsiders" were not welcomed in that third room. For the greater part of our five-day rest, its inmates came out only on rare occasions, to borrow a sheet of writing paper, to talk for a few minutes, perhaps to eat in common with the rest of us. Sam Benton, Jr., became the ring leader in there, and if any of his men left the door open, he got off the bed and slammed it

333

shut, giving the outsiders a stern, reproving look for glancing in. No one ever remarked on the division in our ranks.

Phil Schaeffer awoke one of the first mornings in Wiesbaum, took a look at his watch and scrambled out of bed. "Good God," he said, "I'm late! I've got to shave! Where's my stuff?"

"What's the matter?" I asked.

"Oh, some damned idiotic foolishness."

"Phil's going to get his Bronze Star today." Ted smiled. "Aren't you, Phil?"

"Now, Fatso, I don't want anyone bothering me. If you'll just do me a favor and keep out of my way—"

"I can tell you what you have to do, Phil," said Teddy, who had been through the ceremony, but he wanted to sell his information for questions.

" 'Do'? What's there to do?" Phil emptied his canteen into the big washbowl.

"Well, for one thing, you have to know when to shake hands with Colonel Mauck. You go out like in a field," Teddy said, "and you line up with some others, some officers and all, and then he comes along and he has written down what you did to deserve the medal, and you all stand at attention in a row while he reads it out—"

"Suppose I don't stand at attention?" Phil demanded. "What's the old ninny going to do, shoot me?" But Phil was rattled, and Ted was delighted. Phil cut himself twice shaving in a hurry, and he covered the lower part of his reddish face with white talcum powder.

"Now where's—? I *did* have a helmet. Every man was issued a helmet leaving the United States."

"Here, hurry up, take mine," I said. As he started out the door I called after him to ask if he weren't going to brush the coating of white powder off his face. He looked around at us, frowning through his cracked glasses.

"No!" he said with determination. "No, I'm not!"

When I saw him again it was just before supper, and the four of us were getting out our mess kits to go down out onto the street.

"There it is," he said, taking a small case out of his pocket and tossing it on the bed. "Greatest fraud ever known to man. Give him a medal, sure! But keep him right up there till he's killed, or shot to pieces or his nerve is ruined. And why

334

single me out? Every man in the line companies deserves one."

"Still, it's very good-looking," I said, picking it up. "And it's five points toward your score getting out."

"Getting out? D'you think for one minute anyone's getting out of this alive?"

"Well, of course. Don't you?"

"We'll *all* be wiped out. You mark my words—*all* of us. Sooner or later. It's only a question of time. The law of averages runs out. Sure, give them all medals; let them shake the great man's hand."

"Phil, don't you want the medal?" Ted asked. "Aren't you going to send it home to your mother?"

"Oh," he said wearily, "I suppose I will."

Each day, as soon as I had had my breakfast, I set off for the aid station at the top of the hill.

"Isn't this the filthiest place you ever saw?" Warren Troy asked in disgust as I came in. "You hate to put your hand on anything. What a spot to pick out for an aid station! Pure stupidity."

The floor of the tiny, crowded living room was uneven and splintery and there was a small, flat, dusty fireplace with a crack running through it. Little many-paned windows, cobwebbed and gray and spotted with rain, framed views of the manure piles in front and the latrine, the rubbish, the barbed-wire strands on the side. The wallpaper here was navy blue with gobs of blackish gold.

Each day till noon there was sick call, the routine of the company sickbook, the dubious necessity of checking rifles in the dark hall and pistols in my pockets. The officers from Battalion Headquarters drifted in and out, flung themselves down to talk to the captain and groan about the dullness of the town, but since they spoke to the enlisted men only as a last resort in their boredom, I continued with my rule never to be drawn into their conversations if it could possibly be avoided.

Lieutenant Kane was in charge of Battalion salvage, among other things, and was therefore my superior officer. He was an unself-conscious, pleasant-looking young man, a former basketball player in college, off-hand, relaxed and popular. He knew that someone named Atwell existed and worked for him. We had held many telephone conversations about the disposition of the salvage equipment, and he had been in and out of the aid station frequently, but I had always let him pass without bringing myself to his attention.

In the dirty little farmhouse I was sitting on a bench one morning, nursing a stiff knee, when he came in and dropped down beside me.

"Hello," he said, and I answered. There came a pause and he said, "Say, what's your name anyway?" When I told him, he looked astonished. "Then you're my man!" he cried. "How're you getting along, Atwell? Got everything under control?" From what Chris Taylor had already told me of the lieutenant, I realized I knew one of his college professors as well as several of his family friends. "Good God," he said when this came out, "you know all my best friends and we have to come all the way to Germany to meet!"

The fact that we had friends in common did not lead to friendship between us. The fault was mine. After a little excited, happy talk on his part, an exchange of news, the conversation floundered. "You know," he said, somewhat apologetically, "you're supposed to get a sergeant's rating for this job you're doing. The T.O. calls for it. I'll have to see about it right away." I laughed. "What's the matter?" he asked. "Don't you care about that?"

"They'd have to make me a full colonel before I'd even begin to care one way or another. Of course, if you could manage that, fine."

Whenever we met after that day, we exchanged a few sentences, asked if we had heard anything of our mutual friends, and that was all.

Captain Christoffsen, the long-waisted, short-legged man who cursed like a trooper about the crowding on the chow line, was Lieutenant Kane's superior and therefore mine too. To facilitate paying me, I had recently been transferred to his company. I liked him and enjoyed watching him in action, yet we passed each other many times a day in constrained silence. Saluting had gone out during combat, so we glanced in opposite directions when we came abreast in a narrow street or lane.

Young Lieutenant Stuart Martindale was another officer whose path crossed mine quite frequently. Back at Fort Jackson, when Chris Taylor and I were working on visual-training aids with little Haas as our boss, the lieutenant drove up almost daily to collect the charts and drawings or to notify us of any changes the colonel, the major or the captain wanted on them. His manner of arrival was always the same. His jeep stopped outside with a loud squeak of tires on the sand and he catapulted himself over the side. His heels rang out downstairs as he started through the Carpentry Shop, and from the moment of entering he bawled, "Haas! Haas! Haas!"

"Don't answer. Make him come up," Chris and I urged, but with a flustered, "Yes, sir! Coming, sir!" nervous little Haas dropped what he was doing and ran down the stairs for the instructions.

When Haas went home on furlough and I was put in charge, the same procedure held forth: the sudden halt of the jeep, the loud heels, the louder voice calling, "Haas! Haas!"

Stripped to the waist in the heat, lying on our stomachs, working on the large brown-paper charts with speedball pens and colored inks, Chris and I waited in silence until the lieutenant shouted two or three times from the foot of the stairs, and then I said, "Haas isn't here. Who is it?"

"Lieutenant Martindale."

"What can I do for you, Lieutenant?"

After an inward struggle, he came up the stairs to deliver the message. Chris had been his jeep driver at Regimental Headquarters for some time, but the lieutenant gave no sign that he had ever seen him before. We lettered footlockers and packages for him to send home to the Midwest, and during the last days in camp, on request, I had even painted for him on a wooden plaque a replica of the regimental insignia. Here in Europe, though we were frequently billeted in the same house, we passed each other without a glance of recognition.

Aside from Captain Stettner, little Lieutenant Serletis and Lieutenant MacKenzie of C Company, the Death's-Head Lieutenant Millbank was the only officer I talked to. Each meeting brought back the picture of him running along the road in the Saar Valley between a messenger and me, saying, "Horrible! Horrible! My God Almighty!"

"Soon's you hear the shells poppin' close, ole *Lieu*tenant Millbank comes a-duckin' in the door," Preacher used to say with a laugh and a slap to his thigh. The lieutenant came in now, seeming exhausted, and flung himself down at the opposite side of the table from me.

"How have you been, Lieutenant?"

"Oh, all right, I suppose." I knew he had been given a job of little importance following his crackup in the Saar, but I had never understood why Captain Stettner, knowing his condition, had not evacuated him to a hospital or had not sent him home. "You know," he said, taking up the conversation where we had last left off, "no matter how long Ah stay, Ah never seem to get used to it." He removed his helmet and set it between us on the table. His face, malarial and finely lined like that of some Southerners, had a tragic look, and the hopeless way he rolled his head when he spoke only added to the impression. "Ah see these young boys bein' shot up, killed, all maimed—ruined fo' life— It's horrible!"

What of himself? Would he, after that one day's combat, be ruined too for life, or would he recover from this? And the thing I always wondered about: why hadn't he been better prepared? What had he expected of war? He seemed too to be bothered by the foul language, the cruel streak, the dishonesty in many of the men, and it appalled him to discover that America was made up in part of such. Yet he was an educated man, he was not young, he had taught in a college and had coached its football teams. I could not help thinking that his war had not been won on any playing fields.

Every day at lunchtime I went down the hill to eat, and walked up again afterward to wait around the aid station till four-thirty in case I should be needed. A painful stiffness had begun in my left knee, but, thinking I had banged it while climbing into a truck, I ignored it at first. When the stiffness grew worse, I started to hobble when going up and down the hill. The captain met me on my way up and asked what was the matter. I told him and he said, "Let Preacher look at it tomorrow if it isn't better."

The next day I was limping badly, and after sick call Preacher said, "At, let's see that ole knee of yours." The captain was standing nearby and came over. I took off my legging and pulled up the pants leg and long drawers. The captain examined my knee, poked it, had me stand up and sit down while he prodded again.

"Uh-huh," he said, nodding. "Just as I thought: arthritis."

"How would I ever get that?"

"Oh, at your age," he said casually, "you'll have to start expectin' that sort of thing. Preacher, put an elastic bandage on him. Bind it good and tight."

No one ever had to tell Preacher to do that. Exerting full

338

strength, he bound quite a distance above and below my knee and asked how it felt.

"Fine," I said. "But now it's as if I had a whole wooden leg to the hip." I couldn't bend my knee at all.

"You jes leave that on three, four days, and you'll be all better."

Walking became almost impossible. I lurched and staggered, and zigzagged on my trips up and down the steep hill; I had to sit with my leg straight out before me and push myself up by my hands when getting off a chair. When Sam Benton, Jr., announced that he was once more in the business of washing mess kits, I became his steadiest customer.

The days were growing longer, and in the blood-and-orange living room the windows stayed open during the early evening while the sunset brightened the lurid colors of the walls. We had attached to us as extra driver for the white German ambulance a light-haired, surcharged young man from one of the line companies, named Buchta. He was short, with a missing front tooth, a voice like gravel going down a chute, a ready laugh, and a tremendous interest in motors. The broken portable phonograph we had been carrying along with a few records in the pocket of its lid he took apart the first afternoon, repaired it, put it together again, and then for the rest of our stay it went almost constantly, with one scratchy needle, playing "Lili Marlene" and an English record made in the twenties of Irving Berlin's "Always."

Striking like a clap of thunder one noontime came the news that we were waiting to cross the Rhine. I suppose if any of us had seen a map, we would not have been so surprised. As it was, the lazy, relaxing boredom gave way at once. A chill went through the crowd.

I came stumping into the room in time to hear the tail end of the announcement. There were sharp intakes of breath.

"Can you swim?" Sam Benton, Jr., whispered to Tom Lawlor, who was standing in front of me.

"No!" He gave a nervous laugh. "Can you?"

"No."

"Don, kin you swim?" Bob Russell was asking.

"Hell, no! You?"

"Cain't swim a f---in' stroke." He went suddenly white about the mouth.

"Jeez, I don't even wanna *think* about river crossings," said

Jimmy McDonough, moving away as the meeting broke up.

There came to mind a summer day at Fort Jackson when C Company was driven out in trucks to a small muddy lake whose tan water seemed no more than a degree or two cooler than the sweltering air. We had come for a swimming test now that we were getting ready to go overseas.

"All the men that can't swim—that can't swim—put up their hands. Anyone that can't swim fifty yards—out to that raft—put up their hands."

Hands went up from fully half the company, ashamed at the admission.

"Sergeant, take the names. You men who can swim, strip down and line up here on the dock."

In our swimming shorts we dived off in groups of four and swam out to the raft while a lifeguard rowed inexpertly along. We climbed up on the raft, dived off and swam back to the dock again. The non-swimmers splashed each other and paddled about the shallow muddy edge of the lake. The mud gave off a glare and a smell, and huge, iridescent dragon-flies swooped over the banks.

Demorest, a black-haired young Southerner who had been elevated to sergeant that day, stepped up in new yellow las-tex shorts when his name was called, and, at the signal, his group of four dived in with a great splash. Three of the four men came to the surface and struck out for the raft. A half minute passed. "Gee, Demorest must be good!" someone finally remarked. We kept waiting for him to surface halfway to the raft, when slowly, almost in the spot where he dived, his face came up pale under the water and then sank away from sight again. "Good God! That was Demorest!" "He went down!" "He can't swim!" "Lifeguard!" cried an officer. "The rest of you stand back. Lifeguard!" There followed a paralyzed moment when nobody moved. The lifeguard, who had secured the job through pull, soon showed that he did not row well enough to back-water and bring his boat around; neither did he make any attempt to dive in for the rescue. Completely flabbergasted, he stared toward the dock. Several men then dived in after Demorest. In the midst of their splashing descent, the drowning face appeared again near the surface and sank. He was finally hauled out unconscious, given artificial respiration on the dock, and, on coming to, admitted that he could not swim a stroke but had not

340

wanted to say so for fear his new rating would be taken away from him.

Arrangements were made to have the non-swimmers take instructions, but beyond that nothing was ever done and that ended the swimming tests.

That night in Wiesbaum, at about seven-thirty, the door of the inner room opened and a procession came out led by Sam Benton, Jr. He stooped and whispered something to Phil Schaeffer, who was sitting beside me, writing a letter. Phil looked astonished, then said, "Now? Why, yes. Yes, of course!" but he glanced around at me as if I suddenly presented a problem. I noticed that Warren Troy was in the room and, for the first time that I could remember, Preacher had left his aid station to come down and visit among the litter bearers.

"All right for us to hold a meetin' in your room?" Sam asked me.

"Yes, of course." A meeting?

"Thank'." But pointedly there was no invitation for me to come along. Sam walked out, followed self-consciously by most of the others. In all there were about ten.

Tom Lawlor, Jimmy McDonough, Mike Nowak and I were left behind in the sitting room.

"What's happening?" I asked.

"Aah," Mike Nowak said, "Sam's holdin' some kind of church services."

"*Sam* is!" We started to laugh, then I remembered that the Protestants hadn't had a chaplain since December, with the exception of the one who had appeared that Sunday in Olzheim only to be shot up an hour afterward.

"The bastard!" Jimmy McDonough said with feeling. "Goin' around sayin' his was the best religion, he'd prove to everyone it was the *only* one. He tries any of that on me, I'll knock his goddam block off."

We looked at each other and laughed at the choice of language used by the Defender of the Faith.

The last man out had been careful to close the door, but after a short spell we began to hear Sam's voice, muffled at first, growing louder and louder in exhortation until he was shouting, and there were emphatic thumps as if he were pounding his hand on a Bible. I looked up from my letter.

"Boy, he sure is whooping it up in there."

"Sounds like a revival meeting."

Our door suddenly opened and Don Stoddard came in with a rush, a deserter from the prayer meeting. After a first startled glance at him, we bent our heads again. No one spoke: the pens scratched away. Don sat down, picked up a tattered, well-read copy of *Stars and Stripes* and give it his whole attention. The silence in the room was unnatural.

Through the door the declaiming, high, shouting voice could be heard, but except for "the Good Lord" or "Lord God a'mighty," no words were distinguishable. Then chills of embarrassment raced down my spine: Sam, in a high, shaky tenor, led off in a hymn. Other voices joined in uncertainly, holding together for a while, then dropping out long before the finish. Don didn't move or turn a page, and the rest of us kept our heads down, writing steadily. Sam's solitary voice, quivering, straining, off key in the high notes, finally brought the hymn to a close and, after a few words, the meeting broke up.

Feet tramped along the hall. The door opened and in they all came, Sam with a Bible in his hand, looking satisfied, stern, rather glittery-eyed, his light hair damp with sweat. The others tried to appear casual.

"One thing's sure," Bob Russell was saying, worried, edging over toward me and trying to prolong the discussion, "with this river crossin' comin' up, Ah'd sure like to git straightened out befoah Ah stops that bullet with mah number on it. Don't you think that's right, Les?"

"Yes, I do."

"What Ah'm worried about though is mah past! I jes ain't led a good life, an' Ah got a lot of sins on mah soul."

"Well," I said, not wanting to get into it, "if you're sorry for them, that's about all you can do—and that's all that's expected of you. That, and trust in God's mercy."

" 'An eye fer an eye, an' a tooth fer a tooth,' " Sam Benton suddenly contradicted from across the room. Everyone stopped talking. He fixed me with a glare. His words seemed to shoot through Bob Russell.

"There, that's it," Russell said, rubbing his hand over the back of his neck and giving a desperate laugh. "Cain't git away from that."

I said to Sam, "What the hell do you want to be frightening him with that for?"

" 'Cause that's what the Good Book says. 'An eye fer an eye, an' a tooth fer a tooth'! A man sins, he's gonna burn. No

342

two ways about that. Good Book says."

"But that's in the Old Testament!" I could hear my voice getting loud with anger. "The New Testament doesn't say a damned thing about 'An eye for an eye.' In fact, Christ preached the direct opposite. His whole theme was forgiveness! Why don't you tell them about that if you're going to tell them anything?"

"You're right! I agree," Warren Troy said, evidently dissatisfied with the prayer meeting. Bob Russell and several others began to range themselves on my side.

But Sam, holding himself rigid, said in a loud, unyielding voice, "Ah believe what the Good Book says!"

"Well, don't you believe in the New Testament too? Don't you believe God's mercy is above all His other works?"

"Ah believe—" His voice rang out sharply. "Ah believe what the Good Book *says!*"

"But do you or don't you believe in an all-merciful God? Above everything else . . ."

He looked at me, his whole face stiff and tight with disapproval. "Russ?" he said, calling his disciple from my side, and after a moment, when I did nothing to detain him, Bob Russell walked across and followed Sam into the inner room. The door slammed. Conversation suddenly broke out, but not a word was said about the prayer meeting.

The next night at approximately the same time, Preacher again came down from the aid station. The sitting room was crowded. Sam walked out of the bedroom and gave some sort of signal to the men. They put away their writing materials, got up and started to file out. Don Stoddard, sitting to one side of me, continued to write studiously. Sam stepped over and placed a hand on his shoulder. "Don, you comin' in?"

"I—I want to finish this letter first," Don replied; and at the same time, Ted Jameson to my other side was trying to squirm down and hide behind me.

"Cliff, are you going?" he whispered.

Cliff sat upright, looking straight before him, evidently listening to the voice of conscience. "Yep!" he said, unsmiling, getting to his feet. Teddy sighed, got up too and went along, martyred. The door closed behind them. The four of us who were Catholics, silent because of Don Stoddard's continued presence, joined in the elaborate pretense that nothing unusual was happening, although we could hear Sam's voice, louder than on the night before, shouting away, and later raised quiveringly in hymns.

This time, halfway through the service, it was Ted Jameson who deserted. "You know, I don't like the way he—" he started to say, but when none of us looked up or spoke, he subsided in silence. And afterward when they all came in, several of them gathered in worried little groups to talk the thing over. I heard Phil saying, "Well, yes, I do admit Sam's inclined to be a bit too unyielding; I don't think he's right on all his points, but in the main—"

Coming into the sitting room late with Sam, Bob Russell, eyes cast down, continued straight into the inner room for what I imagined was further and individual instruction.

Before dinner the following evening, Bob Russell came out of the bedroom and, after hedging around for a while, said to me in a low voice, "Well, Les, Ah guess the only thing fo' me to do if Ah ever git back is to stick to mah divorce. Ah'm gonna write an tell mah wife Ah'm not comin' back to her."

"Oh. Have you decided that definitely? You yourself?"

Avoiding a direct answer, he said, "Ah guess it's the only thing to do." He appeared upset and he glanced at the closed door.

"Won't that separate you pretty much from your children?"

"Gosh, Ah wouldn't want that to happen. Last time Ah was home they wuz gettin' to be right cute little kids." Under the mustache his mouth relaxed in a half-smile. "They wuz sure proud of their daddy bein' a soldier. Mah wife, you know, she had 'em all filled up with stories about how brave their daddy was—"

Sam Benton came out suspiciously and sent us a quick, disapproving look. Though it was much too early, he said, "Russ? Comin' down to eat?"

After a moment Bob Russell gave in. "Yeah, Sam," he said, low, walking away from me. I continued to sit there, my stiff leg up on another chair.

On their way out of the room Sam announced for my benefit, but without looking in my direction, "Ah'm *through* washin' mess kits. No more!"

Bob Russell, Preacher, Phil and Cliff were the only disciples that night at the prayer meeting, and when it was over, Phil came back to the orange living room, rattled, nibbling on his finger, looking as if heresy might have been preached.

He and Cliff dropped out from further meetings. Sam surveyed the fallen-away with a pitying smile; and the services continued for some time with Sam, Preacher and Bob Russell, and were held out in the dark parked ambulance.

I came hobbling back from the latrine the last night we were there as Silly Willie opened the ambulance doors to toss something inside, and I caught a glimpse of the three figures: Sam, with the Bible open, a flashlight in his hand, an Army blanket hooded over him to shield the light; Bob Russell and Preacher were sitting opposite him. "What the f--- goes on?" asked Silly Willie, beginning to laugh.

Following a moment's silence, Sam snapped, "Prayer meetin'!"

"Oh!" Silly Willie walked away, staggered.

At night our room was often winter-cold. Getting ready for bed, we sometimes lit a candle stump and placed it far back in a corner, away from the open lace-curtained window. Tired of wearing our clothes month in and month out, we undressed as far as our long underwear. Each night, before putting out the candle, Teddy and Cliff had a romp and a pillow fight.

"Silly children! Aren't you ever going to grow up?" Phil asked, crawling around on all fours, looking for his receptacle.

Ted and Cliff were jumping in unison on their double mattress until their heads almost touched the ceiling, then they lunged at each other, pinching and swatting. Cliff flung a pillow at Phil.

"Now look here!" Phil cried. "You've hit me with your damned pillow! Why can't you watch what you're doing? Annoying young ones!"

"Oh, don't be such an old fart!" Teddy said, shying another pillow at him in the hope that Phil would retaliate. Phil did, and Ted and Cliff jumped off the bed and fell on him, and there was a tussle all about the room, ending only when they had knocked his glasses off under one of the beds.

"Is that how you sleep?" Ted asked a few minutes later. "One on one side of the bed and one on the other? It is? That's not how we sleep, is it, Cliff? See, Cliff sleeps on his side and I fit right up against him like he was sitting in a chair, and when he gets tired we turn around, and then it's my turn to sit in the chair." It was seldom quite that peaceful.

Long after the candle went out, there were cries as one pinched or punched the other, and often they played "last tag," with Teddy saying, "Now, that's the end. There. You started it and I—Cliff, you dirty bastard! There! Now stop!"

"Oh, for *God's* sake," Phil would cry, "go to sleep!"

In the middle of the night I awoke and the cold dark room was filled with piercing screams, one following the other. They seemed to be coming from a shell hole in the ceiling. I sat up in the dark, astonished, half under the impression that all the London air-raid sirens had gone on. Then I thought someone in the room was shot and that the rest of us were being taken prisoner by the Germans.

"My God, what's happening here?" I shouted. Phil too had leaped up, asking, "What? Who? What?" The wild full screams continued from the ceiling.

"There's a *mouse* in the room!" Teddy screamed hysterically above us. "A mouse, a *mouse!*" He let out the whooping screams again. He was dancing on the pillows at the head of his bed, trying to leap over to the marble-topped night table beside ours.

"A mouse!" Phil cried. "Is that all it is?"

"Well, it ran right over my face and I don't like it!"

"Well, shut up and go to sleep. You're a damned pest!"

"No! Someone's got to catch it! It was after the Nabiscos, I think."

His shouts had awakened the others far around in the opposite side of the house, and some of them came tearing down the hall, their bare feet thudding. The door crashed open.

"Fer crissake, what's happened? Who's *hurt?*"

"No one. It's just Teddy," Phil said. "He thought a mouse ran over him."

A series of blistering curses met the explanation and the men retired along the hall. It took about ten minutes of persuasion before Ted would lie down again. I had to close the box of Nabiscos that had come in an overseas package to Phil, and at last Ted pulled the covers up. Just on the point of drifting to sleep, the suspicion crossed his mind that Cliff had tickled him across the face to pretend it was a mouse, and that precipitated a fight, a tussle and hair-pulling that lasted another five minutes.

American combat men, I thought. A holder of the Bronze Star for outstanding bravery . . .

When I heard we were leaving Wiesbaum, I asked Preacher to loosen the bandage on my knee, for I knew I wouldn't be able to climb up into the trucks with a leg that stiff, nor would there be enough room for me to hold it out straight. He loosened it so that I could bend my knee a little.

We rolled for hours toward the Rhine, passing white surrender flags hung from the upper windows of farmhouses, and burned-out German vehicles strung along the roads. But no one took heart from these signs. Everyone felt the enemy had retreated to the east bank of the river to make a last stand. When we arrived during the late afternoon at Mulheim, I was surprised to hear that we were on the west bank, not of the Rhine but of the Moselle River, at a place near where the two came together. The city of Coblenz lay just across the Moselle and we were to capture that before attacking the Rhine.

Prolonged artillery barrages made a continuous dull booming, with the heavy shells going in and coming out, but since we couldn't see where they landed—the hilly town cut off the view of the river—we paid no attention to the sound. It was impossible to keep up for long any pitch of feeling; the softness of the spring weather itself acted as a soporific and lulled the nerves. We were quartered in a cobbled street of three-story tan tenements hung with white surrender flags. A long twilight bloomed all pink and rose and violet over the flats, and everywhere men sat at doorways or up at open windows, lolling at ease, smoking, talking across the street to each other. In the dusk, one man rode a large white draft horse bareback through the street, smoking a cigar. A slightly warm, sour smell of the past owners' living floated up out of the windows, open perhaps for the first time that season.

As darkness came over the sky, the yellow circles of candlelight grew more noticeable in the various rooms where men were washing or writing letters or cooking on the stoves. Soon the guards patrolling the streets called, "Lights. Put out the lights," and here and there blackout shields went up. In other cases the windows remained open, but the candles were snuffed out and the tips of cigarettes glowed inside the unlighted rooms. Voices talked on and on in the darkness; then the moonlight came down, softening and bleaching everything.

Our particular two-room apartment belonged to an old

woman, one guessed from the musty clothes hanging on pegs, the push-pedal sewing machine, the numerous plants in tin cans, the clutter. The contents of an entire house, heavy dining-room furniture and all, seemed to have been packed into the two rooms.

We were gathered together there when Captain Stettner came in, unfolded a big crackling green-spotted map, and with his nicotine-stained finger pointed out the city of Coblenz on the opposite bank and traced the triangle of ground formed by the juncture of the Moselle and Rhine rivers. We were to make the amphibious assault on the city the following night at midnight in utmost secrecy, not from our present location but from a smaller town a few miles farther down, called Gulls. Again he impressed on us the need for secrecy. The litter bearers, he added in the heart-thumping stillness, were to be attached to the line companies for the operation. "You're goin' over in assault boats. You're gonna paddle over, and you'll have your shoes unlaced, your packs loose, ready to slip off at a moment's notice. How many can swim?" Uncertainly, a few hands were raised. "Better still, how many can't?" Most of the hands went up slowly in the silence. "Well, I'll tell you. If—y-you get in any trouble, don't lose your heads. Just hang onto the side of the boat until someone comes along and picks you up."

That concluded the meeting. The non-swimmers pushed past each other blindly.

The next day after lunch we were marched up the cobbled street to a farm just beyond the town, and, turning up the wide driveway, we found C Company holding a class on the edge of the first plowed field. Most of the men were sitting in a wide semicircle under the budding trees, but a group was out in the field and an officer was addressing them in a loud voice.

"First Battalion Headquarters? Medics? All right, you men, just fall out around here and watch what's going on." Major Gregory, taking Colonel Hessig's place, and several members of his staff, had come out to observe. Before my stunned eyes, there was a large rowboat lying in the lumpy field. "All right, Lieutenant, if you'll go on now with the lesson. I want your men to pay strict attention." Out in the bare sunlight, Lieutenant Dobrozek, C Company's new commander, was instructing his men how to get in and out of the boat.

"Awright, you men, now here's how you're gonna *do* this!" The lieutenant, sweating and red-faced, had an extremely loud voice and there was something wild and disheveled about his gestures. "Now pay attention! This line here, when I give you the signal, you start forward, you understand?" For no reason he began to push at the line, shoving one man one way, pulling another another way. "All right now, begin!"

"Look at the crazy bastard," a C Company man said. "He's drunk and they're trying to keep him away from the brass." There was a little convoy about him, consisting of a few lieutenants and staff sergeants.

The first man of the line stepped over the back of the boat, walked up to the front and knelt down. Three men followed after him in silence, then three more, and three more, until the boat was filled. Those near the oarlocks passed their rifles over to the men kneeling down the center.

"Now tonight, when you get in these boats, you wanna be absolutely quiet." The lieutenant, slightly unsteady, raised his elbow and wiped the sweat from his red face. "D'you get that? Quiet!" His voice came out in a roar, and, sitting nearby me, De Vroom gave a sudden good-natured peal of laughter. "Your entrenching tools are gonna be all padded so they don't make any noise banging against the boat. We don't want a sound because the Jerries will be waitin' for us on the other bank, and you know how noise travels at night. Now the idea is to all row in time. The first guys set the pace and the rest all follow."

"This is the most f---ed up thing I ever saw," the men on the sidelines were saying.

"All right now, begin! One, *pull!* Two, *pull.* No, *together!* Try it again. One, *pull! Two,* pull!" Some of the oars flailed out and struck clumps of earth; others rowed swiftly above it. None was in unison. "Four, pull! Fi— *That's* not how you hold an oar!" He rushed over to a man who was gripping the oar from underneath. "This way, like this! You got it? All right, *pull!*"

"Jesus, this is gonna be a slaughter."

"And when you bring the oar back, you turn it so it don't hit the water flat and make a big splash. You feather it, you understand?"

Most of them didn't understand at all. And this time when they tried, one man dropped his oar out onto the dirt and

349

leaned out to retrieve it, flinching, as if he expected a blow from the lieutenant.

"Are you men watching this?" Major Gregory asked sternly.

"Oh, yes, sir!" De Vroom replied for all, and then gave his clear, happy laugh of amusement.

When it came the turn for our group to practice getting in and out, and rowing, I knew I wouldn't be able to swing my stiff leg over the boat. Rather than add the final note of grotesquerie by stumping forward and hauling myself aboard like a crab, I melted across into the group that had already gone through; and I decided to remove the bandage entirely.

During the day Bob Russell had begun to feel sick. He threw himself down on a pile of folded blankets in the living room, missed the rowing lesson, and when we started down for supper he was not able to join us.

"What's the matter, Russ?" Tubby asked. "Gittin' a li'l nervous 'bout this here river crossin'?"

"Ah feel sick to mah stomach," he answered. "Mah heart's pumpin' powerful fas' an' that's what's makin' me feel so sick."

"Could we bring you back something to eat?"

"No. Ah think if ah jes stay here awhile, near this open window . . ."

Sam Benton, Jr., went over and sat beside his disciple, who fell asleep face down, and then began to sweat and groan and thrash around a little. Preacher came up after dinner, took his temperature, frowned at the thermometer, and went down to get Captain Stettner.

The captain, in high spirits, brought with him the news that a bridge across the Rhine at Remagen, about eighteen miles north of us, had been captured by the Americans and that so far the small force was hanging on despite fierce enemy attempts to annihilate it. Not only that, but one of our own regiments had already got across into Coblenz and was trying to clear a place for us to land. As we listened, the sounds of a sustained, heavy barrage floated across the river.

Over in the corner near the windows, Bob Russell, drowsy-eyed and sweating, was on the verge of delirium, and the captain ordered him to be evacuated. The ambulance was to rush back to us as soon as possible. Russell, wrestling with his conscience, put up a halfhearted fight to stay, but he was carried downstairs and out into the ambulance.

"Pure case of buck-fever," Warren Troy said, looking calmly about. No one disputed it, though later, because they liked Bob Russell, everyone said he "musta picked up a bug of some kind."

Darkness came down, the few candles were lighted on the table, and the blankets were pulled over the windows. The constant booming and crashing from across the river gained in intensity, but our room was quiet, with most of the men attempting to rest, their heads down on the table. I had been given several bundles of unpressed, cleaned uniforms to distribute to any men from the battalion who might fall into the water. The candles burned on in silence.

"It's this waiting!" someone said in a low voice.

"Yeah, if you could only get it over!"

"Hey, shut up, you guys; I'm trying to sleep."

Suddenly Sergeant Campbell walked in. "All right, you me-e-en, better git off to your companies. They're gittin' ready to pull out. Formin' on the street now."

We all stood up. The litter bearers buckled on their full field packs, slung on the medical bags. There was a look around, face turning to face, as the squads were about to separate.

"Well, I guess this is it. So I'll say so long, guys." Some began to shake hands, but the others were ashamed to follow suit.

"Les," Ted whispered, "pray for us. Take care of the binoculars I found. They're right there. And my other pack."

"All right. And I have your flag, Cliff, and your bag of coins."

"Well, we all set, guys?" They were, but none wanted to be the first to start for the door. They turned to the few of us who were not leaving as yet. "You lucky bastards, you!"

"Look, we'll be going over too. We'll see you on the other side."

"Yeah." They seemed relieved to find any unemotional words of farewell. "See you guys over there! See you all on the other side. Come on, Don. Come on, Ted. All right, Sam. We'll be seein' you."

"Good luck!" we called.

"Yeah, good luck," a few answered bitterly. They all went out and clattered down the stairs. We stood in silence until the front door slammed behind them.

And now, down below on the street, we could hear the troops falling into line, roll call being taken, orders given in sharp, half-whispered voices. Feet began to tramp quietly as the companies went by, then the last sounds faded away.

"We cross right after the rifle companies," Warren Troy said. "We're the first vehicle to go over."

"Are we going to row the damned thing over?" I asked.

"I don't know. I never thought of that."

We sat around the table for perhaps a half hour listening to the shells across the river.

"All right, me-e-en, get them blankets downstairs now. Take your 'quipment along. We're gonna leave. Ambulance is outside."

"Who've we got driving? Silly Willie?"

"No. Two new boys we don't know."

A convoy of vehicles had formed on the dark street. Motors were running quietly; headlights were blacked out. A shielded flashlight went on for a moment. Up ahead of the convoy, Captain Stettner was sitting in the jeep with Tubby and Mike Nowak.

"You boys follow us along. Stay close. We can't show any lights."

Sergeant Campbell climbed up with them, while Preacher, Warren, Phil and I got into the ambulance. The unknown driver closed the doors, turned up the back step, and we started off. The moon was shrouded and visibility poor; once outside the town, I didn't know how the driver could make out the captain's jeep ahead. Relax, I told myself; there's no use worrying over their job. Let them do the driving.

"C'n you see 'em?" the driver asked a few minutes later.

"No, but they must be right up there."

Two or three minutes of silent driving.

"I don't think we're on the road," the driver cried, and we smashed into a sapling. "Goddamit, I must have missed the road some place!" We began to lurch and bump through a hilly woods, crashing down young trees, narrowly sliding between old ones.

"Can't you find the road?" Preacher asked.

"No!"

"Well, don't you know where we *are?*"

"Yeah. *I* know where we are. We're behind the German lines!"

"Oh, good God!" My first reaction was one of annoyance. Couldn't we go any place without getting lost? "Aren't the Germans all over on the other side of the river?" I asked as we nearly tipped off our seat.

"No. They're all over this f---ing place."

An inward constriction came—a fear that we were riding in among their foxholes, that we would be halted, ordered out hands over head, and be marched off for separate questioning.

"Well, you must have seen a map." Warren Troy was impatient with blunderers. "Start bearing to your right till you get back on the road, and then drive ahead on. God!"

The driver accepted the rebuff in silence. We jounced up and down, crashed into heavy underbrush, skidded a little on a stretch of pale sand, and shortly after found a road. Whether it was the right road or not, we didn't know, but after driving cautiously along it for about six minutes, a guard suddenly materialized, bringing a rifle up almost against the driver's face. My heart gave a jump and stopped, then beat on in a rush of relief.

"First Battalion medics?" the guard said in a low voice. "Go down this next street to your right. Don't make any noise."

"The line-company guys here yet?" The driver's voice was equally hushed.

"No. No one's here. Something's wrong."

We rolled quietly and slowly through a silent, unlighted town where the houses were close together.

"In here." Mike Nowak's voice was hushed in the dark. "Bring it up the driveway." The narrow driveway between two flat plaster houses curved around toward a large barn in the back yard. As the driver let us out, the captain appeared at the top of the cellar steps.

"Men, get down the cellar here. No noise. Driver, run the ambulance inside the barn there and close the doors on it. Then come downstairs."

Carrying our packs and some extra blankets, we went down a wide flight of very narrow steps into the cellar.

"D'you guys get lost?"

"Yes, sir. For a little while."

"Well, I don't know what's happened here. No one's in town but ourselves and a couple of C.P. guards. Don't know *where* the companies could be." Someone had lighted a can-

353

dle far back in a corner: the two high, oblong windows had wooden blackout shields clamped in place. The cellar, though neater and larger than most, extending under the whole house, was glacial and damp and it had a dirt floor. I could dimly make out a large crib, or bin, with white slats. The two drivers came down from the yard. "Sure you men closed those barn doors good?"

"Yes, sir."

"Well, how about movin' your stuff upstairs into the kitchen, and lettin' us know when the companies come along?"

The drivers looked at him a moment and, without answering, turned and went upstairs. Shortly after, the captain interrupted his nervous pacing to ask Phil to go up in the kitchen too and stay with the drivers. "Be sure, if they have any light goin', that the place is blacked out good."

The chill cellar depressed me, and I asked if I couldn't go along too. We went up the steps into the yard, around and in through the back door of the house. The drivers were lying in a cleared corner of the kitchen, away from the shuttered windows. They were leaning on their elbows, in their sleeping bags, smoking. A lighted candle was beside them on the floor. The crash of artillery shells came clearly from across the river.

"He send you up here too?"

"Well, yes, but we don't like cellars, so it doesn't matter." We spread out our blankets, making a wide bed beside them.

Probably about midnight, when the crossing should have started, I was awakened by someone shaking me. My eyes flew open; I remembered at once where I was, but at first I didn't recognize the captain's voice. He was squatting down, speaking to me in a whisper.

"You four men. Quick! Get down the cellar!"

"Cellar?"

"There's something wrong! The companies didn't show up. We're the only ones here except for a couple of C.P. guards, and there's small-arms fire comin' closer every minute. Wake those guys up and tell them to take all their stuff down. Don't leave anything up here. Nothing! Be quick!" As he was whispering, I could hear the pop and zing of rifle fire and the stuttering of burp guns. He tiptoed quickly out, down the three steps into the yard. Why had he come up himself to warn us? The drivers awoke and wriggled out of their bags, cursing.

"Don't strike a light! Get everything, and get downstairs. You ready, Phil?"

"What was it he was saying? There's no one here but some C.P. guards?"

"Yeah. The aged, the ruptured and crippled, but it's all right. Old Man Owens is probably among them." We began to shake with laughter.

"Old Man Owens will protect us," Phil said as we started out of the house, our arms burdened, the blankets trailing.

"And looking like the 'Spirit of Seventy Six' doing it." Our laughter stopped at once: there was rifle fire in the back yards further down the street; one could see the scarlet flash of tracer bullets in the dark. We tiptoed across the stretch of paving and began hurriedly to go down the narrow steps sideways.

"Hurry up!" the captain whispered from the bottom. The drivers, coming down after us, closed the slanted doors of the cellar board. "Put out that candle! Everyone get down. Lie down."

Complete darkness now; the cold damp floor; the feeling of being inside a refrigerator. I began to shiver, not alone from the cold. The rifle fire had grown appreciably nearer.

"All you men got your Red Cross identification?" the captain whispered. We were lying close, facing the flight of steps.

"Yes." The whispers came back.

"I haven't got mine," Phil murmured to me. As I recalled, he didn't even have an armband.

"Atwell, is your rifle down here?"

"No, it's somewhere in the truck, I think." And where was the little truck? In the barn too with the jeep?

"Well, I'll try to explain." Did he mean he'd try to explain me?

A sudden light exploded in front of my eyes. Cliff's swastika flag and the collection of German coins. But where in God's name had I dropped my pack? Off somewhere in the blackness, in the middle of the cellar floor. There was no time to search. A loud chattering of small-arms fire had broken out in the next back yard. And who were they firing *at*? A few C.P. guards?

"No one move or speak after this," the captain was whispering. "If they come down here, I'll do all the talking. *If they let me talk.*"

The moment, I thought, had come. I could feel my heart racing and pounding, and my mouth went suddenly dry. Loud footsteps ran gritting up our driveway to join the others moving over the cement in the back yard. Hard-breathing voices spoke in German. A pair of German boots went up the three steps onto the little back porch and into the kitchen just over our heads. Breathless, I was waiting for the barn doors to open. And a moment after they discover the ambulance there'll be a search, the cellar doors will be flung back with a crash, a German voice will shout something . . .

My God, I thought, how often could one go through this strain, this sensation of fear wrenching and bucketing up from the pit of one's stomach? Part of my mind, racing ahead in disconnected exploding pictures, heard the captain saying, "We are all medics, except this one man," saw my pack with my number on it being ripped apart to disclose the Nazi flag, saw us all being shot down in the dark against the barn wall. At the same time I hated to be caught lying there and would have got to my feet but I was afraid of making a sound in changing my position. Give nothing but your name, rank and serial number, I thought, hoping that I as well as everyone else would behave well.

A consultation was going on upstairs at the cellar doors. Footsteps gritted. One of the Germans spat. The boots came down the backporch steps, and rifle fire opened up in the yard beyond us. The Germans at our cellar door moved up to join in.

After a long silence, a voice whispered, "They've gone." When nothing happened, I stood up. Somewhere a knee bone cracked. Several men got to their feet.

"I guess they're gone."

"For the time being."

But it was not possible to grow tense again in anticipation: the emotion had worn itself out.

"Phil," I said, "let's spread out a blanket. The floor is freezing. Put one down and one over us." We settled down to wait for more Germans. Bursts of rifle fire sounded from time to time, but I felt myself dozing off to sleep.

When I awoke, the cellar doors were open and gray morning light showed at the top of the stairs. Cocks were crowing in the back yards.

"The boys are comin' in now," someone was saying. "Yeah, I can hear 'em!"

"All right, upstairs, everyone! Upstairs! The boys are here!"

As I came up yawning into the back yard in a thin fog, it seemed for some inexplicable reason that a whole new era was beginning. I looked down the driveway and saw a few sheets hanging out of the windows of the houses across the street where there had been no surrender flags last night, and a scattering of soldiers and a few vehicles went by.

The captain came into the kitchen smiling with relief as we started heating our K-ration breakfasts. "Everything's all right. The companies are just startin' over now."

"What held them up last night? Where were they?"

"Oh, at the last minute G-2 found out the Jerries knew we were gonna cross from here at Gulls, so they rushed after the companies an' headed 'em off from comin' here, but they forgot about us, or couldn't find us, or somethin'." It was already in the past, no longer important.

The kitchen became crowded with drivers, sergeants and messengers dropping in, giving reports on the crossing taking place unopposed, just above the town. Then a messenger came hurrying to ask if there were any dry clothes here in the aid station: an entire boat had capsized and gone down. Eight men out of the thirty-odd had been drowned. Some of the rescued had been taken to the opposite shore; the others were being sent up to us.

Someone else came in to report there was a girl at the front door asking if anyone inside could speak German. Phil Schaeffer was sent out and I followed him along the hall. The fog was gone and the sun was coming out. It was nearly seven o'clock.

The girl, prettier than any German we had yet seen, dark-haired and blue-eyed, with finely chiseled features but a bad skin, bowed and gulped and began to talk rapidly to Phil, twisting her hands. She wore ski pants under a fitted winter coat, and a dark-blue scarf bound tight around her head, showing only the tips of her ears and the dark widow's peak of her hair.

"She says," Phil said, turning to me, rattled, "that she has two wounded men over in her house about a block away, and they need attention. She's done what she could for them

357

but she thinks they should go to the hospital. I don't know whether she means soldiers or civilians or what." Phil went back to report to the captain, and I waited at the open doorway with the girl. She stood clasping and unclasping her hands, shaking her head. She looked as if she had been sitting up all night. When a few civilians went past, fleeing with milk carts crammed with possessions, she turned and gave them a tired smile of greeting. They glared at her, standing with me on the front step. She sighed and shook her head, and tried to tell me, I think, that now they'd think she was a collaborationist.

Phil returned with two of the hangers-on from the kitchen who had each been given a litter and were told to commandeer litter squads from the passing infantrymen and bring the wounded men back.

They had just gone hurrying off after the girl when eight or ten dripping, shivering men came waddling in, some still clutching onto their wet weapons. I went out to the ambulance to get the bundle of dry clothes and when I came back one man was saying with chattering teeth: "I don't know. We were overcrowded, I guess, and when we got out in the middle, the boat just—just went down. The first thing I knew, I was in the water. I don't know."

I brought them down to one of the rooms toward the front of the house and gave out the dry underwear and socks, the unironed uniforms. "I didn't get any towels, so I guess you'll have to dry yourselves off with the draperies here." It was a side room, still shadowy and chill with imprisoned night air. The furnishings were cheaply ornate and there was a large pier mirror. With numb fingers the men began to peel off their wet uniforms. The room in front of this turned out to be a butcher shop, depleted of stock, with empty showcases, chopping block, hanging scales, and a suspended beam of sharp hooks.

The temporary litter bearers were back, carrying through the narrow hall a light-haired, delicate-looking, frightened boy about twelve years old and a wounded German sergeant with his hands clasped behind his head. They were set down on the kitchen floor, and the infantrymen who had carried them took themselves off. The young boy had been wounded by an exploding shell two days before; he had a broken arm and a bandage around his head. The soldier, who was about twenty-eight, blond and hard-looking, had a bad wound in the thigh, but he answered no questions as to where or when he had been hit. Plainly it had not been his idea to come to the Americans for help. Preacher finished the dressings and Warren Troy was making out the evacuation tags when someone came in and said the same girl was outside, crying, asking again for the man who could speak German.

When we went to the doorway, she poured out a sudden tearful story to Phil. He listened, frowning through his cracked glasses and making crowing noises half aloud.

"Yah, yah," he said from time to time.

"What's she saying?"

"I don't know," he said to me.

"Then tell her to go slower! Gnädiges Fräulein, langsam, langsam!"

"She keeps saying 'erinnerung,' and I don't seem to remember what that is! Keepsake, I *think*. But it's all mixed up with her grandfather and a watch—I don't know."

The girl kept showing us her wrist, tapping it, and pointing distractedly to the passing soldiers.

Phil asked her if the "erinnerung" were a watch, and in great relief she said, "Yah, yah. Americanische soldaten—"

"Oh, God. She's telling us the American soldiers just stole the watch and she wants us to get it back for her." The watch had been a family heirloom. "It was either her father's or her grandfather's—probably both's—and she gave it as a keepsake to the soldier inside—evidently her boy friend. And just now, coming along the street, some of our guys held up the litter and took the watch from him." Phil turned back to her and explained that there were now too many soldiers moving through the town for anyone to be able to find out who had stolen the watch.

She was about to turn away when she asked if she might see her two charges before they were taken off to the hospital. The young boy seemed to be either her brother or her cousin.

I went back to the kitchen to inquire for her, and, surprisingly, the captain gave his consent. The girl came hesitantly down the hall, passing with a shock the open door of the room where the rescued men were rubbing themselves dry, the pier mirror multiplying their naked bodies. Unprepared for the number of men in the kitchen, she nodded once, then moved over to the foot of the young boy's litter and, bending toward him, hands pressed between her knees, she spoke softly, trying to encourage him, trying to smile, while tears formed in her eyes.

The German soldier, still with his hands behind his head, angrily refused to look over at her, but at her entrance a wave of color swept over his face. She moved away from the boy, over to him, and began apologetically to speak to him. He answered once in a monosyllable but stared straight before him. She spoke a few more sentences, pleading with him. With us staring at them, he would not answer. She kept trying to coax a smile or an answer from him. A tear splashed down onto the blanket.

The captain, grinning, said, "Ah, what the hell," and turned his back. Everyone then moved off a little and looked somewhere else, leaving them together. They spoke swiftly, in whispers, her voice continuing soft and caressing, while he seemed to be telling her what to do, how to keep out of sight. She, not thinking, not caring about herself, kept telling him she loved him and would wait for him.

The drivers came in and announced they were ready to go with the ambulance. The captain turned and told the girl it was over, that she would have to leave. The men picked up the litters. She bent over and kissed the young boy. To the soldier, whose face had gone hard again, she put out her hand and then burst into tears. He was carried past her, his hands raised in surrender up in back of his head. She turned to bow to us, tried to say something but could not manage it, and walked blindly out and down the hall.

Without waiting for the ambulance to come back, Preacher, Phil and I set out in the jeep with Warren Troy driving. We went through the little town and down to the riverbank where the last of the line companies was crossing. There was no resistance on the opposite bank, and no rowing either. Boats, such as we had practiced in yesterday afternoon in the field, had outboard motors attached to the backs of them, and they putt-putted back and forth, three or four of them, manned, I was surprised to hear, by our Navy. "What's the Navy doing in the middle of Germany?"

"Beats the s--- outta me," someone replied, but the fact, I gathered, was so. The men, in Army uniforms, wet almost to the waist, were members of the Navy, attached to the Engineers for the river crossings.

It was a clear, fair morning, the 17th of March. I was shocked to discover how calm and unimportant the Moselle

River looked. Even without my glasses, I could clearly see the men getting out of the boats and scrambling up the opposite bank. The river, olive-green, flowed slowly past the muddy banks and budding bushes with a serene ripple and glisten. One could hardly imagine eight Americans drowned in it, pulled down by the weight of their equipment. Would their bodies remain there always?

A not unpleasant smell of mud and river water met the nostrils. A large bridge close to where the boats ferried back and forth had been demolished and it hung down in a ruin of stone and twisted metalwork. Lieutenant Kane, my superior officer, was standing at the water's edge with a small group of men. Somewhere, in honor of St. Patrick's Day, he had found a piece of Kelly-green ribbon and had tied it through the buttonhole of his field jacket.

One of the boats came back for us. Two planks were laid crosswise over it; another two formed a ramp. Warren Troy drove the jeep up onto the boat, and Preacher, Phil and I followed on foot. We sat down between the planks, made ourselves comfortable, and the boat started off. A fair breeze blew and the Red Cross flag unfurled on the front of the jeep, making a tutting sound. It was like going on an excursion, slow and untroubled.

Phil and I grinned at each other. It occurred to me that though Charley Heydt had returned two days ago from the hospital following his migraine attack, Phil had not gone back to litter-bearing. I asked Phil if he were going to continue as Preacher's assistant in the aid station.

"Oh. No! Good God, no! That one siege back there at Olzheim was enough for me. I—I couldn't take it. I was no good at all there. I realized. No, I asked the captain to let me help Joe Mortara with the supplies." Joe Mortara, with only the medics to supply, had no need for an assistant, but the captain had given his consent. "I *think*," Phil said, "I'm being carried along now as excess."

"Well, that was damned nice of the captain."

"Yes. I don't know how long it will continue, of course. It's an odd feeling, being excess."

"I've grown used to it. I feel as though I'm being taken along just for the ride."

We sailed serenely across the Moselle. On the far bank we waited for the ambulance, and when it was ferried across, its red crosses on their white fields standing out clearly in the sunlight, we boarded it and rode up steeply into Coblenz, passing badly smashed, flat-faced gray stone houses, and several dead German soldiers lying against the curbs. Slates, fallen from the roofs, were everywhere.

Our first stop in Coblenz was at a large, deserted red-brick hospital that had been run by Dominican nuns. The wards in the upper stories had been bombed and splintered, but the ground floor was almost intact. In the cellar, in a maze of narrow aisles between coal bins, emergency quarters had been set up with an operating room, diet kitchens, small laundries, and thirty or forty close-packed cots where the sick had lain staring up at the branching pipes of the furnace. In one aisle we came upon jars of homemade jam, and boxes of Ry-Krisp; a tall chest of drawers opened to reveal winter-stored pears and apples and magnums of champagne. A sudden ruffling movement in the dimness startled us: on top of the chest there were three or four hares in improvised cages.

Carrying the food and champagne, we came racing up to the Mother Superior's office. There we joined Captain Stettner, Preacher, Sergeant Campbell and Lieutenant Serletis, just back from the hospital, and we sat about eating the rather crisp, dry, yellow-brown pears and apples and washing them down with full canteen cups of champagne. Outside on the streets there was artillery and rifle fire, but a vast relaxation stole over us in the Mother Superior's office.

Phil loved champagne. "Have more," I kept saying, filling his aluminum canteen cup. "Have all you want. Champagne at noon: it's like being at a wedding. Here. Open another bottle." I had begun not to see very clearly, and not to care. There was a constant desire to go into bursts of laughter, and from time to time a swirling darkness seemed about to come down.

At some point, most of the litter bearers showed up in a delegation at the Mother Superior's office, feeling their job was accomplished when they had crossed over with the companies.

"The boat that went down?" Sam Benton was asking. "That was A Company. *Mah* company. Ah was standin' raght on the shore an' Ah could tell that boat was overcrowded. Only had to look at it. It gets out in the cenner, starts to rock. Next thing, everyone was in the water, all splashin' an' tryin' to swim."

"Didn't anyone go after them?" I asked somewhat thickly.

"Them li'l motor boats put out from each shore, but by then the men were too scattered. All excited. Boats picked up as many as they could, but some of the boys, they struck right out and swam for shore. Made it, too! Ah saw one boy step outta that rescue boat still holdin' onto his grease gun. Pourin' water. Yes, sir, they lost eight men."

The litter bearers had slung off their equipment and were about to join us in the party when the captain returned to the room and ordered them out at once with angry instructions to rejoin their companies and stay with them. It was the iron door closing in their faces. They picked up their equipment, put it on in furious silence, and went out. But instead of returning immediately to the companies, they took shelter in the cellars and houses nearby, where they too found liquor and started celebrations of their own.

The fall of a city the size and importance of Coblenz was nothing as one had imagined it. The windows of all the houses were shuttered tight; a few dead German and American soldiers lay in the streets; jeeps raced by; artillery barrages screamed in, bringing houses down in a thunder of rubble; fighting continued from street to street. But there was, over all, the chaotic air of a drunken, end-of-the-world carnival. Infantrymen who had been down in the cellars ran crookedly past, firing anywhere, and shrill, overexcited young German girls, impatient of rape, ran after them through barrages, ducking into almost flat doorways as tiles fell from the roofs in crashing showers.

A Free French newspaper photographer drove up in a jeep, brandishing a revolver, and staggered out drunk to take pictures. In a shuttered house directly across the way from us we heard someone banging out "Lili Marlene" on the piano, and, going into a rage, the photographer entered and pulled open the living-room door with a shout. On the point of firing, he found himself aiming at two American soldiers: Ted Jameson at the piano and Paul Clifford standing beside him. The photographer came over to us, shaking from his narrow escape.

In another house, Jimmy McDonough and Horse-face Fogarty, an aid man temporarily taking little Jenkins' place, were looting the contents of a living room. They had learned to say, "Achtung! Macht schnell! Kommen Sie hier!" and approximations of several other German expressions that they repeated to each other over and over. While Fogarty had his back turned, rifling through the ornaments in a corner whatnot, Jimmy McDonough, with mock German gruffness, said just behind him, "Achtung! Macht schnell!"

"Hey, cut it out; you make me nervous," Fogarty said, but a moment or two passed and the harsh German voice resumed. "Cut it *out*, I said!" Fogarty repeated. "What the hell's the matter with you anyway, always f---in' around." Then he felt something poke him in the back, and when he turned he saw that Jimmy McDonough was at the far side of the room, speechless and shivering, his hands trembling over his head. Four armed German soldiers had come into the room after them, and it took both Americans a few jibbering moments before they realized the Germans were poking their rifles at them in an attempt to hand over the weapons and surrender.

In a living room up the street, a group of American soldiers were fast getting drunk. Going tipsily out into the dark hall to look for the bathroom, they found themselves, in confusion, bumping into German soldiers who had been holding wassail on the second floor and had come downstairs on the same mission. " 'Scuse me. Beg your pardon. Wanna get through here," one American found himself saying to an equally drunken German in a polite, Alphonse-and-Gaston act.

Don Stoddard dashed in off the street to escape a heavy artillery barrage, and, running into a dining room, looking for the way to the cellar, he came upon one of his litter squad having sexual intercourse with the woman of the house. It was Bob Lozlo, of Hungarian descent, a young expectant father, dark and thin-faced, who was replacing Dick Gann as litter bearer.

At intervals between the shelling, the cobbled street just outside the hospital rang with the heavy clatter of German boots as long streams of prisoners came past. There were as many as forty or fifty at a time, hands up, being chevied along by two small infantrymen, one of whom invariably was unsteady on his feet. Many of the prisoners themselves were drunk; their canteens were filled with cognac.

Once German 88s screamed in and a long line of prisoners, four abreast, hands over their heads, though badly frightened, broke into an orderly run. There were some wounded among them, being helped or carried along, and far behind, shouting, running for all he was worth in his long overcoat, came one enormous, tipsy clown of a private, eager to join his fellow prisoners.

By four in the afternoon Coblenz proper had not been cleared, but the companies, still engaged in street-to-street fighting, were ahead of us. The captain had Tubby drive him forward in the jeep, and shortly after he telephoned for us to pack up and join him at the Municipal Hospital, which had crammed itself, the patients from the Dominican Hospital and many civilian refugees into one bunker that extended several floors beneath ground level.

A wide horseshoe drive led up to the hospital past sloping lawn, trees and flower beds. The building had two large forward wings, and in the stout cement foundation of the one on the right the narrow entrance to the air-raid shelter was located. On entering it, one came into a long, windowless, prisonlike hall. It was crowded with families bedding down for the night much as English families must have done in the London subways. Doctors in white uniforms with stethoscopes hanging around their necks, and nurses in mobcaps and long starched aprons, were trying to get the people settled, or visiting those who were ill. The more affluent families had brought with them blankets, beach chairs, back rests, air cushions, small mattresses and pillows, and hampers of food. Some elderly couples, already wrapped in steamer rugs, looked like ocean travelers riding out a storm on an inside deck. Children, enjoying the novelty, ran back and forth, playing under the feet of the American soldiers. You could hear the crash and explosion of shells outside.

A patient was trundled out of one of the rooms that opened off this hall. Captain Stettner was there, ordering three or four more of the rooms to be set aside for our use; the largest of these was to be cleaned and prepared for him. Two nuns were listening attentively to the instructions. The younger of the two—slender, pale, and serious—spoke English, and she appeared to be in charge. Her companion, about thirty-five years old, was red-faced, with glasses, and lips that tried to close firmly on her protruding teeth. The younger nun translated the instructions for the other to carry out, then she hurried away. Shortly after, the captain left with Sergeant Campbell and Lieutenant Serletis to examine the hospital. There were several American prisoners of war in it and the captain had given orders for them to be moved out of the wards at once, out of the jurisdiction of the German doctors and nurses.

"See that they get this room fixed up," the captain said to Phil and me as he departed.

The eyeglassed, buck-toothed nun found two porters and put them to work sweeping and mopping the floor in the captain's room. She left after stripping the beds, and presently a frightened young nurse's aide showed up with clean sheets and pillow cases. She wanted to leave them and run, but one of the porters, with a laugh, grabbed her by the wrist and made her stay.

As I took a look at him from the hall, I noticed that he wore on his dark uniform a small diamond-shaped patch over the breast pocket with OST on it: the badge of a slave laborer from the East. He was a man in his late twenties, of average height and good-looking, with heavy, wet, smooth black hair. Although a slave laborer, he appeared to be on excellent terms with the hospital staff, and the young girl was plainly afraid of him. Smiling, holding her close from behind, he whispered something to her and gave her a sudden push. She picked up his mop and began his work. He strolled out into the hall, snapped his fingers at another young girl as she tried to hurry past. She stopped, cringing a little. He brought her in and put her to work too. The other porter, who had no slave laborer's badge, kept his head down as he worked and studiously paid no attention to what went on.

The assured black-haired young man went into the room and closed the door. A second later, one of the girls opened it. He closed it, and, after a scuffle, it was opened again. As the girls worked, he kept untying their aprons, slipping his arm about them, running his hands over them. Somehow I caught the impression he was not exercising any new-found liberty, but that this sort of thing had been going on for some time and that he had become a minor power in the hospital. Why else, I wondered, hadn't he walked out, now that we had arrived and he was free?

When the homely, bothered nun returned, the girls made no complaint but, on finishing their task, took their mops and went out.

The captain had left orders that he wanted a table moved into the room for his latest acquisition: a large German radio.

There was a white metal washstand in the room and the nun said something about it, evidently telling the porters to carry it away. I told Phil to tell her to leave it, and somewhat haltingly he did.

Leave *this?* This was not a table. This was a washstand! "Wasch-tisch!" she said. "Wasch-tisch!"

"It's good enough," I said. "Ist goot."

Her eyes stared, magnified by the glasses. "Nein! Nein!" She was horrified at the thought of the captain using a makeshift. The two porters carried the offending little washstand out and disappeared.

Phil and I went out again to look at the civilians, and in about ten minutes the buck-toothed nun came searching for us, wringing her hands. The porters had not come back. There was no table for the captain!

I said to Phil, "Tell her he can keep the radio on the floor."

Phil tried to explain that the table didn't matter, but I could see she had an inborn high regard for Army officers; besides, she had been told to get a table and nothing short of a table would do. She was pigheaded, determined, and completely Deutscher in that respect.

"She wants to know if we'll come with her and get the damned table," Phil said.

She was a nun and it was awkward for either of us to refuse. Asking us to follow her, she took off at a rapid clip down the hall, up the stairs through an arch and down another equally crowded passageway. The people this far back had never seen American soldiers and they scrambled flat back against the wall drawing their children in close to them. We went down two or three flights of stairs and along corridors lighted by dim, infrequent bulbs. Everywhere stone, cement, steel doors. Then up flights of stairs, and the atmosphere suddenly lifting and changing, the air growing fresher: we were on ground level again, in the center of the original hospital, hurrying along a spacious waxed reception hall. Where a large stain-glass window was blown out, one saw the gardens, the boughs of trees, the clouding, twilight sky.

The nun went into a large parlor where there were sofas under sheets and several pieces of hospital equipment, including a ponderous white metal chest of drawers. The nearest French window was smashed and hanging from its frame. I believe one swift glance showed the nun that the table she had been counting on was gone, and instantly she had settled on the chest. Near it was a "wash-tish," the mate if not the very one that had been removed from the captain's room. She put her hand down on the heavy chest of drawers and indicated that we, she included, were to carry it back.

"Das ist zu gross!" Phil said.

"Es ist *nicht* zu gross!" she protested.

"Look, Schwester," I said, "this— Dies ist *goot!*" I pointed to the familiar little washstand.

"Nein!"

"What are we going to do?" Phil asked. "We can't lug this big heavy thing up and down all those stairs."

Buck-toothed, obstinate, she would not budge.

"Could we get the damned thing out the French window here and across the courtyard? There's the entrance to the bunker. Come on. Nein. Danke, Schwester. Danke." We showed her she need not help, that we were going to take the short cut overground. She held open the window frame and we started out under the trees, trampling through flower beds, straining under the heavy load. Because she was a nun, Phil was moderate in his comments. "Nuisance!" was about as far as he would go.

When we were halfway across the garden, a wild shelling began to rake toward us. "Drop it or not?" Phil asked.

"Can you hurry with it? My hands are nearly falling off." It had cut in so deeply I did not think I could put it down in a rush.

We just made the entrance to the bunker as the shells came in close. Deep red marks had cut into our hands.

"Can you imagine," Phil asked, winded, "being killed carrying this damned chest just so the captain could have something to put his radio on?"

Then when we got it to his door, we could hardly get it through.

The room had been left immaculate. We saw Lieutenant Serletis' belongings and claimed one of the twin beds for him, placing his child's-size overcoat on it, determined for once he was going to sleep like a human being. The captain's radio we left on the floor and returned to our own room.

What long, strange days they were, I always thought, compared to those in civilian life. About this time last night we were in— I had to pause and think back. We were in Mulheim, and the litter bearers were waiting gloomily to cross the river with the companies. I remembered how in civilian life someone could ask, "What's new?" and you could often look back over a whole week and truthfully answer, "Nothing."

When we had driven up in the afternoon, Tubby brought the champagne along with us, and the captain announced he was giving a little party for some of the hospital staff. The radio had been connected by the black-haired Yugoslav porter, who had been a mechanic in peacetime. Among the hospital officials and doctors who showed up in their white uniforms, one was a young, tired, quietly good-looking woman doctor whose husband was fighting on the Russian front. Another young doctor was from Luxembourg. He had been taken prisoner by the Germans during the Battle of the Bulge and had been assigned to work in the hospital wards here in Coblenz. He did not appear overjoyed at the thought of liberation or of returning to his own country. There was so much to do here at the hospital, he said, he had so many patients . . . No, he said to the captain, he did not think he would leave immediately for home.

Though I was not a member of the party and saw it only in glimpses from the open doorway, I longed to walk in and go over to the light-haired doctor from Luxembourg and say, "Look. Tell me about it. Why are you staying here? What honestly are the German people like? What is the truth about them?"

The radio crackled and waltzes played. By prearrangement, I think, the doctors and officials all had arrived at approximately the same time. Tired-looking, unenthusiastic, they sat about on the beds and the few chairs, answering the captain in German. He was an expansive host, but after they had had a glass or two of the looted champagne and a cigarette, they got up, thanked him and left. Plainly, it was a duty call: he was the victor; he had asked them to come, and they had.

The captain, with his enthusiasm for new people, especially those who were open in their admiration of him, had now become the sponsor of the black-haired Yugoslav porter. "He knows everything about motors," the captain told us. "Brilliant guy." The man had asked the captain if he couldn't accompany us in the fight against Germany, and attach himself to the medics; he could drive any of our vehicles and keep them in perfect order. The captain did not exactly promise, but said he was going to look into it and would give his answer in the morning.

I went back to my cell-like room and talked awhile to Phil and Tubby. Tubby was affably drunk. He was starting to be fat again now, and he had a way of sitting on top of a chair seat with both legs crossed, one above the other, like Buddha. One hand supported his elbow, and the free hand was raised stiffly as he smoked a cigar. He still wore the coonskin cap with the one permanently curled-out ear flap. "No, now listen, Phil. Listen, Phil, listen to me." The chair he was on was a small, folding metal one and he was in danger of toppling off it at any moment. "Listen, you don't think she —she minded, do you, Phil? All I did—I saw 'em all goin' along the hall, all these p-pregnan' women, and I—all I did, I went over an' I just patted her. A little. Like this. Just light. On the stomach. I didn't mean—you know, like, just to be friends. As a compliment! She laughed, so she wasn't sore. That's all. So, Phil, you think that was all right?"

"Yes, Jim, I'm sure it was all right. She understood. You meant it as a compliment."

"I whistled a little too. Like this: Whooo! Was that all right?"

"Yes, that was fine, Jim, but I couldn't advise you to go around doing that as a matter of course."

"No. Listen, Phil—just between us. What—what d'you think of the cap'm takin' all the champagne an'—an' keepin' it now for himself? Not that *I* care, y'know, 'cause I got somethin' else, better—I got kickapoo juice—but—but what d'you think? I mean he didn' go down the cellar an' *git* any. He'd never do that. But he s-sen's me over to Firs' Battalion with some of it, to make a present to the officers. 'With his compliments.' Hell, them f---ers *had* all they wanted. That stuff belonged to the boys!"

"Well, I guess you have to expect that, Jim."

"Mmm. Have to expec' it." Tubby looked about him. "Roughtie-toughtie, right, Phil?"

"Right, Jim."

Just before nine o'clock, Phil and I went back to the doorway of the captain's room to hear the news bulletins that came in with crackles of static over Radio Luxembourg. A crowd of officers from First Battalion Headquarters had gathered with the captain to drink the rest of the champagne.

370

The bed we had set aside for Lieutenant Serletis was occupied by Sergeant Campbell, lying on it in his underwear; the lieutenant's belongings were on the floor. If Sergeant Campbell was still angling for a battlefield commission, I felt sure, after seeing him in action among the officers, that he would never get it. In an attempt to establish himself on their level, he overplayed his hand; he was loud, brash and familiar, talking far too much and far too fast, cursing freely and resorting to obscenities for hard-won laughs. I was surprised, for with the litter bearers he had never shown any signs of crudeness.

Phil and I stood against the doorway and the news bulletins came on, but there was so much loud talk and laughter in the room that we could hear only parts of it, enough though to learn that the Remagen bridgehead still held fast and was expanding as troops and materiel poured across the Rhine.

The lights in the hall were dim and the crowds slept, most of them sitting with their backs against the wall. Here a woman walked silently up and down carrying a baby; there another sat gazing tiredly ahead, with two or three children leaning against her, relaxed in sleep.

I slept in the top bunk, Phil in the one below me. Howard Mason and Tubby were out. I woke up when they came in and heard them undressing in the dark. Tubby was very drunk and stumbled about as he tried to take off his pants. Getting into his bunk, he cracked his head. Phil had awakened and was carrying on a conversation with him, then there was silence for a while. Soon Tubby was up, pattering around barefoot on the stone floor, bumping into the metal furniture, and then came an entirely different sound of pattering.

"Jim! Jim Cuff! What are you doing?"

"Taking a leak here, Phil."

"Yes, but have you a receptable?"

"I'm usin'—I'm usin' a helmet, Phil."

"Are you sure?"

"Least I—I *think* I am."

"Jim, you're drunk, and I'm very much afraid you're peeing on the floor!"

"Gee, am I?"

He was.

In the morning we dressed and left our equipment packed on the bunks in case we should move out, but we hoped that we would stay at least a few days: the contact with so many assorted civilians was too interesting to leave. Surely some of them must speak English, and if we stayed long enough we might find the answer to some of the questions about the German people that had disturbed us since the start of the war.

In our cell-like room there was no way of heating a breakfast. We ate some K-ration crackers and a few hard candies, but airlessness and the lack of coffee made us feel tired and dispirited in starting the day.

Most of the civilians in the hall were folding blankets, putting away picnic baskets and lining up to use one of the two small toilets. What of their businesses and shops? I wondered. And what would happen when the picnic baskets were empty? Where would the food come from for a city the size of Coblenz?

The halls had grown more crowded during the night. One of the city's prostitutes, who was said to have done a rushing business with American troops the day before, was pointed out to me as a recent arrival in the bunker. She appeared to be in her early thirties and wore dark glasses even when indoors. She had dry, springy, shoulder-length hair and a chapped-looking face. Her mouth, though brightly painted, was scarcely any redder than the rest of her complexion. She wore a heavy tweed suit, white woolen stockings that came to the knees, and polished moccasins; a Glenplaid topcoat was thrown over her shoulders. She sat on a camp chair with her bare knees crossed, her face with the staring blind glasses fixed on us. Now and then, chain-smoking, she shook her wrist, which was loaded with silver bracelets.

The civilians knew before we did when the order was given for us to leave: a whispering in German ran all through the hall. About five minutes later the order reached us and we began to carry out the equipment. The prostitute, abandoning hope of American soldiers, loitered about the line outside the men's room, soliciting there among her compatriots.

Outside the hospital a squad of infantrymen, done up in full field pack, hurried past to join their company about to move out of Coblenz. "Sure," I heard, "you hurry up and

372

take the town and then you get kicked the ass out of it. Service company or some other bunch of rear-echelon bastards move in and have all the fun while we go out into foxholes!"

"Yeah, well we're not gonna be so f---in' smart after this. We're gonna take the towns nice an' slow."

Late the same afternoon we got down out of trucks and, with Battalion Headquarters, started hiking through the woods about a mile from the Rhine. The sun in its descent threw almost horizontal beams of golden-white light in among the dark trees and shadows. A few loud shells crashed nearby. The whole line sank down and after a few minutes arose and continued. No one any longer bothered to comment on the distraction. At twilight we came to a large ramshackle country house in a clearing and we stayed there for the night.

In the morning I was called halfway through breakfast to go around and check rifles for the lengthy sick call. Preacher was working in a room so small and crowded that I remained outside with the weapons. The stone barns and sheds of the house almost enclosed the passing dirt road and turned it into a courtyard. In its center stood a pump and a trough for horses, and there was a constant flashing activity and noise: men pumping water into their helmets for washing, jeeps and trucks driving past, two repaired motorcycles racing up and down the road, and men in groups, bareheaded in the sun, cleaning their rifles for an inspection.

A truck drove up, bringing new equipment and clothing. Now that the weather was mild, winter hoods were distributed for the first time.

"I don't want any, sir," the men were saying.

"I don't give a goddam whether you want 'em or not!" shouted the explosive Captain Christoffsen. "They're issued and you're going to take 'em and *sign* for them! They're part of your equipment and you're going to be held accountable for them."

Many of the men threw them away at once; others put them on over their steel helmets and wore them with the neck band unbuttoned and flapping. A second issue of the much wanted combat boots had also arrived. About a month before, a limited supply of them had come up and there had been fierce competition for their possession. Phil, Warren Troy and I were still wearing leggings and overshoes, and now, in an exchange out at the truck, I fell heir to a pair of used combat boots a size or two too large with a gash across the toe of one.

Some men went unswervingly for new clothing and equipment, and from its acquisition derived a keen sense of satisfaction that had little to do with personal fastidiousness: it seemed more a case of greed. Staff sergeants at Battalion Headquarters, men who worked indoors in clerical positions, pulled strings to secure articles of clothing intended first for combat troops. You saw them, ahead of anyone else, striding about in stiff new yellowish combat boots, brand-new pants, new shirts, new field jackets: Big Time Operators, easily recognizable through their minor victories. Since I disliked these sergeants for their conniving, their tyrannies and their toadying, I never spoke to them and, rather than request new clothing through them—whether one received it or not often depended on their favor—I wore what I had or could find. I had come by a field jacket of Captain Stettner's that he was turning in for salvage. Though enormous on me, it was fairly new and far cleaner than my own, and, unknown to him, I wore it, with the secondhand combat boots, for the remainder of the war.

After lunch some of the litter bearers and I carried wicker chairs out and sat in a hollow, secluded from the wind, at the bottom of the garden where there was a sundial and the remains of a strawberry patch. A rustic fence separated us from the dirt road, and every now and then a former cowboy galloped past bareback on a horse that he had just lassoed in the woods. At times he lost control and came thundering along, hanging onto the mane, the wild-eyed horse bucking and rearing in its efforts to dislodge him, while men sitting along the rustic fence swung up into the trees or took to their heels with shouts and curses for the rider.

Quantities of furniture had been thrown from the upper windows of the house by the retreating German Army. Bureau drawers had been rifled over and over again, and as we sat lazily talking and watching the shadow move around the sundial whose inscription we couldn't translate, snapshots kept blowing down among us, and past, and out across the road, and far into the woods. Someone who had lived in the house had been studying architecture, and they were photographed reproductions of his plans and models that were blowing away. There were also stacks of family photographs. Late nineteenth-century wedding pictures. Babies in long christening gowns. Class pictures. Tennis parties. A city house with lace curtains, with the older brothers and sisters looking down fondly at the new baby in the family. A boy in uniform. What good faces, what a happy, solid family. And what were they all doing now? Was the student of architecture in the Army? Or dead perhaps? Were the other boys in S.S. uniforms, pushing helpless, tortured people into gas chambers? If health and environment and a happy childhood had anything to do with forming a good character, wouldn't this family of boys, and any like it, strongly refuse, rebel against such inhumanity? I put the question to Phil and he said, "Ye-es, I should think it would. Providing, of course, that they knew the inhumanity existed."

The next day the trucks came for us and we rode to Boppard-am-Rhein. Our battalion was to cross the river at midnight. We walked down the long main street toward the unseen river, toward a green stucco bungalow set back from the road, where Mike Nowak was waiting for us, hands in his pockets, smiling. "C'mon in," he said. "It's a good deal." He led the way up the driveway and around to the back of the house, where three young children were swinging on a rustic fence. The long spine of a hill rose up behind the house, cutting off some of the declining sunlight. Facing the last of it, a thin, attractive, vaguely cheap-looking, black-haired girl was lying in a beach chair with large black glasses on; a coat was bundled about her and she wore gray silk stockings and high-heeled shoes. Her face was made up, her lipstick applied in a generous, moist sweep beyond the outer corners of her mouth.

As we approached, the children immediately stopped playing, the back door of the house opened and a more reliable-looking girl stepped out tensely and halted.

"That one up there's the mother of the kids," Mike said, and he tried to present us to the two girls. The children ran to their mother, who drew them close to her and waited to see what would happen. The sun-worshiper smiled when we were introduced and pulled down her skirt a half inch or so; the other girl, her older sister, bowed a little and released the children. The older girl had a quiet, intelligent, unsmiling face. She wore a plaid skirt, a dark sweater, plain green sports jacket, silk stockings, woolen socks and saddle shoes. Her hair was drawn back simply and there was no make-up on her face.

"See the little kid there, the girl?" Mike pointed out a child about three years old. "She's deaf. Stone deaf. Can't hear a sound, so she don't know how to talk." The three children were playing in a grape arbor that climbed part way up the hill.

The married girl, whose husband had been in the Africa Corps and was now a prisoner of war in Kentucky, at first was uneasy about coming into the house with us and remained outside with her sister and the children. The interior was neat, comfortable, and reminiscent of American cottages of 1927. The floors shone. There were scatter rugs, rough plaster walls, bookcases crowded with books, a desk with a painting above it, and good prints on the wall. The profusion of books and prints gave the place a masculine air. In putting my equipment down, I noticed that many of the books were on art and architecture.

The boys walked carefully over the clean rugs and polished floor, and they stacked their equipment neatly away against the wall. For a while, we hung about outside in the late sunlight, watching the children and making attempts to become friendly. Dark-glasses began to enjoy herself and stared up smiling into the sun, but the married girl remained watchful. The children swung on the fence and accepted bits of ration chocolate and gum. Dark-glasses accepted cigarettes and kept arranging the skirt over her knees even when it needed no arranging at all. It dawned on me that the older girl was watching her as much as us. Dark-glasses looked like the early pictures of someone who might later land in moving pictures. Right now her hair was too kinky, her mouth too made up, and there was no variety to her smile.

When the sun dropped entirely behind the hill, we stood up to go inside. Sergeant Campbell arrived in the ambulance with Lieutenant Serletis and Silly Willie and his assistant; the litter bearers were out with the companies and were to make the river crossing with them. I wondered what the girls thought as the companies went past their house on the way to the Rhine bank two blocks or so away. From their faces, you could tell nothing about that.

Through Phil, I asked the married girl if her child's deafness had been caused by the recent bombings. She explained that the child had been born deaf; she had been taking her to Bonn for treatments which had seemed to be helping, but then when transportation of all sorts had broken down, the visits had to be discontinued. "Everything's kaput," the girl said. "Deutschland's kaput." She shook her head while her sister, Francesca, laughed.

"Hitler kaput," said one of our men brightly.

"Yah," the married girl said grimly. "Hitler kaput." She looked bitterly about her as we piled into her house.

Lieutenant Serletis had been immediately struck with the tall Francesca, and he trotted after her, letting out approving barks and whistles. A little conga line formed after her, and Lieutenant Serletis kept pushing the others out of his way, pointing to his bars to impress her, which made her and all of us laugh. Francesca swung her hips as she walked and she walked about unnecessarily. The married sister kept trying to catch her eye, to tell her to sit down.

At one point, to stir up flagging interest, Francesca entered the bedroom that opened off the living room and closed the door. "Where's she gone?" Lieutenant Serletis asked. "Where's that sexy bitch gone?"

"In the bedroom."

"*What?*" He trotted in after her and there was a pleased little scream. She was changing her dress, and made him leave. She came out a few minutes later in a gray silk dress; she had touched up her eyelashes, put on a fresh wide mouth, and had sprayed on a lot of perfume. She enjoyed moving through the rooms, having the tiny lieutenant trot after her saying, "Kommen sie here, Fraulein! Hitler kaput! Guten morgen! Hey, Fraulein! Boy, I'd like to get hold of that bitch. Kommen sie here!"

The older girl was out in the kitchen preparing supper for the children as some of us heated our rations. From the packages, we gave her lemon powder and dried bouillon, a can of cheese, a can of stew, things which puzzled and interested her. The kitchen door opened and a tall, clean-looking blond girl walked in. She was about twenty years old and looked like an American college girl. She was better dressed than either of the girls of the house, in a tweed suit, heavy white sweater, white woolen stockings and highly polished moccasins. Her long shining hair was caught in a snood. Her manner was not so much bold as assured, independent and unflirtatious. She spoke to the girls in German, bowed to us, and sat down in a chair against the wall.

The married girl explained to her that we were medics.

Red Cross. The blond girl looked interested, accepted a cigarette with thanks, still not flirtatious, but rather like a girl who had many brothers. Her name was Marie Elizabeth. To Phil she explained that she did not live in Boppard-am-Rhein. She came from the Boden See, but had been sent to visit an aunt here. Her father was a bellmaker. She had been in a finishing school when the war started and had wanted to be a fashion designer. Yes, she had been drafted into the Girls' Army and had not liked it: she had worked on a farm. She had falsified an illness and had come to Boppard ostensibly to recuperate. She did not believe she would have to go back into the Girls' Army—Deutschland was kaput. Everything was kaput. Poor Deutschland! Hitler! What Hitler had done to them! Her younger brother, like her mother, father and herself, had hated Hitler and the Nazi Party. Her brother, at sixteen, had hurled a stein through the window in their town hall while a party meeting was being held, and he had been forced to disappear, to hide out. They had not seen him or heard a word from him in two years.

This Phil explained to me while he waited through the translation to say something else.

"Do you believe it, Phil?"

"I don't know. She *seems* honest. That business about the brother—I don't know." Phil and I stood near her; some of the other men stood about in an awed semicircle, looking at her.

She launched suddenly into a defense of the people of Germany, none of whom wanted, or deserved, Hitler. She became quite heated and her voice shook with emotion. From time to time she banged her fists on the arms of her chair. The married girl, with an annoyed glance at her, went on with the preparations for the children's supper. Phil told Marie Elizabeth that the German people were, nonetheless, responsible for Hitler and would now have to start rebuilding all the countries they had ravaged. Yes, yes, she knew! She knew that! And decent Germans wanted to do that. They would also have to start rebuilding Germany, too. With this she grew so overwrought that tears came to her eyes. She started to push her hand through her hair and it became entangled with the snood. She ripped it off, flung it down into her lap and cried stormily. After a few moments, she dried her eyes with her fingers and sat staring.

Phil tried to comfort her by saying now that the Nazis

were about to be exterminated, she and all the good Germans should feel better; Germany itself would be in for better days. Marie Elizabeth shook her head. The United States, Great Britain, France and Russia would never let Germany lift her head again. They would grind her down, and keep her down; there would be no hope for anyone. Germany would be thrown helpless to the Russians.

The door opened and a worried middle-aged woman came in—Marie Elizabeth's aunt. She gave a startled look at her niece in tears, but a few words from the married girl put her at her ease. She sat down at the kitchen table and carried on a low-voiced conversation. So far, I gathered, the American soldiers were not as bad as had been expected.

Marie Elizabeth got herself under control, gave up politics for the time being, examined a box of rations and tried a stick of gum. Brightening somewhat, she stood up and went inside to see what the other Americans were like. Two more women arrived at the back door, each with a child, and, seeing their friend at the stove, calmly cooking in the midst of the enemy soldiers, they smiled as if to say, Maybe it won't be so bad. They had stories, small incidents to relate of what they had seen of our Army. The general air was hopeful.

Francesca, in the meanwhile, continued with her teasing, her moving about, and Lieutenant Serletis kept chasing after her, trying, as he said, to talk business. Our blankets were added to the blackout curtains the married girl already had. Candles were lighted in the living room, the heated rations were opened, and three more women came in to visit. The small house took on the air of a family party. Everyone milled about, talking and smiling affably. Phil started to laugh. "Good God," he said, "*look* at us getting ready to cross the historic Rhine! Do you realize every one of us could be fined sixty-five dollars for fraternizing with these people?" The noise and friendly laughter had grown suddenly in volume, drowning out the sound of shelling from across the river. "They'll be able to hear us out on the street. If Colonel Mauck ever stepped in, he'd fine Nick Serletis a *hundred* and sixty-five dollars!"

A few minutes later, at the height of the noise and the laughter, with a group of mixed voices singing "Ach Du Lieber Augustine" in the kitchen, the captain arrived, asking what the hell went on here. We pointed out the two girls who lived in the house, but we could hardly explain the

others. After a moment of puzzlement and indecision, he began to smile and soon was talking in German to the married
girl. Sitting around the dining-room table, the other women
were watchful, and Lieutenant Serletis did not know
whether to continue or abandon the chase. The married girl
made a favorable impression on the captain. He looked at
the sister, and, turning to me after a while, said, "These are
about the most intelligent ones we've struck so far." I said
that of the two I preferred the appearance and general manner of the married girl. "Oh, definitely," he said. "The other
one's nothing."

Since we had all gathered around the table and had started
to share our rations with the women and children, the married girl came in with a candle, explaining she wanted to get
some wine from the cellar. The captain produced his flashlight and offered to go down with her. After a slight stiffening, she agreed.

At the moment, I was wedged in at the large table; there
was a row of German women beside me, and a little girl
about three or four years old, light-haired, dressed in a white
rabbit hat and coat, had made her way over and leaned
against me. I gave her a chocolate bar. "Choco*lada!*" the
women cried in wonderment. "Choco*lada!*" When I looked
down at the little girl, I saw from the blind dazzle of her blue
eyes in the candlelight, and from the meaningless smile, that
she was simple-minded. Her hands were almost powerless,
yet very slowly, still smiling, she took hold of my finger.
Her mother leaned out of her chair to watch, to smile.
"Shoen!" I said, and after a moment I lifted the child up on
my knee.

One of the women, pointing to the departing captain, said
to me, "Jude?"

"Yah," I said. "Gut mann."

"Yah," they said softly.

"Catholic?" I asked them.

"Yah," came the reply.

I asked Phil to ask them what had happened to the Jews
who had lived in or around Boppard. At the question, a look
of blankness, real or assumed, came over their faces. "They
say," Phil said, "that the Jews have all gone."

"Ask them where. What happened to them?"

The reply came uncomfortably from the women: they

did not know where. The Jews had just gone somewhere else.

Before we could go further into that, the captain returned with the married girl, who carried three bottles of wine. She brought in some small, modern crystal glasses. The noise and laughter were again high and the corks popped; the wine was poured out. It was delicious, strong, golden wine. Lifting their glasses, the women instinctively looked at each other and then, with a little intake of breath and a shake of the head, they drank to the new regime. Most of the women now were smoking American cigarettes, chewing American gum, and laughing at the sensation, their heads together. This whole enemy invasion was starting off so differently from what they had been led to expect.

I always wondered why they hadn't tried to get away from the path of the approaching army, why they hadn't bundled up their children and belongings and rushed into the hills. Had they talked it over together, decided there was nowhere to go, that it would be better to stand their ground, hold their houses? Put out a sheet, or a tablecloth? And what must it have felt like to do that, to open that upper window?

Phil and I had often talked over the possibility that, a half hour or so before our arrival, the burgomaster might have gathered them quickly and said, "Look. Everyone. It's all over. There's no way to escape. They're all over the place for miles. The only thing you can do is keep calm. Be brave. Keep your heads. Put out a white flag. And remember— smile! Greet them with open arms. Don't admit anything. No one's a Nazi. Now! Hurry up and get back to your houses."

The family party gained momentum. There were songs from different parts of the room. "Lili Marlene," "Oulette" and "Ach Du Lieber Augustine" again. Family snapshots were passed around in stained wallets. The women were tremendously interested in pictures of American women and children. Getting out of their seats, they brought them forward toward the candlelight, bending over them with delight.

Suddenly Captain Stettner said, "Cut out the noise! Quiet there!" We all paused, astonished. Outside there was no sound. "Too damned much noise! Willie, where's your assistant?"

"I don't know, sir."

"Where'd he go with that girl?"

I didn't even know which girl he meant, and then, looking about, I realized it must have been the tall blond girl, Marie Elizabeth.

"Willie! Where is he?"

"I don't know, sir."

"Goddam it, you tell me or I'll—" He broke off, whipped out his flashlight, stepped out of the room, and pulled open the door that led to the cellar. "Get out of there!" he shouted.

Immediately Marie Elizabeth and the boy came past him and stepped into the room. The callow boy, who was married and the father of a child, was sheepish, grinning; the girl went swiftly through the room past us, into the bedroom and shut the door. In a barely controlled voice, the captain lashed out at the boy, threatening him with court-martial. "If I ever catch you pulling a stunt like that again—"

"Yes, sir," the boy was answering in a small voice, his eyes on the ground. "Yes, sir." The whole thing had happened so swiftly, most of us were still amazed.

"Raus!" the captain suddenly shouted, turning on the women. "*Raus!* Schnell!"

They were on their feet in an instant, grabbing up the children, hurrying out the back door without a word or a glance behind them. Marie Elizabeth had appeared, still proud-looking, and she alone attempted to leave with some vestige of dignity. As if she were at a rather stiff party, she went from one to the other of the men and, with a serious nod, extended her hand. "Auf wiedersehen. Auf wiedersehen." I shook her hand when it came my turn. We each bowed gravely. Giving her head an extra lift, she then faced the captain and put out her hand. He deliberately turned his broad back. Her nostrils flared and the color raced up to her cheeks. Turning from him abruptly, she went to the next man and extended her hand again. Before the captain, Preacher and a few others were now afraid to shake hands with her. Unsmiling, determined, she completed the circle, walked out square-shouldered into the kitchen and then allowed herself to be bundled out the door by her trembling, tearful aunt.

The married girl had spoken quickly to her sister; they went into the bedroom with the three children and came out a few minutes later. All had put on ski pants, coats and scarves. They carried blankets and a child's mattress. "Schlafen," the married girl said quietly in the silence, and, herding the others before her, she went out the kitchen door and up the hill to a neighbor's house.

The captain was still angered and we moved the table and chairs, clearing a space on the floor, and spread out our blankets. An abashed silence held us, and worries about the Rhine crossing came to mind again. The candles were spluttering. The captain, Sergeant Campbell and Lieutenant Serletis went into the bedroom to sleep. The rest of us settled down on the floor; the last man blew out the candles. I tried to visualize the Watch on the Rhine, and the line companies huddled in darkness down at the end of the street, waiting for midnight. How soon after that we were to go across, I didn't know; I thought we were lying down for a few hours' rest. In the silence we could hear artillery shells whistle and boom out in heavy barrages from either side of the river.

There was only the slightest surprise to be awakened and find that it was early morning: delays in plans were usual.

"Did they get across? Does anyone know?"

"Yes. They got across, most of them," the captain said.

"How did they make out?"

"All right, I guess. But there's no communication." Artillery still screamed and roared across the Rhine. "We're goin' over under a smoke screen."

Awaiting the signal, we went out into the kitchen, took the blankets down from the windows, and started a fire to heat the K rations and make coffee. A smoke screen. And German artillery shrieking through it. God! But no, there was no sense in worrying or trying to visualize any part of it. One was such a tiny decimal in such a vast operation, planned entirely and remotely by others, that even if it meant certain death, one would have to go through with it. And one had worried so often before, it was hard to dredge up any real feeling.

The married girl, her children and sister came down the hill in back of the house, carrying their blankets from a neighbor's cellar. The married girl sighed and leaned the palm of her hand against her cheek to indicate she had not slept well on the cellar floor. Francesca this morning was out of sorts, sulky, bored with us, and superior.

By nine-thirty we were told to leave. We said goodbye to the girls and the children; the girls shook hands and wished us good luck. I took a last look at a small framed etching of Boppard-am-Rhein. A little looting took place while the girls remained in the kitchen.

"Atwell, don't you want anything?" Lieutenant Serletis asked. I said I wouldn't mind having the etching as a souvenir of the town but that I didn't like to take it. "Why not?" He stared at me. "Here, *I'll* take it. I'll give it to you." He grabbed it down from the wall. I told him I couldn't accept it, and he was puzzled.

It was decided that Warren Troy was to cross over first in the white German ambulance with Phil and me. I stood on the narrow running board and kept one elbow in the window as we drove down the street. It was a sunny, cool day with a fresh wind blowing. At the foot of the hill the street curbed a little before disclosing the Rhine. Once more, as was the case with the Moselle, I was disappointed that the Rhine was not broader or swifter. The street emptied into a broad, pleasant esplanade with a long row of trees—lindens, I think—above the riverbank. A milky-white smoke screen hid the activities of the rowboats ferrying back and forth, and through the fog the sun looked like a golden ball.

Large hotels and inns made of white or pale-gray stone faced the esplanade. Their walls and high terraces were pitted and gouged by shells. Now and then, when the wind blew part of the smoke screen away, the river could be seen glistening by with a twisting slow ripple. Enemy shells whizzed overhead. There were very few men about, and these had taken shelter behind the hotel walls, out of sight of the river.

When we had waited there about five minutes, we were told it was time for us to cross. It was very much like crossing the Moselle. Warren drove the German ambulance up onto a pair of planks that had been laid across two of the boats. Phil and I sat down on the floor of one of the boats, Warren climbed out and joined us, the outboard motors started, and off we went. I had a box of candy that had just been delivered to me, sent by friends at home. I opened it and passed it around to the others. "Delicious," Warren said imperturbably. I dipped my hand for a moment into the water, which was icy cold, and felt the current run through my fingers. Well, I thought, that's the Rhine. In the heavy white smoke screen, there was nothing to see.

Shelling continued quite severe, from the opposite bank, with no answer from our side. We wondered if there'd be a crowd of casualties laid out on the bank waiting for us. A stiffer breeze sprang up, and the entire smoke screen blew past us downstream, leaving us exposed in the sunlight.

"This is nice," I said. The three of us laughed almost with embarrassment, as if a stage curtain had rung up on us unexpectedly. The Red Cross flag unfurled, and the olive-green water lapped against the boats. "Did you loosen your pack?" I asked Phil.

"No! I forgot to!"

Before doing anything about that, we waited to see if the target we presented would start to draw fire. We began to run into the thinnest veils of the smoke screen. As we neared the opposite shore, the motors turned off and we drifted in. The two Navy men, already wet to the armpits, jumped down knee-high in the water and started to push. German artillery was whistling and screaming in, but most of the shells landed nearby on the bank without exploding. "Another dud," the men on shore were saying. "Good work on the part of the underground somewhere."

The bank was high and very steep, and the activity along it seemed small for so large an undertaking. There were only seven or eight men standing around as we landed, but off to one side the Engineers were already at work, beginning to lay down a pontoon bridge.

The town facing Boppard-am-Rhein—I thought at first it was another part of Boppard—was called Filsen. We rode up to it, passing on the high, steep ramp the bodies of several German soldiers lying in the grotesque attitudes of the dead. One evidently had been hit while riding a motorcycle, for he lay sprawled over it, his entire face as black as his uniform, his black puttees gleaming, his light hair stirring in the breeze. Then we passed two dead American boys. The road was deeply gouged by recent shells; the few suburban houses on top of the bluff stood out in their skeletons.

Filsen appeared to be a very old town, in part medieval. An ancient wall surrounded most of it; the streets were narrow and cobbled; the upper stories of houses bulged out and almost touched those opposite. There were mullioned windows and much plaster and dark beaming. Slates everywhere

385

had fallen from the shattered roofs; white flags, tablecloths and sheets flapped from most of the houses.

The main part of the troops, in pushing on beyond the town, were held up by depressed artillery guns firing down at them from a high castle wall. There was the constant rattle and chatter of machine guns, the twang and zing, rip and whistle of small-arms fire through the streets as the mopping-up process went on. I saw a few infantrymen from C Company slide down over the wall, land in a heap of rubble, extricate themselves and, panting, wary, holding their rifles at port, pause, deciding which way to go. Off they jogged heavily, their faces wine-colored, sweating and dusty in the sunlight.

Coming in through an arch in the ancient wall, we turned down one of the first streets. The ambulance parked, we got out and entered the walled court of a small plaster house. An apple tree grew in the yard, heavy and old, supported by crutches, its branches loaded with white buds.

Entering the house, one came into a primitive squarish hall. A small laundry with stone tubs opened off to one side and an ugly, low-ceilinged living room to the other where a canary trilled and beat its wings against the cage in terror of the explosions. There was a harness in the hall, a few spilled bags of grain, two grinding stones, a bench and some milking stools. The planks of the floor were extremely wide, smooth and dry. A steep, enclosed staircase led up to a second floor which none of us bothered to investigate.

Preacher set up his boxes of medicine and treated several casualties, some of whom were carried in, others who came in limping almost as soon as we were established. I never understood how the men knew where we were a few minutes after our arrival. When there was a pause around noon, we took the milking stools and brought them out into the walled courtyard to sit in the hot sunlight. I glanced up and saw that the apple tree had just bloomed: there were sprays and sprays of white blossoms against the clear, quivering blue of the sky. It was Palm Sunday.

Early in the afternoon, a dumpy, middle-aged German woman presented herself to ask for medicine for her mother. To Phil, acting as interpreter, she explained that her mother had "nicht gestoolmacht" for five days. Preacher had nothing but the large brown bombers he had given me the day we left the Saar Valley, and through Phil he told the woman that her mother was to take two immediately, and if there were no results by evening she was to take two more. With one of his rare bursts of humor he looked at me over his glasses and said, "An' then Ah think we better be a-gettin' the hell outta town." The woman, repeating the instructions, went off. A few hours later, from the doorway of the court, I saw her with her mother—a toothless, thin woman in her late seventies—both of them being dispossessed, making their way through the debris, bent over with Saratoga trunks on their backs, being hurried out of one smashed-up house into another by one of the battalion interpreters. German artillery fire was quite strong at the moment, and there was still small-arms fire in the streets. The interpreter, with shouts and jabs of his rifle, was trying to rush them to cover, but the old one kept turning her head to snap and crab at him. Five days of constipation, brown bombers, Saratoga trunk and all, she could still give back as good as she received.

At about three in the afternoon, following a particularly heavy shelling, in one of the first moments of stillness, I was shocked to see part of the floor rise up. It was a trap door leading into the cellar. An aged man showed his face. We stared down. There must have been twenty-five or thirty terrified civilians in what was not so much a cellar as a square, windowless pit. Most of the people appeared old; many of them were crying, and there were several small children crowded down there with them.

When the old man saw us, he immediately ducked for cover and pulled the trap door down after him. It sickened me to think that people that old had remained silent and motionless for hours under our feet, stilling any whisper or movement from the children—hours and hours of needless terror, crowded against each other, hearing our voices, the tramp of our feet over their heads. I remembered myself in the cellar at Gulls when the German soldiers stood conversing and planning in the back yard; and why I didn't open the trap door and try to tell the civilians we were not going to harm them, I don't recall. Possibly at the time I thought they were better off down there during the shelling.

Another half hour passed, and after what must have been a long, frightened discussion, the same aged man opened the trap door and crept out. Looking down past the ladder, you could see frightened faces palely lifted in the darkness, a mother holding her hand over her child's mouth.

"Wasser!" the old man begged, trembling.

"Yah," the captain said.

The man went in through the living room and returned a few minutes later with a large slopping pail of water which he lowered down; then he climbed down the ladder and closed the trap door after him. An event came along shortly afterward that drove them completely from my mind.

A soft, beautiful twilight was coming on, and a hard, elderly farmer stumped into the aid station and spoke to the captain in streams of rapid German. I caught the word "comraden" several times, but that was all. The captain turned and spoke to Phil. I heard him say, "So take a litter with you." He glanced around and saw me. "You'd better go along with Phil." He hesitated, and changed it with a smile into a request: "Would you mind? We're short of men here."

I said I didn't mind, and we set off with the old German. Phil was carrying the litter, furled on his shoulder.

"Where are we going?" I asked.

Phil frowned. "I don't know." He was in one of his vague moods. "One of our men seems to be wounded somewhere. The old guy's going to show us."

Phil moved along stiffly, frowning, like someone suddenly dropped on a strange planet. We were going through narrow streets, past small crowded cottages showing white flags, cutting through narrow alleys, in through a maze of back yards and cobbled streets. I kept looking back, trying to remember the turns we had taken.

We were in the middle of the town, on a wide street with small cottages and white picket fences. There was almost a seashore air about the place; the ocean, instead of the river, should have been at the end of the street. The dour old man, empty pipe held upside down in his mouth, halted at the gate of a tiny cottage with one enormous round-topped bush, almost a tree, in its front yard. He gestured; I thought he was shooing us up the brick path, then I realized he was telling us that our comrades had carried someone in off the street and up into the house.

Phil looked dazed and didn't see to understand the story at all. We went across the little porch into a tiny hall. The old man, still protesting his innocence, I thought, opened the door and pointed to his living room, but he did not go in, nor did he wish to. I went past him with Phil and was

388

startled to see two American soldiers lying on the floor of the little living room. Both were very young and the fading daylight washed in on them. One of the boys was lying near a small, tufted red-velvet sofa at the front windows. A dust sheet was twisted partly around him; the rest of it was still pulled across the sofa. I thought he must have tried to reach the sofa and had failed. Nearby was a stand that had held a tall glass vase of pussy willows. The vase had fallen onto the sheet, the water had spilled, and the long, stiff branches of pussy willow were scattered on top of the boy. There was absolute stillness in the room.

Nearer us, almost at our feet, the other boy lay on his side in the shadow of a table covered to the floor. Drunk, I had thought in the first flash, but the boy near us had his eyes parted wide and his mouth too was open. His face, which looked yellowish, was frozen in blind surprise and pain.

"My God, I think these men are dead!" Phil said. I stood without moving, looking an inch above the fallen pussy willows while Phil bent over, examining each boy. "Yes, they're dead."

"I know." I turned and went out of the silent room and faced the open front door. At the gate a little knot of German men had gathered to see what the trouble was, or what we were going to do about it. Phil came out into the hall and explained to the houseowner that the men were dead, that we were not allowed to move our dead comrades, that we must go. The grumpy old man stumped out of the house after us; he would not remain inside it with the two dead boys.

"I can't understand Vic!" Phil exclaimed, frowning, on the way back. "I understood him to say there was one *wounded* man. 'Fer-wounded'—I'm sure of it!"

"Well, we can't move the dead ones." I recalled someone stopping by the aid station about an hour ago to tell us Lieutenant Dobrozek of C Company, who had given the rowing demonstration in the farm field, had been killed by a sniper in a street three blocks over from us. The man said he and a companion had carried the lieutenant's body into a house there lest it be run over or blown up by a shell; and he asked us to notify the Graves Registration Detail if they came by.

The way back seemed shorter; we cut through the streets and alleys and found our place with no difficulty, a feat which surprised me. Upon coming in, Phil, placing the litter in the corner with the others, said, "Sir, we found two men there. They were both dead."

"*I* knew that," the captain replied, putting on a puzzled little smile. How, it asked, could we have been so stupid? "That's what I sent you there for." He continued to smile, snorting through his clogged nose. "You'd better go back," he said, "and get them out of there. Take another litter"—which was proof to me he hadn't known there were two men —"and round up some of the Krauts. Carry the men down to the river and have them shipped over to the other side."

This was so contrary to all orders, to anything we had ever done before, that we gaped at him for a moment.

"Yes, sir," Phil said. This time each of us picked up a litter and we started off for the cottage again.

"Do you suppose he thinks one of the men is Lieutenant Dobrozek?"

"I don't know," Phil mumbled, lost.

By now the sound of firing had died down. The deepening pink-and-rose sky dyed all the surrender flags and sheets a paler pink. The branches of trees held tiny yellow-green blossoms that had not yet turned into leaves. A robin broke into throaty troubled song. It was one of those soft, nostalgic times when one wanted to say, "Wait. Let me alone for a while. I don't want to go any farther." Instead we went on, discussing the possibility of recruiting German litter bearers from the burghers we had seen. It was nearly six o'clock— the curfew hour—and there was no one on the streets. As we started down to the house where the two dead boys lay, the owner came out of a neighbor's cottage. Phil explained that we would remove the bodies if the man could round up some litter bearers to help us. The man nodded and started off to get his friends. Phil and I waited on the steps. The front door stood open, causing an inward draft.

Our hearts plunged when we saw the collection of old men who came back with the houseowner. There were about twelve of them, some not too willing, being urged on by our man. Then among them I saw a neat, stocky, dark-haired young man of perhaps thirty or thirty-two, dressed in a dark-blue shirt, light tie and bluish-gray suit with padded shoulders. He explained to Phil in a low, easy voice that he was a Belgian, a slave laborer; yet he appeared to be on terms of ease and friendliness with the old men who stood grinning at us. One was lame, and another put forward a hand from which most of the fingers were missing—a souvenir, I think he was saying, of some previous war. We picked the strongest-looking of the lot to help us, and then there sprang up in their minds a little difficulty. It was almost curfew: would we guarantee them safe passage home past the American guards? Would we accompany them? We would.

With that settled, we went into the front hall, unstrapped the litters, and walked into the room. Phil's group, which contained the smooth-haired Belgian, picked up the body lying near the sofa, and while they were maneuvering the litter out the door, I left to stand in the hall. Before I could get in again, my group had picked up the second boy and placed him on the stretcher. In the interval since I had first seen him, his face had changed. He now looked like a young Chinese, the yellowish skin drawn tight over his cheekbones. One of the old men knelt down and closed the eyes. They carried the body out into the cramped hall, where I took one of the back ends of the litter.

As we started out and down the steps, Phil's group halted. A large crowd had gathered. Phil looked distractedly about for the houseowner and, when he saw him, asked for a covering to put over the bodies, or at least over their faces. The man hurried in while we waited, and in time he returned with two pieces of cloth—one was part of a sheet, and the other piece looked like burlap. The weight was beginning to grow heavy in my hand. "All right," Phil said, bothered, as he placed the cloths over the faces; and we went out the white picket gate, through the crowd, and started down toward the Rhine.

The boy I was carrying was head first on the litter, his feet toward me. The old man ahead of me was very short. He was also lame, with a much heavier sole on one shoe than the other. How had we ever picked him? He hobbled off beat, making the litter pole lurch and wrench in my hand. Phil and the Belgian had two fairly strong men on the front of their litter and they struck off at a decent rate, marching in step down the center of the broad street.

I could feel my arm pulling from its socket when we had gone one long city block. Thinking more of the ignominy of being forced to ask the gaffers to halt than of the difficulties of the lurching man ahead of me. I was surprised to hear the old man opposite take control and call out with a sly grin in my direction, "*Links*, recht; *links*, recht." At once we fell into step. OCS material, I thought. Ahead, Phil's squad finally halted to rest half a minute. We did too, then started off once more. Before we rested again, the Rhine came to view at the foot of the street, and this time, instead of carrying by hand, we hoisted the litter up and bore the poles on our shoulders. Being thin, I could feel the weight at once on my collarbone. The man in front, when he limped, caused the litter to tip, and the body rolled around, in danger of falling off. With my free hand, I reached up and held onto the ankle of the dusty, stiff combat boot.

All the colors had gone from the sky. Evening was coming down over the Rhine, and a chill wind blew. Going slower and slower, and pausing now much more often to rest, we came along the high embankment and finally to the place where the pontoon bridge was going up. The Navy men were still ferrying troops and equipment across in the little boats with the outboard motors. A number of Negro troops was landing as we came along, and when word traveled ahead that there were dead bodies approaching, the men scattered out of the way.

Gripping extra hard onto the dead boy's ankle, I went down the long, steep escarpment to the river's edge, digging in with my heels as a brake. By this time Phil had explained to the Engineers or the Quartermaster men in charge that the two bodies were to be shipped back across the river by the captain's orders, and the burial squad on the other side was to be notified. There was some consternation, cursing, a great unwillingness. And in my mind there kept passing the question: why ship these two bodies back? Was it only a whim of the captain's? What about the other bodies in town?

The men in charge finally agreed, but wanted to take the bodies on the litters. There was another wrangle, with Phil trying to explain that we would need the litters; and in the end, unceremoniously, even roughly, the bodies were thrown onto the wet floor of the boat and dragged like sacks of grain up to the prow. There, one was hurled on top of the other to make more room. Phil winced. We turned away and started back.

Far up the road in the dull mustardy twilight, a procession approached: a long, double file of old men in civilian clothes, their hands up over their heads in surrender. Two infantrymen had them under guard, and as they came nearer, our old men hung back deliberately to laugh and hoot though it was

392

time for us to turn up the street. The prisoners, members of the *Volksturm*, many of them even older than our companions, trudged past, their eyes straight ahead. Mixed in with them were a few gawky, stunned boys in their early teens. Our old codgers choked with laughter and jeered as their townsmen went by. The prisoners had evidently volunteered to hold the town, had been run out into the woods, and there ingloriously captured. Our old men might rock with laughter, but the other old boys held themselves upright: at least they had tried.

"How insensitive these old bastards are!" Phil exclaimed in disgust as we started up the street with them. Since the half-light held, I put the stretcher down from my shoulder and lit a cigarette. Immediately the old men gathered about me, grinning, rubbing their hands and shoulders to remind me how hard they had worked. I gave them each two cigarettes, much to their delight.

Tired, we wandered up the street, and the old men began to peel off, to go into their small cottages. In parting, each extended his hand to be shaken. Phil and I went through the ritual, thanking them in turn. The young Belgian, who had all along been angling for some sort of opening, went into one of the small houses behind two of the men. The door had no sooner closed than the Belgian was out again, tiptoeing down the path, calling softly, "Pst! Pst." Looking about him furtively, he ran up to us and broke into torrents of whispered German. I could understand none of it. Phil finally said, translating, "He wants to know if you could let him have a few more cigarettes."

I gave him one more, the last I had in my red plastic case. As he accepted it with a bow and thanks, our eyes met, and I felt he could see my dislike for him. He seemed to say, "You don't know what it's like. You don't know what you'd do in my place." Then he dropped his eyes, ran on tiptoe back up the path, across the little porch, and let himself silently into the house. Why the secrecy? What was the story? Why, above everything else, was he staying on? Was he a Belgian at all? It was the sort of unfinished, inexplicable story one was encountering at every hand.

The Germans, letting go the Rhine, fell back in retreat, leaving road blocks and detachments of men to engage us in delaying actions. Sometimes during the following week, the enemy dug in to make a desperate stand only to have large numbers of its men throw down their arms and stream toward us in surrender. After a disorganized rout, collapse and retreat, more road blocks were thrown up and the wounded German Army fell back still farther.

One of the delaying actions made by the Germans, though of short duration and of obvious uselessness, stands out as one of the more ghastly episodes of the war. We were advancing down a road in convoy when a German tank drove out of a grove of trees, fired pointblank, killed two of our men, and then retreated from sight again. The convoy halted and two of our rifle companies went forward and surrounded the little grove that contained, they discovered, a platoon of German soldiers in deep foxholes. The German tank kept swiveling and firing, and after a while four of our own tanks came up. Each from a different direction sprayed the tiny stretch of woods with long streams of flaming gasoline. Within a few seconds the place became an inferno, and the shrieks and screams of the Germans could be heard through the high curtains of fire. A few, in flames, tried to crawl through, but they were mowed down by our machine guns. Within a half hour we went on, and all that was left of the little woods was a deep bed of glowing golden coals, hideous to see and to think about in the spring sunlight.

The countryside grew extremely hilly and wooded; small towns, flying surrender flags, lay hidden in hollows. In the swiftness of pursuit, one company by mistake often seized another company's town and had to double back to take its own objective. The convoy of trucks rushed into the towns; the infantrymen hopped down, cleared out the snipers, rounded up the prisoners, jumped into the trucks again and set out for the next town. Some days, in this fashion, as many as thirty miles were covered.

We had been traveling since early morning in the ambulance, jouncing and rolling along in second gear on the heels of the last rifle company—Phil, Warren Troy, Preacher and I. All during the winter the captain had ridden everywhere in the heated ambulance, but now he had transferred to the jeep. The litter bearers were out riding with the companies and we did not see them until the entire convoy pulled up in a higgledy-piggledy village with small, low cottages and a few round, turreted medieval buildings that seemed to have no windows. The place looked like a page from a Mother

Goose water-color book. It was full noon; the dusty road and white cottages, the bed sheets and tablecloths gave back a white glare. When the trucks stopped, the men jumped down and then there were khaki uniforms swarming everywhere over the bleached whiteness of the little street, opening gates, going into back yards searching for eggs, forcing open front doors to loot and hunt for liquor.

Not knowing how long we were to stay, we sat in the kitchen of one of the little houses, having our lunch. The old woman who lived there had just been dispossessed. The litter bearers had come in and Jimmy McDonough gave me a tea bag from a package his wife had sent him. When the tea had drawn I poured a little lemon powder into it. A canteen cup made a good long drink of tea. With it I was eating a K ration of cheese and the oblong hard crackers. The kitchen was crowded with men walking about, eating and talking; Silly Willie was frying a can of C-ration hash and causing a stench. As I ate, I took out a few letters I had not had time to read. Friends at home were asking if I had stopped off at the Monopole-Metropole Hotel? Had I visited Cologne? Had I taken a launch down the Rhine? If I stopped at such and such a hotel I mustn't fail to try a whole peach in champagne; and the next time I was in Paris, would I please send some Chanel No. 5? I had no idea of the privations at home! The things one went through at the butcher shops! Even toilet paper was awfully hard to get.

At the moment, two line-company boys smashed down the flimsy back door of the house with their rifles and came in, asking, "This place been looted yet?" The old woman who lived in the house had returned and there was a commotion behind me in the room. Either someone had burned the bottom out of her only good pot or she had seen someone going out of the house with her only good pot. At any rate, she set up a loud keening about it and taxed Phil, who had promised her that nothing would be disturbed. "Hey, get her the hell outta here," someone was saying. "What's she bitchin' about anyway? Go on, ya old bastard, git out! Git outta here!" She took herself off on her sore feet, whimpering and crying, followed by a few oaths and careless laughter. Sipping my tea, looking out the window at the sunlit back yard, the thought suddenly came to me, "I'm tired of this, tired of war, of human beings, of everything." From the

395

front door someone shouted in, "Snap s--- in there. We're moving!"

At night the rolling convoy stopped; we unloaded and carried our equipment into a large stone community farmhouse on a bare hill enclosed by a corral fence. The litter bearers joined us instead of sleeping in foxholes, and while the aid station occupied the ground floor with Battalion Headquarters, we were given two rooms upstairs. These we did not see thoroughly till morning when we awoke and found ourselves in a separate apartment: there was a stove and sink in a corner of the living room. It was a bright, cold spring day. Intermittent sunlight flashed and dimmed on a worn rug with reds and blues in it; the windows rattled with the wind; the fire was kept stoked up. Word drifted down that we were to remain here for a while. No one knew why, but it was a relief after entire days of jouncing along on the hard seat of the ambulance. We heated water after a K-ration breakfast, shaved, took sponge baths, and sat at the kitchen table writing letters. There was no sound but the bluster of wind pressing against the windowpanes, the scratch of pens, the crackle of the fire. We looked as though we were taking a final examination.

My usual desire to investigate the place we were in had vanished; I did not even look at the other rooms on our floor. Polish slave labor had been used on the farm and work had now come to a complete standstill. Many of the laborers had bolted for freedom the night before when we first arrived, but the eight or ten who hung on after their years of servitude did not seem especially jubilant. Rather they appeared mentally tired and without plans for the future. On the way to the latrine I saw three of them sitting in a little shed; they had a bottle of liquor, which they hid as I passed. On my way back, one was lying in the hay; the other two were smoking cigarettes, staring dully out at the hard dirt of the farm yard. Near the house other slave laborers were saying to some uninterested American troops, "Me Polski! Me Polski!" in the expectation of American cigarettes, but by now the men were accustomed to hearing "Me Polski," and everyone seemed played out. It was difficult to summon up any but the most distant feeling.

And yet, only a few days before, on Good Friday, during the attack a half mile ahead on the town of Eisenach, I had seen the high wire gates of a slave-labor camp being swung open by men of our battalion, and the inmates, with a rush and a tremendous roar, had come pouring out onto the street. For me, it was one of the most thrilling moments of the war. They surrounded the handful of us who were there—I had come down the street with Phil to watch—and they crowded about to shake our hands, to thank us individually, laughing and crying and in their jubilation addressing us in their native tongues. There were no interpreters; we could only smile and smile and continue shaking hands. I offered my cigarettes around until they were gone and kept asking, "Polski? Russki?" In time I could feel my smile growing stretched, but there was nothing to do but go on smiling and smiling and shaking hands. A few of the slave laborers, their meager possessions slung over their shoulder, giving us a wave and a cheer as they came out, pointed to a direction—to the east, probably—and struck off without a backward glance. Then two slave laborers ran up the street, each with a bottle of liquor, and at that they all scattered and began to burst into the nearby houses in search of liquor to celebrate their freedom. The American troops were a half step ahead of them in the search, and a fast-paced looting contest started up.

Later in the afternoon, when large numbers of German soldiers were captured and marched up the street in their long muddy overcoats, hands over their heads, some of the slave laborers ran alongside, catcalling and shouting and pointing out the S.S. troops to the American guards. Other slave laborers, by then happily drunk, were roaming up and down the street, five and six abreast, arms linked, careless of shellfire, singing their national songs. Still others, looking dazed and without plans, leaned against the wire enclosure that had been their home. A few wearily went inside. Within a few hours, all of them seemed to grow as accustomed to the sight of us as we grew to them.

While we were writing letters in the second-floor room, one of the German foremen came to the open door to ask for wood to build a coffin for his young son, killed the day before by American tank fire. He stood in tears, trying to make himself understood. I turned around on my chair to look; a few men from Battalion Headquarters had come along the hall and were trying to puzzle out what he was saying. Was he asking for planks? Or was he asking for permission to use them? No one knew. He was sent downstairs, fobbed off on someone else and immediately forgotten. I turned back to my letter.

For over a month, Ted Jameson and a few of the others had been wearing the almost knee-length, rubber shoe packs which had been issued when the winter was practically over. Originally Ted had put up a loud squawk for them, as he did for anything novel; but almost at once the weather had turned mild, and there was no way of washing—rather, of drying—the one pair of long, very heavy, whitish wool stockings that came with the shoe packs. Further disadvantages soon grew obvious: once water got in over the top of these tight-fitting boots, it never dried out; there was no support to the arch or ankle, and day-long marches had almost ruined his feet. The other men throughout the battalion had turned back their shoe packs for combat boots at the first opportunity, but Ted, with his double-E foot, couldn't be fitted and he had suffered along day after day, limping after the companies, complaining without end. His feet, he said, had grown so soft they felt as though they were melting inside the heavy wool and rubber.

Most of his complaints were now directed to Phil, who was swinging into action as Joe Mortara's assistant. With lists that never seemed to get anywhere, Phil asked over and over again what size underwear, socks, shirt, pants and field jackets the men wore. Joe Mortara made out duplicate lists that somehow did not tally with Phil's. Adding to the confusion, the men invariably gave a different size for almost every article of clothing each time they were asked, causing Phil, flurried and red-faced, to start another list; and while that was going on, Teddy kept up a steady yammering to ask if Phil had put him down for combat boots, size 10-E.

"Yes, yes, for God's sake!" Phil cried. "Now I'd like to check all you men for the last time, just to make sure we have this right. If I could have your attention here? Jimmy, I'll begin with you. I have you down for a size fifteen and a half shirt."

"Fifteen and a half? Better make that sixteen, Phil. I think that's what I wear."

"It is? Is that—? Wait a minute. Which list have I got here now?" There were so many items rewritten and crossed out that he could barely decipher it. Wholly confused, he started another new list.

On the first night of our arrival, Ted had complained of

being ill, but he had complained so often and had emoted so about his twinges and aches that no one paid attention to him. All the next day he lay on the sofa, sighing loudly, rolling his eyes up, groaning and asking to be waited on. "Would someone please get me a drink of water? A blanket? Would you fix this pillow under my head? Would you go over and ask Phil if he put me down for a pair of combat boots, size ten, double E? Do you think you could get me some coffee when you go down?"

That night he was tossing and groaning while the rest of us sat around the oil lamp writing letters. "Somewhere in Germany," Sam Benton Jr., was dictating slowly and distinctly to Paul Clifford, who was writing for him. "Dear Mother and Dad. Ah am well. Today Ah read Job, chapter eighteen, verses one to seven. Your loving son, Sam."

"Is that all you ever write?" I asked. "Wouldn't your family be interested in hearing what sort of a place you're in, or anything about the slave laborers here, or the fact that we crossed the Rhine and took Coblenz?" Censorship had just been lifted to that extent. He favored me with a pitying smile.

"Jes long as they know Ah'm well, an' read m' Bible today, tha's all they care about. 'S all that matters."

Suddenly from the darkness Ted Jameson cried out, "No! No! Please don't send me out! Please! I don't want to be an aid man!" We turned around. There was no one near him. Someone went down for Preacher, who came up, took Ted's temperature, pursed his lips, came back and administered sulfa pills. The captain came up to look at Ted, stared at his eyes, pushed the eyelids back, and turned away with a shrug.

"Get Warren to make out an evacuation tag. He's got yellow jaundice. No, it's not fatal," he said in answer to a question, "but it can be damned contagious. Get him out of here right away."

Teddy was pleased with all the attention at first and had us rushing about, gathering up his toilet articles, his writing paper, borrowing a towel to take along. Then a sudden sharp fear occurred that he might not be able to make his way back to us on leaving the hospital: he might be assigned somewhere else as an aid man; it might all be a trick to get rid of him. "Cliff, find my helmet. Oh, pray that I get back. Oh, Les . . . Oh, I'm so sick. Will you write to me? Cliff, will you write? Tell me if they put anyone in my place."

"Sure," said Cliff, but he grinned. After an inseparable friendship they had come to a point where Cliff was growing restive and, I believed, looked forward to some peace without Ted, to friendships with the other boys which Ted's tagging presence precluded.

Assisted by Warren, Phil and Cliff, he went down the enclosed staircase and out into the waiting ambulance. "Don't forget to write—pray—put in a good word for me—and, listen, if any—"

Silly Willie, bored, cutting short the entreaties and instructions, slammed the doors, kicked up the step and drove off with him.

The two long seats in the dim ambulance were so stiff that we put a folded blanket down to sit on, and hour after hour passed as we jolted along. My neck ached from looking through the windshield at the hilly farm country. Every now and then, when we stopped while a road block was being removed, streams of surrendering German soldiers came clattering loudly along the road, their hands raised over their heads. The sight had grown so commonplace that it attracted no attention.

Back in the days of the Siegfried Line, men had been proud to march the prisoners in past the long lines of American troops. Soon, though, they began to duck that assignment, for usually they had to take the prisoners—as many as forty of them—three or four miles back to an improvised pound, then turn around and run to catch up to their companies again, only to continue on along the road. Those taking in the prisoners now wore a shamed smile and drew horse laughs as they went by.

Whenever our troops stopped for a rest along the road, we asked to be let out of the ambulance to stretch our legs.

"Lucky bastards, riding," said the tired line-company men, but often Phil, Warren Troy and I would have preferred to walk, for our backs ached intolerably from sitting bolt upright. Preacher was the only one who enjoyed the experience; just as long as no shells were exploding and he had enough ration food, he was happy. Every few hours he opened and devoured with gusto a can of cold hash or stew. "Mmm! Could eat another," he said on finishing one, and with a laugh he opened a second.

"Preacher is nothing but a damned *pig!*" Warren said in

400

a fury as we walked up and down beside the ambulance. "Just because the stuff is free. He'd eat manure. I'm perfectly serious! *Preacher would eat manure!* God! I get so I can't even look at him."

Someone had been sent a few pocket editions of mystery stories, and Phil, Warren and I read them as we bumped slowly along, straining our eyes in the poor light. For some reason I could not get interested in the thrillers; neither could Phil, and often after a break we exchanged books, picking them up at any page and reading without knowing one character from another. This was the monotony of war.

We talked in bursts, for a half hour or so, and then sat in dull silence. Either Phil, a political liberal, had more faith than I in the Russians, or else he did not like to face unpleasant facts. We argued daily about the Red Army's course. Why, after driving forward all winter, was it now immobilized for so long on the banks of the Elbe within artillery fire of Berlin?

"Well, now, I don't know," Phil said, concerned. "Of course, their communication lines are enormous and perhaps they're waiting to—"

"Yes, but in the meanwhile, one after another of the satellite countries is giving up. They say, 'We surrender unconditionally.' They throw down their arms, and what happens? Instead of pressing on Berlin, the Russians send an army into these countries to 'subjugate' them. Their supply lines aren't too extended for that."

"Well, now, that might be necessary. For all we know there might be guerrilla bands there."

"The hell with guerrilla bands. You never hear of any large-scale fighting or of any fighting at all! They sweep through the whole damned country. And those places aren't surrendering just to the Russians—it's to all the Allied Command! If it's just a question of occupying, why don't we all do it on an equal basis? It looks to me as if the Russians are prolonging the fall of Berlin until they've grabbed off everything they want."

"Now, I don't agree," Phil said. "I don't think it can be that. There must be some other reason."

"All right, well, listen. What do you think we should do with the Germans once this war is over?"

Preacher had no thoughts ever on any such subject. At its mention, his round face tightened; a guard went up. If obstinately pressed, he said, "Ah think they ought to fix 'em so there'd be no more war," but that was all.

"Well, of course, they'll have to smash the military machine," Phil said. "And see that they never arm again. And the Germans will have to rebuild the countries they've ruined. I'd be all for sending labor gangs, culled from the S.S. troops—make 'em go from country to country—"

We got along better on this argument.

"Leave one badly smashed-up city as a monument so they'd never forget. Have one day a year when every student through grammar school, high school and college would have to sit and look at all the war films showing what Germany did to the other countries, and then what happened to dear old Deutschland as a result."

From that usually we passed on to a discussion of our failure as an invading Army to present a favorable picture of ourselves.

"The fact remains, we were poorly indoctrinated," Phil insisted. "We should have had a separate Army of Occupation ready to move right in behind us, made up of specially trained older men. Married men with some idea of—"

"From what I can see, the older men and the married ones too behave as badly as the young."

"Yes, I'm afraid you're right there. The whole thing is certainly complex."

"I wonder what future historians will have to say about it," Warren Troy said with a smile. "Wouldn't it be interesting to read about a thousand years from now—"

"They'll probably say, 'The first half of the twentieth century was marked by unrest and wars.' They'll slide over all of us with a single sentence."

Riding through the country around three o'clock in the afternoon, we noticed that the sound of artillery shelling was rapidly growing loud. Explosions went off all about us. Preacher, as usual, had noticed the sounds first, and while the rest of us sat up listening, he became panicky. "Hey! Let's out of this buggy!" he cried to the driver. "Stop it, and let's git out!" The whole convoy came to a halt. We alighted and stood indecisive beside the ambulance. The companies ahead of us scattered off the road. The men whipped off their packs, fitted the handles onto their entrenching tools and began to dig foxholes.

402

"All right, me-e-en." Sergeant Campbell came along. "Cap'm wants you medics set up a station here. Don't know how long we'll be stayin', but jes sort of temporary set one up."

Our own mortars, close at hand, began to fire. Shells slammed back and forth. We carried the medicine boxes, some blankets and our packs, and followed Sergeant Campbell off the road and down a wooded slope. The trees were all young, tall, with new, large, flat leaves that made a harsh clattering sound in the breeze. We approached a green stucco house alone in the sloping glade. The ground was bare around the back door; a German police dog had been tethered to a pulley line, and either it was a good watch dog or it was frantic with the sound of shelling, for it barked loudly and made wild lunges at us, only to be yanked back by its chain. Gauging the distance it could cover, struggling under the weight we carried, we made a semicircle around the animal and went up the back steps of the house into the kitchen.

In the confused first impression—the kitchen was small for so sizable a house, and painted deep apple green—I could tell we had arrived in the middle of an emotional crisis. There were a few infantrymen present, but they were baffled onlookers. Two women held the scene, obviously mistress of the house and her just-freed slave laborer. The mistress was in her early thirties, slender, with fine features, no make-up, and a lot of light-brown wavy hair. At the moment there was a blanched look of terror on her face. The slave laborer, with a cigarette in her hand, had her mistress backed into a corner and was giving vent to an impassioned tongue-lashing. Her hair was straight and black, and there was a dark-blue handkerchief tied tight about her forehead. Turning at our entrance, she thumped herself on the heaving bosom and cried, "Polski! Polski!" and, going up close, snapped her fingers under her mistress' nose. "Bah!" she shouted. "Bah!" and let loose with a scream of laughter, forcing the woman still further into a corner.

Without speaking, really without interest, we pushed by her and entered a bedroom. At this, the mistress grew more frightened and made a move to stop us, but the slave laborer pushed her back into the corner, laughing theatrically in the meanwhile. The bedroom, though rather small, we thought would have to suffice for the captain; he had ordered one set aside for himself. There was a bed high with mattresses, and

403

Sergeant Campbell was about to throw his full field pack on it when something stirred. There was a woman lying in the bed who appeared to be a hundred and fifty years old. Or was it a man? I wondered, aghast. A baby in a carriage beside the bed started to wail. We backed out hastily. My arms were tired from the load and I wanted to set it down anywhere.

We struggled across the hall, went down a step, and walked into an enormous studio with slanting glass skylights. It had a great cobblestone fireplace and was furnished with a grand piano, tables, low sofas, easy chairs, easels. There were six or seven men in the center of the room with their officer, who was listening in on a telephone and directing the mortar fire that crashed and slammed outside. Through a side window, I could see one of the gun emplacements. Infantrymen were hastily digging foxholes among the saplings.

"Synchronize your watches," the officer was saying. "It is now 16:13." A minute or two went by. Then the mortars started blasting off. Four rounds, and four rounds, four more, and four more.

"Really pourin' it on!"

And while some men outdoors went ahead digging their foxholes, others were slanting down the hill, prowling about for eggs and loot. Again the guns went off. The dog barked frantically, the slave laborer continued to shout in the kitchen, and the baby wailed.

When the shelling lifted, Lieutenant Serletis came trotting into the studio. "Hey, guys! There's a German officers' supply dump down here in the hollow, an', Jeez, they got everything. Fish, chocolate—'chocolada'—schnapps—everything! Do one of youse want to come with me? We'll bring some up before it's all gone. You want any bathing shorts?"

The ambulance drivers went with him while the rest of us stayed to hold the place. The mortar crews were notified to fire off a final series of shells straight down the road. Outside all forward traffic was stopped. Again the minutes ticked by; the instructions were repeated and a desultory conversation kept up with the batteries, one of which, maddeningly, refused to answer for long stretches of time. "Listen, are you *awake?* Well, *stay* awake! Whyn't you answer? What the hella you doin' out there? Now you got the order: four rounds. All right now, stand by. Keep on the phone."

At the appointed minute, the guns roared out as one series of explosions followed another. The fourth gun seemed a little late and there was cursing in the studio, but no complaint was made and the men stood up, preparing to leave. Vehicles up on the road began to drive on again and suddenly the fourth gun, for no reason at all, fired off an extra round through the moving traffic, throwing everyone into a panic. Some of the men in the room burst into helpless laughter, but the officer howled into the transmitter, "Who the goddam hell did that? That's how you kill your own men! What the f---'s wrong with you?" At the other end there was a coy silence. The officer flew into a choking rage.

At length the voice must have said, "It was a mistake, sir."

"Mistake! Goddamit, I *know* it was a mistake! I want to know who's responsible!"

Again there was no answer. The line went dead.

Phil and I laughed, but we were appalled. "Good God, so that's how it happens!" Phil said as the men left.

Lieutenant Serletis came back laden with booty from the fast-diminishing dump of supplies. There were sardines from Sicily, fish from Norway, olives, butter and cheese, semi-sweet chocolate flavored with coffee, orange, or vanilla, extra-large dark-green rayon handkerchiefs and triangular navy-blue cotton swimming shorts. The ambulance drivers brought in bottles of sparkling burgundy.

"Here." From his pocket, Lieutenant Serletis took out small packages containing four chocolate drops each. "Candy. Maybe they're poisoned."

"We'll soon find out," I said, and popped some of them into my mouth. He had brought back enough handkerchiefs to give each of the litter bearers one for a souvenir. The dark swimming trunks I could use as underwear, for I had taken off the long drawers and had only one pair of shorts.

The gray afternoon was waning; the studio was damp and chill. We poured out some of the wine, opened up the delicacies and started to have an impromptu party. The captain arrived and stood looking down at us from the narrow arched doorway.

"D'you get that bedroom?" He was obviously in an ugly mood.

"No, sir. There's an old woman in there."

"Get her the hell out! Come on, get busy. Start blackin' out this place." He turned and began shouting in German for the mistress of the house to clear out the bedroom.

The party broke up at once. Phil and I hurried out to the

ambulance to bring in more blankets for the blackout. When we came in, the captain was still shouting at the woman, who, in fright, was backing up the steep enclosed stairs that led to an unfinished attic, dragging the baby carriage up after her. The wailing baby, held only by its straps, dangled forward half out of the carriage. The Polish slave laborer, sneering and laughing, stuck up her nose, refusing to help.

A few minutes later, upon returning from another trip to the ambulance, I heard Phil groan, "Oh, for God's sake!" The young woman was trying to get the hundred-and-fifty-year-old woman up the stairs too. Germany has the oldest women in the world. This particular one was skin and bone and totally bald. She was toothless. A white cloth was wrapped several times over her head and under her chin, giving her the appearance of Marley's ghost. The cloth had fallen loose. Feeble-minded with age, she did not know exactly what was happening but kept up a series of mewing little cries and whimpers at being disturbed, trying feebly to struggle out of the girl's arms as she was being pulled up the stairs. Her knitted bedroom slippers fell off. She had the thinnest feet and ankles I have ever seen, and of a peculiar, unalive, brownish-yellow color.

We were part way through the difficult job of blacking out the studio when word came that we were to leave at once. On the way out, we were treated to a last burst from the slave laborer. A few restless infantrymen were loitering in the kitchen, waiting for her to finish with politics so that they could get her into the bedroom, but she, unaware of their designs, kept proudly pounding her chest.

"Me Polski! Yah!" she cried. "Me Polski!"

April

Sundays in combat were so like any other day that one was seldom aware of them, and this unbroken continuation of our day-to-day routine wiped out the normal time limits and gave one the feeling of walking tiredly on a treadmill.

Easter proved something of an exception, for we were in reserve and the day was free. We had arrived and put up at a secure, small farmhouse on a slope that was enclosed by a white picket fence, just beyond the town of Gravenswiebach. A pair of dark glasses, ground to my vision, had reached me by mail the night before.

I stepped outside the house to try them for distance and saw Mike Nowak and Big Steve Brudzinski, who had just come back from the hospital. They had been down in the town and reported that they had been talking in Slavic to great numbers of slave laborers who had been freed the night before. They were both standing at the foot of our sloping path, and up the road, waving to them, hurried two girls in slacks and heavy sweaters. One girl was husky, dark-haired, and vivaciously pretty. I went down to the foot of the path with Phil.

"Ollo!" cried the vivacious girl. She and her companion wore the familiar diamond-shaped patch with OST on it.

"Hello!" we all said. "Polski?"

"Naw! Me *Russki!* I talk English leetle." She laughed. "Mooter, fater, zist, brooder. Von, du, dree, fo, five—I *luff* you!" She had expended her whole vocabulary and went into peals of laughter. Both girls accepted cigarettes and sticks of gum. They were in highest spirits. Mike and Big Steve joked with them in Slavic but seemed uncomfortable, not knowing what next to say. I asked Phil to talk to them in German. Between Phil and Mike, we got something of the vivacious girl's story.

She had been a slave laborer in town, working in a textile factory making Army uniforms for the past four years. Before being carted into Germany, she had been a student at a dramatic school. She had then been fifteen. At the realization that she had given away her age, she went into peals of laughter again. She wanted very much to visit the United States. To go into the movies? I asked in German. She did not know. She laughed in surprise as the idea grew on her.

Often the questions addressed to her—one in Slavic, one in German—were so conflicting, she did not know which to answer. She and her sister had been carried away from school. No, she did not know where her sister was, nor had she heard at all from her family.

"Ach!" she cried, answering Phil. "Arbeiten! Arbeiten!" All she had done was work. From early morning till late at night. With never a day off. The factory was unheated; they froze there all through the winters. Their lodging place in the camp was cold and drafty too, and they had but one thin blanket. They had worked until they became too ill to stand, then, the moment they were better, back to work they went. She hated the Germans—hated them! Yes, the S.S. were the worst of all.

"But she must have been fed well," I said to Phil. "You couldn't find a healthier-looking girl. Ask her about it."

Yes, she said with a shrug, they had fed them, but not well. Nothing good. They fed them so they could go on working.

Were any of the Germans kind to her, I asked through Phil, or were they all equally cruel?

Some were kind, she replied, and they tried to slip the girls extra food when the S.S. weren't looking. The few who were kind, though, were just as afraid of the S.S. troopers and had just as much to fear from them as she herself.

Aside from the long hours, were any of the girls maltreated?

No! She glared to show how she would have flown at the Germans.

"Ask her more about the German people trying to befriend her," I told Phil, but this time the girl tossed her head and wouldn't answer at first.

"They wouldn't let us ride on the trolley or the bus," she said. "There were streets we could not walk on. Only certain streets. And always we wore this." With her thumb she indicated the OST. "Some people sneered at us on the streets."

But what streets? I could not find out. In the factory, had they worked side by side with the Germans? I gathered so, but couldn't be sure. I was even surprised they had been allowed to walk on any streets, for this indicated there had been at least some measure of freedom. When I tried to ask more about it, Phil grew rattled and couldn't form the translation; besides, I could see the girl didn't want to dwell on her slave-labor experiences. She was zesty and lighthearted and more interested in flirting and visiting about. She bid us goodbye and strode off toward the town again.

I saw her later in the morning, this time with a German officer's leather jacket over her sweater, walking gaily, arm in arm with her friend and two young men who had also been slave laborers. She smiled—her teeth were superb—and went past on high, runover heels, the bottoms of her trousers flapping, her curly dark hair blowing in every direction.

Toward eleven o'clock I went with the Catholic litter bearers to Mass, which was offered on the opposite edge of the town. The men from C Company, quartered in foxholes in the woods, were already there with their rifles, sitting or lounging about on the gray stone steps of the building—it was not a church—in the blustery sunlight. I left the litter bearers and went over to speak to them.

A day or two before, our outfit had overtaken a section of the German Army that had about a month previously, at Olzheim, captured some of our men, including several from C Company. George Gaynor was one whom I knew, and Sergeant Ziegler was another. All the recaptured men reported that they had been used well and that their main hardship had been in keeping up with the Germans, who were retreating constantly on foot. Many of the men—I believe there were ten or fifteen of them—had been wearing shoe packs at the time of their capture and now were hardly able to walk. When first taken prisoner, they had been questioned briefly, then separated and attached to the various German rifle companies and told not to try to communicate with one another. They had received the same rations as the Germans and had carried the squarish, heavy loaf of bread inside their shirts. Some German soldiers had shared cigarettes with them.

"That I find hard to believe," I said, but the C Company men swore it was true. They thought our men had been treated well because the Germans expected to be overtaken any day, or to be told the war had ended. At any rate, none of the men had been beaten or tortured, or even cross-questioned, and all had been allowed to keep their personal possessions: wedding rings, watches, fountain pens, wallets, pictures and money—which was seldom, if ever, the case with prisoners we captured. After a few days, the close guard on the Americans had gradually relaxed, and during halts or while the Germans lined up to fill their canteens after dark, they managed to talk to each other and pass verbal messages back and forth.

It irritated me that I could not speak to any of the recaptured men. All of them were held separate and questioned by our G-2 upon their return, and, we heard, so favorable toward the Germans were their reports that they could not be united with their companies, but instead they were to be shipped to Paris and from there rushed home, to be released from the Army.

"Sure," the boys from C Company were saying. "It would break down the fighting morale. One of the guys said the German guys were friendly—just like us."

It seemed I was always running into accounts of German kindness, and yet each time there was some reason why I could not find out the full story: either we moved out, or Phil's translation broke down, or, as now, the witnesses were unavailable. I knew great cruelty abounded: there were the slave-labor pens and the torture and gas chambers, and there was no way to reconcile them with these acts of kindness. How much did the average Germans know of what went on? To what extent were they guilty? And over and over again there was the question: where did the German High Command find the large numbers of people to run the concentration camps? To claim they put the criminally insane in charge did not strike me as the truth. Insane people can't run vast camps over a period of years. Somewhere lay the truth about the German people, if only one could find it.

Sergeant Jack Ziegler, one of the most popular men in C Company, had been on the point of receiving a battlefield commission at the time of his capture, and the boys told me he had been commissioned only the day before. While we were talking about him, he came along with a group of officers to Mass.

"Hey! There's Jack Ziegler with his bars on! Hello, Jack! Nice goin', boy!"

"How's it feel, Jack? Hey, Jack, over here!"

The group, warm and friendly, stirred, grinned, got to their feet, expecting him to come over and join them and receive their congratulations.

Embarrassed, convoyed by the other officers of the battalion, he glanced over, smiled and said, "Hello." That was all. There was a moment of shocked silence, then: "Did you get that! Wouldn't even come over to say hello!"

"Wouldn't even shake hands! This is the first I saw him since he was captured!"

"Boy, it don't take 'em long, does it?"

"He's got to do that. They must have told him. That's not how he is."

"We'll be salutin' him now."

As uncomfortable on their part as he had been, they watched him in the group of officers threading his way through the gathering throng.

410

We had traveled so fast and so far in the past two days without mopping up that pockets of resistance had been left in our rear. By order, vehicles were not allowed to travel alone for fear of ambush. The chaplain was not exempt; he was driven up, preceded and followed by a jeep, each containing three infantrymen and a mounted machine gun. Because of the unusually large turnout for Easter, Mass had to be offered outdoors at the foot of the steps.

There was a stretch of hard pale dirt, as unyielding as cement to kneel on, with sharp pebbles imbedded in it. The sun shone and you could feel its warmth on your back for a second or two, and then the wind blew chill again. The chaplain's vestments flapped and fluttered; the altar cloth kept blowing. By the time Mass was finished, I looked behind me and saw a wide semicircle of freed slave laborers, all men, standing self-consciously, I thought, gripping their hats or kneeling, bent forward on one knee. They looked at us and backed up as we dusted off our knees, put on our helmets and started to leave. No one spoke to them. I wished that the chaplain, when he had turned to us for his sermon and saw the slave laborers, who must have been at Mass for the first time in years, had asked for an interpreter to convey to them some sort of greeting. The way it was, it seemed cold and unfriendly.

In the afternoon, the day turned milder. I was starting out to take a walk with some of the litter bearers when Phil drew me aside and told me the captain had just asked him to write a novel about the aid station.

"I told him," Phil said, "that I didn't know anything about writing novels, and he said to get you to help me." It hadn't been an idle suggestion, Phil went on to explain; it had been one of those half-smiling direct orders and had been put to him in this guise: Phil was overstrength in the group and had no real work to do; he was being kept on the captain's whim. "He said to get each of the men and ask what he was doing before he was inducted and how he came to be a medic."

"What's this thing for?" I asked. "Does he just want a record of the men? To keep for himself?"

"No. I asked him that—if he just wanted a history of the men—and he said what he wants is a novel!"

"But no one writes a novel and *gives* it to someone. It sounds crazy."

411

"I know, but what can I do?"

"Tell him you can't write a novel. If he asked you to do a painting, you couldn't do that, could you? He's not here as a patron of the arts. You're not at his beck and call for that."

But Phil was bothered. He blinked and bit at his dry finger-tip with a little clicking sound.

"He said to get you to help me."

"Tell him I can't write a novel either or I would have done one long ago. It's just one of his passing ideas. He'll forget all about it in a day or two."

I left and started for the walk. It was late in the afternoon and the wind had died down completely. The townspeople had been out all afternoon strolling soberly up and down the sidewalks. There were men in knickerbocker suits, white golf stockings, black shoes, bluish felt hats with the brims turned down; little girls in big round hats with streamers longer than their pigtails; farmers in polished bluchers, bow-legged pants, stiff collars, and ties with rings on them. The women wore thin cotton summer dresses, with their winter coats open to show them. At first, I didn't understand; then I realized it was the Easter parade.

By the time I was returning from the walk, it lacked a few minutes to six. Over the small houses, the spring sky was suffused with deepening color, and, looking down the streets, you saw the families in profile in their front yards, at their closed white picket gates, standing motionless as statues under the surrender flags, unwilling to go indoors until the curfew hour had actually struck.

For some time we heard that we were approaching one of the famous German highways: the Frankfurt-Berliner Ring Autobahn. Once we hit that, we were told, we could really expect to roll. The days had turned beautiful. The willows were showers of pale green; the fruit trees were in pink and white bloom; forsythia made yellow fountains on lawns, and in the countryside, on the hills, the dogwood was out. For days, it seemed, we had heard no firing. We were up early in the mornings in the cool semidark that was loud with waking birds, eating our breakfast outdoors, standing in the fields. Then the men piled into open trucks, while Phil, Preacher, Warren and I climbed into the ambulance with our K rations and canteens of water, and by daylight we'd be rolling and bumping along.

Since crossing the Rhine we had been going through one

dull farming town after another. Now, making a sudden turn off a country road, we drove onto the broad new Autobahn, which, disappointingly enough, was very much like the parkways at home, with long narrow islands of grass and shrubbery between the traffic lanes. The character of the towns too began to change. We could catch only glimpses as we sped by in the convoy, but they were cleaner, more prosperous, more pleasant to see. There was no sign of war damage. Red- or orange-tiled roofs of suburban houses showed between the green domes of trees; there were flashes of gardens, monuments, blossoming fruit trees, forsythia bushes, a church spire rising up. Then on, and perhaps five minutes later there'd be a similar town.

Here and there along the Autobahn, we began to pass groups of slave laborers, now haughtily and antiseptically referred to as Displaced Persons, making their way back home. Sometimes four jaunty young Frenchmen in berets, with a sack slung over their shoulders, would wave and make a V for Victory with their fingers; sometimes there would be family groups with big, rickety, two-wheel pushcarts. The women took turns riding on top of the bedding, sacks and cooking utensils, while the others pushed up the long hills. Now and then there'd be two girls and two young men.

"Oh, boy! Shackin' up!" you'd hear from the truckloads of soldiers. "Yay, Polski! Yay, Russki!" And occasionally loose cigarettes, a chocolate bar, or part of a ration would be thrown across to the opposite lane, and you'd see the slave laborers running forward, stooping, then waving and waving, making the V with their fingers till they were tiny dark dots far behind on the road.

Some days we traveled without sight or sound of the enemy; on other days there were many rabbitlike hops, stops and starts. Here there was a stop in a narrow house on a modest rural side street, in a living room with a blue-and-silver scrolled wallpaper, oriental rug, large carved curio cabinets with plate-glass shelves holding a collection of china dogs, Scotties and Dalmatians predominating, all new like the oil paintings and everything else in the place. Out of respect for such elegance, Preacher had the oriental rug rolled back. The troops were a short distance ahead in the town, and there was the bark and rattle of small-arms fire.

Presently two wounded infantrymen were carried up the street and into the living room. They had been ambushed

413

and shot down by snipers a few blocks away at a crossing.

"Yeah, they got the snipers," the men who had carried in the wounded said. "Four of 'em. They were layin' in the bushes there and they opened up as we came along. Jeez, we sprayed the place, and then the sonsabitches come out with their hands up. Three of them had farmers' clothes pulled on over their uniforms, and the other one was a major or a colonel. He was still in uniform, an' he wouldn't give up. One of our guys shot him in the leg. And just as we closed in, he tried to kill himself, but his pistol jammed."

I helped Preacher bandage our men, and they were no sooner driven away in the ambulance than the wounded German colonel was carried into the room. He lay perfectly still on the litter, a middle-aged man, severe-looking, with a tight, bony, gray face and a small waxed mustache. Hollywood never overdoes it when casting German officers.

While Preacher dressed his leg wound, the colonel, hands over his head, looked up at the nearby table with the boxes of medicine and the five-gallon can of water. I had just finished a drink when he spoke. "Wasser."

I hesitated. It always seemed to me one brought the thing down to a petty level and demeaned oneself and one's country by refusing such requests, so I drew the cup of water and bent down to hand it to him.

Captain Stettner, on his way in the front door, barked suddenly, "Don't give that sonofabitch anything!"

I got up and poured the water back. The German watched; a gleam came into his eyes and then died away. The captain, walking in circles, throwing in that heavy foot, shouted out questions in German to which the man replied in monosyllables. The captain then began a series of threats, telling the German officer that for the act of sniping he could expect no mercy. The man remained silent and expressionless.

The captain expected a trap, some sudden violence from him, perhaps another suicide attempt. "You search this man for a hidden weapon?"

"No, sir." Preacher was astonished. "We never—"

"Well, *do* it from now on." The captain bent down, roughly ran his hands over the man's chest, arms, pockets, legs, genitals. The German let out a short, involuntary cry of surprise or pain. The captain stood up and cast the long coat back over the figure. Dissatisfied, and perhaps feeling as I did, that the prisoner had gained a slight advantage, the captain

414

told me to go and find Heimer, the battalion interpreter. I put on my helmet and dark glasses and started out of the house, wondering why Heimer was needed when the captain spoke German quite fluently. Had the colonel refused to answer any questions put to him by a doctor? It seemed so.

It was clear, fresh morning, growing warmer by the minute. The row of little suburban houses—white, pale green, cream-colored and yellow—looked, as usual, inappropriate as a background for such a huge war. Some German children, ready to run, stood at the side of the road, looking at the Americans. At the corner, I turned to the right and saw the spire of the town hall flashing white in the sunlight through the haze of budding trees. Jeeps and little trucks raced up to it and then raced away.

"There's where they captured the snipers," an infantryman said, pointing to a spot beside the broad dirt road. It looked undramatic; a little triangle of dead weeds, thick bushes and trees not yet fully in leaf, hardly large enough to hold four men. But what a morning there for the colonel! Being wounded, then surrounded, and then trying to kill himself, with the pistol jamming . . .

Captain Stettner overtook me on the road. "That's big game we got back there," he said.

"Yes?" I felt my lack of interest failed him somehow. But to me, the Germans, once captured, became impersonal, scarcely worth a glance.

Captain Stettner began to curse the German colonel. "Do *you* think we ought to turn him in?" he asked.

Did I? I stared at him. The sun shone on his face, which, at the moment, was frowning and greasy. Staggered, I repeated his question in my mind, wondering if he meant what I thought he meant. Was he suggesting that we—he or I—*not* turn the man in? That we kill him?

"Why, we've got to turn him in. What else could we do with him?" I asked.

Without answering, he cursed out the German colonel again, and we walked the rest of the way in silence.

The town hall was a maze of activity, wires, soldiers running up and down the stairs. I found the interpreter and returned with him, and the captain followed along a short distance behind. Outside our house, a little crowd of infantrymen had gathered, buzzing and talking, waiting to see what was going to happen to the German colonel.

The German officer was questioned again by the interpreter, but he gave no information beyond repeating his name, rank and serial number. Captain Stettner, furious, ordered him off the litter, and, getting up, the man staggered badly on his wounded leg as he put on his long overcoat. He hobbled out into the jeep, and under armed guards was driven off to Regimental Headquarters, hands over his head, for further questioning. That was around eleven in the morning.

Late in the afternoon, after several other stops, we rode into a fair-sized town and, led by Mike Nowak, entered a tavern. The taproom was quite bare, with an unvarnished floor and plain walls. It ran across the front of the house. At the rear you went up a step and along a passageway into a big kitchen. A side door opened off this into a surprisingly large farm court with barns and big sheds forming the sides of the rectangle. The German family had retreated into the barn adjacent to the house.

The litter bearers had joined us, dropped their equipment and had rushed out all over town searching for eggs. Infantrymen, too, were out on the tireless search, breaking into chicken coops, banging on doors with their rifles and demanding eggs at gunpoint. German women keep eggs fresh for months in crocks of salt water. Sometimes our men departed with a few eggs—a dozen or so. At other times they took from the frightened civilians the entire crock of forty or fifty, along with all the lard, potatoes and bread the house contained. Careless of how the conquered women and children would eat after their departure, the men gorged themselves, eating ten or twelve eggs at a clip in addition to their regular food. The number of eggs they ate seemed to enhance their reputations.

Whenever the cooking started, the captain became childishly pleased. "Mmm! Hey, that smells good out there! What you cookin'? Eggs?" He was sitting in the taproom trying to play one of the two piano-accordions he had picked up and carried along with his saddles and loot in the German ambulance. A linesman was connecting the long gray portable radio the captain had recently acquired. "What have you got out there? Eggs?" He leaned out of his chair, but there was no answer.

In the kitchen they had heard him the first time. "If that sonofabitch comes out here lookin' around for eggs," someone swore, "he won't git any. Let him git his own."

"Mmm! Eggs!" The captain walked in, sniffing. He beamed, pretending to be unaware of the dark looks he drew, the mutters that were loud enough to hear. "Who owns all the eggs?" No one answered. Thick-skinned, still smiling, he asked, "Who's gonna give me some eggs?" After a long, turgid silence, Tubby broke down and said that he would. Pleased, the captain left, going inside to be waited on, and he picked up the big glittering accordion again. Tubby was cursed up and down in heated whispers.

"Aw, what was I gonna *do*? He asked, didn't he? He was lookin' right at me! All you bastards made b'lieve you didn' see him!"

The stove was kept roaring hot. The men worked in teams, not telling the other teams how many eggs they had hidden away. Potatoes, provided by the Hungarian slave laborer, a man in his sixties, were peeled quickly, with thick, careless parings that were left anywhere. The sink soon became clogged and the slave laborer was kept on the hop bringing in more and more potatoes, more firewood, more "grease." He had become their slave laborer temporarily, and their attitude toward him plainly showed it.

Now everything that could be used for frying was crammed on the hot stove. There were pans overcrowded with spluttering frying eggs, and skillets filled with frying potatoes. Tubby was in a sweat, cooking away, shoveling three or four eggs onto a clean plate to bring them inside for the captain.

Sergeant Campbell had joined up with the ambulance drivers, and the three of them, friends only for this occasion, crowded at the stove, almost trembling with eagerness, waiting for the panful of eggs to be done. Waiting not long enough, they slid them off onto soiled plates, wolfed them down, then hurried back to get a place again at the stove. The whole atmosphere was noisy, brawling and pushing. The men sat down at the dirty table, shoved back a heap of potato peelings, gobbled, and jumped up to fry more eggs and potatoes.

Wiping the back of his hand over his mouth, Sergeant Campbell said to me, "Ate thirteen aiggs today!" He nodded his head as if he had the whole situation satisfactorily under control.

"I don't mind taking champagne or schnapps," Phil said,

voicing my own feelings. "The civilians can get along without that, but I couldn't grab the eggs from the women and children. They have nothing else to live on, and won't have until the crops come up. We always have the rations, lousy as they are." Oddly enough, Sam Benton, Jr., strict, puritanical in all other matters, saw no wrong in robbing the defenseless civilians of their last mouthful of food.

After about an hour the cooking and eating finished almost simultaneously, and, sweating a little, belching, the men made their way inside, leaving the mess of shells, dirty pans, greasy paper and potato peelings behind. Tubby, the easy mark, had spent all of his time cooking for others who professed not to know how, and now, tired, he began to fry himself four eggs, the last of his hoard. Phil and I were heating water for coffee. The captain appeared in the doorway. "You men, clean up all that mess. Get all that garbage and everything out of there." He turned and left.

"Hey, Howie, how 'bout givin' us a han', cleanin' this place up?" Tubby asked when his friend, Howard Mason, appeared.

"Let the DP do it," Howard Mason said carelessly, and went inside.

Tubby, who was rapidly gaining back all the weight he had lost at the height of combat, swore a solemn oath never to cook for anyone again. Just within the last warm day or two he had, at long last, laid off the coonskin hunting cap his wife had sent him. During a break, in the middle of a town, some German women had laughed at him. "Hey, what's so funny?" he had asked me. "What the hell're they laughin' at? What're they sayin'?" I told him. They were saying, "St. Nicholaus! St. Nicholaus!" and going into shrieks of laughter at the sight of him sitting, fat, befurred and red-faced, in the jeep.

"Goddamit all, they must be laughin' at my fur cap!" he said with what I felt was admirable self-confidence.

A stout, lame woman, white-haired, with a pretty, giddy, bright-pink face and OST on her roll-collar sweater, hobbled in from the barn and made signs that she had been sent to clear up for us, but we told her not to, and she limped out mystified and startled at the sight of Tubby in an apron, standing over a pan of dishes. By the time the place was clean again, the captain's radio was going. Radio Luxembourg was on, giving messages in code and playing Viennese waltzes through roars and crackles of interference. It was almost time for the news broadcasts which were given out both in English and in German. The elderly slave laborer came in from the barn and asked in German if he might sit down to listen. Phil told him he could. The man slipped in behind the table and lit his pipe. "Another one who's not taking off," I said to Phil. "Wouldn't you think this would be the last place he'd ever want to hang around?"

I went into the taproom for a while where the captain was still trying to play the accordion, and when I returned to the kitchen for a drink of water the slave laborer was jabbering away in Hungarian with Bob Lozlo who was Bob Russell's replacement. Bob Lozlo broke off to ask me if the owner of the farm or tavern couldn't come in too to listen to the radio. I asked why the slave laborer should care whether the German owner came in or not. The slave laborer replied that the owner, a man of his own age, was not a Nazi and had been especially kind to him. When the Hungarian had first been seized and sent into Germany, he had become separated from his wife and daughter. The owner, hearing his story, had bent every effort to locate the man's wife—the stout, lame, white-haired woman who "obviously," as the man said, was not of much use about a farm. Rather than request another male laborer, the owner had had the lame woman assigned to him. She, in turn, had become separated from her young daughter, and the German owner went through all the same efforts: months of searching, wire pulling, interviews and petitions to discover where the fifteen-year-old daughter was. Once he found her, he had her assigned to him so that the family could be reunited. How anyone who was "nicht Nazi" could do all this in a police state, I could not imagine. What reasons could he have given to the Nazi officials in making his search and requests? Friendship with slave laborers was a criminal offense. There was a mystery somewhere in the story.

"He says," Bob Lozlo continued, translating a few phrases after the man, "his daughter and the daughter of the house were treated as equals in every way. They were the same age; they were like sisters, and shared the same bedroom." The wife, I gathered, was as giddy and talkative as she looked and was a cross to all concerned. "He says that if the man was his own brother, he couldn't have been better to him. Should I tell him to bring him in?"

"Yes, go ahead."

The owner, dressed in corduroy farm clothes, was a quiet man, smaller than the laborer, pink-faced, with mild, hooded blue eyes. Sucking his empty pipe, he slid in beside his friend without a word to us. As we were leaving them, unsure what the captain might say, the owner took out of his pocket a small, worn, folding checkerboard and a box of checkers, and in silence they began what was evidently an evening ritual.

How was this case possible? The tavern was in the center of a town; neighbors must have come in to buy a drink, to sit around and talk. What had they thought of this friendship? In a country where children were said to have informed on their own parents, why had no one turned the tavern owner in to the officials? And again one thought of the officials themselves who had been instruments in permitting the slave family to reunite. Why this exception, while other slave laborers by the thousands were herded into crematoriums?

Nothing out of the ordinary led up to the events at Tambach. The entire battalion was on the road, the litter bearers out with the companies on foot. The ambulance rolled slowly along at the heels of the last infantrymen. It was an average day, with the usual stops and starts. We were to make Tambach, a small city, by nightfall—not only make it, but take it. The countryside had turned extremely mountainous, the growth of pine very heavy. We were in the Thuringer Wald.

As the afternoon was fading, there came the sudden loud explosions of German tank fire around a forward bend, and then machine-gun bursts. The convoy came to a halt. There was firing back and forth. We sat talking in the ambulance, expecting shortly to pass through the road block and on into Tambach. Within a half hour, though, word came down that we were going to spend the night where we were.

"Dig in, boys. Dig in."

The infantrymen got to their feet and moved off the road to dig foxholes. There was talk of sending the ambulance a short distance back to a tottery shack perched up near the top of a hill, and so we waited, doing nothing. There was a long, winding stream of vehicles behind us, almost bumper to bumper; two trucks and Captain Stettner's jeep were ahead. "We're jes sittin' ducks," said the worrisome Preacher. "If the Jerries ever send one of 'em shells over here— mm-mm!"

Still, as soon as he had eaten and it was thoroughly dark, stout, eyeglassed Preacher, worried or not, prepared to go to sleep on one of the ambulance benches. At the edge of the woods, Cannon Company's howitzers set up an almost constant blasting roar that thundered through the night as over six hundred shells crashed across a short, open plain into the city of Tambach.

At about nine o'clock that night there came a thump at the ambulance doors and Sergeant Campbell announced from the road that there was a wounded man who must be lifted inside to be treated.

To make room, Phil and I hopped down onto the road. The captain came along from his jeep and climbed in after the wounded man, and as he did so, I caught a glimpse of Preacher trying frantically to rip open a Carlyle bandage while gripping a flashlight between his knees. The doors closed.

The night had turned suddenly cold. Phil stood shivering, his shoulders hunched, wondering how the man was to be evacuated. "Not in the ambulance?" I asked.

"It'd never get past all the trucks in this dark. And Collecting must be miles in back of us. I don't know what they're going to do."

He soon found out.

"Phil Schaeffer," said Sergeant Campbell, opening the ambulance door, "we're gonna send you back with Tubby in the jeep. Take this wounded man to Collecting."

Tubby approached the task with great unwillingness. He succeeded in turning the jeep around on the narrow road, and with Phil and the wounded man aboard he began to maneuver it past all the stalled dark trucks and artillery pieces. In the stillness the sound of his motor gradually faded into a distant hum.

I waited on the road for Phil to return. The captain had invited another officer and a few master sergeants from Battalion Headquarters to join him in the blacked-out ambulance for a game of cards. About an hour later, Phil returned on foot with the news that driving past the convoy had been so nerve-wracking that Tubby had not tried to get the jeep up again to the head of the column. Waiting for the card game to break up, Phil and I hung around on the road, shivering, listening to the laughter from inside the ambulance. Near midnight, Paul Clifford walked up with the news that his team was bringing in a casualty.

This time, in Tubby's absence, a jeep and a driver from farther back in the column had to be commandeered to drive the new wounded man back to Collecting. The driver showed up, stocky and rather nervous. It had taken him a short while to find out where we were, and the captain, showing before his little audience of card players more feeling for the wounded than was his custom, gave the driver a dressing-out for being late. The man took it in silence, standing at attention, facing the pitch-black opening of the ambulance. The audience within sat in silence.

"Phil Schaeffer, go back with this driver and show him where Collecting is."

The wounded man was lifted out and placed across the back of the jeep on his litter. "Remember," I said quietly to the driver at the last minute, "the litter poles stick 'way out. You'll have to take that into consideration when you're getting past the trucks."

"Yes, sir."

"And at ease with that 'sir.' " Phil and I laughed.

Slowly, carefully, they started off, and almost at once the poles became entangled with a truck. I ran back and straightened them out. The wounded man had not been hurt.

A half hour passed. The card game broke up, but the captain did not leave. Instead, he settled down and went to sleep in the ambulance. I grew tired of waiting for Phil and was about to take a blanket and lie down on the road when the jeep driver reappeared on foot.

"Hey, medics here?" From the way he spoke I could tell that he was nervous.

"Yes."

"Is—is the captain around?"

"He's in the ambulance, asleep."

The man took off his helmet, wiped sweat from his face, took a breath and knocked on the ambulance doors.

"Who's there?" came from inside.

"Sergeant Harrison, sir."

"Well, what the hell d'you want?"

"S-sir, I had an accident. My—my jeep went off the—off the road, sir."

The ambulance door opened. "Where's the wounded man?"

"He—he's layin' down in the— He's beside the road, sir.

422

The medic is down there with him." The man swallowed noisily. "I couldn't get by, sir."

The captain cursed him for a fool, berating him more, I suspected, for disturbing his slumber than for dumping the wounded man out. "Goddamit, *who's* your superior officer? Lieutenant Lloyd, hey? Well, there's gonna be a complaint lodged against you in the morning! What the hell d'you come back here for? Why didn't you do somethin' about gettin' your goddam vehicle up on the road?"

The moon appeared and shone on the sergeant's husky shoulders, sweating face and neck.

"Because I'd need a winch, sir, and a—and another jeep to pull me out, an' I couldn't get it without the Traffic Officer's okay. No one knows where he is. He's sleepin' somewhere."

"Well, goddamit, you go an' *find* him!" The ambulance doors slammed.

In time Buchta's jeep was procured and the same desperate, sweating sergeant was told to see to it that the wounded man got back to the field hospital without any further mishaps.

Howard Mason, our own truck driver, heavy-set, smiling and cagey, who avoided all work and embroilments, was sitting awake in the cab of his truck directly behind the ambulance. The seat beside him was vacated by Charley Heydt, and I climbed in to see if it would be any warmer there. I smoked a shielded cigarette and then tried to sleep.

At about four-thirty Phil returned and I got down on the road to speak to him.

"God, what a time!" In a low voice he described the jeep going suddenly down off the road, turning over, hurling him and the wounded man out into the ditch. The man's arm was in a splint and he had suffered no further injury. Phil remained with him until the doughty Buchta—"Buchta the wild man"—showed up. With his jeep and a block and tackle, Buchta hauled the first vehicle up and onto the road, where it was discovered that it couldn't run. Buchta then offered to drive Phil and the wounded man back to the field hospital in his jeep. That part, Phil said, except for a little erratic, high-spirited driving, had gone all right. On the return trip, though, at high speed, Buchta suddenly jammed on the brakes, whipped out a pistol from his shirt and fired it off rapidly at a German patrol running in silhouette beside the road. Emptying the pistol, he shouted to Phil to hand him his carbine, but Phil, who had bundled himself Indianlike in a blanket, became entangled trying to throw it off and couldn't get to the rifle in time. The Germans disappeared, much to Buchta's sorrow.

Phil reached for the handle of the ambulance door, tired and ready to climb in.

"Uh-uh," I whispered. "Der Arzt is schlafing in there and he's not in a very good mood."

Each of us took two blankets from the back of the truck and carried them down to the bank of a small rushing stream. Men were lying in sleeping sacks all about on the frosty grass. I wrapped myself up and lay down on a blanket, hearing the stream splashing past a few feet away, and awoke for the day two hours later to the same sound just as the sun was coming up.

After waiting around with no orders to move out, we knelt over the stream and washed our faces in the icy water, letting the breeze dry them. The sky grew paler, and all along the stream tiny fires were lighted as the men began to heat canteen cups of water for their coffee.

After wasting almost the entire day, we drove away in the ambulance at four o'clock, cutting in ahead of the rifle companies by taking a side road and riding up and down steep hills with hairpin turns, with deep gorges and misty chasms falling away abruptly from the narrow trail, until we came to a halt very near the road block that was holding up the battalion. Some of the companies and all the vehicles were still behind us, strung out along the winding road in the positions they had occupied during the night. A and C Companies were a little ahead of us. They had been picked to demolish the armed road block at daylight and beat back any counterattack in the meanwhile.

The spot where we stopped was scenically the most notable we had come upon. We were very high up on a road outside an inn; a little above it rose the peaks of the mountaintop entirely covered with tall, identical pines. A deep gorge dropped away below the road, while directly opposite, mountain peak after mountain peak stretched up, eye-level, their outlines jagged with the same straight, dark-green pine trees. Evening was approaching and the deep valleys had begun to fill with mist. There was a constant sough of wind.

The inn had a small bar and a restaurant dining room with windows overlooking the ravine and the mountains opposite. All the tables were covered with soft-looking, red-checked cloths and were set with cruets, thick white plates, knives, forks and spoons. Old prints of race horses hung on the walls, and there was one large, dark still-life of fowl and fruit. Behind these public rooms were the living quarters for a nervous family: an old man, his wife, their daughter, her small children, and what appeared to be a few elderly aunts; they were packing in haste to clear out and leave the place to us.

In the bar there was still a little of the frothy, thin, pale, raspberry-colored beer, and we took turns at the pumps, filling the crested steins and scraping the foam off professionally, though no one wanted more than a few swallows of the unpalatable brew. With blankets and baskets of food over their arms, the family left by a back door and I saw them toiling up the steep side road that went higher than the inn, on their way to a rustic summerhouse. Two of the women were trying to make the small children carry some of the load, and the children, too young to understand what was happening, kept straggling and stumbling, looking back at the inn.

It was growing darker and a mountain coldness could be felt in the air. We fastened the shutters and, as an extra precaution, nailed up the Army blankets too. On a shelf above the bar, there was a long radio in working condition. We tuned in on Radio Luxembourg, heard the news of Berlin's bombing and imminent fall, heard waltzes and a long speech in German. There was seldom any detailed news of the Pacific, and now no news at all of the Russians.

The captain, getting ready to retire to a small room at the head of the stairs, turned to me and said, "By the way, did Phil say anything to you about writing the novel?"

"Novel?" I looked surprised.

"Yes!" He looked even more surprised.

"I thought he was just gathering notes for a sort of history of the boys here for you."

"No! He's gonna do a novel while he's hangin' around. I wish you'd help him."

"Of course. I've never written a novel, but I'll help him all I can."

This was not quite satisfactory. "You know," he said, "no one's ever done a novel about an aid station, and some pretty dramatic stuff goes on. Seems to me there's a good thing there. We might be able to make some money on it. A lot of money." I longed for enough nerve to say, "Who's we?" He

425

said, "So see what you can do. Get the boys together the next time they're in, and get each one's story."

He went upstairs. I walked into the taproom and said to Phil, "The novel's on again."

"Oh, good God! No, is it?"

"All we can do is get the boys in and start taking notes. And that's all we'll ever have to do. Whenever he asks what we're doing, we're taking notes. We can stall on that indefinitely."

At daybreak, C Company was to push through the road block, and then the whole battalion was to roll on again and take Tambach. The artillery had come forward and everything was poised. I took off my shoes, put my belongings in my helmet. Phil found himself a "receptacle," and we lay down beside the others. The lantern went out.

We awoke at daylight and heard the shattering roar of the artillery barrage opening up just a little ahead of us on the road. Mixed with it were concentrations of small-arms fire. After a short while there was silence. Automatically we began to fold the blankets and do up our packs.

We ate a K ration for breakfast. Lieutenant Serletis, in better spirits these spring days, put on his helmet and went out; so did Charley Heydt and Sergeant Campbell. Phil started out to admire the view by sunlight, when a door opened at the top of the staircase and Captain Stettner appeared, sleepy-eyed, his clothes in disorder. "Phil . . ."

"Oh! Yes, sir!" Phil started up the stairs.

The captain was dragging, half on the floor, an armful of blankets, eight in all. "Here," he said without any particular tone, "fold these up," and he let them drop over the banister on Phil's head. With that, he walked back into his room. Phil clawed the blankets off and emerged scarlet-faced, whether with asthma or humiliation, I couldn't tell.

"Can you *imagine* that?" he asked, his eyes dilated behind his smashed and half-repaired glasses. " 'Fold these!' "

Even had a few hours passed, I thought, it would not have been so bad, but it was lowering to have thrown on you the blankets still warm from someone's body. Talking, mumbling to himself, Phil folded the eight blankets and put them away.

The family who owned the inn had returned from sleeping outdoors in the summerhouse; they had let themselves in through a back door and all were crowded in the narrow kitchen, preparing their breakfast and making very little noise about it. The captain came downstairs and stood leaning against the kitchen doorway, laughing and talking amiably in German with the family, eating pancakes and drinking coffee with them. Shortly after, he went out.

There was activity now on the road outside the inn. A few jeeps went by toward the blasted-out road block and messengers began to drift back. Then long, long streams of prisoners came by, their arms upraised and a few infantrymen guarding them. They were halted on the road a little past the inn. We were surprised at the extreme youth of some of the prisoners, not all of whom were even in full uniform. They appeared to be boys from fourteen to seventeen. Some of the infantrymen called in to say that many of the prisoners had been recruited from the town of Tambach, or from a military high school nearby, and had been told to hold the Americans off from their mothers and sisters. A sprinkling of the Regular Army had been left to strengthen the ranks under the control of some S.S. troops.

The sun rose higher, giving promise of a beautiful, warm, pine-scented day. Striking among the trees, broad slats of sunlight fell through the open door. Lieutenant Serletis returned, smiling widely, his eyes alight. "Boy, oh boy," he said with a laugh, sitting down on the floor with his back against the wall like a gnome in a patch of sunlight, "the line-company boys sure are gettin' tough." He nodded his head approvingly. "They just took about sixteen Jerry prisoners out in the woods, right out there, and shot 'em down. Killed every f---in' one of 'em. They're not taking any s--- from *no* one!"

We stared at him.

"But that's murder!" Warren Troy pointed out.

"Murder?"

"Simple, cold-blooded murder, that's all it is."

As if the words sank in slowly, Lieutenant Serletis scratched his head. "The boys are pretty pissed off," he said tentatively.

"I don't give a damn what they are, anyone who'd do that is a murderer," Warren Troy repeated.

Lieutenant Serletis looked at us. Phil, Preacher and I agreed with Warren, and at this Lieutenant Serletis became more and more confused.

"Well, *gee*," he said, "I don't know . . . It's different for them: they're under a strain." Most of us tall, we stood look-

427

ing down at him. He scrambled to his feet. "Of course, it's nothin' to *me*."

"Who did the murdering?" Warren asked sternly. The word did not sit well with Lieutenant Serletis.

"Well, C Company guys, and some tankers, and—" He named a new aid man at C Company.

"Damned brave of them," I said, "shooting down a bunch of unarmed high-school boys."

"Well, it's—it's the war," he said. "You know how it is. If you were there, you'd—"

"No, I don't think so. Not even if I were there."

He looked at us a moment, ill at ease, and then trotted out.

Three or four wounded men were carried into the station, and while their wounds were being dressed, this was the account of the shootings we received: The artillery barrage had gone off shortly after daylight and small-arms fire had joined it, mowing down many of the advancing Germans. As the barrage lifted, streams of the Germans came forward to surrender. When they were close to the foxholes dug in around the road block, some snipers in their midst suddenly opened fire, killing the Artillery Observation Officer and his sergeant and wounding the men here on the litters. As soon as the snipers had fired, they threw down their weapons and raised their hands in surrender. The infantrymen shot them down without hesitation.

Had the killings which Lieutenant Serletis mentioned happened immediately, it might have been understandable, but a half hour or so had gone by. More and more Germans surrendered or were rounded up. Lieutenant MacKenzie, following the death of Lieutenant Dobrozek, had at last been made Commanding Officer of C Company. He and a replacement officer, Lieutenant Morse, stood watching the prisoners stream in. A short distance away stood Captain Reddy and some members of his staff. Lieutenant Morse suddenly said, "Let's kill some of these sonsofbitches. Do I get any volunteers?"

Many hands went up. Lieutenant MacKenzie shook his head but said nothing. Captain Reddy and his staff, within hearing distance, looked the other way and likewise remained silent. At that moment a file of young prisoners was being led past. Lieutenant Morse halted the line, and, with his six or seven volunteers, marched the first ten prisoners out of sight into a little glade formed by a circle of trees, and shot them down. Returning for the remaining eight prisoners, they marched them into the same glade. The eight, seeing their comrades lying dead, let out screams and started to run. All were shot down. Lieutenant Morse, with a grease gun, killed most of them.

Immediately after the wounded infantrymen were carried out to the ambulance, some walking wounded came in, helped by their friends. All were talking about the killing of the prisoners, and, from a first boastful, excited chattering, a complete reversal of feeling was apparent. "It wasn't the C Company guys that done it," said a man from C Company. "It was A Company!"

"No!" said an A Company man. "It was the goddam tankers, that's who it was!"

Suddenly no one wanted any part of it, and those who a little earlier had boasted of sharing in the massacre now were said to be denying it at the top of their lungs.

The troops had gone forward to clear Tambach of snipers, and the captain returned, telling us to pack up and be ready to leave. At that moment the last of the German prisoners came along under guard, carrying six or eight of their own wounded, whom they deposited in the bare sloping yard outside the inn. A Third Army photographer had arrived at the same time in a jeep and came in to arrange for some moving pictures.

Captain Stettner, who up until then had personally ignored treating all German wounded, suddenly showed a great willingness to help the men in the yard. He was all genial co-operation, and he sailed out with the photographer, calling for Preacher, Phil, Joe Mortara and Warren Troy to come with him and bring out a box of medicine. A stream of infantrymen paused to look on while the camera ground away. I watched from the doorway. The captain strode around among the litters, pointing, giving instructions and a short talk on the nature of the wounds, and he permitted Preacher to help him with the bandaging of a German high-school boy while the cameraman came nearer for a close-up. The moment the cameraman stopped and said, "All right, thanks. That's all," the captain stopped too and walked unself-consciously away, though several untended Germans still remained on the ground.

As soon as the ambulance came back, we started to pile in

the blankets and medicine boxes. Phil and I made a last trip to the inn to see if anything had been left behind. The captain was bidding the family goodbye and there were many good wishes on both sides. In the midst of the speeches, he turned and said over his shoulder to us in English, "Grab that radio. Quick!" He turned back smiling to the family, blocking off their sight by standing in the kitchen doorway and keeping the door partly closed. The voices still continued in German, very gemutlicheit.

After a little hesitation, Phil and I reached up onto the shelf above the bar, got hold of the radio and started to lift it down. Wires held it. I gave them a yank, and it came free. Quickly we carried the radio out and gave it to Howard Mason to put in the white ambulance along with the rest of the captain's loot.

"What the goddam hell's he want this for?" Howard Mason cried. "He's got one."

"Well, he wants another. He likes things in pairs."

Leaving the inn shortly after, I passed beside the sloping glade where the shootings had taken place. Everyone on the marching line turned to look. The young trees were just coming out in tenderest leaf; the sun dappled the sward where the bodies lay riddled amid uncurling young ferns. Tambach itself, a mile farther on, with its open windows, sunlit lawns, rustling trees and spring-flowering shrubs, looked timeless and peaceful. The people all remained indoors; that was the only strange note. I wondered how many of the homes were plunged that day in mourning, or in how many of them were the families still frantically awaiting word of their schoolboy sons, some of whom were even now lying dead in the glade near the road block.

Stutzhaus, or what we saw of it, might have been anywhere in the country, in any country: a dirt road bordered by trees, some fields, a few houses such as a child draws. An aid station had been set up; Phil and I left Preacher minding it and went down to a nearby field. The battalion had halted and Regimental Headquarters had also arrived in the town.

It was the first time we had seen the litter bearers in several days, and, while talking to some of them, I was told that over in the next town, Ordruf, just outside our sector, there was a large concentration camp with the remains of hundreds of starved and mangled bodies lying unburied in the yard:

the gas chambers and crematoriums had been operating at full speed until the very last moment, but there had been no time for the S.S. to bury all the ghastly signs of their guilt.

"Some of our guys over there saw it. They were pukin'. They said it was awful! But they're gonna let everyone over to see it. If you wanna go, they say you ought to see it before they clean any of it up."

The field in which we were standing was overgrown with knee-high dead, bleached weeds, and the crowds of men trampling on them made constant loud crackling sounds. Nineteen-year-old Konrad Hausner, one of the regimental interpreters, a refugee who had been born in Germany and had spent his childhood there, came quickly through the straw-colored weeds with his superior officer, a man in charge of Military Government. Letting the officer go past, he stopped to shake hands and talk for a few minutes. He said, "I've just come from Ordruf, from the concentration camp."

"I hear they're going to let us all go over and see it."

"Don't. Don't go. Do yourself a favor—stay away! It's the most horrible thing—worse than anything you ever heard of. Bodies all over the place—women, kids, men—all heaped together, half burned. They must have been living skeletons. God, what bastards to do things like that! I tell you, I'm sick! Take it from me, it's all there; none of it's exaggerated, but don't go."

As it turned out, we were not permitted to go over, but toward evening Jimmy McDonough and his friend Horse-face Fogarty returned to Stutzhaus. Forgart was slack and expressionless; Jimmy McDonough looked awed. "You're lucky you didn't go," he said, passing me. "God, it was awful. Honest, I'm sick."

We had our mess kits out, getting ready to line up, and someone asked if he were going to eat.

"Eat?" He put his hand on his stomach and turned his head away. "Listen, I don't even wanna *think* about eatin'." He went on into the aid station to lie down as Fogarty had done. When we were going to sleep that night, he was still lying on his stomach, his head buried in his arms. They didn't eat all the next day, but sat in the aid station, dazed and silent.

About a week later, some rear elements of our division were present at Ordruf when the burgomaster led his towns-folk out to the concentration camp for a burial ceremony.

431

By then the place had been considerably cleaned up. The starved and half-consumed bodies had been gathered together and placed in coffins, and there were even a few floral offerings. When the people saw what the camp was like and were led through the torture chambers and past the ovens, men and women screamed out and fainted; others were led away crying hysterically. All swore that during the past years they had had no idea of what had been going on in the camp just outside their town.

And yet, one heard other stories. One heard that it would be impossible not to know what was happening, that the greasy black smoke and the unmistakable odor of burning bodies could be detected for miles around such concentration camps, that villagers got up petitions to have the camps moved elsewhere.

I never knew what to believe.

Near the field of tall dead weeds there was a fenced-in yard that was being used as a temporary prisoner-of-war pen. German soldiers of all ranks were crowded into it, their hands raised, while the regimental guards searched them and their meager belongings, opening their packs, flipping through their army booklets, robbing the prisoners of rings, watches, money, souvenirs and pen-and-pencil sets, occasionally tossing the articles they didn't want over the fence to begging, jumping infantrymen.

Among the prisoners was one strapping blond young S.S. man who doubtless cursed and hated himself now for surrendering, and, in an attempt to save his pride, he put up a public challenge to beat any four Americans in an honest fist fight. Believing fanatically in the myth of his superiority, he begged and shouted for the chance and caused quite a disturbance in the compound.

A passing American who reminded me of the former Sergeant Janovic of C Company, shorter than the German and not too prepossessing in appearance, heard of the vaunt, walked in quietly, put down his rifle, took off his helmet and field jacket, squared off, and beat the Nazi all over the enclosure. He battered him so that at the end of three or four minutes the German was lying on the ground, heaving, his face cut, nose bleeding, his fists pressed against his eyes, trying to shut out the acknowledgment of this ignominious day. The infantryman, whom no one seemed to know, rubbed his scraped knuckles, put on his helmet and jacket, shouldered

432

his rifle and walked away without saying anything. The German was left on the ground. The rest of the prisoners formed a distant, expressionless circle around him.

Near one o'clock one warm afternoon the whole long convoy of jeeps and trucks came to a halt beneath the first surrender flags of a shabby, damaged little town, and the road immediately became thick with soldiers. Clouds of dust rose up in the sunlight. Preacher, Phil, Warren Troy and I got out of the ambulance and had taken only a few steps when we heard, "Medics! Hubba hubba! Down here, medics, on the double!"

We ran down through the crowd to a wide courtyard that opened off the road. Small flats formed three sides of the court, and German women were at the open windows, staring down. So many of our troops were milling about, pushing past each other, uninterested in what was happening, that at first we couldn't get through to see why we had been called. A shouting officer was clearing a path through the men while a fifteen-year-old German boy and a woman pushed a large two-wheel hay cart ino the courtyard.

"Get out! Get out!" the officer was shouting. "All you men, get out, and let these medics through!"

In the cart, lying on the hay, was a stout, strong-looking German woman who had been shot several times through the face and neck. She appeared to be paralyzed as a result. Her mouth was tight shut, but in the full glare of the sun there was a strangling vitality about her: her eyes protruded, her coarse, sandy hair seemed to boil out of her head; a large vein stood out pulsing in her full neck. She was struggling to say something but her jaws couldn't move; she gritted her teeth and a horrible sound came from her throat. As if to emphasize the look of someone ready to burst, her black dress had ripped apart at the neck.

There followed into the court, through the scattering crowd of soldiers, a weeping young girl drawing a little express wagon in which a dead child was lying: a boy about four years old, the son of the woman who had been shot through the face.

Some relative of both—sister, perhaps, of the woman—came running out of one of the flats, beating her hands. Seeing the woman in the hay cart, she let out a loud scream and gaped at her, transfixed. The wounded woman, unable to move, again gritted her teeth in an effort to move or say something. Some blood dribbled out the corner of her mouth.

A second later the aunt saw the little boy, who had died, I believe, on the way over. The girl who had brought him cried so hard she could answer no questions, but could only indicate the child with both empty, open hands. The aunt suddenly fell to her knees and held the little body to her, rocking with it and covering the face with kisses. From all the windows there came the sound of women crying. Their gestures, the whole scene took on a biblical aspect.

"My God!" Phil whispered. "This is awful!"

Preacher and Warren had gone over to the wounded woman, and after a first glance Preacher called, "At! Phil! Someone! See 'f you kin round up the cap'm. Tell him we got a woman here in purty bad shape, 'n' see what he wants to do. I think he's down with the officers at Battalion. Tell him he better come right up."

Glad for an excuse to leave the sight and the sounds of lamentation, we hurried down the hill through the throngs of soldiers idly bumping into each other, searching for eggs and loot, and we entered the crowded court of a small, white frame house on the corner. The officers were there with Captain Stettner in their midst and a group of noncoms and privates about them.

"I hope he'll come back with us," I started to say to Phil as we stepped into the court, but halfway through the sentence a series of loud warning shouts went up.

"Look out! Look *out!*" Everyone was frozen, looking at me. For an odd split-second, I found myself staring aghast at the captain, who had whipped out his revolver and seemed about to shoot me between the eyes. At the same time, I knew something was hurtling at me through the air. I flinched without knowing what to expect. Something large, swift and dark landed with a crash of bone, muscle and nails almost on top of me. A huge dog, part Boxer, tethered by a long metal chain to a pulley line, had made a long flying lunge at my throat as I came into the yard. At the last moment, its chain yanked it back midway through the leap. I stumbled against Phil, and the dog was up, again trying to leap for me. The captain, about to shoot it, had been stopped by one of the officers, who had grabbed his wrist and held it aloft.

"My God!" I said in astonishment. It took a moment or

two before everything settled down for me. The hideous dog, looking like a cross between a beast and the devil, with undershot jaw, bared teeth, bloodshot eyes and small pointed ears, was still snarling, scrabbling and choking at the end of its chain, rearing up on its hind legs. If I had made any motion, I thought, or had put my hand up to my face . . . But I hadn't been doing anything. Why should it single me out of the crowd?

The captain, his face still watchful, black with wrath, had not put his pistol away. The back door of the house opened and a man came running out, crying, "Brintz! Brintz!" The captain snarled something to him in German; the man reined in the dog, trying to quiet it. Under the captain's order, it was taken down the cellar and locked up. Phil and I advanced—I somewhat shaken—and told about the wounded woman.

"The hell with her," the captain said shortly. "Damned Krauts."

"What's that?" Major Gregory, temporarily in charge of the battalion, had caught the story. "A wounded civilian? A woman? You'd better hurry right along, Captain. We're moving out in a few minutes."

"Oh! Yes, sir!"

We returned, and, in a bad mood, Captain Stettner came about five minutes later. To Cody, the Kentucky ambulance driver, he said, "Where's Collecting? How far away is it?"

"Five, six mile back, sir."

"Well, listen. Don't take her all the way back there. Dump her off at some nearer town an' let someone else worry about her."

"Yes, sir." The driver, tall, light-haired, straight-featured save for a dent in his nose, returned a level, expressionless glance. He was the man who had gone back the second time and rescued the ambulance when Silly Willie let it run off the road coming out of Olzheim.

Preacher had the woman plastered with bandages and she was carried up to the ambulance. The child's body was gone. Referee whistles blew, companies lined up quickly, a roll call was taken, and the men piled into the trucks. The lead-off vehicles started to roll. Preacher and Warren Troy went along with the captain in the jeep. Phil and I were instructed to wait down at the corner outside Brintz's house, to flag down the ambulance on its return trip and tell the driver to bear along to the left till we caught up again with the convoy.

I was surprised to see how quickly all signs of a battalion could disappear. Brintz's house was one of the last in town; a meadow stretched behind it and there the road took a sudden left turn and was shielded from sight by a heavy growth of trees. The last vehicle disappeared around the bend and we were left alone.

"They said there was an air raid here last night that lasted twenty minutes and knocked *hell* out of this place," Phil said. "And then there was another raid just before we got here."

"Why would planes come over this place?" I could see nothing worth bombing. Unless I had missed the greater part of it on our way in, it was a most insignificant town—four or five short streets in all, surrounded by trees, meadows and low hills. "Do you think there could be any hidden factories? Phil?"

He hadn't heard me. A scowl came over his face and he looked about him slowly, as if puzzled, then he started mumbling to himself. After a while I tried him with another question, but again he didn't know I had spoken.

The white house and its lawn were raised about two feet from the road on a little walled terrace. We sat on it, our feet in the dusty road.

Two French slave laborers hurried down the street to our left between the rows of flat, narrow houses. They were dressed in berets, sweaters, corduroys, and had such heavy sacks over their shoulders that they were stumbling. One, with Cuban heels on his shoes, was carrying about fifty pounds of flour, some of which spilled out when he swung it from one shoulder to the other. Intent, without seeing us, they went past on the opposite side of the street, close to the houses, and out through the meadow.

"Loot," I said to Phil, who did not understand. It was turning into one of his bad days.

A few minutes later, a narrow door of one of the small houses opened and a tall, elderly man came out—a surprising man, well set up, dignified, military in bearing. He was perhaps seventy, with strong aristocratic features. He wore a navy-blue suit, a starched collar, dark tie and black shoes. He had a short, white beard which shone in the sun. Holding himself with dignity, he started up the street toward us. A doctor, I first thought, but he was hatless, had no bag, and was too citified for his surroundings. There was something in the way he struck out, veered a little, looked lost for a second or two and then set his course again that made me think he had escaped from the house and was in a daze.

He had got past us, marching rigidly, head high, toward the empty meadow, when the same door opened and a young man in his early thirties, dressed in a tan knickerbocker suit and cable-knit sweater, came out distractedly, looked up and down the street, spotted the old man and set off after him on a run. Seeing us at the corner, he stiffened, dropped into an enforced walk and continued past without glancing at us again. He had heavy light-brown hair pushed back from a face as resolute and handsome as a movie actor's. His clothes had a look of great expense.

I watched him go by on the opposite side of the street, but I did not turn my head to see what happened, for just then there came around the corner from behind us a boy about seven years old and a girl who was eleven or twelve. The little boy's face was dirty with dried tear streaks. The two children stopped before us.

"Hello," I said. "Guten tag!"

The girl, stringy and fair, smiled, showing large pale gums. She wore a faded, too-short summer dress and an open cardigan sweater. Phil, picking up interest, also greeted them. I had a few hard candies from a ration in my pocket and I handed them over, along with two sticks of gum in khaki wrappers. The girl took them and divided them with the boy. It was obvious that she was taking care of him, obvious too that she had a story to tell. She was self-important, scraping one foot in the dirt. We had got past questions like How old are you? Do you go to school? Do you live here? when suddenly the story unfolded. The little shaven-headed boy stood with his eyes fixed on us. The girl smiled throughout, twisting and scraping her foot, addressing Phil, who translated for me.

The American planes, she said, had come over last night. They were all in their cellars. The boy here, a neighbor of hers, was with his mother, his aunt, two older sisters and a baby brother in the cellar of their house when a direct hit landed on top of them. All, except the boy, were killed. The girl's family had rushed over as soon as they could and had dragged him out of the wreckage; he had spent the rest of the night in her house. She was minding him now.

Through her recital, he stood with hard bright eyes, pale in color, fixed on us as if looking for a clue how to behave, waiting to see what our reaction would be. Even if I knew the words in German, I would not have known how to offer sympathy to a child that young.

"God!" Phil said. We stared back at the little boy. I found myself trying to smile at him. He opened one grubby hand and offered us a lump and a half of dirty gray sugar.

"A lady gave it to him," the girl said. "She gave him four pieces! He says you can have it."

"That tears it," I said to Phil. "Tell him Thank you, but he'd better keep it for himself." And when Phil did not speak, I said, "Nein. Danke, danke, but nein. Is gut, but nein, danke."

The girl added a few sentences which Phil either did not hear or did not feel were worth translating. He began to talk to himself again, to shake his head and frown, and the girl watched him with a growing awareness of his trouble. She kept smiling and scraping her foot, but her eyes were suddenly unchildlike, delighted and cruel.

"Goodbye," I said. "Go on. Goodbye. Auf wiedersehen."

The girl started to leave, but the little boy did not understand why she was tugging at him. His small dirty face crumpled as if he were about to cry. At the same time, from behind us on the road came the young man in the golf suit leading the upright old man by the arm, trying to reason with him and hurry him back into the house. He halted halfway through a sentence and stared from Phil to me, and then from the little girl to the boy. She swung her head around and almost in astonishment saw him trying to manage the bedazed old man. There was a curious moment of recognition among the three of us. It was as if each of us realized in the other a kinship: each of us had a charge; we were all in the same boat. Then the moment fell apart. The girl, tugging and twitching at the little boy, got him past us; the young man hurried the old man down the street, into the house, and kicked the door closed behind him.

After a minute or two, I turned my head and as if materialized out of the air there were five or six German men standing where a moment before there had been no one. Their eyes were trained on us. I looked away and said to Phil, "I haven't got my rifle, and there're some odd-looking customers closing in on us. From your left."

When I looked around this time, there were more than a dozen. My heart stopped. Where had they all come from so quickly and silently? And in that small space of time, they had crept very much closer. Phil looked at the men, seemed interested, then looked away, made a crooning sound and laughed a little.

The men, few of whom looked old enough to have escaped military service, were too close to be ignored, nor could one pretend they were doing anything but staring at us. I had visions of them making a sudden rush, dragging us down a cellar and beating us to death in reprisal for the bombings. "Say something to them," I said to Phil, but he was rattled and said nothing. They gathered silently about us in a tall semicircle, cutting off the sun. I was about to strike out in my own abominable German when I could feel the courage go draining out of me. One of them had sneaked up behind us and I could feel his breath on my neck.

As calmly as I could, I turned my head and then almost let out a cry. It was the dog Brintz, with his head virtually between Phil's and mine. I was too shaken then to know whether Phil spoke to the men or not. At all cost I didn't want to show fear of the dog before them; I hunched up the shoulder next to Brintz, expecting him to sink his fangs into me at any moment. In the meanwhile, one of the men, broad and swarthy, said something to which Phil was silent.

Behind me a screen door opened.

"Brintz! Brintz!" called an excited boy. He ran up, grabbed hold of Brintz's collar and dragged him away toward the cellar. With a great lightening of spirits, I heard myself saying, "Guten aben!"

The swarthy man said, "Soldaten? Infantry?"

"Nein," I said, pointing to Phil. "Ein Sanitater: Roite Creutz. *Ich* bin ein Infantry soldat."

"Infantry. Yah." He shook his head, smiled; he knew what that was. Then he asked if American soldiers were coming here—to stay, I gathered. I told Phil to tell him, "Yes. Later this afternoon."

Phil muttered to himself, so I said, "Der krankenwagon gehen zu ein Americanisher lazarette mit ferwounded Deutscher frau, und commen—here—ahere fir us." I indicated Phil and myself.

That satisfied their curiosity. They nodded their heads. All was clear. They stood and discussed us quietly and I found myself gazing out over their heads with all the simple blankness of a freak in a sideshow. Now that I had got a grip on myself, I began to see that we must have presented an odd sight: two unarmed soldiers left behind for hours alone after the rest had driven off. What could we have seemed? Deserters?

The young man in the plus fours had come out again and he hung about on the outskirts of the group, giving them and us sharp, nervous looks. He wore a heavy gold identification bracelet on his wrist. Taking one of the men aside, he asked who Phil and I were. Upon being told, he shot us a glance and walked quickly back to the house. Through Phil, I asked the Germans who he was. They looked uneasy and said they didn't know. In a town this size they wouldn't know?

"His wife is sick," one of the men volunteered.

The man had gone back into the narrow little house. An army officer making an escape? Burdened with a sick wife, a shell-shocked father? Changing out of uniform, trying to avoid the American Army only to run headlong into it? Wondering now whether to travel on, where to go, how to hide out?

The spokesman for the group came toward me and reached out his hand—I thought in begging for cigarettes. Deciding to give him one, I remained motionless. He said something smilingly.

"He's saying he's a tailor, I *think*," said Phil.

The man reached out and felt the material of my trousers. "Excuse. I am—tailor. Gut!" He pointed to the trousers. "Wool—gut! American. Gut!"

"You've been to America?"

"Yah. Yes. Seven year. Detroit. In Detroit, tailor. Gleen and bress." In German, he pointed out to the others the quality of my combat boots, empty pistol belt and so on. I wished the uniform looked more spruce, that I was not so tired-looking, so old and coated with dust.

An American plane zoomed over the trees, flying low in our direction, and with a simultaneous cry of terror the men broke and ran, dashing into the houses across the street. The plane dipped, circled around and then flew away, but the men did not reappear for the rest of the afternoon.

"P-38. Notice the fuselage," I said to Phil, who snorted

440

with laughter. To me, all planes interchangeably were P-38s or Mitsubishi Bombers.

A little later, people came out cautiously, eyes lifted up to the sky, and a dignified promenade began. I was struck by the number of pretty girls who appeared, walking sedately, escorted by an older member of the family. There had not been one at large while the troops were in town. Several people passed by us to go to the side window of Brintz's house and knock on the glass. Each time the owner raised the window, said something, and the people walked away. Noticing that I craned to watch the performance, the owner came to the window directly behind us, opened it and explained to Phil that he was the town baker; this was the hour when people called for bread. Our men, however, had carted off everything he had baked, and "others" had made off with his last sack of flour. The man spread his hands. He was out of business.

Another hour or two passed and we began to feel hungry. We had had no lunch and our K rations had been left in the ambulance. Phil didn't even have his canteen. I had a little water in mine, which we split. I had three cigarettes. We began to talk of going to the CBI after finishing up here in Europe.

"Of course," Phil said, "I don't ever expect to get there. I'll be wiped out here first."

"Don't you feel it's all over here but the shooting?"

With sweeping pessimism, he said, "We'll *all* be wiped out. Here or there. No one will last any time there."

"I understand the litter bearers are all armed there and have two riflemen with them on every haul. Do you think you'll have to take rifle practice?" Until I spoke, I had forgotten he was a conscientious objector. "What will you do if they issue a rifle?"

"Oh, carry the damned thing and not use it. They can't force you to fire it at anyone."

"When you came into the Army, did you have to explain—?"

"No, as a matter of fact, I was picked right off the bat to be a medic."

"I suppose if I'm kept with the medics in the CBI, I'll be your guard of honor on litter hauls. We'll see if we can't get Old Man Owens to be the other. Preacher, you know, wants me to transfer over into the medics; he says he'll train me to

441

be his assistant in the CBI. I think I'd break in here on corns and bunions."

"We'll *all* be wiped out."

The conversation kept sputtering and dying like that. The warm afternoon wore to a close. An enormous red sun shone in its descent straight into our eyes. We began to talk of where we would spend the night.

"Not in any of the houses here."

"No," Phil said. "It's too soon after the air raids, and the people might get ideas of reprisal."

"We'll wait until dark and then I think we'd better go out into the meadow there." We were convinced the ambulance had taken the wrong turn and had missed us. But if so, why hadn't the captain sent back for us? "Maybe we'd better stay here on the corner all night."

The western sky flamed with color. The baker's wife threw open the window and asked if we'd like to come in and have dinner with the family. We declined with sincere thanks. We had been sitting outside on their coping then for about five hours.

The ambulance finally came down the road. We stood up and waved. The driver had disobeyed the captain's orders and had driven the wounded woman all the way back to Collecting. There he had visited with his friends for a while, and, on leaving, had got into an accident that knocked the ambulance partly into a ditch. Something had broken—an axle, I think—and he had been forced to wait for repairs.

We rode out of town along a dusty road that wound through the green meadows, churning up behind us in the last of the sunlight a coiling pinkish cloud. Taking left turns all the way, we drove through quiet farming communities, through cool dark woods, over shady rustic bridges. About fifteen miles farther on, we came upon our outfit in a town; we had missed our dinner and had to eat another K ration. Our battalion went into regimental reserve and we were granted a two-day rest.

The early morning was chill, with the sun coming up pale gold through a thin silvery fog. We had lined up at five-yard intervals on a country road, shivering and yawning, waiting for the cooks to start serving breakfast. First Battalion was there and the medics had formed behind them.

"Men—" an officer came quickly along the line— "I have

an announcement. I'd like your attention there! I have an announcement to make: President Roosevelt died last night."

"What?" You heard it from all sides. "What? President Roosevelt? Roosevelt's *dead?"* We were astounded.

The officer's voice continued, "We don't know any of the particulars, except that he's dead. I think it was very sudden. Probably a stroke. Truman, the Vice President, will take over."

"Who? Who'd he say?"

"Truman, ya dumb bastard. Who the hell you think?"

Phil was behind me and I said to him at once, "I wonder what effect it will have on the war—whether it will make it drag out, if the Germans will take heart—"

"I don't know!"

"Just when we'd really need him! With peace conferences coming up—I wonder what Truman's like."

The beginning of the line moved ahead, but one man, taking too long to wash his mess kit, held up our part of it. "Come on there, Mitchell, let's not wash our leggin's," someone called; and one of the cooks came past, carrying the big steaming strainer of coffee grounds. "All right, out of the way! Hot stuff! Hot stuff! Lady with a baby!" he cried.

We started forward. Late-comers, jangling mess kits, were greeted with the news. "Hey, did ya hear? Roosevelt's dead."

"Wha—? When? Ya kiddin'!"

"No! Ask the lieutenant."

"Jeez! Too bad it wasn't Hitler, hey?"

"Did ya vote for him the last time?" someone was asking.

"I voted for him all the time. How about you, Skeezix? What'd you do?"

Skeezix was a small, tough, disgruntled figure with a sagging fish mouth and dark rings under his eyes. "What're ya—wise guy?" asked Skeezix.

"I'm askin' ya!"

"F——," said Skeezix bitterly.

"So what's the matter with you?"

"He means he wasn't old enough to vote."

By the time we had rinsed our mess kits and were standing along the edge of the dirt road, eating, the subject was practically forgotten. It had caused a ripple of surprise and interest, no more than that.

From my experience, the speech and reactions of the fighting man to any stirring or dramatic moment were seldom as

443

they were depicted by the war correspondents, the play-wrights or radio dramatists, in whose words GI Joe spoke with deep feeling and wisdom about Democracy, One World and the nature of the peace to come. In this respect I was reminded of the night last October when in secrecy we were boarding the *Queen Elizabeth* to sail for Europe.

Everything about the scene was sufficiently moving to bring forth sentiments of patriotism or rushes of free verse if ever they were to come. On the brackish cement pier, companies of infantrymen were lined up, facing the gray steel wall of the ship. Naked electric bulbs cast down a harsh, lonesome light, and shadows made by steel helmets turned even the most commonplace faces dramatic. In the dark harbor, boats mooed sadly, a bell tolled. I listened particularly to hear what the men were saying.

"Well, this is it, fellas." "Yeah, I guess they got us this time." "Jeez, I'm sweatin'." "Wish the f--- they'd let you smoke." "I hope we don't pull any KP, that's all I hope, I hope, I hope." Red Cross women had appeared to give out coffee and doughnuts, and the youngest of them drew wolf calls and appreciative whistles. "Hey, look at the ass on that one. Ooh, my f---in' back!"

Though the autumn night was mild, we were dressed in long underwear, new woolen uniforms, sweaters, field jackets and overcoats. Stonelike full field packs were strapped to our backs; gas masks were slung on; our belts were heavy with ammunition, bayonet, entrenching tool and filled canteen. As our names were called out over an amplifier, we answered, hoisted up the heavy duffel bag, grabbed the rifle and, in single file, began to toil up the long gritty cement staircases. On the first landing, as a boost to morale, a swing band comprised of garrison soldiers was playing "Amapola, my pretty little poppy." Staggering up the stairs like beasts of burden, the infantrymen cursed them roundly and bitterly. "Goddam 4-F bastards!" "Lucky sons of bitches!" "Hope the f--- they git you too!" The golden instruments glittered and seemed to laugh.

All at once in the dimness I came face to face with a short, steeply inclined gangplank, and as I set my foot on it I heard behind me on the stairs the loud, desperate Texan voice of little illiterate Shorty Witherspoon bawling out in farewell, "Youah boyas will *nev-ah leave these shores!*"

For weeks the litter bearers had been living out with the companies and sleeping in foxholes. During this two-day rest, Captain Stettner permitted them to join us in a small, snug farmhouse, but he had not been overgenerous in his welcome and he remained shut off in a room with Lieutenant Serletis and Sergeant Campbell.

Out in the small living room, everyone had notes to compare, stories to tell, opinions about rifle companies, officers and noncoms. I remember that while we were talking of a small city we had captured Don Stoddard told us of an odd thing that had happened to him. The streets had been jammed with fleeing civilians, many trundling little milk carts piled with their possessions. Don had been making his way through the crowd during a ten-minute break, when a girl ran out of one of the apartment houses, took him by the sleeve and asked him to come in. Thinking someone was sick, he went in with her and up a flight of stairs to an extremely neat apartment. Her husband was there, standing at a table where they had been having lunch. They had come to the dessert; the girl had baked a large cake and had iced it that morning—and there it was. They explained that it seemed a shame to waste it, that they could not possibly eat it all. Would he like to join them?

"Weren't you afraid it was poisoned?" little Jenkins asked.

"Hell no!" he replied in rising inflections, as if he were asking a question.

"And how was it?" I asked.

"Swell!" They had sat there and, laughing at themselves, finished the entire cake while the rest of the town took to its heels. Don thanked them, they left the table, the husband and wife took up their bags and all three walked out of the apartment and down the stairs. On the street they said goodbye and separated.

"How'd she come to pick you out of the crowd?"

"Be damned if I know! It was the damnedest thing that ever happened to me."

Someone in the meanwhile was describing an attack when the lead-off company had ridden ahead, clutching onto the sides of rumbling tanks. It had been one of the days when we covered thirty miles, capturing town after town, and at its close the men were jolted up, soaked by rains, tired, with blinding headaches. They had dropped off at their destination. "An' then we come up the path of this house, and

445

there's this old, old woman sittin' there on the doorstep cryin', an' she gives us some sort of a long, sad story about somethin' and Fogarty said to her, he says, "Don't tell *me* your f---in' troubles; give us some eggs."

Sam Benton was saying in another conversation, "Hey, 'member that place? Where the MP was, got killed? No, not that place, the place where McDonough got all the eggs. Boy, 'member that? Six men ate fifty-two eggs. Yes, sir!"

Jimmy McDonough said to me in a low voice, "You know that Sam Benton's a crazy bastard? He's gonna get us all killed. He doesn't give a damn about himself, but I want to get home to my wife and my little Jimmy. A guy'll be wounded, see, shells comin' in from all sides, maybe machine guns cross-firin', and to make a big shot of himself in front of the lieutenant, he wants to run in an' carry the guy out. I says to him, 'You can have all that s--- you want, but you ain't gittin' *me* in there. Wait till it lets up a little.' But no, he says out loud so everyone can hear, 'I'm goin' in after him. Do I git any volunteers?' Then Tom here always volunteers."

Tom Lawlor was listening with a smile. "Gee, sometimes it's pretty bad. Each time I think, well, here goes . . ." A little shiver ran through him while he smiled. "I'll say this for Sam, though: he certainly is brave."

"Brave me ass. He's gonna get us all killed. You're a damn fool for volunteering."

"He's a fahn lieutenant," Sam was telling someone across the crowded room. He had a mild way of raising his left hand that had the injured fingers, as if he were being sworn in on the witness stand. "Go through anything for that lieutenant—go through fahr. Yes, sir!"

"Say," Phil said to me, "now that the boys are all in, what do you say we start on our notes?" He had some loose sheets of paper. I searched around the room, and, in an open bookcase, I found a penny notebook with a limp blue cover. Since Sam Benton, Jr., was sitting near us on the floor, we began with him. The others listened at first in surprise, and then continued to talk among themselves.

"Ah'm twent' seven," Sam Benton was answering, "an 'Ah come from Colfrey, Kentucky. Kentucky hillbilly, that's me. Ah went to Colfrey Seminary an' then Ah worked in a lumber mill for m' dad for 'bout two years, an' then Ah comes in the Army." He ran through the list of camps to which he

446

had been assigned. "Yes, Ah was a medic right off, because of this injury to my han'. Got it in the lumber mill. These three fingers have no power in 'em. Yes, Ah went through the Tennessee maneuvers. Had the bes' meal ever ate in the Army there. I 'member we were lost, and come up to this shack in the country an' a woman, a Mrs. Kelly—she had 'bout four li'l shavers, and she says, 'Boys, could you eat a meal?' She fixed us the bes' meal Ah ever sat down to. Coming over to Europe? Was Ah *seasick?* Tell you, Ah was too sick to dah. Ha, ha, ha, ha. Yes sirree, wouldn't a-cared if the *Eliz* had hit the bottom."

After the first few days in the Saar he arrived to join the First Battalion medics. "That was a tough place. 'Bout lak Valley Forge, guess. An' Ah remember the trip *out* of the Saar. Open trucks. Oh, man! Coldest Ah ever felt. Yes, day before Christmas. Christmas Day," he said with restraint, "we had a very good dinner. An', remember, we kept poor ole Phil runnin' into the kitchen for water, 'cause none of us could say it in German? An' remember that ride when ole Burrell lost his helmet an' thought his head came off? Ha, ha, ha, ha. Never forget that long's Ah live. Each stop we made, Ah got out and double-tahmed beside the chaplain's jeep to keep warm.

"The toughest litter haul? Ah think at the chateau. Got a boy named Brill, came from Chi. Was shot through the knee. Snow almost up to our waist there. We got him out of the foxhole, and comin' back, we kept stumblin' into other foxholes: couldn't tell 'em in the snow. An' all the way back, Phil here and O'Rourke, they had some kinda labor dispute.

"Most *dangerous* litter hauls were at the Crossroads near A Company, when A Company didn't take the hah ground. Saw more fireworks ever saw in all mah life. Mortars everywhere. Boys were scared to go in. Ah started out one time with twelve litter bearers, and got to A Company, on'y had four.

"And the next place, Neurendorf, right nearby, when C Company's C.P. got hit the same night. Nine litter cases, and two guys killed. Couldn't *count* the walkin' wounded.

"And Ah'll never forget that boat goin' down on the Moselle. Terrible thing, seein' those boys tryna swim. One guy climbed out of the rescue boat still had his grease gun in his han'.

"We got lost in Coblenz, got lost in the dark. Thought the

squad and me were in enemy territory. Got sniped at there, walkin' with Lawlor along the street.

"Felt best at the town where the MP was dead. Had the bes' bed there of mah whole European trip. An' then just the other day, riding on tanks into Frankenhein was a thrill. Crashin' through the woods thirty mile an hour."

After the war, he said he thought he would like to drive one of his brother's trucks. His brother was somewhere here in Europe, a lieutenant in a tank outfit; on two occasions he found they had been within a few miles of each other without knowing it. "Think the world of m' brother, and if Ah could just drive one of his trucks, Ah'd settle down and marry m' girl. Yep, got her all picked out: Miss Lucy Lee. M' brother married Miss Martha Lee. Ah don't care much about money, 'bout how much Ah make. So long's a man's happy—"

"*Chow-w-w!*" someone shouted, and there was an upheaval in the room, a scramble for helmets, gas masks and mess kits. We put our notes away and rushed out to get on line.

After dinner some of the litter bearers, on a second hunt through the cellar, found several bottles of liquor and brought them upstairs. "Now listen, guys. We keep this for ourselves. No sharing it with Stettner or Campbell."

"Hey, pipe down; they'll hear you."

It was vodka they had found. Whispering, laughing silently, one eye on the closed door to the captain's room, we began to drink it.

"What the hella they talkin' about? This stuff ain't strong. Give us some more. Open the other bottles."

"Hey, *shh!*"

Our room was very small and next to it there was a toilet slightly larger than one on a train. And soon in our midst there was a vast relaxing, a milling about, considerable stumbling. Voices grew louder.

From the captain's room came "Cut out the noise in there! We're tryin' to go to sleep!"

There were suppressed giggles in reply and a whispered voice saying, "F--- you," then more silent laughter. Another round of drinks followed, and more stumbling, protestations of undying friendship, handclasps. Jimmy McDonough began to stagger outside for air, but he fell and crashed into the toilet door, and once more there were sharp commands from the next room.

"Can't be more quiet in nere," Sergeant Campbell was saying, "y'll all go back to the companies. If I have to git up and come in there . . ."

Phil and I dragged Jimmy out of the house and stretched him out on the cobblestones. The moon turned them, and him, a ghostly pale green. We stayed outside with Jimmy for ten or fifteen minutes, hoping the cool air would revive him. The experience took me back years to college dances. We tried to wake him, sat him up and began to slap his face.

"Jimmy, wake up. We're going to try to lift you up and get you back inside." While Phil opened the door, I started in with him, warning him to be quiet. Once inside, in the box-like pitch-black hall, he became sick and started to vomit. "The toilet!" I whispered to Phil. "Where is it? Open the damned door!"

"Here. Can you get him in?"

"Yes. Jimmy, hold it just a second." We got inside, but someone was sitting in there. "Get the hell out of the way!" Luckily, it was not the captain. In the confusion and stumbling, Jimmy proceeded to throw up in all directions, fainting in between times. Later, by candlelight, we bathed his face, brought him outside again for a while, and as soon as he started to shiver with cold, we returned, half carrying him.

The lantern had gone out. Men were sleeping sprawled on the floor over a welter of equipment, full field packs and unopened blankets. We lowered Jimmy into an empty place. In the corner, someone was vomiting. Phil and I dragged a couple of blankets out and prepared to sleep in the hall, halfway into the toilet.

Don Stoddard, who had missed the party while out visiting friends in another battalion, came in, stepped over us and began to undress in the dark. "Hey, what the hell goes on here?" he asked. "Is someone sick?" There was no answer. "Smells as though someone's *sick* in here!"

"Shh! Don't wake the captain. He's sore."

"This is the worst damn billet we ever had! It stinks! Hey, Pancho," came Don's aggrieved whisper, "what'd you do, puke? What's the matter with you?"

Miserably came the answer "I couldn'a help. I'm seek."

Early in the morning when we got up, Sergeant Campbell of course saw what had happened. He was angry, but, to his credit, he said nothing. We got ready to move out at once. Pallid and sick, the litter bearers put on their equipment and dragged themselves out to rejoin the companies.

Pössneck, a fairly large city, was not yet cleared of the enemy when the battalion convoy arrived on its outskirts that afternoon. After a twenty-minute halt, we were told to set up for the night. We were parked just outside an inn and we began to move the equipment into the taproom. Two women in tears disappeared, frightened, seeing the men rush to the beer pumps, which turned out to be dry.

Mike Nowak wanted to get the walkie-talkie inside, and in handing it to me through the window I knocked a large spider plant from the sill to the clean floor. The jardiniere broke and the dirt poured out. The stout proprietress rushed popeyed into the long room and stared down at the plant in tears. I told Phil to tell her that it was an accident. The woman called to her daughter, who appeared, took a look at the broken plant, pointed to it and she too began to cry. Why, I wondered; what did the plant mean to them? The girl hurried out, returned with a dust pan and a broom made of twigs, and, while sweeping up the dirt, for some reason she turned cheerful, blinked her tears away and began to smile at herself. She was about nineteen; both she and her mother were dressed in mourning.

"Hey! She's not bad," the men were saying. "Chocolada?" "Have some gum, chum?" "Hey, Frawleen, don't look at him; look at me!" "Hey, this one's all right!"

The girl was surrounded and was pleasantly surprised by the friendly advances. There was nothing bold or flirtatious about her: she was a thorough home girl. She had pale-blond ringlets, rather prominent pale-blue eyes, soft contours of face and the beginnings of a double chin. Her lips were bland and smooth, and when she smiled, one saw too much of her gums, but she was defenseless, soft-looking, feminine, with sloping shoulders and a slim waist. Her legs and feet, in black stockings and shoes, were fairly good. One saw many girls like her in America behind the counters of German bakeries. Yet not quite like her: the docile softness would be gone, and, with it, some of the femininity. It was this sheltered quality, this lack of aggressiveness or emancipation on the part of many German girls that appealed so strongly to the American men.

"Wie haisen sie?"

"Irma."

Irma made no attempt to be the mental or physical equal of any man.

"There's something about these girls," the men said as she went out with the dust pan. "Say what you want, they got it all over the girls back home, be damned if they don't. I don't know just what it is—"

"They look up to a guy."

"They been brought up right. They ain't been allowed to run around."

"They're more natural; more like girls should be."

There were two floors upstairs, let out as apartments. The first of these was rented to a stout, elderly woman who had fled out of the taproom with the proprietress as we entered. In looking for a place to sleep, Phil and I came upon her, standing alone in the middle of her living room. She jumped with terror, thinking we had come up to shoot her.

With the outside of the place poor and rural, it was a surprise to find expensive ornate furnishings in her apartment: tapestries, lace tablecloth, silver candelabra, oriental prayer rugs, vast cut-glass punch bowl and cups, quantities of ornaments. They looked like the possessions of a woman, widowed, who had given up a large house.

One of the tenants on the third floor was a woman perhaps thirty-four, the mother of three small boys. At our first entrance downstairs, she had looked old, gray-faced and sick, with the children peeking from behind her skirt. Now that the little boys had been running around with chocolate and gum, and friendly relations were being established, her color came back and the tenseness went out of her. She proved to be a thin, attractive, embittered-looking woman with a sharp widow's peak, light brownish hair to her shoulders, and high-heeled gray suede shoes with many buttoned straps over the instep. Her apartment was poor and plain-looking. She had herded the little boys inside to give them an early supper. She sat at the table while they ate, listening to their stories. Passing along the hall, I could see her warning them not to annoy the soldiers.

A shorter, rough-looking, dark-haired woman of a similar age had three rooms across the hall from the mother and children.

Out behind the inn there was a large garden, planted with vegetables and fruit trees. The wooden washtubs were there, also a tethered goat, and hares in boxes covered at one end with wire screening. It seemed to be a communal garden, and the women all got along well together. I had seen them for a moment in a wide dark hall, shortly after we came in; they were all crying quietly, or drying their eyes. Sometimes I thought that not until we were actually in sight, living in on top of them, did they believe that for them all was lost.

On the first floor, behind the taproom, the proprietress and her daughter had their apartment. Tubby was in the kitchen boiling up his kickapoo juice. It was a narrow room, over-looking the back garden. Irma was there washing dishes, and the dark-haired married tenant stood drying them for her. Howard Mason and Joe Mortara were paying court to Irma, though neither of them could say more than "chocolada," "Fraülein" and "kaput" in German.

Leaving the field to Howard Mason, Joe Mortara applied himself for ten minutes or so to the little German booklet the Army had given us, and he returned to the kitchen, very serious, took a last look at the booklet, put it behind him, and said, "Fraulein, schlafen with me? Chocolada. Nize choco-lada." The two girls went into peals of laughter. He looked surprised and glanced again at the book to see if he had made a mistake. Irma, with a laugh, showed him a piece of choco-late someone had already given her for nothing; she kept it on a shelf above the sink. "Hey—" In his despairing voice, he appealed to anyone present, "how'm I going to say to her, 'Come on to bed'?" Everyone laughed. He went outside again with his little book for further study.

Irma's stout mother had revived, and while starting to pre-pare dinner she and Phil fell into conversation. The woman disclaimed all knowledge of politics or party affiliations. She knew nothing of what went on, and had never asked.

"What did she think of the concentration camps?"

"She says she knew nothing about them. Never saw one, or *knew* anyone who saw one. She doesn't believe they existed."

I asked Phil to ask her what she thought when she saw slave laborers with OST on their shirts assigned to the farms in the vicinity.

"She says," said Phil, " 'they are all poor unfortunates whose homes were destroyed by war. They would have died if they had been left where there was no food or shelter. It was a kindness to bring them here, to give them clothes and food and shelter. They gave them work to do.' "

"Yes, but so much work! Zu *fiel* arbeiten. Tell her!"

He spoke in German and she answered him. "She says, 'We all work hard. Everyone works hard.' " That was life.

"But it's a question of being forced to work, against your will. Tell her about it. Go ahead!"

While he explained, she listened with uncomprehending gooseberry eyes. Her mouth was an astonished O. The theory was evidently entirely new to her.

"She's hopeless," Phil said, turning away, disturbed. "They're all hopeless." She stood looking at us, trying to understand. When, at my suggestion, he started to ask her about the Jews, she became excited, threw her hands up over her head and didn't want to listen.

We went out for a while in the rear garden, and when we came back Joe Mortara was trying to teach Irma to jitterbug. Irma could waltz—that was about all. "Hey, for *crissake*," said Joe, his arm about her. He was a vigorous dancer, and when he tried some of his steps with her, twirling her away to arm's length, then snapping her back, passing her under and between his legs, she let out a shriek, and both of them fell on the kitchen floor. She and the dark-haired tenant screamed with laughter. Joe wanted to try again, to go on with the lesson, but Irma laughingly declined. "Don Juan!" the older girl cried, taking in his dark, intent good looks. "Don Juan." Both girls kept laughing.

The next time I passed the kitchen doorway, it was evening. The kitchen was silent and unlighted. Irma was sitting on a chair, her back to the window; there was a nimbus about her pale blond hair, and her arms and neck had a soft milky gleam. Howard Mason sat on a low stool at her feet, his head in her lap, his eyes closed. In her mourning dress, she was looking down at him, smiling her sad little smile, while her fingers moved over his ears and through his black wavy hair.

"Boy, oh man, look at that Howie Mason!" said Preacher, slapping his thigh. "Mm-m-mmh!" Howard Mason had heard him, but did not open his eyes or smile.

Lieutenant Serletis, jealous, it was thought, that Irma had paid no attention to him, stepped into the kitchen and said, "Hey! Nix! Cut that out! Git outta there, Howie! Don't you know there's a fine on for stuff like that? That's fraternization!"

Smiling regretfully, Howard stood up, stretched with his arms clenched over his head, raised up on tiptoes, gave a sudden laugh and walked out.

Some wine had been found in the cellar and we drank a few bottles with our K-ration supper; the rest the captain impounded. When we went upstairs to spread out our blankets on the floor of the stout old woman's living room, the captain came up to look the place over. He sat down and started to play the grand piano, looking over at us and smiling, and gradually we drifted toward him. Tom Lawlor, Jimmy McDonough and little Jenkins were there, but their squad leader, Sam Benton, Jr., had refused to join us at the aid station, remaining instead with A Company. Only a few candles were lit in the room, one on the piano.

"When I was at college, I played with an orchestra for dances around White Plains," the captain said, alluding for one of the first times to anything connected with his past. "What would you like me to play for you?" It was one of those moments when he tried to be particularly friendly, but no one could respond. "Come on," he urged. "What's your favorite song? What would you like?"

"Oh, I don't know," they said. "Anything'll do—whatever you like."

Finally I said, "How about 'Lili Marlene'?"

He began the mournful tune, playing it softly and slowly. For me, it always brought to mind sifting February rain, and the pillboxes in the Siegfried Line. "Come on," he said, "sing, all of you."

But they grinned and backed off, abashed. Before he was finished with the little recital, most of the men had lost interest, had moved off to open their blankets for the night. They began talking and laughing among themselves in another part of the large room. He got up, closed the piano lid with a loud bang and went downstairs.

When we came down a short while later, he told us we'd better go up to bed. Though none of us was tired and we were looking forward to a social evening with the tenants, we trooped upstairs and, after a half hour, took off our outer clothing and lay down on the floor. "C'n you imagine him tellin' us to go to bed—as if we were kids!"

"Don't you know why?" Jenkins asked. "He wanted to get us out of the way so he could have a party with the women! Listen."

In one of the small front rooms on our floor, we heard voices and laughter. A stream of light came out as the door opened and closed. The wine corks popped. The captain had invited Irma, the dark-haired tenant and the mother of the three children to join him in drinking the wine from their

454

cellar. Lieutenant Serletis and Sergeant Campbell rounded out the party. There were songs and toasts and the clinking of glasses, with occasional horseplay from Sergeant Campbell, whose voice, loud and farmerish, shouting in English, could be heard clear above the others. The little party lasted about an hour and a half, making up for its brevity with noise, high spirits and laughter. We heard them all separating in the hall, the three women whispering Guten-nachts, going upstairs together, the three men going down.

The next morning was clear and warm, with the little fruit trees rustling their blossoms in the breeze. There was no sign of moving on, so some of the men heated water and started to wash out their socks, underwear and shirts. Irma's mother was shocked to find men engaged in such work, and, with cries of "Ach! Ach!" she elbowed them out of the way and did the large heavy laundry herself. She would not even permit any of them to carry out the tub of steaming wet woolen clothes, but struggled out with it alone and hung the things up on a line in the yard. I was lying on the grass when she came out.

"I call her 'Mom,'" Jimmy McDonough said. "These people are all right. She wouldn't let us wash nothin'. *They* never wanted a war."

"But I'll bet if you had been a flier and dropped down here in the road about three months ago, Mom and all the others would have fallen on you in a rage and cut you to pieces with knives and forks."

"Yeah, maybe you're right." He laughed and went past, unconvinced, not wanting to think about it.

The morning went by peacefully, in idleness. We wandered in and out of the house. The hallways were dark, cool and damp, with a clean toilet at the end of each floor. A deodorant or a disinfectant that had a sweet smell, almost like cheap talcum powder, was used, and that, though faint in the rooms, wafted by currents of air, was the smell of the entire place.

We washed and shaved out of our steel helmets in the sunny garden. The breeze blew the clothes dry and by noon we were told that we were to leave. At the last minute Irma appeared—despite the short time and the language difficulty, it seemed we had known her for years—and she passed out carbon copies of the words to "Lili Marlene." At Warren

455

Troy's request, she had dictated the lyrics and her mother had typed them.

> Vor der Kaserne, vor dem grossen Tor,
> Stand eine Laterne, und steht sie noch davor,
> So woll'n wir uns da wiedersehen—

There were five or six choruses. Men from Battalion Headquarters asked for copies later on, and by the close of the war the German words were sung everywhere. Men who couldn't speak or understand a word of the language could, while writing a letter, chime in thoughtlessly at the end of a line with "das *sah* mein gleich daraus."

With the women and children gathered in the hall, waving us goodbye, we left for Pausa, the next large town. "Friendly relations make all the difference in the world," Phil said, satisfied with our stopover.

"But if the roles were reversed, if we were losing the war and the United States was invaded, would you think our women would be as friendly to the Germans as these are to us? Would you want them to be?"

"No-o, I'd hope they wouldn't be."

"I'd hope not too." Though it was more pleasant for us, it showed a poorness of spirit on the part of the women while their husbands and brothers were still fighting.

Pausa, like Irma's town, still had not fallen, and once more we had to wait on the outskirts at the head of the column of vehicles while two of the line companies went forward to clear out the snipers. The steep broad street we were on, whitish in the sunlight, was clogged with fleeing civilians afraid the town would become the scene of a large battle. They surged up the hill and turned off into the country, hurrying the aged on canes and crutches, carrying their children, trundling after them little milk carts piled high with bedding, clothes, pots and pans. The infantrymen, hot and weary from the hike, continued along in single files on either side of the street, and up at the top of the hill an officer raised his hands over his head and broke an imaginary stick.

"Break." The word was passed down. "Take a break."

The men sank down along the curbs, dully watching the civilians hurry up the middle of the street. The hot sunlight beat down and some of the men crawled into the shade of the buildings. Everywhere helmets came off; faces were hot, sweating, coated with dust. There was very little talk. The men stared before them. I wondered if they were going to have to go through the parched heat and dust of a summer campaign. Would Germany never give up? A few of the men took a ration box from inside their shirts and began to eat. One man was feeding a little dachshund he had picked up and had been carrying for the past week or so in the front of his field jacket. A breeze sprang up, and suddenly all the new leaves on the trees sighed and rustled with an unmistakably summer sound.

Great formations of American planes, flying almost wing to wing, had been surging overhead all day long with a steady drumming might. The infantrymen stared up at them, and those who had once been in the Air Corps cursed loudly and gazed after them with longing in their eyes.

At the top of the hill, an old man who evidently had forgotten something slapped his hand across his forehead and started down again on the opposite side of the street while the rest of his family waited, fretting nervously. The infantrymen on that side began to say, "Watch. Watch," passing the word down from one another until finally some of them were interested. They stood up, closed in around the old man and took his heavy gold watch and chain from him.

Ten or fifteen minutes later, when I thought the last civilians had gone and shells began to fall near the top of the hill, the door of one of the houses opened and a tall girl in a large slouch hat, tweed coat and flat shoes—I was reminded of Greta Garbo—came out, leading a bareheaded young man in a dark suit who, with the aid of a cane, was obviously trying to walk on two brand-new wooden legs. *Smash!* went the shells landing in at the top of the hill. *Smash!*

The girl and the man got out into the center of the empty street and started up. A feeling of tenseness, of dread, gathered within me, watching him lurch and stagger for balance, trying to hurry. The muscles on his jaws stood out rigid. The distracted girl was breathless, and, against her will, she kept plucking at his sleeve. Before the audience of lounging infantrymen, he would not let her take his arm. Part way up the steep hill, they came to a halt and had an argument: he was urging her to run, to go on without him. She would not do it.

Lieutenant Morse of C Company, remembered for the

Tambach killings, walked out to the couple, I first thought to inquire if he could be of assistance. The girl turned to him gladly in entreaty, but instead of helping her, he snatched the watch from her wrist and returned to the sidewalk, holding it up to the sunlight, swaggering before a laughing audience. The girl bowed her head, crying, and hunched her shoulders, and the pair crept slowly up the hill; the man did not care now whether she took his arm or not.

The following afternoon there was a hot, plodding, seventeen-mile march with full field packs for the infantrymen and litter bearers. The entire regiment was on the road with tanks, trucks, jeeps, kitchen equipment, bulldozers, tank destroyers and heavy and light artillery pieces. There was a sensation of coming to the end of our combat days in Europe; Phil had a map which showed we were approaching the Czechoslovakian border. There was no elation among the men, and for my own part I was conscious only of a flat burning anger that any of this had been necessary. Fundamentally patient under their griping, more silent than usual, the men walked along hour after hour, up hill and down, dull-faced and weary in the heat. We in the slowly rolling ambulance, with the captain's jeep before us, headed the column of vehicles for our battalion. When several sick or exhausted, limping infantrymen had to be picked up, I got out to make room and rode on the hood.

Late in the afternoon, in the face of the strong, hot, reddish sunlight, we made our entrance into Plauen, the last city of any size this side of the Czechoslovakian border. Coming down a long incline into a choking pall of dust, we saw the havoc caused by yesterday's fleets of planes. Whole climbing city blocks were devastated; everywhere there were smashed-in buildings. Beside us on the main thoroughfare, a huge department store lay crumbled; similarly a furrier's, a bank, a theater, rows of office buildings, apartment houses, an armory, tenements. There were two overturned, half-buried trolleys. The air grew thicker with churned-up, acrid plaster dust, smoke, whirling flame-bright sparks and ashes. Whole sections of the city were still on fire, and the stricken civilians were dodging through the heavy military traffic with little milk carts and express wagons, heading for shelter in the park or the cemetery. Others, in shock, stood at the jumbled corners, staring openmouthed at the victors.

The din was tremendous. Bulldozers were clearing part of the road; tanks clanged and rattled abreast of us, climbing over great piles and slabs of cement, only to crash down on the other side, banging and bumping crookedly over heaps of rubble. Infantrymen seized their opportunity to skin past us, and a terrified thin woman, trying to manage a piled-up milk cart, a young child and a palsied feeble-minded old grandmother, got the whole ménage caught in the narrow space between the ambulance and the tanks, where they all barely escaped being squashed to death.

A few feet away on the tilted sidewalk, an infantryman appeared to be in the throes of an epileptic fit. Two others were holding his arms as he writhed and strained against them. Just ahead of us, Lieutenant Serletis leaped out of the jeep and ran toward them to see if he could help. The man broke away from his captors, fell down, rolled over and bit Lieutenant Serletis on the leg.

"It's all right, sir," the captors were saying in the smoky din. "He's just drunk."

"It's all *right?*" Lieutenant Serletis cried. "What the hell ya mean?" Captain Stettner jumped down, took a bottle of liquor from the man's pocket and smashed it against a section of blown-up paving.

As he began to take the man's name and serial number, the signal came for us to proceed. We started up the next long hill past the ruined skeletons of tenements. There was a clear view through to the back yards, where huge shattered trees stood choked with debris halfway up to their branches. As far as the eye could see down the long side street, there was not a single house undamaged.

Just before our arrival, the city had gone through its sixteenth pulverizing air raid in which as many as fifteen hundred planes at a time had participated.

This was our regimental objective.

We settled on the final and least-damaged block in the city, facing a wooded hill that was torn with shell holes. The city's water supply had been ruined, and, fortunately for us, the only well within a vast area was situated in an alley between the back yard of the small tenement we moved into and the one adjoining it. A dark passage ran from the street between the two houses, and civilians came all day long in shifts to pump out buckets of water. The women were the ones to do all the drawing and carting of water for the crowd in the distant schoolhouse. What the men did, I never heard. Perhaps scavenged for food, or sat and smoked their pipes.

In the morning we learned that no further objective was in store for the division, that we were to remain in Plauen for some time, perhaps until the Germans surrendered. The usual division took place within our immediate ranks: those who lived on the first floor remained shut away from those of us on the second; the men upstairs were similarly cloistered. In the two weeks that we were there, I don't believe I ever saw the third-floor rooms.

The large back bedroom downstairs had modern taffy-colored twin beds and a large oil painting above them of twisting, red and pink tulips in a silvery frame. The civilians had left clothes here in the wardrobes, and all day long you'd see Charley Heydt and Mike Nowak dressed in strange un-matching garments: dark-blue plus fours with a white over-check, worn with a top hat and a rayon satin sports shirt; striped morning pants; felt hat turned down all the way around; a small, tight topcoat; and a cane. Seeing each other lounging about the back yard, swinging long, zoot-suit watch chains, they reeled with laughter. In these outfits, they admired themselves endlessly in the mirror attached to the wardrobe doors.

Here an odd and rather sad thing came to pass. After being the closest of friends for months, Mike Nowak and Jimmy McDonough had a falling out and no longer spoke to each other. Neither would allude to it beyond saying, "Ah, he's a lotta crap. I'm through with him." Both, I think, regretted it, and did not find their new friends as stimulating, yet neither would give in. Mike stayed for the greater part of the time in the shady back bedroom; Jimmy roamed around outside, rather stout, in the too small helmet that perched high on his head, with just the fingers of his hands in his trouser pockets.

On one of the first mornings in Plauen, I went out into the fenced-in back yard. It was a windy, rather chill, sunshiny day and all the new leaves on a little beech tree were fluttering and shining. There were two very large rabbits in boxes in the yard, and some of the litter bearers were stuffing grass and leaves in through the screen mesh. Others were strolling idly up and down. A wash of khaki socks and underwear blew in the breeze. An open door in the side fence disclosed civilian women coming down the narrow passageway to draw water from the high pump. My heart went out to two. Elderly—in their late sixties or seventies—they were thin and dressed in cheap cotton house dresses, shapeless hats, one of which was a sunbonnet, and hand-me-down men's overcoats. Their faces were pale, drawn and saintly, with sunken, shriveled mouths. Each carried two large, empty pails to fill.

"See 'em?" asked Eddie Jessup, a new young litter bearer from Georgia. "They're the ones the boys had a line-up on the day befoah yesterday while you were all at the movies. Them ole things. 'Bout fifteen, sixteen guys. They had 'em up in the barn there. The guys give 'em a chocolate bar, or a can of haish. Ole Tuttle-eye was one, wasn't you, Tuttle-eye?" Turtle-eye was the other new litter bearer, a tall, thin, coppery-colored hillbilly with a bad skin, greenish-black eyes, crooked teeth and lank, black, oily hair. Turtle-eye, also known as Robbie, did not answer, but turned his head away and hurriedly left the back yard. His young friend laughed. "Ole Tuttle-eye, he was so sick when it was over, he like to puke. He jes come in and lays down without a soun'. He don't want to go out on the chow line to eat, or nothin'. He jes says, 'Lemme alone.' 'Bout four times that night he gits up and pukes. He don't even wanna see 'em now."

The two thin, aged women, looking neither left nor right, staggered past with their heavy pails of water.

Shortly after, two young women came along with their children, and after drawing the water they stood at the open doorway, looking into the yard, half troubled, half smiling. They did not permit the children to come in, yet something held them. We said, "Guten morgen!" and they answered. One of the young women was dark-haired, fairly well built and good-looking; her companion had a waxy pinched face, tiny mouth, pale-blue eyes and masses of pale-blond hair. They pointed tentatively into the yard, and their shoulders asked questions.

"Sure! Come on in!" Jimmy McDonough said. "We're all friends here. Come on!"

They held back at first, then the dark-haired, more adventurous one, with an embarrassed pat to her cheap clothes, as if she were stepping out onto a stage, entered and crossed quickly to the rabbit cages. Assured that the rabbits were still there, she poked in two large, wilted leaves from her pocket and hurried out with a nod of thanks. Some of the men in the meanwhile had given the children C-ration crackers, a few sticks of gum, and a hard candy or two. With laughs and Auf Wiedersehens the little group moved off, the women carrying their pails of water.

Phil and I were standing upstairs at our window a day or so later when the same two young women came down the passageway to draw water. When they peeked into the yard and saw that it was empty, they put down their pails and ran over to the rabbit boxes. Someone had let one of the rabbits out and it had escaped. The little blond woman mourned, with her hand up to the side of her face. From a crumpled brown paper bag the other took out vegetable tops and poked them in between the wires.

The attention of both was attracted by someone in the window directly below ours. The women, trying to understand, looked at each other, looked back, shrugged. "I think you might be needed as an interpreter downstairs," I said to Phil, and I went down with him. Joe Mortara was at his window with a half a chocolate bar in his hand, trying to entice one or the other of the women—perhaps both—into the bedroom. "Schlafen?" he was saying. "Schlafen? Chocolada?"

The women, finally understanding, laughed and went out. Not too discouraged, Joe covered up the little chocolate bar, knowing he would see them come down the passageway again. Even under ordinary circumstances, I felt half a chocolate bar was niggardly, especially when the whole bar was there; but when one considered that Joe Mortara was the supply sergeant and had free access to cases of ration food, the thing was staggering.

"Now that's a damned shame," Phil said, "to tempt women with little kids who haven't enough to eat." That morning on the chow line, a thin, sick-looking woman had stood silently begging, with a baby in her arms. We had passed her at our five-yard intervals and with terrible eyes she had looked from man to man. Captain Christoffsen was there with one of his lieutenants, and it had just been announced that the fine of sixty-five dollars for speaking to any German civilian was to be strictly enforced once more. For the first time in weeks, an orange was given to each man on the line. Phil took his, walked up onto the road and handed it to the woman. Immediately after, she was sent away. "They want to fine me, court-martial me, let them!" he said. "I don't care

462

who they are or what they've done, if it's a woman or a child, and they're hungry, they can have half of anything I've got."

The next time the dark-haired woman and her waxen-faced friend came for water, Joe Mortara was in the yard with half the chocolate bar in his hand, trying to lure them down the cellar.

Phil was outraged. He had received four or five packages from home, and he gathered together some dehydrated soup, some tea bags, lumps of sugar, K-ration cheese, crackers and a few cans of chopped pork-and-carrot which no one could eat, and brought them down in a paper bag and gave it to the women.

"Fer der kinder," Phil said. "Mit obgekochter wasser: Suppe."

The blond woman burst into tears. The other woman, crying, "Ah, danke! Danke," wept also, and tried to kiss his hand. Then both hurried away with the food, leaving the pails of water behind them.

"Hey, what the hell's the matter with you?" Joe Mortara asked. "Here I am, I got the chocolate bar all ready, you come along and spoil everything."

"I'm sorry, Joe," said Phil, "but I'm going to continue spoiling it for you. If they want to go to you voluntarily, well and good; that's their business. If it's through hunger, no."

Joe Mortara accepted it as one of his assistant's eccentricities. "Jeez, you don't have to be so friendly with them as all that," he said, walking back toward the house, wrapping up the chocolate for use some time again.

Up until now, whenever we stayed for any length of time in a town, it was always an empty one. Plauen was the first place where there were large numbers of women, and in the general chaos of a recently destroyed and disorganized city, licentiousness broke out on a tremendous scale. Countless girls and married women who under normal circumstances might have led provincial monogamous lives—here deprived of homes, sometimes bereaved of family, thrown out of employment, afraid of approaching starvation and surrounded by conquering troops—turned nymphomaniac or prostitute at every opportunity through the day or night in return for a chocolate bar, a C ration or a few cigarettes. Frequently it was for no profit but through hysteria or the despair that impels some people to hurl themselves in advance at the fate

463

that might never overtake them. Some held forth in certain condemned, half-ruined tenement houses on the main road; others, more tattered, hung about in the debris of large buildings; still others in the hilly woods surrounding the city.

Every morning a battalion formation was called and we were marched over into the lumpy field opposite our row of flats to pass in review at the ceremonies while Bronze and Silver Stars were awarded, mainly to the officers and first sergeants, "whether," as someone said, "they deserved them or not." One officer wrote the other up for the awards until almost all in the battalion had received the Bronze Star, the Silver Star, or both. None of the men cared when the awards were even vaguely justified, but very often they were not, and on the way back from the field, hoots, oaths of disgust and coarse laughter rose up all about the newly decorated officer.

One morning Captain Stettner received his Bronze Star for extreme bravery in establishing an aid station at Olzheim. As I recalled, he had set up the station at Olzheim in direct disobedience to the Acting Regimental Surgeon's order, and for a much lesser infraction an enlisted man would have been court-martialed. Yet I felt he was more deserving of an award than many other officers who had been given them; and while he stood, newly decorated, the battalion passed in review before him, turned "eyes right," and stumbled over the lumps in the field. Though all along he had promised the litter bearers to see to it that they were each awarded a Bronze Star, when the time came he did nothing about it. Of the lot, only Teddy Jameson and Phil Schaeffer received a medal, and in each case an outside officer had arranged for it.

For a few days, Captain Stettner complained of not feeling well. His sinus condition had become aggravated, and when I was on duty at the aid station one morning, I asked him if there wasn't something he could do for it.

"Well, I don't know," he replied. "Nothin' seems to help very much. It's a tough thing to treat over here."

When he went out, snorting through his nose, Silly Willie said, "If you ask me, he don't want it to get better. He just wants *out*. He's not fixin' to go to any CBI with the rest of us. He's gonna pull that sinus business on 'em and get the hell out of the Army. D'you ever see him *take* anything for his f---in' sinus? *He's* no dope."

464

At the same time, he did not look well. His eyes, generally puffed and watering, had become inflamed. He came back into the room, went over to one of the bare windows with a shaving mirror and stared at himself. We watched the performance in seemingly casual silence.

"Atwell, come here. Do you notice a yellowish tinge to my eyes?" I said I thought I did. "You know what it is?" he asked with a little smile. "Jaundice. Yellow jaundice."

"Do you think you've had it long?"

"A couple of days. It's just gettin' to the yellow stage now. Warren, is Captain Baylor comin' up this morning? I think I'd better let him see me."

The men lounging in the sunny, cheap little living room with the cut-velvet sofa scarcely looked at each other until he went back to his bedroom.

"D'you git a load of that? He got 'jaundice.'"

"Well, boys—" Howard Mason picked up two empty five-gallon cans to take out to his truck—"there goes the ball game."

Captain Baylor was driven up about an hour later. The two held a private conversation up in the captain's room, and then came down into the aid station.

"Yep. Captain Baylor says it's jaundice. Warren—" Captain Stettner smiled—"you want to make out an evacuation tag for me?"

Lordly, unsmiling, Warren filled in most of the information from memory. "What is your serial number?" was his only question or remark.

"Think you'll be gone for long, sir?" Tubby inquired.

"Just for a week or so. . . . Well, I'd better get my stuff together."

He went upstairs again, but since Captain Baylor remained in the room with us, waiting to drive the captain to the Collecting Station, the talk remained general. Captain Stettner came down in a few minutes wearing his short overcoat and helmet.

"Let me see now. Have I got everything I'll need? Howard Mason, you'll take care of all my stuff till I get back?" He said goodbye only to those of us who happened to be in the room at the time and he made no ceremony of it. "See all you boys again. So long."

"Goodbye, sir." "So long, sir."

He went out into the pale-tan glare of the street and

climbed into Captain Baylor's jeep, which was parked directly outside our half-open windows.

"Bet you a thousand bucks that's the last we ever see of him," whispered Silly Willie. Preacher, with his arms crossed, shifted uneasily on the little sofa. I knew his feelings: it was as if those who were to escape the CBI were making their getaway now. The jeep's motor started up and the Red Cross flag unfurled.

I watched the jeep start off with the captain, with the leather case of toilet articles he so seldom opened, with his writing portfolio, his smooth melton overcoat. Complex, contradictory, intelligent, always interesting to observe, he was more likable than dislikable; yet, while lifting a cigarette to my mouth, I could watch him drive past the windows without any feeling.

We never saw him again.

In the afternoon a formation was called that no man could miss. Officers, cooks, guards, drivers—everyone was compelled to attend. We were lined up outside the houses next to the Battalion Headquarters men, marched down the street and across into the farthest hilly field. The Inspector General of the division and several high-ranking officers drove up in jeeps.

Because of the shameful nature of the subject, the Inspector General explained in a brief address, he had purposely requested that we be marched outside the town where no civilian could overhear or see what what was to take place. There had come to his attention, he added, a report that a number of German prisoners had been shot to death by men of our battalion at a place called Tambach.

"Now, I'm going to ask each man the following two questions, and I'm going to place you individually under oath. The questions are: Did you *see* any German prisoners killed at Tambach? Do you *know* any man who killed any German prisoners at Tambach? Now I don't want to know what you *heard* or what someone told you."

What had prompted such an investigation? Didn't the Inspector General realize that the prisoners at Tambach were not the only ones who had been killed? Time and time again in combat we heard, "The boys aren't taking any prisoners today," and that always meant the prisoners were being shot down.

We were taken in groups of five, marched a short distance from the others. An officer held a Bible open and we were told to raise our right hands. "Do you swear to tell the truth, the whole truth and nothing but the truth, so help you God? Answer 'I do.'"

In turn we said, "I do."

"Now. Did you see any German prisoners killed at Tambach? Do you know any man who killed any German prisoners at Tambach?"

The answers came back from man after man. "No, sir." "No, sir." "No, sir." "No, sir." "No, sir."

"All right, the next five men."

After everyone had taken the oath and answered "No, sir," the Inspector General's party drove off to question the line companies, and we returned to our billets.

We did not hear what happened when the party arrived at C Company, but a day or so later young Lieutenant Morse, who had asked that morning in Tambach for the volunteers, stopped by at the aid station in highest spirits to have a breaking-out on his leg dressed. He was beaming widely. He, of all the officers in the battalion, was to be flown back to the United States for a forty-five-day leave of absence. The thing was obviously rigged, for he had come up as a replacement, had not served very long, and if any furloughs were to be given, there were many officers, in combat from the start, who were more deserving. It was an attempt to spirit him away before the search into the Tambach killings became too hot.

Preacher changed the dressing and the lieutenant ran out, hopped into his jeep and was driven off at full speed toward an airport. He had gone only thirty or forty miles back out of Plauen when an order, telephoned ahead by the Inspector General, stopped the jeep on the road and the lieutenant was ordered to be held for further questioning. The next thing we heard, both he and Lieutenant MacKenzie, his Commanding Officer, were placed under arrest to await court-martial proceedings, one for perpetrating the murders, the other for standing by and permitting them. I felt deeply sorry for Lieutenant MacKenzie, who had been endlessly gallant, kind and decent to his men, and I could not think of him in his present circumstances without recalling the night at Metz when Smathers had cooked the goat and Lieutenant Mac-

Kenzie told us how eager he was to make a good name for himself in combat so that he could measure up to his long line of military ancestors.

We were told that the next few days everyone must exercise the greatest care. The guards on night shifts were particularly notified not to fire on any foreign soldiers until it was certain who they were. Russian patrols, coming through Czechoslovakia, had set out to make contact with our division. No one knew what road they might come down or when they might link up with us. Men who could speak Russian were stationed in outposts to greet the Allies. There were several days and nights of alert waiting, and then disappointment, for when the Russians did come through, it was just outside our sector.

The days of idleness came to a sudden end: a training program began which was like garrison life in the United States. One needed an excuse and a pass to leave the area, and the days began with reveille and a police-up of cigarette butts and scraps of paper in the shell holes opposite. There were calisthenics and classes in Military Courtesy and the Care and Use of the M1 Rifle. The rooms of the house and the halls had to be swept and kept clean. Lieutenant Serletis, for the first time, went up to inspect the top floor and his shouts could be heard out on the street. The two new Southern litter bearers—young Eddie Jessup and his friend Turtle-eye —were living in a slice of a room they had turned into a sty, with opened ration cans, cigarette stubs, dirty socks and filthy, unmade beds. "Where the hella you two guys think you are—Tobacco Road?" he shouted.

"Well, Ah didn' know, sir," the nineteen-year-old, indolent Eddie Jessup drawled. "Ah guess we jes forgot about cleanin' the place up a li'l."

"A *little!* Goddamit, get all that crap outta there! Open the window an' *sweep* the place! You ought to be court-martialed!"

In our house in Plauen, there was constant speculation as to how the point system was to work.

"Well, I hear for every kid you get twelve points."

"No, five points."

"A guy outside just said twelve. He saw it in *Stars and Stripes*."

"An' for every year over thirty, you git two points extra."

"What for? Why should you old bastards get anything extra? How about us? About me? I'm nineteen!"

"Oh, Jesus, you," said Tubby. "You're gonna be in for the next forty years. You're hopeless. Hey, but you know what I just heard from a guy next door? I heard they're gonna let all the married guys over thirty go home. I'm all packed, just waitin' for the good word."

"For every battle star, I hear you get five, and five for Purple Heart, ten if you got a Bronze Star—so let's see. Who's got a paper and pencil? I'm in thirty-two months, so that's thirty-two points there . . ."

One of the men next door was a recent friend of Phil's and a former New York high-school teacher named Irving Strauss. He accidentally set fire to the house while cleaning a field jacket with gasoline he had come by illegally, and as a punishment he and all the men in the house were turned out to sleep in tents across the street. The men grumbled and cursed against Strauss, whom they disliked anyway, and that night, making himself scarce among them, he showed up in our second-floor kitchen as a guest of Phil's.

"Oh, it was nothing, nothing," he said of the fire. "An accident that might happen to anyone. People build these things up." He was in his early thirties, heavy-set and freckled, with a head slightly bullet-shaped, thick features, greenish eyes and a crew cut of sandy hair beginning to grow out into a Napoleonic fringe over his forehead. He was married and he had a young daughter, a curl of whose shining red-gold hair he showed in a locket. For part of the time during combat he had been on an ammunition relay detail, driving up through storms, through mine fields and under shellfire, in the back of a truck loaded with high explosives, and he was perfectly contented with his record. "Under duress," he said, "a man learns his own measure, and I'm satisfied now that I could meet any eventuality. Not, of course, that I'd like to." At present he was an orderly for one of the officers in Battalion Headquarters, and he accepted the menial job philosophically with the statement that all things pass.

His descriptions of life among the officers of Battalion Headquarters were, while detached and fair, highly entertaining. In general he was acute and civilized, but there was a broad streak of the fraud about him too. "I am a little man," he said from time to time, placing his hand over his heart. "Yes, I am just a little man."

469

"But you don't honestly think that you are, do you? Wouldn't you resent it if you overheard someone referring to you as 'just a little man'?"

"Why?" he asked. "Do you object to the term?"

"Yes. As I say, I can't believe it's sincere when it's used by someone to apply to himself, and it's damned patronizing when it's used to describe someone else. It puts the user on such a superior plane. It's like that 'Ask the little guy in the foxhole.' Why not 'the man in the foxhole,' or 'the soldier in the foxhole'? There's nothing condescending about either of those terms, but the other's one of those easy catch-phrases probably turned out by some patriotic writer who's made damned sure *he's* not going to be in any foxhole."

Strauss, smiling, puffed on his pipe. "Yes, perhaps."

"I dislike all those tags. I even resent being called a GI, and particularly by someone who isn't one. It's always demeaning. If I were an officer, I'd always speak of my company as that—as the company, or the men, or my men, but never the GIs, as if we were two separate races of beings."

"I'm very happy to meet you, by the way," Strauss said. "I noticed you having lunch yesterday with two Jewish boys. That's very unusual, you know, in our 'democratic Army.' Very unusual."

At the moment I couldn't remember who the two men were. Lilliencron and—someone else. "It never crossed my mind that they were Jews until you mentioned it just now. And I don't think it's so rare."

"You haven't come across anti-Semitism in the Army?"

"Well, no, I can't say I have. We *hear* there's a lot of it, but I can honestly say I've seen damned little of it."

"You haven't heard 'Jew bastard'?"

"Yes, but no more often than you'd hear Guinea bastard or any other kind. Certainly not often enough to make a big issue of it."

"Ah, but the particular *venom* behind it when it's used about the Jews!"

"I think you read that into it where it doesn't exist. I've been far more aware of anti-Semitism outside the Army than inside."

Phil frowned as he did when any touchy subject came up. Tubby, Tom Lawlor and Jimmy McDonough kept staring in surprise.

"Ah, no, my friend, it's inside too. Haven't you heard the

470

remarks that used to circulate about Colonel Hessig? Jew this and Jew that?"

"No! My God, I tell you honestly, I thought all along he was a poor Catholic. I've known Catholic Hessigs."

"And your own Captain Stettner! He was disliked!"

"If he was, it wasn't because he was a Jew. He might have been disliked; I never heard of him being discriminated against. The officers all thought he was wonderful! I think you've got that on the brain. You separate people into Jews and non-Jews when others aren't even aware of it."

He puffed on his pipe, nodded noncommittally and passed on to something else. Within a few minutes he was assuring us that when we got back to the United States, there was much that we would have to do; there were still many wrongs we would have to right.

"There is native Fascism to wipe out. You must *all* realize that," he said, moving his index finger slowly from Tubby to Jimmy McDonough to Tom Lawlor, Phil and me. They gazed at him blankly.

"Sure," I said, "let's wipe it the hell out. Communism too. One's as bad as the other."

Strauss smiled again, but uncomfortably, and he changed the subject. He had a normal New York way of talking, but at times his voice deepened and his pronunciation broadened with long As. He became theatrical and spoke then as if he were weightily addressing a multitude.

"Yes," he intoned, "when President Roosevelt died, I felt a personal loss. A very *deep* personal loss. It was as if someone in my own family had passed away. Ah, that was a blow, my friends, a very great blow. I felt it here." Slowly he tapped his heart. His little audience looked at him uneasily. Tubby plucked at the seat of his pants, shook it a little and sent Phil a troubled glance that asked, What have you brought in on top of us?

I said, "Strauss, I'd be more ready to believe you if I hadn't read almost your exact words about 'a death in my own family' in several of the newspapers from home. You borrowed that. Next you'll be telling us, 'Many a little guy in the fox-holes wept,' when actually they didn't give it five minutes' thought."

He had the grace to admit it and laugh.

He stayed on for several hours. The men wanted to go to sleep, but he liked to spin his talk out and to hear his voice interweaving and balancing his involved dependent clauses.

In talking of his German girl, he said, "In the midst of one of our first moments of intimacy she whispered to me, 'You are not the enemy,' and she used the 'du,' the very personal 'du,' for the first time between us. I was—well, it affected me very deeply."

Most of the audience looked more puzzled than ever, with no idea what the "personal du" was all about, but when he left, shaking hands in a circle and thanking everyone for the hospitality, out of politeness to Phil they did not discuss him.

For the first time since leaving England, Sunday was by plan a day of rest. Mass was said in a big shattered factory; the midday meal seemed larger and better than usual, and in the afternoon we sat talking and writing letters in the second-floor apartment with the windows open, Tubby, somewhat tipsy, sat curled on a kitchen chair, his legs folded like Buddha's, while he regaled Phil with an account of his business progress in civilian life. He was the proprietor of a pool parlor in his small Missouri town, and, along with this, was a man of property: he owned two houses. His wife, a district nurse, was, in his absence, rapidly paying off the mortgage on the second house. Tubby figured that after the war, what with the income he received from his rents, the soft-drink concession in the pool parlor, and a part interest he had in two gas pumps outside a friend's house, all he needed was thirty-five dollars a week more and he could live like a king. The tiny amount he paid his help and the ruses whereby he moved in on one "Lglew," and eventually took over the pool parlor from him, left Phil profoundly shocked.

"But, Jim!" he cried. "Do you consider that *honorable?*"

"What? You mean—you mean how I got the pool parlor away from Lglew? Sure! That's—that's business, Phil. Right?"

Down in the yard we saw the two women coming in to feed the rabbit. They looked up and we called back and forth. Tubby had got off the chair and was starting to fry potatoes; he told us to invite the women up. They were extremely doubtful about accepting the invitation. The dark-haired one, the bolder of the two, finally consented, and with a toss of her head came in and up the back staircase with the other one at her heels. They stepped into our bedroom and crossed over to the kitchen. Their manner by then had

472

become rather formal and at first they weren't going to sit down. By the way they glanced about, looking for things that were missing, or that we had moved from one place to another, I was sure they had been the former occupants of the house.

At length they sat down with us at the kitchen table, amused at the sight of Tubby, now up to his full weight again, fussing around the stove. In their honor, he began to heat up a brew of kickapoo juice. They watched the preparations with puzzled interest: the GI alcohol, the dash of water, lemon powder, the lumps of sugar. Jimmy McDonough opened a K-ration cheese and the crackers that came with it. "Nein," the women said. "Nein."

"Yes! Go ahead. It's good. Gut. What's the word for 'cheese'?"

"Kayse."

"Kayse!" They looked doubtfully at each other as Jimmy sliced the round cheese in half for them. They sat blinking down at it. Finally they looked up. "Der kinder. Please." They wrapped the cheese up and put it into their pockets. I told Jimmy what they were doing.

"Then here! Have some for yourselves!" He opened another and Phil brought out a can of sardines from his overseas package. We made up a little bag of food for the children, and when the women were assured of that, they relaxed completely and began to talk and eat. Tubby shoveled out a plateful of hot French-fried potatoes.

The husband of the blond woman had died of tuberculosis in a hospital near Vienna following a winter on the Russian front. She cried a little, telling Phil about it. For Sunday, she wore beneath her jacket a white shirt like a man's and a striped tie. The husband of the more vital dark-haired woman was a prisoner somewhere in the United States. Through the breakdown of mail service in Germany, she had not heard from him in several months.

The kitchen was extremely narrow and someone squeezing past the table knocked down a man's felt hat that hung on a series of crisscross pegs. The dark-haired woman picked it up, brushed it off and sat holding it. After a moment, tears flooded her eyes. The blonde, looking at her, shook her head sadly. "Her father's," she explained to Phil. Had the father been killed in the bombing? We didn't ask. With a sigh, the woman stood up and hung her father's hat back on the peg.

Tubby's kickapoo juice was finished, steaming hot. He poured out a generous shot all the way around, and even Tom Lawlor, who didn't drink, decided to try it. The women by then were laughing, and when the pinched little blonde took a swallow, she let out a shriek and clutched her throat. Everyone roared with laughter, she included. She tried to explain that she couldn't drink very much, it made her too dizzy, while her friend seemed to be saying that she would welcome both dizziness and forgetfulness for a good long while. The fact they spoke in German and we in English, and yet we could understand each other, or at least thought we could, struck us all as enormously funny. The women went on eating, going into peals of laughter.

Warren Troy came up with a huge stack of mail. There had been a long delay and everyone was glad to get the letters. The women at first didn't know what was going on, but as soon as they understood, the sight of men ripping open letters, eagerly looking for news from home, sent both into tears again. They sat thinking of themselves, blinking their tears away, slowly eating French-fried potatoes and sardines with their fingers.

When we were all talking again, little Lieutenant Serletis suddenly appeared in the kitchen doorway. "What the hell goes on here?" he asked.

"We're havin' a little party," Tubby said cheerfully. "Here, have a drink."

"*Out!*" the lieutenant shouted, making a gesture with his thumb. His square face had darkened. He glared. "Outside! get 'em out!" He turned to the women. "*Scram!*"

Astounded, frightened, they jumped up from the table, and in their excitement to get out they ran past him and down the stairs without taking the food we had set apart for their children.

"I'm the only officer here," Lieutenant Serletis was shouting, "and what happens if someone comes in? They chew *my* ass out! I'm not gonna lose my bars 'cause of this! You guys know how tough they're getting!"

I was called down to the telephone and instructed to pack up all my belongings and report at 17:30 the following evening in front of Battalion Headquarters. What for? For a new assignment, a temporary one, it was thought. I would be gone for about two weeks, maybe more.

May

When I walked down to the corner that grayish evening, wearing a full field pack and carrying my rifle, I found Chris Taylor standing dejected, apart from six or seven others culled from the various companies through the battalion. All seemed glum; there was no conversation. Chris understood we were being farmed out to Personnel, situated about fifty miles back, to work on service records for the division.

"And 'o's to do for the captain while you're gone?" I asked. Chris, whose despondency went deeper than that of anyone I knew in the Army, did not reply.

A small truck came for us and in the growing dusk we slung up our equipment and climbed aboard. We drove through shattered, bombed-out Plauen, swung onto the Frankfurt-Berliner Ring Autobahn, sped along it through the country for a few hours, turned eventually off onto a dirt road and accomplished the number of miles intended for us, but found that we were lost, more than sixty miles off our course, on the wrong end of a V. This was so normal for us that it drew scarcely any comment. We retraced our way and started out again. Two hours later we crossed a rumbling log bridge and entered a dark, silent, leafy town. Montclair, New Jersey, I thought. The truck stopped at a corner before a fair-sized suburban house almost obscured by shrubs and trees behind a plaster wall. A generator was chug-chugging in the darkness.

"Jossnitz?" the driver asked hopefully of a guard.

"Yeah. What do you want?"

"Personnel."

"Right in here."

We were led inside by a tall, beady-eyed master sergeant with slick, light-red hair, a Barrymore profile, a shirt taken in under the arms and a gleaming brass buckle on a belt washed almost white. The rooms on the first floor were closed, showing strips of light under the doors; those on the second floor were open, and passing along the dark hall we saw clerks typing or gathered in groups talking at green steel filing cabinets. Stumbling up a narrow servant's staircase, we came into an unfinished attic with a sloping roof, two naked electric lights hanging down and long planks laid across boxes to form work tables. Seven or eight other men had arrived before us.

This was our office, the mettlesome master sergeant informed us—his eye was expecting trouble—and it was also to be our bedroom. We would be working steadily for the next few weeks, day and night, with an hour off for meals. "An' when I say an hour, I mean an hour. No more. Any of you guys think you come down here to kid aroun', waste time, get that idea right outta your head. You're here to work! Sooner you get finished, the sooner you get back to your companies. A few a ya, ya work hard, there might be a permanent place for ya here in Personnel. Sergeant McMahon here will get the work started right away."

Dejectedly we sat behind the planks while frowning, serious young Sergeant McMahon set up a fan belt of work, placing before us ink, pens, blotters, mucilage, and match sticks to use in place of brushes. While waiting to begin, we were told to practice copying Captain Donald A. Sarsfield's signature.

"Now get it to look as much like his as you can. Here's some for you to follow. You copy that, how he signs his name and initials."

In his neat hand, with no attempt at imitation, Chris wrote once on the scratch paper, "Captain Donald A. Sarsfield, Jr.," threw down his pen with a little bark of laughter and read through one of the narrow white-covered service records.

The men at our plank were set to writing, very tiny, on a certain page of each record: Left USA 10/17/44, Arr. Scotland 10/22/44. Left Eng. 11/26/44, Arr. France 11/27/44. Left France, Arr. Ger. 12/15/44. On the margin went the initials, D. A. S., Jr. Captain Donald A. Sarsfield, Jr., I gathered, should have attended to this six or seven months ago.

It was nearly ten o'clock before the work began to go smoothly and then it was time to quit: the electricity was about to be turned off. Just before it was, Norman Harris, small and Machiavellian in appearance, whom I had last seen with C Company in the apple orchard, came running up the stairs looking for Chris and me. We greeted him with surprise and shook hands, and he informed us it was at his suggestion and through his special efforts that we had been se-

476

lected to work for Personnel.

I had forgotten that I had ever known him. I hadn't known him very well. He came into the infantry just before we sailed overseas, and on his first day in C Company he asked me some directions: he was setting off at once to see the Jewish chaplain about getting out of the infantry. I was the first man he spoke to, and, for a long while in his subsequent discouragement, the only one. Later he began to talk to Chris Taylor. I showed him one night how to take his rifle apart and clean it, and on another occasion I taught him the Manual of Arms.

"See? I always said if I could ever do you two boys a favor, I wouldn't forget. The hours might be long, but I know it would be better for you here than in a line company."

"Gee, that's swell of you, Norm. Thanks a lot!"

"The lights are going to go off. I'll see you boys tomorrow." He ran down the stairs.

Chris and I looked at each other. "He meant well," I said.

"Yeah. There's no use telling him."

"I wonder if there's any way we could get out of here, get back."

"No, I'd say we're stuck. And stuck good."

The lights went out. We slept anywhere on the attic floor, badly crowded.

Chris and I awoke with the others on the attic floor to a chill, rainy day. Unwashed, we went outdoors for breakfast, a few blocks up the street, into the rose garden of a big gray stone house with espaliered trees trained up against it. There was a huge crowd of men standing there eating, in new-looking raincoats and unscratched steel helmets, with clean rifles on their shoulders and clean gas masks slung over their chests. They tramped in among the young rose bushes, cracking them off under their feet.

From the first moment of leaving the house, I had noticed a difference in the atmosphere at Jossnitz. The town bristled with military courtesy and discipline. Five and six times during the length of one street arms snapped up in stiff salutes. There was an absence of smiles or laughter. Uniforms were neat, combat boots were polished and the men themselves looked cleaner and far healthier, though less open-faced, than those in the line companies at the front. Sergeants bore themselves with a pompous importance and did not mingle with

477

their inferiors or deign to greet them in passing.

After breakfast, we reported at once to the unfinished attic. It was cold there and drafty and the tiny windows ran with rain. The bare electric lights were on and the wooden boxes made uncomfortable seats. There was pasting in of inserts, more tiny writing, more of Captain Donald A. Sarsfield's signature. Then in one service record after another we wrote: 1 Bz Star, Battle of the Ardennes; 1 Bz Star, Battle of the Rhineland; 1 Bz Star, Battle of Central Europe, with the dates of the campaigns and Donald A. Sarsfield's initials. There were hours of 1 Bz Star, then hours and hours of Left USA, Arr. Scotland; Left England, Arr. France, with dates again and initials. The narrow white-covered service records passed from man to man, for some worked on the insurance page, others on pay, on court-martial, and absence without leave.

One tall, pallid, light-haired youth named Junior, with parrot eyes, enormous gums and warty hands, kept up an incessant barrage of boastful talk about E Company and the rough time they had had in Bonnerue, Belgium. He was an extremely fast worker and by the end of the morning he had made the identical mistake, in ink, on four or five hundred service records before anyone was aware of it.

Most of the men who had come down with us to Jossnitz worked diligently, hoping to worm their way into Personnel for the CBI campaign. Burke summed up the general attitude when he said, "Sure! I'm not ashamed to admit it. I had enough of that s---. Let someone else tote a rifle for a change. I have a wife and kid, and I'd like to get home to them in one piece. I've *done* my part."

Outside, despite the burst of leaves and flowers and a big cherry tree in bloom in the front yard, thick wet flakes of snow came down, and within a half hour the streets and green lawns were blanketed with white. Over the radio in one of the second-floor rooms, a tense-voiced news broadcaster suddenly announced Hitler's suicide in Berlin. There were no particulars at the moment, but the flash was repeated several times: "Attention! Attention! It is just announced that Adolph Hitler has committed suicide in his bunker in—" An excited jabbering broke out in the attic. "What the hell's the matter with them they let him get away with that?" "It was too goddam good for him!" "They should have taken him alive, stuck him in a cage, and dragged him from one country to another and charged admission to—" "Yeah, but now who'll be in charge? Who'll they get to sign the unconditional surrender?" "Jeez, now if only Tojo'd take the pipe—"

The excitement lasted about ten minutes; ten minutes afer that the topic seemed forgotten, no longer of any importance. The end of the war was expected any minute; the Russians were to pour in on Berlin; but it would not be the end of the war for us, and each step forward from now on made the CBI campaign loom up that much nearer. Reminded of this, the men in the attic grew quiet and went on writing steadily, blotting, writing, blotting. Left USA, Arr. Scotland; Left England, Arr. France; Left France, Arr. Ger. . . . 1 Bz Star, Battle of the Ardennes; 1 Bz Star, Battle of the Rhineland; 1 Bz Star, Battle of Central Europe.

The harsh light sent the shadows of our heads down on the service rocords. At lunchtime and again at dinner, out came the mess kits, on went the gas masks, ammunition belt, steel helmets and rifles, though we were fifty or sixty miles behind the quiet front in a town where not a single shell had ever fallen.

"Yes, this has always gone on," Norman Harris answered that evening when he was taking me on a brief sightseeing tour of the parts of Jossnitz that were not marked "Off Limits." "You can't stir around here without being a-a-amed to the teeth. There's so much brass all over the place. Salute? My God, yes! You salute everything back here from a Pfc. up. D'you mind stopping in at the Gift PX with me? I'd like to send some ties home to my father for Father's Day. You never heard of the Gift PX?" He laughed, shifting his M1, which always seemed too tall and heavy for him. "A warrant officer and a couple of sa-agents run it."

"Who ever knew about it?"

"Oh, men in the rear here." His tone reminded me that they had to live too.

We walked up the path of a small house, opened the storm door and stepped into the living room, where a warrant officer was passing the time of day with a few lieutenants sitting near the windows, bored, with their feet up. There was a counter displaying gaudy compacts, rhinestone pins and triple strands of pink pearl beads, all cheap-looking but expensively priced.

"Sir, I'd like to look at some ties," Norman said, and the

warrant officer opened a thick, highly colored catalogue.

"These are very nice," he said professionally, showing us a page of wild scrolly designs. "Bow ties and four-in-hands."

"Could I have flowers wired home?" I asked, noticing a placard to that effect on the counter.

"No. Not any longer," he said. "We're not doing that any more."

"How about candy?" I was going to surprise him by having it sent myself.

"We've discontinued that too." He smiled.

While Norman hesitated over the page of ties, I listened to the group of officers talking about a rotation plan then under discussion at headquarters, whereby officers here in the rear echelons were to take a turn of duty up at the front.

"I been there!" said one. "I went up!"

"And how was it?" another asked with studied carelessness. "Pretty rugged?"

"Well, they were in a rest or a holding position when I drove up, but things didn't look too good to me! All these jokers were walking around, talking, you know? But I could hear shells falling, and believe you me, I got the hell out of there fast!"

On the way out Norman told me he had spoken to his roommates and they had offered to let Chris Taylor and me move in with them. He came back to the unfinished attic, where Chris and I gathered up our packs, and then he led us down the side street to the next house, which was separated from the Personnel building by a large garden. In the warm twilight, the snow was fast melting from the wet cherry blossoms.

We went up a dim staircase and into a bedroom on the second floor; Norman introduced us to Bill Eyerly, a neat man of medium height, with a whispery, husky voice, and to Ken Dahl, a tall, casual, light-haired, pleasant young tech sergeant. The fourth occupant of the room had not as yet come in.

The room looked familiar, with its short double beds, tall green-tiled stove, bureaus and chests, and a big round dining-room table crowding the rest of the furniture. There was a long green serge cover on it and a brass and crystal epergne holding an unlighted candle stump.

"Now that we've invited you here," said Ken, "I don't know where-all you're going to fit. There are four of us in here already and we've only got two beds. It's a hell of a thing to ask, but do you—well, do you guys think you could manage to sleep on the floor for tonight, till we see what we can do?" When we told him we didn't think we'd be able to sleep any place else, ever, he said with a smile, "Oh. Well, of course, we wouldn't know about that. You'll have to excuse us for not being up on the war. We're all suffering here from Rear Echelon Fatigue."

There was something defensive and at the same time apologetic in their attitude toward us because they had spent the war at the rear. They had seen no action, had never dug a foxhole, had never heard a shell go off, and yet, as they told it, their lives had been miserable. Moving only three times since landing in Europe, remaining always in safety fifty or sixty miles behind the front, they had lived under a constant strain, in an atmosphere of office politics and intrigue, afraid for their jobs, working day and night goaded by the ever-present threat of being sent up to the front as combat troops.

"Back here it's all cliques, all politics. The damned lack of security eats at everyone. It's that business of seeing a few guys whispering in a corner over here and there's a few guys whispering over there. Everything is whispers and secrets, and someone always trying to f--- someone out of his job."

In the midst of talking, the fourth occupant of the room showed up and was introduced to us: a burly, red-faced truck driver in his early thirties named Zubek. At once a wild argument broke out and for the first moments I thought it was serious.

"Say, Zubek, what the f---'s the matter with you? Why don't you get on the ball? Where's our wash water? What the hell d'you think we got you around here for?"

"Go on, ya pen-pushin', 4-F bastards! Just because I didn't get it one day, ya hop all over me. Go an' get your own f---in' water from now on an' see how you like it! There ain't one of you could lift the pail without strainin' yourselves!"

"Well now god*damit*, Zubek, you understand that we're all intellectuals here, and the only reason we'd have an ignorant bastard of a truck driver in with us is because we need someone to do the dirty work. That was the agreement, and if you're not sportsman enough to live up to it—"

The argument boiled up with all their voices raised in abuse. Zubek, defending himself, roared back at them as he changed out of his work clothes to go on a date with his

German girl. Shouting curses, he ripped off his shirt and hopped from one foot to the other in taking off his pants to disclose a strapping physique in women's pale-pink rayon underwear: a low-necked shirt with a slotted ribbon tied in a chaste bow on his hairy chest, and a pair of short pink drawers. The three other roommates were too accustomed to the sight to notice it, and they continued strenuously with the argument.

"Zubek, that's mighty pretty underwear," I said.

"Oh, this?" He looked down at it and laughed, explaining that some weeks ago in a German house he had come upon a stack of women's underwear, and, since his own was dirty, he had made the change. "It's good," he said. "No trouble washin' it. Dries overnight. I always have a clean suit ready to put on."

"Yes, but what's your girl think of it?" one of them asked.

"Oh, she says—" He had to search for the word. "She says, 'Shon! Gut!' The first time she saw it, o' course, she laughed. Yestiddy I give her a pair of drawers for herself."

In Jossnitz, where high-ranking officers abounded, the MPs themselves were under constant surveillance to see that they enforced the nonfraternization bans with utmost strictness. To discourage the men—for the sake of the rising venereal rate—from sleeping with the German women, soldiers caught saying as much as "Good morning" or "Good evening" to anyone on the off-limits side of the street were arrested and fined sixty-five dollars. It was a losing battle, for large numbers of men continued to sneak out of their billets at night, and "fraternization," as it came to be known, grew so widespread that higher brass threatened the captains and lieutenants with the loss of their commissions if any of their men were found with German women. To protect their rank and their salaries, guard shifts of lieutenants, driven by MPs, patrolled in jeeps hour after hour at night, up and down the dark, leafy streets. Any man abroad was stopped and questioned. Several times each night the officers made concentrated raids into the woods surrounding the town, driving in between the trees, turning on the headlights and their flashlights, flushing the men and the girls, leaping out of the jeeps and racing after the men on foot. It was still a losing battle.

In general, the lack of morals on the part of the German women was attributed to the fact that their men had been away from them so long, but this could have been only partly the reason, for the towns were not depleted of males. There were surprising numbers of men out of uniform. Nor, in most cases, was it hunger for food that drove the women into the woods to wait for enemy soldiers whom they had never seen or spoken to before. Very often they received no more than a few cigarettes. There was seldom any love, any knowledge or selection of partners. It was all chance in the dark, which gave rise to the saying, "Copulation without conversation is not fraternization." The fact that so many of the German women were wanton was not surprising to our men; even the very young accepted it without question as the way human beings all over the world normally behaved. Anything like romance, chastity, an honorable courtship, actual love, or faithfulness to marriage vows were to them but literary figments or surface conventions in which no one had ever really believed.

Almost every night when Zubek came in, he woke us up for ten or fifteen minutes of talk. Once he asked Chris and me what regiment we were in, and when we told him he asked if we knew of a Captain Hillier.

"Know him!" Norman said with a laugh from his bed. "My God, yes! That was our Company Commander. How'd you ever hear of him?"

The blackout curtains were looped back, and in the dim light there was the sheen of Zubek's pale-pink underwear.

"Well, 'bout a month or so ago, I was told to report down to drive some officer some place in the jeep, an' out comes this guy, Captain Hillier, with all his stuff, an' he tells me to drive him over to the 244th. I thought he was actin' kinda funny, but I didn't pay no attention, so off we start. An' all the way over—I had to drive him over a mountain—he keeps tellin' me how he was always with the 243rd an' how he hates to leave it, an' don't I think it's a disgrace to git transferred from one regiment to another. I says, 'Hell, I don't see no disgrace; one regiment's the same as the other,' but he says won't all the men *think* it's a disgrace. See, I didn't know he f---ed up; I didn't know what was the matter. Then he starts tellin' me how he hates to have this happen, an' how he always done the best he could. Damn, you know, by the time we got over there, I got to feelin' *sorry* for that guy. Seemed like a nice young guy. An' when we git over there, he don't want to go in an' report. You know, you could tell by the

483

way he stands there. He just hates to do it. Well, I had to drive away, an' when I look back, he's still standin' there outside that buildin'."

Once the service records were brought up to date, we, the temporary workers at Personnel, began riding out early in the mornings to the various companies throughout the division to check each man's service record against his own statements. We went in open trucks and ate at midday with whatever company we happened to be interviewing at the time. Since the companies were scattered over a wide area, as far as the Czechoslovakian border, it was a fine way of seeing the countryside, then at its peak of spring beauty.

On May 8, with rumors on all sides that the war was ending, we checked service records outdoors near the abrupt edge of a wooded bluff looking off to the distant mountain peaks. The sun brought out a tangy smell from the pines, and a constant warm breeze blew. A long board table had been set up for us on the grass, and the company was lined up alphabetically waiting to come through.

At one end of the table the men working on the first page of the service records began by reading off rapidly, "Your name is John Peter Abbott. Your serial number is 3277627, and you're a Pfc, okay? Now. You were born June fifth, 1922. Your home address is Route 2, Culver Falls, Missouri. You're 5-11, weigh 162; you have blue eyes, brown hair, ruddy complexion. No scars. Your father's name is John; your mother's name is Elizabeth Wycoff. In civilian life, you were a garage mechanic. You finished elementary school and had four years of high school. You were inducted January fourth at Camp Rucker, and your active service began January eighteenth. You're a Protestant. Okay? Go on to the next man. All right, your name is Arthur no-middle-initial Antonson. Your serial number is—"

Within a few moments other voices on our side of the long table were saying, "You have ten thousand insurance. Your wife's your first beneficiary, your mother's your second, your father's your third. You have two kids, the first a son, Robert, born August twelfth, 1940; the second a daughter, Alice, born December twenty-seventh, 1942." "You have no bad time to make up for the Army." "You've had all your shots." "You were last paid May first, 1945." "You've had two furloughs." "You came over with this outfit." The voices were mingled, all reading aloud at once. "You're six-one, and weigh—you have ten thousand insurance—a son, Edward, born—you were a farmer—fourteen days bad time still to make up—you came as a replacement—your serial number is—going AWOL—your mother's name is—receive partial pay on—have an eighteen-seventy-five war bond—"

Chris Taylor, the tall, blond, rabbitty Junior, and I worked on the Awards and Citations page. Picking up the service records that were slipped along to us, we read out, "You have a Good Conduct Ribbon, a Combat Infantry Badge, a Unit Citation. You get three Bronze Campaign Stars: one for the Ardennes, one for the Rhineland, and one for the Battle of Central Europe."

"How about the Bulge?"

"That's the Ardennes."

"An' how about Metz? Don't we git one for that? The Battle of Northern France?"

"That's not decided yet. They're working on it. Next man. You have a Good Conduct Ribbon, Combat Infantry Badge, Unit Citation. You get two Bronze Stars. Were you a replacement? Yes. One for the Rhineland, and one for the Battle of Central Europe. Next man."

"Wull, uh . . . don't I git more than t'ree battle stars?" a battered, heavy-set man was asking Junior. "See, I—I come over with the Foist. We were at St. Lo. Nen, 'bout a week after, I got wounded. Nen I was inna hospital, an' I got sent, you know, up tru the Reppo Deppos to this outfit. An' I got a letter from my buddy from the ole outfit where it says all the guys got a star for France. Northern France. An' I shoulda got a Purple Heart, on'y—"

"Tough!" said Junior, a Hanging Judge. "If it's not on your record, it's just tough s---. Next man." Junior, like several others working with us, quickly forgetting his own days in combat, acted as if every man on the opposite side of the table were his mortal enemy, and he gave them no quarter.

"Hurry it up," the officers cried. "What's all this piling up here? Move right along! Keep this line moving!"

"Wait a minute, Junior; I'll take that man's record." By looking back through the blotched and crossed-out pages of the temporary record—an act that never occurred to Junior —one could find substantiation for the man's story: the date he landed in France, the division and the company he had been assigned to, the time of his hospitalization, his course

485

through the Replacement Depots and his eventual entry into our own outfit.

Chris Taylor was untangling similar difficulties, thumbing through the pages, writing in Purple Hearts and Battle Stars if they seemed deserved, and signing Captain Donald A. Sarsfield's signature. This we were not supposed to do, but we both felt it was better to err on the side of generosity.

That evening back in Jossnitz again, Chris and I were sitting with Ken and Bill in the dimness at the green serge-covered table, eating our supper, when Norman Harris came in late. Taking the rifle off his shoulder and not quite meeting our eyes, he said tiredly, with his flat Bostonian accent, "Well, boys, it's all over. The war's over. I just heard the announcement."

"Really over?" I put down my spoon in the mess kit.

"Honest to God?"

He raised his eyebrows, accepting no responsibility. "So they say. It's over." His helmet-liner stuck a little coming off his head. "There's to be no more fighting."

We sat in silence. I searched for some feeling, waited for it to develop. There was hardly any sensation at all. A moment later I was aware of an inward caving in, followed by a sore-throat feeling when I thought of those who had been forced to give up their lives for this moment.

"It's funny, isn't it," Bill Eyerly was saying, "how you can't feel anything. 'The war's over.' I thought I'd be hopping all over the place."

"And I have another cha-a-a-ming bit of news," Norman added. "You'll all have to work tonight. The captain wants everyone to report to the house at seven o'clock."

Leisurely, late, we went over to the attic and worked for a few hours, getting the records in order for the following day. The radio on the second floor, tuned up high, proclaimed London, Paris, New York—the entire world—delirious with joy, and there was a New Year's Eve blare of noise, voices and horns blowing in the background. "We switch you now to London, where the crowds in Piccadilly—" The radio snapped off and voices downstairs talked. The clerks were planning a celebration: someone was offering to buy liquor if any could be found for sale, and someone else long ago had cached away a bottle not to be opened till this night; but we upstairs in the attic had nothing, and no means with which to celebrate.

Our voices gradually quieted as we worked, and a peculiar long silence developed. Looking down, working automatically as the service records passed before me, I saw snow falling, fine, intent and unending, out of a cold, colorless sky. Where had that been? The trenches outside Rheims? Dominic's house? The chateau? The schoolhouse? None of those places, and yet all.

Finishing our own work ahead of the others, Chris and I left and went down the dark stairs, out into the spring night. The streets were cool and silent and leaf-shadowed. The guards were out, walking slowly up and down, and the generator chugged away in the stillness. A plane—the first in Europe we had seen with its lights on—throbbed across the sky. The entire town was blacked out.

"Do you feel like walking down as far as the corner?"

"To celebrate?" he asked.

In Norman Harris' airless, warm bedroom we sat alone, with one short candle lighted in the epergne, and had a canteen cup of cider that Zubek had left for us. Norman, Ken and Jim were visiting friends in one of the rooms downstairs. The dark Army blankets remained stretched across the open windows. There was nothing to do but write a letter home while the candle was still burning. Up at the front, would there be any sort of a party? we wondered.

One felt the need to say something extraordinary in the letter, yet even that somehow emerged false and forced. "Here, there's no great feeling of elation," I wrote. "There's merely a tiredness and a sense of relief. It's as if one had sat too long at the bedside watching the death throes of a gangster who hung on and hung on so that even one's hatred became dissipated. And now that the end has finally come, all you want to do is get up, walk away, and not think about it."

The candle spluttered out. We got up and swung back the blankets from the rear windows. In the pretty moonlit garden next door, the family sat out in their glider and on white iron furniture, murmuring and laughing softly, entertaining friends, serving drinks in tinkling glasses.

"They're having a better time over it than we are," Chris said.

By day the family next door drifted aimlessly, taking sunbaths, reading outdoors, going for picnics and swims to the nearby lakes. The machinery of their days had run down; there was no business for the men of the house to attend to. All were waiting, without discernible anxiety, to see what would happen.

Early the next morning on our way to breakfast, a small, humorous-looking, middle-aged German saw us, grinned and came across the street toward us into forbidden territory, his hand outstretched.

"Ofer!" he said. "War ofer. Gut! Friends!"

We stopped. The man he had addressed, who worked in the attic with us, looked around, saw no MPs and permitted his hand to be shaken.

"Now," said the German with his codger's grin, "togedder we fight the Russian, no?"

The soldier fell back and let out a roar: "Get outta here, you sonofabitch!"

We burst into laughter and went on.

By seven-thirty we were in the open trucks with our mess gear, rifles and the boxes of records. Starting off, we ducked our heads under the low boughs in town, then drove out and onto the Autobahn, cold at that hour, rising and dipping, with the air fresh and swift past our faces. The sun was coming up and former slave laborers were already on the road: groups of them pushing their rickety, piled-up carts, on their way back to France and Belgium, passing in silence and without a glance the German farmers and their families who waved to us from the fields as we rode by.

We drove up through Plauen, where now the choking plaster dust was gone and the main thoroughfare was cleared of debris. In the sparkling morning sunlight, ruins and skeleton walls stood out stalagmitic, in long dwindling perspectives, in an aching Dali-like landscape where, far down, the tiny figure of a civilian picked among the rubble and far behind him a still tinier figure walked beside a bicycle. Lilac bushes bloomed and tossed in the destruction, and several damaged trees were in leaf. The little park, a sudden green oasis, was filled with becalmed civilians sitting on the grass, watching the military traffic speed by. Before doorways of caved-in houses and apartments, cardboard signs had been planted, lettered in German, bearing the names of the dead still buried within. Soon, it was said, the stench of bodies would become terrible.

The civilians who were not in mourning had blossomed out overnight in thin summer clothes, though the weather was not mild enough for that. Some of the men wore Tyrolean shorts with dark-green jackets; the women went hatless, in full cotton skirts and sandals. As yet there was no sign of starvation on faces that showed the first reddish sunburn. All waved and smiled, relieved that we, and not the Russians, were occupying the Province of Thuringia.

There hadn't been any big victory celebration the night before, Preacher told me when I stopped off at the aid station to see him. He was alone. Tubby, he said, had cooked up a batch of kickapoo juice, and some of the boys had got to feelin' a little high, but by eleven-thirty everyone was asleep. The whole neighborhood was quiet. Before Battalion Headquarters had released the news of the war's end, all live ammunition had been called in. A few men had held out extra clips, had gotten drunk and had fired their weapons off toward the dark sky, and that had been the extent of the wild time on the front lines.

Nope, he said, there was no other news of any account. No one had heard from Captain Stettner, and Howie Mason was thinkin' of gettin' rid of the captain's loot because it didn't look as though anyone was gonna see him again.

"Yup." Preacher laughed. "I'm still holdin' down the fort, case we git any customers. Be movin' in a day or two to a great big place the other side of town here. Ah hear it's a pretty fine place." Would it make any difference to him, I wondered, when he never stepped outside, no matter where he was? It was not only combat or the fear of shells that kept him indoors and away from the windows and the view of foreign streets.

Part of the day Chris and I spent checking records at C Company, where the office was established in a long T-shaped, one-story shack in the country not far from a DP camp. Lieutenant MacKenzie was still absent, standing trial for the Tambach killings, and Lieutenant Ellis, who had thought he had a million-dollar wound the first day in the Saar, was temporarily in charge. Soft, warm wind whistled through all the open screened windows; dust and sand blew along the floor. Outside, stockpiles of German army equipment, gas shells and empty drums rusted in the hot sunlight. The screen door banged with double notes as the men, growing fat and lazy, drifted in and out with no visible purpose. Someone, lifting his voice, sang, "Sweet Eloise has a social disease . . ."

Everywhere there were plans in undertones about women and the approaching night. "Some of these guys," Atanasio said with a smile, shaking his head, "every single night in the week. Listen, you want some chocolate? We found a whole Jerry supply of it. Here, do us a favor: take some of it back with you. Everyone's sick of eatin' it." There was an air of appalling lassitude about the place.

At sunset we rode back through the bombed section of Plauen, standing up, bareheaded, hanging onto the swaying hoops above us. Out again along the long ribbons of the Autobahn that was restricted to military traffic and had no speed limit. We went so fast it was almost impossible to keep one's eyes open. Up and down hills, climbing into broad red-gold sunlight, dropping down into cool lonely shadows, flying past DP camps, past the many-porched country club where once we had set up an aid station, past towns and farms and empty rolling fields. On a side road there was the fringed surrey I had seen that morning setting out on a picnic, now coming back slowly, one wheel wobbling, with children lying asleep on laps and big wilting bunches of field flowers.

Our eyes grew bloodshot; we were coated with dust, tired, windburned and dizzy from the rushing air, glare and speed. By the time we reached Jossnitz, it was dark and we had missed our dinner again. The cooks gave us bread and jelly and a cup of coffee; and before reporting back to the attic for work, we went down to the brook on the edge of town to wash the grit from our faces and arms and the stiff dust from our hair.

As if it were a stupendous undertaking, Personnel moved up to another town, called Schleiz, into a fair-sized yellow plaster suburban house. The drawing room was in the rear, a stagey oval room with French windows giving out onto a flagged terrace. The bare parquet floor squeaked loudly. All the furniture, except a desk in the windows, had been taken out to make room for our work tables and the files of company service records.

A bedroom opened off one side of this oval room and was set aside for Captain Sarsfield and his two lieutenants. At the other side there was a pleasant library they used for their office. Upstairs there were bedrooms and a fairly modern bath, but a new ruling had come down: all enlisted men were to sleep outdoors. Pointless as it seemed—we worked indoors till ten o'clock every night, Sundays included—we pitched tents and slept in a stretch of neglected high grass that bounded the far end of the back garden.

Chris and I had the first tent in the second line of them, and, by some odd accident, my shelter-half, which was one I had dug out of the salvage, proved to be lacking one of its triangular flaps, so that on my side the tent didn't close in the front. It was, like most of the tents I had ever had, different from its neighbors, wrinkled, discouraged, makeshift and unmilitary.

We worked in the oval room, giving everyone in the division, sight unseen, and without a physical examination, a perfect bill of health for the war in the East. Later on, perhaps, a perfunctory examination would be given, but the findings would be immaterial: the results were already transcribed on the service records.

Captain Donald A. Sarsfield, Jr., was a notably handsome man, thoughtful-looking, tall, broad-shouldered and spare, with smooth dark hair and a Ronald Colman mustache. "One thing you gotta say for him," everyone said, "he's a hell of a good-looking guy." In his favor they had not much else to add. He craved attention and admiration, and his staff, though despising him in secret, played up to him at every opportunity.

"You've got to," Norman Harris told us cynically. "You've got to, to hold your job. You're constantly feeding his vanity." His clawlike hand made dredging motions.

"Tell them about the time he put himself in for the Bronze Star. And got it too," said Bill Eyerly, proceeding to tell us about it himself. "That was one of the rawest things I ever heard of. He was being driven up in his jeep to some town where Regiment was—he hates those trips forward, though he was still a good thirty miles behind the front—and as he gets out of the jeep, a Jerry soldier steps out of some bushes and walks across the street to surrender. Well, the driver told me Sarsfield goddam near died. Shook from head to foot and almost fainted. Went dead white and fell back against the hood of the jeep. Stayed there cowering for his life. The driver was ashamed of him. Then when Sarsfield finally sees the guy is surrendering, saying 'Kamerad! Kamerad!' and putting his hands up, Sarsfield gets out his pistol, still shaking like a leaf, and marches the guy up the street, and turns him over to an MP. Then the first thing he does, he goes in and demands a Bronze Star for overpowering a German soldier singlehanded."

"One thing about him, though," said Ken Dahl, "he tells on himself. I heard him tell that whole story. He always admits—"

"Admits, admits," said Norman. "What the hell else could he do with the driver there as a witness ready to tell it on him everywhere?"

"No, but I mean he has no pride. He doesn't care who knows—"

"God!" said Ken. "Will you ever forget during the winter the letters he got from the WAC?" Ken turned to Chris and me. "This was a WAC he met back in Jackson. He has a beautiful wife, but he's a chaser; he's got to be shacking up with someone on the side or he's a louse to everyone in the office. It's easy to tell how he's making out. Well, he met this WAC back in camp and he didn't tell her he was married, so they start shacking up—he told us all about it at the time —and the next thing you know, the gal's pregnant. That was just as we were clearing out to come overseas, and when we get here, the gal starts writing him, God, the most pitiful letters, how she was in a hell of a fix with her family and she had been booted out of the WACs; she didn't know what to tell people—whether to say she was married or not. They'd tear your heart out, and at night—I remember we were in Belgium—when we'd all be working, he'd come out of his office roaring with laughter, to read these letters out loud to us. We all gathered around, and that bastard laughed till he cried over the parts where she was begging him to marry her, and telling how much she loved him and how worried she was over him in combat, but please couldn't he write to her." Ken's voice suddenly hardened. "And we all joined in and laughed with him and made believe it was the *funniest* thing we ever heard. Boy, how we laughed! You do some goddamned lousy things to hold onto your safe little desk jobs, don't you, men?"

There was no answer.

After a week of cold rain, a leaking tent and soaking blankets, the days turned fair and warm and there was a burgeoning of flowers everywhere. Flowering shrubs and flowering trees burst out. The French windows stood open and birds sang in the May stillness. Sometimes I'd find myself looking up from work, wondering what I was missing and waiting for. It was for the scream and fall of a shell. Walking up and down the garden paths at the noon hour, thinking of the war in the East, I had the feeling that I was on the grounds of a convalescent hospital, resting up to undergo a second and more serious operation from which I had no hope of coming out alive.

Though we now had been together for the better part of a month—more than sufficient time for anyone to be assimilated and to feel at home in a rifle company—the permanent workers at Personnel still for the most part either loftily ignored us or else watched us and listened as if from a higher, more intellectual plane, shook their heads in puzzlement and said, "Characters." Yet their service records showed that in civilian life they had been the least important clerks, earning usually far less than thirty dollars a week. As opposed to the men in the rifle companies, predominantly they were strapping youths, very few of whom even wore glasses. On the first day we saw them, all had been wearing the blue-and-silver Combat Infantry Badge, which by right they should not have been issued; and such a howl went up from some of the new arrivals that the clerks were instructed to put their combat badges away until they were home on furlough.

They were warlike enough with the conquered civilians. It was not unusual for the clerks at Schleiz, shouldering a rifle, to halt a middle-aged or elderly housewife on the street and thrust on her their dirty underwear, their second woolen uniform and a small bar of Ivory soap, with grim instructions for her to wash and iron the things and return them before eight the following morning. No matter that the day was ending, overcast and rainy; the woman, shaking with fright, rushed home to boil, scrub and rinse, to wave dry the heavy pants and shirt over her slow kitchen stove. The next morning one saw her, nervous, hiding in the garden shrubbery where by law she was not supposed to be, looking for the clerk, with his clothes freshly ironed. For her efforts she received no pay, but was likely to have two or three more men hand her their alternate uniforms and a small bar of soap. Pointing menacingly to their watches, they shouted, "Tomorrow morning, verstehen sie? Now scram! Bastards!" And by night, for all they knew or cared, while the woman was sitting up trying to dry their uniforms, they might have been sleeping with her daughter, for, immediately after the sergeant major's flashlight bedcheck from tent to tent, men sneaked off through the dark garden to visit the off-limit houses where the German families were quartered.

Behind the picket fence that enclosed our property there stretched a large victory garden with a broad path running down its center, and during the day shifts of women and girls came to work in the rows of vegetables. Often at mealtime, though it was against the rules, we scaled the fence and went down the broad path because it proved a short cut to the parade grounds where our food was served.

One day at noon, in the bright sunlight, Burke and Oppenheim, two married men who had come from A and C companies were taking the short cut when they stopped to watch a curly-haired, three-year-old girl working with a tiny rake just beside the path. Her pregnant mother, in a smock and large straw hat, worked at a considerable distance. While the two men bent forward, trying their German on the child and occasionally on the mother, the telephone rang in the Personnel office for Captain Sarsfield. Colonel Mauck had been spying through binoculars from his bedroom window opposite and in a fury he ordered Captain Sarsfield to rush down and bring the two men over to him, where they were to be placed under arrest for fraternizing with the enemy.

Captain Sarsfield, cursing and in a dither, raced through the room to put on his belt, pistol and helmet; he ran out across our lawn, then scaled the fence and pelted down the path in time to grab Oppenheim and Burke as they were leaving the victory garden. He was by then too winded to explain to the bewildered men. "Colonel Mauck!" he gasped. "Mauck—Mauck's house. Quick!" Unable to fathom any of it, the two men led the trembling captain over to the colonel's house.

"On the way over," Burke later reported, "he started saying something about 'arrested—Colonel Mauck.' I thought he was saying Mauck had been arrested! I thought Sarsfield was in the middle of a fit."

They found Colonel Mauck trembling, striding up and down his bedroom, livid with rage. "You—you men!" he spluttered. "Desk workers! Clerks! Having it easy here in the rear! Fraternizing with the enemy while your buddies on the front lines have been sacrificing their lives! They would be ashamed of you! Ashamed! If you knew the privations they suffered! You wouldn't find one of *them* fraternizing with German women!"

Colonel Mauck was deaf, and at the moment overwrought, and it took Burke and Oppenheim some time to make him understand that they had not been clerical workers during the months of combat. When it finally seeped into his consciousness that they were riflemen who had come over with the outfit, that both had been wounded in action, had been awarded the Purple Heart and had returned again to the front lines, he was struck dumb and dismissed them without an apology.

The heavy duffel bags that we had last seen at Metz were delivered to us, and, opening mine, I came upon the rifle rod I had made of a thick wire coat hanger back in the United States and the tube of MacLean's toothpaste I had bought in England, the hundreds of rifle patches Sergeant Hill had given out, the little cans of bore oil and rifle oil, the two fatigue uniforms, the other pair of leggings, a K ration. Over all was a smell of canvas and mud that brought back memories of the chill, moist, twiggy apple orchard near Rouen, of Dave Rossofsky and the B.A.R. with the chronic malfunction, of the villa at Metz where Smathers cooked the goat and we first went into combat.

June

The work was finished at Personnel and we were sent back to our companies. A small truck transported Chris and me about three miles outside Schleiz into the country where Battalion Headquarters and the medics were established in a gray stone meeting hall that stood in a grove of elm and chestnut trees. Stretching before the hall, bounded by woods, was a grassy parade ground now dotted by long, straight double rows of little tents put up by the men of Battalion Headquarters. The training program, with its tiresome classes in military courtesy, personal hygiene, nomenclature of the rifle, its ten-mile hikes and night problems, was still in progress. Only the aid-station complement slept indoors, I was informed on reporting back; all the litter bearers were out in tents in the little woods between the road and the parade ground.

I toted my duffel bag and rifle over to pitch a tent near them. It was almost twilight. The medics' tents were not in rows, but scattered haphazardly under the trees on either side of a winding footpath near a circular, rustic summerhouse or bandstand with a gray stone foundation and three steps leading up to the dirt floor.

Ted Jameson ran up enthusiastically and we shook hands. Immediately, though, he became withdrawn and embarrassed, as if he regretted his first impulse.

"How was it at the hospital?" I asked.

"Oh, stinky. Had to do a lot of KP, and—oh, I don't know." His eyes flashed accusingly behind his glasses. "You never answered my letter."

"I know. I was working at Personnel."

"And neither did Cliff or Phil. I'm mad at all of you!"

"Where is Phil?"

"I don't know. He's always off someplace by himself. And I don't know *what's* the matter with Cliff, he acts so funny."

"How?"

"Well, he's not a bit friendly, the way he used to be. Everything's different. I almost wish I'd stayed in the hospital. I'm going off to see my friend Lynch, in A Company. I don't even hang around here any more."

In looking for Phil, I discovered that he was living alone. He had not pitched a tent with anyone, but instead had put up an Eastern bazaarlike canopy, open on all sides, by stretching his shelter-half over four thin stakes. The ends had been lashed down unprofessionally with yards of medical bandage. His equipment, duffel bag, and six or seven packages from home were partly covered by a blanket. Some of the boys, laughing a little, waited for my reaction.

"What does he do when it rains?" I asked.

"Just stays there under it. Campbell, Serletis, everyone told him he'd have to put up a regular tent, but he says he can't be bothered."

"You know what he does all day long? He takes *bird* walks!"

Phil came along a few minutes later, shoulders hiked up,

496

glasses still crossed with adhesive tape. He smiled and shook hands but seemed uneasy. He said he liked his Eastern shelter, and since he showed no inclination to strike it and join me in making a tent, I went back to the station, borrowed a shelter-half, a pole and some pegs from Warren Troy, and put up a tent of my own. I spread my raincoat down, my two blankets, stowed my equipment inside, and found myself smiling. The low little tent was dim and it smelled of canvas, of crushed grass; drafts blew in along the bottom edge, but here was privacy, privacy for the first time in—how long? In five months, since the icy room at the chateau. Once inside there was no necessity to speak to anyone, see anyone, consider anyone, or compromise on space. That alone made for one of the happiest intervals in the Army.

At this time the men seemed relaxed, walking about lazily, talking to each other in half-finished sentences, yet their tempers were apt to flare without warning. Best friends had violent disagreements and sulked for days. The two new Southern litter bearers, though from different backgrounds, had been inseparable since their arrival.

"Here comes ole Tuttle-eye with some drah wood," Eddie Jessup, the young, mild and likable one, remarked one day as his lanky, villainous-looking friend approached the bandstand, carrying an ax and some kindling.

"Don't cohll me Tuttle-eye!" the older one suddenly said in anger.

"But that's what I ohlways cohll you," the younger one pointed out in his plaintive drawl. "Youah eyes *are* jes lak a ole tuttle's, an' that's why Ah say 'Tuttle-*eye*.'"

"Well don't you say it again, goddamit!"

"Tuttle-eye . . ."

Turtle-eye let out a roar and chased young Jessup across the grass toward the barrier of trees. Seeing himself outdistanced, he raised the ax and sent it with all his force whizzing after his young friend. Missing by only a hair's breadth, the ax lodged with a sickening thud into a tree trunk. Turtle-eye turned and plunged cursing and swearing into the woods. We didn't see him for the rest of the day.

He came back toward nightfall. We were gathered around a little fire on the bandstand, slapping at mosquitos. Eddie Jessup, sorry he had caused the disturbance with his tentmate, opened his mouth to greet him and make amends. I could almost tell what he was going to say.

"Hello, Tuttle-eye" came out fondly before he could stop himself. This time, however, though everyone scattered, Turtle-eye merely cursed him viciously and us for laughing, and went by into his tent. The two were never friends and never spoke again.

"And how about you and Mike Nowak?" I asked Jimmy McDonough "Did you ever get over your argument?"

"Aah, if he says somethin', I answer, but that's about all. I'm through with that guy."

"What'd you ever argue about in the first place?"

He stared at me. "You were there! Don't you remember? He says, 'That was a ninety-millimeter shell.' I says, 'You're crazy, that's no ninety,' an' he says it was. I says, 'You're full of s---', an' he says, '*You're* full of s---', an' that was what the argument was about. I don't want anyone telling me when I know a thing is right."

But it was something more than that. It was something in the air. We knew each other too well and were tired of the companionships that had carried us over the months of combat. Friends fell out for no known reason, tried new friendships, clung fast to them for a few days, dropped them, and went off to look up their earliest acquaintances in the division.

After Bob Russell had gone to the hospital, Sam Benton, at loose ends, tried friendship with Cliff for several weeks, and when that fell apart—Sam was an intense and demanding friend—he turned to young Eddie Jessup. For days they went everywhere together, and then there were signs that young Eddie Jessup too was growing restive.

"Yes, but listen, Sam," I heard him complain one afternoon as I was passing his tent, "Ah cain't towk religion *ohll* the time. Whyn't you ever want to play cards with me? Ah git *tired* of religion, an' it's not a sin to play cards, hones' it isn't."

After that, they played blackjack by the hour, the two of them. Sam did not like it, but it was either that or nothing for him.

I was awakened one morning before seven by Sergeant Campbell. He bent down and called into the tent, "Laslie, git yer 'quipment, rifle, all yer stuff, an' report over to Sergeant Smathers, First Battalion. You move over there. Medics ain't busy now. We don't need you no more." He went away.

The kiss of death, administered by Sergeant Campbell. At

Battalion Headquarters I would be overstrength, coming at this late date, and overstrength men, we heard, were being shipped out to the 30th Division, which was said to be sailing straight for the CBI without any thirty-day furlough in the United States. I realized what it was. Sergeant Campbell, with his mind on the job of Medical Administrative Officer and without Captain Stettner to block him, was establishing himself anew, showing his astuteness to the officers at Battalion Headquarters.

I took down my tent and after breakfast dragged my duffel bag out of the woods and across the parade ground. I found Virgil Smathers in his tent. A short distance off, the men were wheeling and marching, performing close-order drill. Smathers, following an act of outstanding bravery some months back at C Company, had been awarded the Silver Star, had been raised to staff sergeant, and placed in Battalion Headquarters.

"Hell, I didn' send for you, Atwell. I don't know nothin' about it. We cain't use any extra men here; we got too many. Far's Ah'm concerned, you jes lay low an' make yourself scarce. Lotta chicken s---'s goin' on here."

I stopped off at the aid station and found that no one there knew anything about the move. Lieutenant Serletis, who was nominally in charge, was surprised that Sergeant Campbell had taken it upon himself to dismiss me. The more he thought of it, his surprise turned to anger, and, jamming on his helmet, he trotted over to the yellow plaster country house to see Captain Christoffsen about it. He came back rather nettled.

"Just as I thought! It was all Campbell's idea! He tells 'em over there we didn't want you any more an' he asks Christoffsen if he couldn't use you as an extra C.P. guard. Christoffsen didn't give a damn, but he thought we were tryin' to get rid of you. So here's the best I could do. You can stay here, live with us. Hell, I told him you were like our brother! You won't train with them or anything, but you will have to pull guard. Your name was already up on the guard list. You're on today. You'll have to go over an' see what time you start."

I returned to the little woods where the bandstand was and put up my tent again. Checkmated by Lieutenant Serletis, Sergeant Campbell never alluded to my continued presence with the medics, nor did he ever address a word to me again.

The big yellow plaster house into which the officers and clerks of Battalion Headquarters had moved had white stone facings and was set down in bright flower beds quite a distance in from the road that led to Schleiz. Jeeps raced up its driveway, made a screeching turn in the back courtyard and came to a halt; messengers ran up the steps under the colonnaded portico and into the house. There was constant traffic coming and going.

There was a large barn to one side where the Sergeant of the Guard figured out the shifts and sat with a pistol on his hip. Each time that I was on duty we had the same sergeant: a studious-looking youth, round-faced and eyeglassed, with a stern, small mouth. He had just been made sergeant and appeared to expect mutiny from his men at any moment.

At four o'clock he set out with the new guard shift. We were talking, which bothered him, yet he didn't like to say so. "Hey, fellas, kind of get in step there, will you? Hup. Hup. Hup."

"So what the hell is he huppin' us for?" asked Skeezix.

When we came to my post at the front of the house, there was a pause. I had forgotten the ritual of serious face, present arms, and the question "What are the special duties of this post?" Instead I said, "Hello."

"Listen," said the sergeant, "you're supposed to present arms! Tell him your special orders."

The guard said, "Well—oh, yeah. Just to see nobody that don't belongs—no civilians get in the house."

"Do you have to salute the officers now?"

"Yeah."

It was a walking post. I went slowly round and round the house, down the garden paths with the carbine on my shoulder, the flat pistol belt, empty of ammunition, around my waist. Whenever officers started into view, I glanced the other way to avoid saluting them. Toward six o'clock, slanting golden sunlight blazed on the brilliant flowers. The many-paned windows on the first floor stood open, afire with gold, and from inside I heard officers' voices saying, "Whatta we coming to? They got a medic on guard!"

"Hey, Nick, isn't that one of your guys out there with a rifle?"

Lieutenant Serletis came to the window. "How's it going?" He grinned affably.

"Fine."

"Oop! 'Scuse me!" His head ducked out of sight and then he reappeared to say, "Forgot you're not supposed to talk to a guard."

On my time off I dropped in at the large kitchen where Chris Taylor, his friend Bill Burnside, Strauss, Shrimp Mitchell and Engle, the orderlies, held forth. Bill Burnside, broad and strapping, was standing at an ironing board, sponging and pressing an officer's uniform. Strauss, who frequently talked for the sake of hearing his own voice, was sitting down addressing an unseen audience. The kitchen, with its huge copper-hooded stove, its lead-glass cabinets and pantries, resembled one in a prosperous American house of the early twenties. Chris Taylor and the others were preparing the officers' food.

"Don't they eat whatever we eat?" I asked, sitting down on a kitchen chair, laying the rifle on the floor.

Chris shot me a glance. "They do like hell. They wouldn't eat that s---. Even if it's the same food, they want it cooked some other fancy f---ing way. And every day for breakfast, bacon and eggs."

"Where do you get them around here?"

"What the hell do they care? You just get them! You scout all over."

Thirty-three-year-old Shrimp Mitchell, with his shining, snub-nosed, deceptively angelic face and little-boy's hair comb, said, "If Colonel Parkhurst don't have his two eggs sunnyside up every morning, there's hell raised, I'm tellin' you." Shrimp kept a small wicker Red Riding Hood basket with straw in the bottom for carrying the colonel's eggs, and he had become a familiar figure during the last few months of combat, running for his life through a town as shells whizzed in, carrying his rifle in one hand and the basket with the breakfast eggs in the other.

"Here, these are for the colonel," he'd say to the busy cooks at breakfast time when we were living in the field. "He wants them sunnyside up. Don't forget, sunnyside up."

"Sunnyside s---! We got more to do than fry this f---in' eggs for him." The cooks took a perverse delight in breaking the yolk and flipping the eggs over, making Shrimp's own yoke heavier to bear.

And there was the memory of Chris through combat: shouts going up in the snowy night in the midst of the flurry

501

of moving. "Taylor! Tay-y-lor! Where the hell is Tay-y-lor?"

"Coming, sir!"

"Got my equipment?"

"Yes, sir."

Captain Reddy had not proved an unreasonable taskmaster in any way, but he was a short man and had difficulty in adjusting the straps of a gas mask to make it small enough for him, and invariably in the dark and confusion, while Chris was carrying his own equipment as well as the captain's, toting the captain's bulky sleeping roll which contained a mattress and eight blankets, the little gas mask would be lost. "That's the only time he really ever got sore."

"What burns my ass," Bill Burnside was saying, "is this sonofabitch Mainwaring! I'm not *his* orderly! He's only a looie; he's not supposed to have one!"

"You're talking now of Katharine Hepburn," Strauss said. "He has *such* disdain."

"He comes down here, throws a lousy old dirty uniform at me, sticks his nose up in the air and says, 'Clean this.' I sweat on the goddam thing all day long, use up all my own cleaner, press it, get the creases down the shirt, really make it look sharp. He comes in to get it today. I give it to him, and he takes it, just takes it without even saying thanks."

"Why'd you do it for him?" I asked.

No answer at first. Then: "Aah, what can you do?"

"The thing I object to is washin' out their goddam dirty socks and drawers!" said Shrimp Mitchell.

"Ah, democracy, democracy!" cried Strauss with a ringing stage laugh.

"Every f---ing day," said Chris, ignoring him, "they've got to have their ice cream. You'd think they were kids. 'Where's our ice cream?' The goddam pigs would eat it for breakfast! And they fight over who has the biggest portion. Here, have some." He heaped up a saucer of chocolate ice cream. It had been Strauss's turn that day to drive down to the factory to get it. It was a special ice cream made only for the officers with ingredients from the ten-in-one rations.

"Well," I said to Chris, "I don't envy you your life."

He was morose. "Anyway, I did what I set out to do: I stayed alive. But Christ knows how many times I was set to fling it up."

"Would you take this job again in the CBI?"

502

Fine-featured, despairing, he stood thinking perhaps of his injured foot, perhaps of the promise he had made to Mary one night in my presence to come back to her at all cost. "I —I don't know," he finally said. "I hate to think about it."

"Oh, there were times when it wasn't so bad," Bill Burnside said.

"When wasn't it so bad?" Chris demanded, flaring up. "When?"

"All right, all right, it was lousy all the way through. Jesus, you talk about touchy guys!"

The conversation swung around to the stout, middle-aged woman who had been given the job of scrubbing up the place. The burgomaster of the town had come up to the house a few days before and with Strauss had concluded the deal. Though it was now against the law to have a civilian in the house, and the five orderlies were there to do the work, Strauss, with the permission of Captain Reddy and Captain Christoffsen, had arranged to have the woman come in to scrub in return for her three meals every day.

From the start, the woman had complained bitterly. For one thing, she said, she had never wanted the job and that it had been forced on her; she said she owned a store in town and she wanted to run it. Instead, she had been ordered to report to the yellow house at six-thirty in the morning, and from that moment until eight at night she had been kept working steadily. The flagged hall was in constant use, and on rainy days she was ordered to scrub it five and six times over. In addition, there were floors and halls and carpets to sweep, three or four bathrooms to scrub, all the beds to make, the officers' rooms to be cleaned, the windows to be polished—the entire work of a large house overcrowded with careless guests—and in return for her labor she was given three meals.

"And mein Gott, the appetite on her!" Strauss exclaimed. "I have never seen a woman eat so much! She shovels the food down. And now she's complaining because we don't give her food to take home! Here she is. Wait till you see her eat."

The woman came in, stout, angry and red-faced; her eyes were a sharp blue. She wore a blue-checked dress, limp black bedroom slippers and a white bandanna pulled tightly low over her forehead. Getting out a plate, a knife, fork and spoon, she muttered in German. Someone gave her a plate

503

of food and she took it to a small table at the window, sat down and began to eat, turning around every now and then to glare at Strauss.

"Look at her!" he cried, feigning delicate disgust. The woman ate quickly and angrily, that was all. "Really she's a horrible character. I can't look at her."

"At that," I said, "you have the better part of the bargain. By our standards she's working for you for nothing."

"For nothing! She's getting her three meals a day."

"Yes, but how much would your wife pay for the same sort of help in New York?"

"We never had any! We are just little people, Atwell. We are not of the class that has help come in."

"Well, if you ever did have any, you'd pay about seventy-five cents an hour with carfare and meals thrown in. So, from six-thirty in the morning to eight at night—"

"But here, my friend, it's a very different thing."

"Why should it be? You're the one who's always talking about the underdog and the little people. And we're not here in the role of conquerors, remember? We're supposed to be here to spread democracy by our good example, and yet with the first chance that comes along, you turn opportunist and start oppressing—"

"*Me? I'm* oppressing?" He shot out of his chair. "*I* turn opportunist?"

"What else can you call it?"

"Why, only the other night," Strauss said heatedly, "she stole a coil of rope! I know she did! She could sell that in the black market. And Burnside here, like a damned fool, gave her a pound of coffee one day. A whole pound of coffee! Gutt in Himmel, she could get six to eight dollars for that alone!"

"I'm talking about you, and what you're giving her. You made the deal, and it was a damned unfair one. You're no better than the Germans themselves. You've got a slave laborer here and you can't disguise it."

"Yay! Yay! Get after him!" Shrimp and the others were cheering and chiming in from time to time. Strauss was flushed, badly rattled, trying to laugh the thing off.

"Hey, cut out the noise. We're making too much noise. The officers are waiting!"

We quieted down and the boys began to rush the food in on the table.

I heard that the next night at dinnertime the woman and Strauss had a furious argument, at the height of which the woman spat on him and said in German, "Rotten Jew!"

"Good God! What did Strauss do?" I asked.

"Not a damned thing!" Shrimp reported with relish. "He just got white. White as a sheet. Didn't say a goddam thing. He got out of the kitchen; then she lit out for the night and wouldn't do any more work."

To get from the yellow plaster house to her home, the woman took the winding footpath that led through the woods, past the rustic bandstand where the medics had pitched their tents. I saw her on her way home in one of the strange endless twilights, muttering darkly to herself. I had no doubt she was a difficult and belligerent woman, but it seemed to me that she was being victimized. I told Phil who she was, and he, perhaps ashamed of his friend Strauss, perhaps just sorry for her, stopped her the next night and gave her some food left over from his package from home. In return she gave him such a turbulent recital of her grievances, and poured it out so rapidly and emotionally, with such floods of angry tears, that he could understand only a sentence here and there.

She began to bring her daughter along to help out with the work. The girl was about nineteen, extremely pretty and golden-haired; she wore a black mourning dress with black shoes and stockings. Chris Taylor told me the mother then spent most of her time chasing after the officers who were chasing after the girl. If the girl went in to make a bed, one of the officers slipped in after her and locked the door. The mother, never far off, dropped her scrubbing brush, came tearing down the hall and shouted the house down, banging on the door until it was opened and the officer got out. The girl was shrinking and timid at first, but within a few days she grew to enjoy her popularity and the chases round and round the bedrooms; and the mother's watch-dog tactics had to be doubly increased. In return for helping with the work, the girl was also given her meals.

Then a second girl was permitted to accompany the mother and daughter to the house. She was supposed to work in the vegetable patch and the garden. We saw the three of them coming and going through the woods and we used to say hello. The second girl was tall, slender, and not pretty: her face was too long, and her wavy brown hair was combed back from a forehead too high; but her features were delicate, she moved with grace and distinction, and she wore well-fitted country clothes. She was friendlier than the other two; she spoke English fairly well and often hung back to talk to us. At the yellow house, no one had ever heard her say a word.

Previously, in showing me through the house, Chris had brought me up through the bedrooms, and in one I had noticed a framed pen-and-ink sketch of a young girl. This, I was certain, was the same girl, eight or ten years later, yet when I mentioned one day seeing her picture in the house, she pretended to be surprised. "Mine? My picture?" She raised her eyebrows. "Nein! No!"

"Yes, it must be."

"Not mine." She tore a leaf from a branch and laughed. But she would not explain who she was beyond telling us her name was "Elisabet" and that she lived in the same house with the others in town. They were her friends, she said. They had been her servants, I was sure, but she would not say so. The peasant woman and blond daughter seemed to be protecting her. Whenever Elisabeth stood talking to us, she kept smiling and stripping leaves with her long manicured fingers. One day she wore two beautiful rings: a square diamond that flashed and sparkled in the sunlight, and a large amethyst in a heavy gold setting. She was the only one of the three who smoked.

"Elisabeth, are you married?" Jimmy McDonough asked.

"Married?" She stripped a leaf and smiled. "Yes."

"Where's your ring?"

"Here. Around my neck." She showed us the thin chain and the ring.

"Is your husband in the Army? In the Navy?"

"He is—he was—in the Diplomatic Service. In Berlin. My family once lived here."

Daily she accompanied the mother and daughter, but she never went into the house any farther than the kitchen. On the days that I was on guard, I never saw her do anything but watch an elderly German hoeing and staking in the vegetable patch. They talked together, and he seemed to be explaining what he was doing. At other times, she walked through the flower beds, but beyond trying to straighten a flower that had bent over, she did not seem to know what to do. At mealtime, Chris said, she came in, ate in silence with her eyes on her plate, got up, and walked out again.

All this while, the older woman had kept up a steady demand for more and more food. There were eighteen people in her house to feed! Eighteen! Crammed into a tiny house with no food, and no way of getting any! Why couldn't she take them some of the food left over from the soldiers? As long as she worked so hard all day long, and was prevented from running her store—I did not believe, somehow, that she had ever had a store, but it was true that food was going to waste.

Out on the parade ground after each meal, the food that was left over was thrown into the sump and lye was poured in on top of it. This the sharp-eyed woman had spotted from an upper window of the house, and she did not cease her caterwauling until in the end she was victorious. She, her daughter and Elisabeth were permitted to go over with a pail each and stand by while the food was being thrown away. They were allowed to fill their pails. After one of the meals at lunchtime, there was nothing left over and the woman berated the cooks, crabbed and complained and banged things around the house for the rest of the day.

The mosquitos were troublesome at night and we stood slapping our ankles and arms and faces, hanging around the little fire on the dirt floor of the bandstand. In the long deepening twilight, the older woman and Elisabeth came past carrying their pails of food. A little after, the blond daughter came by, humming to herself. Phil and I were leaving to go to our shelters. Talking quietly, the mother and Elisabeth disappeared around the bend; only the daughter was in sight, now walking past the tents. A flap turned back and, in the dim silvery light, Joe Mortara scrambled out, minus his shirt, holding up half a chocolate bar. "Pst! Hey, frawleen," he whispered, gesturing toward his tent, "Schlafen? Chocolada? Schlafen mit me?"

We burst into laughter. The girl tilted her nose and went on with her pail. Shaking his head, discouraged, Joe crawled back into his tent.

The news was published in *Stars and Stripes* that the Russians were to occupy our sector as well as the rest of Thuringia. The 67th was named as one of the first divisions to be rushed back to the United States; and there, following a thirty-day recuperative furlough at home, we were to be given a brief but intensive training in jungle warfare and the technique of assault landing, and then were to be shipped to the East.

The classes, hikes and calisthenics came to an end; the heavy equipment started to be crated for the trip home. There was an air of ending to everything here in Germany. The days turned perfect: one long hot June day burned into another.

I was talking to Phil Schaeffer one day when Don Stoddard passed me, then turned back from a short distance and said, "Les, excuse me, but could I talk to you for a second?" When I joined him, we walked quite a way in silence before he said, "Well, it's this. I wanted to ask you about a Protestant marrying a Catholic. Does it ever work out?"

"Yes, of course! Lots of times."

"I wouldn't have to change my religion, or anything?"

"No. You'd have to sign, though, that your children would be brought up as Catholics, and that you wouldn't discourage your wife in any way from living up to her religion."

"And there's nothing else?"

"No."

But there was something else on his mind that he didn't mention.

"Well, thanks very much. I—I just thought I'd ask you."

I saw him, far off, walking around by himself most of the afternoon, thinking, switching the tops off of the weeds, and later in the day, as if out of a clear sky, he said, "Did I ever show you a picture of Anne Marie?" He had written to her constantly, and she to him, but he had never discussed her with the rest of us. "Well, here are two pictures. This one just came today."

"She's beautiful!"

He hesitated a long while. "Yes, she is, but . . . doesn't it strike you that she . . . smiles too much? Shows her dimples too much?"

"No, I don't think so," I said, not quite truthfully. "She *has* a beautiful smile."

"Yes, but in every picture! It's the same goddam expression, the exact same smile, the same dimples, as if it's something she just turns on. I don't know. You see, there's something else. She writes to say that she, her mother and father can't wait to see me again. They expect me to come straight from the boat to their place up in New Hampshire—that's where I met her, at A.S.T.P.—and she thinks I'm going to spend my whole furlough with her. She's been looking forward to it, of course, and making all sorts of plans, but—but hell, my family's going to think it's funny if I don't come out and see them. They're waiting for me too!"

"Couldn't you spend part of the thirty days with each?"

"I don't know." He took the pictures back. "Sure you don't think she has one of those annoying smiles?"

"Oh, no! Not at all."

But after all the waiting and letter writing, I could tell it was the end of Anne Marie.

At every turn there was that sense of things that had sustained us, falling apart, ending. Lieutenant Serletis, forgetting the dark days, spent most of his time at Battalion Headquarters and reverted suddenly to being an officer again. In passing the litter bearers, he nodded briefly and sternly, addressed them by their last names and was never seen in the aid station he had once so hated to leave. Warren Troy reached a point where everything Preacher said and did grated on his nerves to such an extent that he spent as much time as possible in the woods with us. Phil was off on his long, solitary bird walks. Mike Nowak returned from a pass to the Riviera, cheered by the fact that while there he had contracted a case of malaria which would prevent him from being with us in the CBI. Young Eddie Jessup grew tired of playing blackjack and began to avoid Sam Benton, sneaking away from him guiltily, leaving Sam to wait for hours outside the little tent to see if he would return.

Men who had been sick or wounded as far back as the Battle of the Bulge were returned from the hospitals to make the trip home with us. Unexpectedly one still, warm evening when the little fires before the tents burned as straight as candle flames, Bob Russell walked into the clearing near the bandstand. Sam Benton, sitting in front of his tent, sprang to his feet, startled, and then, going into cackles of happy laughter, jumped up into the air and raced over to shake hands, capering around in his joy, pounding Bob Russell on the back and calling to the rest of us to come and greet the returned wanderer. Bob Russell seemed confused by Sam's display of happiness, and, working his hand free, he mumbled something, turned on his heel and went away. Suddenly friendly with everyone, Sam ran from one to the other of us. "Hey, d'you boys hear the news? Ole Russ is back. He's gone up the aid station t' say hello t' Preacher! Yes, sir, old Russ's back again! Sure did miss ole Russ. Glad to have m' friend back again. Hey, d'you hear the news? Ole Russ is back."

But memories of religious fervor, of combat, of dangerous river crossings and the possibility of drowning were far behind Bob Russell. From the field hospital he had been sent to a convalescent one in Paris; and in Paris he had had a wild, wild time. He had found one French girl so enamored of him that on nights when he couldn't sneak out to her she climbed through, or over, a high iron picket fence to be with him in the shrubbery of the hospital grounds. Sitting around a campfire that first night back, giving a graphic description of the affair, Bob stared straight at the fire, his eyes large. He did not see any of us, and, above all, he was completely forgetful of Sam and the prayer meetings out in the ambulance. By the firelight I saw Sam's face, stunned at first and incredulous. Then it turned wry with pain, and before the recital was half over he had faded away from the circle of listeners.

I felt sorry for Sam the next day after lunch when, completing a full circle, he came to me and said, "Les? Like to come to the movies with me in Slice?" The others had arranged to leave in a truck, but Sam did not want to go with them. I didn't have the heart to turn him down.

We set out together on foot. The countryside looked beautiful, with distant blue hills melting into the perfect sky, with nearer blue-green fields and yellow-green fields and fresh green meadows sending up breaths of fragrance. Daisies and buttercups grew in drifts along the roadside, and at a little distance a few naked children splashed in a stream that carried away the rippling reflections of their sunlit bodies and the tall poplar trees along the banks.

"Sure *is* beautiful all right," Sam Benton agreed, "but Ah don' lak it. Be glad get back home Kentucky. Wouldn't mand switchin' out of this outfit neither. Lak to get back to mah ole outfit. Got some good friends there, yes, sir! *Real* frien's. We get back to the States, Ah'm puttin' in for a transfer. Wouldn't want to go the CBI with these boys. Rather have frien's aroun' me there. Need 'em there."

"But if you could switch back, you'd probably be disappointed. People change; your friends would be scattered or have new friends. It'd be the same everywhere. When you first came here, you thought everything was fine." I recalled the irritating cheerfulness of his " 'Bout lak Valley Forge, guess" when we were living under the snowy pines near Rheims. "Sometimes I think we just get to know each other too well; there's never any relief."

"Wouldn't be that way if you were 'mong real frien's."

"How long did you know the boys in your old outfit?"

"Ah was with them 'bout three, four months."

"Well, there it is. Even after three or four months here, everything was still all right. It's after that that the strain becomes apparent—" But Sam never liked to be convinced once he had made up his mind, and rather abruptly he changed the subject.

Sam's brother, who had courted Miss Martha Lee while Sam courted Miss Lucy, was now a first lieutenant in a tank outfit that was stationed not too far from us. Sam had often spoken in terms of glowing hero-worship about his brother. Recently he had been loaned the medics' jeep and had driven over to visit him for the day. Yes, Sam said, his brother looked fahn. The former Miss Martha Lee had presented him with a young son, and he was sure anxious to get back and see them. Was Sam, I asked to make conversation, going to marry Miss Lucy Lee during our thirty-day furlough?

"Well, tell the truth, Les, Ah don't know. Thought Ah was sure—jes as sure as a man could be, but—" Some inward working showed across his face, which by now had lost all its appearance of first youth. "D'you know this German girl Ah visit? Margaret?"

"I don't *know* her." I remembered hearing that he and some of the other little bearers did go down—though not together—to a small country schoolhouse where six or seven German families now lived and that Sam had found there a quiet girl whom he liked.

"Right pretty girl. *Good* girl, too," he was saying. "Not like the others. Don't drink, don't smoke—real good girl. Ah jes talk to her mile a minute in English, an' she talks right back to me in German, an' we unnerstan each other. We unnerstan each other! If the Army didn't forbid it, Ah'd—" he hesitated—"swear Ah'd marry Margaret tomorr'." I was shocked after hearing all the talk of Miss Lucy Lee. "Ah mean that!" he said. "Man could be happy with that sort of girl. Make a fahn wife. But Ah don't know—" He gave a

511

high inconsequent laugh. "Never was so shook up in all mah life, guess. Can't figger on not fallin' in love. A man jes *does* it! That's why Ah'd lak to get home, an'—an' forget all *about* this. Get straighten' out an' start all over." I realized suddenly that he was close to tears and I was struck dumb with embarrassment.

We went into a large turnhall, sat through a poor film about the Falcon in Mexico, and filed out into the late-afternoon sunshine. I had a slight headache and the dragging sense of depression that comes from having been in the movies in the afternoon. We were offered a lift back in one of the trucks, but some of our own men were in it and Sam preferred to walk. Once we had passed the houses, though, and were in the open country, his feet began to drag and he was dispirited and almost silent. He did not in any way refer to his huge disappointment in Bob Russell.

Far ahead of us, two frisky German girls with bare legs, high heels, bare shoulders and very short skirts were walking along the side of the road. The line of crowded, open trucks returning from the movie slowed down and drew over, passing close to the girls, and the men whistled, howled and gestured. A jeep bearing an officer rode up out of line, and he shouted to the vehicles to speed up and continue. The girls laughed and walked along, rolling into each other as the little convoy passed them. One jeep toward the rear of the line had managed to drop back out of the officer's sight around a bend, and, a little later, on a clear stretch, it drove up beside the girls. They turned into the woods and the jeep drove in after them. Sam Benton let out an involuntary tortured exclamation of disgust.

Mass was celebrated that Sunday morning for the last time in Germany in the large meeting room beside the aid station. I stopped in afterward to speak to Preacher, to tell him that I had decided not to become a medic, and I came upon several men I knew slightly, facing the wall in the midst of a prophylaxis treatment. Embarrassed, I turned around and went out. In the shade under the elms and chestnuts that bordered the parade ground, the chaplain was sitting in front of his jeep on a camp chair, his face turned away as he heard confessions. A line of men had formed, waiting. As the penitent's turn came, he took off his helmet, walked out across the grass, knelt down and blessed himself. Non-Catholics looked on with curiosity. Farther down, on the other side of the field, the cooks were working and the KPs were scouring the long wooden trestle tables and benches that had recently been made for us. The wet tables glistened in the sunlight like sheets of mirror. Overhead the American flag fluttered in the breeze. There were all the smells of a summer Sunday: of grass, of chestnut blossoms drifting down, of honeysuckle, of Sunday dinner cooking.

It was pleasant eating outdoors at the long tables, and sometimes there for a half hour or so we were all together as we had been in combat. "Les! Over here! We're all over here!" Ted Jameson's voice, and other voices were calling, "Save room for Don and Tom Lawlor. Wait, here's Jenkins. Push down. Preacher! Warren! Hey Pancho, over here! Eat with us! We all together now?" The sun beat down hotly through our khaki wool shirts. The KPs were lazy and they didn't care if, after eating, those at our table sat on, smoking and talking. Now that censorship had lifted, cameras were returned to their owners, and someone in the group got up to take pictures of us all together grinning and squinting into the sunlight. Sam Benton was the only one missing. He had gone over again to visit his brother.

After lunch, Warren Troy and I went for a walk far outside Schleiz. We got back to the woods long after supper and parted at the aid station; I continued on toward the little bandstand. Big Steve, Charley Heydt, Tubby, and Jimmy McDonough had been drinking kickapoo juice and were sitting around a fire outside their tents, talking and laughing. Jimmy called me over. Big Steve was telling a dirty joke to annoy Tom Lawlor, and Tom, clapping his hands over his ears, kept jigging, shaking his head and shouting, "No! No! No!" trying not to hear it.

"Les, you missed it," Jimmy said. "Jeez, did we have fun! We go down to the schoolhouse this afternoon and we take along one of the cooks—you know, the big black-haired guy with the teeth out in front. We bring along some GI alcohol an' lemon powder, an' go in an' make a great big batch of kickapoo juice an' start handin' it out. An' before we know it, *everyone* in the joint is reelin' around, drunk as bastids: kids, girls, old men an' women, everyone. Everyone singin' an' dancin', stumblin' all over. One of the old guys got sore as hell at us for gettin' everyone drunk. An' listen, Sam's girl, you know? Margaret? We give *her* a few shots an' she loosens up an' has the best time of all! She tells us Sam is a pain in the ass. 'No cigaretten,' she says. 'No schnapps, always God —like this.' " He showed me, his hands joined and pointed heavenward. His eyes rolled up sanctimoniously, then he went into bursts of laughter. "Before we left she was loopin' all over the place, dancin', doin' high kicks, pullin' up her skirts an' havin' a helluva wild time for herself."

Sam returned from visiting his brother about a half hour later as I was getting ready to go to sleep. He came into the glade quietly, and, after standing awhile outside his tent, he turned and went down through the woods in the direction of the schoolhouse, to see Margaret. The rest of the men had crawled into their tents, and there were snickers of laughter as Sam walked away.

In about fifteen minutes he was back, shouting into Jimmy McDonough's tent, calling him and Charley Heydt out to fight.

"Git outta here," Jimmy said with pretended sleepiness. "What's the big idea, wakin' us up? What'd we do?"

Sam's voice was shrill with anger. "Who brought the liquor down the schoolhouse? Which one of you did it? Come out here an' faght lak a man!"

"How the hell d'we know who did it? It wasn't us. It was one of the cooks."

"Which one?" Sam demanded.

"I don't know. Git the hell outta here."

In the stillness there was the swift crackling of weeds as Sam went back to his own tent, and from the other tents scattered about there came the sound of half-suppressed laughter.

A few minutes later I heard Eddie Jessup's drowsy plaintive voice asking from inside their tent, "Sam, what you doin', puttin' on yoah shoes again? Ah thought you was goin' t' sleep. Where you goin'?" The voices, though muffled, carried in the stillness.

"Goin' over to A Company."

"But, Sam, that's a long ways, A Company."

"Someone there Ah got see."

I was late going over to the parade ground for breakfast the next morning. The chow line had ended and the men were sitting at the tables eating. As I presented my mess kit before the tall, rangy, black-haired cook with the bumpy skin, he grinned, showing the black space where his front teeth should have been. He owned a partial plate, but he wore it only for dress occasions.

"Had a little trouble with one of your boys this morning," he said. "Sam Benton. He's one of the first ones waitin' on the line, and as he comes up, he says to me, 'You got my girl drunk last night. Step aside an' fight!' An' when I take a look down at him, I see he's wearin' a set of brass knuckles."

"Brass knuckles!" When I thought of Sam, whose principles would not allow him to fight for his country, putting on a set of brass knuckles for the sake of a German girl, the thing was astounding.

"They say he borried them from some guy over in A Company who used to be on the Tiger Patrol. Walked all the way over there seven miles last night to get them. I says to him, 'What, me fight you? Don't make me laugh!' I says, 'Take them brass knuckles off an' behave yourself before I knock your goddam teeth down your throat.' He stands there shakin' like a leaf, an' by that time there's a lot of guys lookin'. 'Come on an' fight,' he says. I says, '*Git* goin', Sunny boy, you're holdin' up the line.' He looks at me, then turns white as a sheet an' walks off the line without eatin'. I seen him go 'way off, 'way over that way." He pointed to the distant screen of trees away from where we were encamped.

In the afternoon, Sam's brother, the lieutenant, drove over to visit him and meet his friends. It was the first we had seen of Sam all day. Set-faced, jaws tense, he led his brother into the clearing and went through the ritual of introducing him carefully to all of us. The brother was a surprise. Sunburned, red-haired, cocky, with a trim muscular build, a crooked smile and an outthrust underlip, he shook hands around the circle, surveyed us all knowingly and asked as an opener, "Well, how's the frawleen situation aroun' here? You boys gettin' plenty?" Intent on showing us he was nothing like Sam, ripping out curses left and right, he went into an anatomical description of his own frawleen. Sam's face was like stone. To make matters worse for him, the brother and Bob Russell struck up a friendship on sight and went into an uninhibited comparison of the ways of French and German girls.

Cutting the brother short, Sam led him away, ostensibly to meet Preacher and Warren Troy at the aid station. The brother's jeep remained for several hours over at Battalion Headquarters, but Sam did not bring him back to where we

515

were and never again mentioned his name. For that matter, he didn't speak to any of us about anything.

One after another, everyone he relied on had failed him: all the disciples from his prayer meetings, Bob Russell, Captain Stettner, Phil Schaeffer, Paul Clifford, young Eddie Jessup, Margaret, his brother. And the loss of face he suffered on the chow line gained wide knowledge, for the big cook took pleasure in repeating the story. Word of it had traveled to A Company by the time Sam went back to return the unused brass knuckles, and his stock there, where once he had been looked on as a hero, fell to nothing.

Leaving Germany the next day to go home was a much simpler operation than I had expected. In my own case, Lieutenant Serletis had arranged that I travel at least part of the way with the medics, and on the final morning we took down the tents, closed the duffel bags, hid the rubbish, then policed the area, put on full field packs and toted our belongings over to the parade ground.

We lined up facing First Battalion Headquarters, and the wait was surprisingly short. The men all wore the newly issued Eisenhower jackets, new shirts, new pants and new combat boots, but orders for these had been taken while I was working at Personnel, and consequently I was in Captain Stettner's voluminous old field jacket, dirty torn pants, and the combat boots with the gash across the toe.

While we stood at attention in the sunlight, the flag came down and Captain Christoffsen in a stentorian voice began to call off the names.

"Andrews!"

"Here, sir!"

"Asadourian!"

"Here, sir!"

"Atwell!"

"Here, sir!"

His head swiveled around: I was not in the ranks before him where he expected me to be. "Atwell?"

"Here."

"He's traveling with us, Captain," said Lieutenant Serletis.

"Oh, yes." While the rest of the names were being read off, the big two-and-a-half-ton trucks rumbled up to the edge of the parade ground. One of the new officers started belatedly out of the yellow house, staggering under the weight of his bedroll and equipment. "Here!" cried Captain Christoffsen. "*Help* Lieutenant Etzweiler carry his stuff there! What's the matter with you?" No one moved. "By God! You four men there! Yes, you!"

I was always one of that four everywhere. We started over, grumbling.

"What the f---'s the matter with him? Is he a cripple?"

"The las' minute! Carry some f---in' lieutenant's s--- for him!"

"Oh! you boys going to give me a hand? Well, that's fine! Watch out—it's pretty heavy."

Back in place again, we picked up our own equipment and climbed aboard the open trucks. There was no pushing, no haste, very little noise; we were almost like men in a silent picture. It seemed there should have been some ceremony, or someone to say goodbye to. Over at the yellow house, the old man working in the vegetable patch did not lift his head; Elisabeth had not come to see us off, nor was there any sign of the belligerent woman and her blond daughter. For the last time I took a look at the gray stone aid-station building, at the little woods. With a jolt we were off, riding down the now familiar rising and dipping road, past the familiar hills, the trees, the stream where the children were bathing, the daisy fields, the pale plaster houses of Schleiz.

This time there was clean straw on the floors of the forty-and-eights, and we were not nearly so crowded as we had been on the trip into Metz. The medics had been given a boxcar to themselves. All day long the wide door remained open, and to the humming *click-click-clock* of the wheels, the sunlit German countryside rolled slowly past: fields and hills fading off to smoky blue on the horizon, towns, streams and woods, waterfalls, dark-green mountains. And now, when it was all over, Preacher stayed glued to the open doorway even while eating, looking and looking, trying to drink in all he had missed. I remember him speaking only once. "Might as well git me a look at Europe," he said with a laugh. "Don't rightly expect Ah'll ever be back."

Don Stoddard too was almost completely silent during the trip. Throughout the long days, he stood alone at the back of the car staring out like a prisoner through the one high little barred window there. Thinking of Anne Marie, of her smile and her dimples? Of his friend Farron, the young aid man who had been killed in C Company? *Click, click, clock. Click, click, clock.* The miles, the stretches of vanquished country rolling by . . .

When darkness finally came down, we spread our blankets on the straw, took off our combat boots, and, by exercising care, everyone could lie down full length. Accustomed to strange beds, we fell asleep easily. Early in the morning as the sun was rising, most of the men were back at the wide doorway, taking their farewell of Germany, each with separate memories of mine fields and litter hauls, slashing rain, deep snow, screaming 88s, river crossings. Big Steve Brudzinski, Charley Heydt and a few others, apparently with no memories at all, sprawled on the straw, ragging and playing cards throughout the trip, leaving without a single backward glance.

For much of the trip, Phil was abstracted and no longer quite approachable. He sat in the straw, frowning over copies of *Amerasia* Strauss had given him to read. Sometimes he put the magazine down and held a mumbled debate with himself, shaking his head one moment, nodding decisively the next. He had, however, continued to lecture Ted Jameson on the importance of further study should he emerge alive from the campaign in the East.

"The whole trouble is," Ted confided to me, "I don't know what I want to study! Phil says I should take just a straight college course. He thinks Hamilton would be a good place for me, but now somehow—" I could detect on his part a weakening of resolve. "Well, I think I'd like to study music. You know how I love to play the piano or the organ. That's what I really love. Phil says though no matter what I do, I mustn't settle down in Lynsdale again, but I don't know." He shrugged, implying that Phil wasn't right on every point. "It isn't as bad as he makes it sound." I could see Teddy sinking back into that country town with his Charleston-dancing grandmother and grandfather, his father who had surveyed him in silence, hands in pockets, from the upper window of the factory, his sister Jan, his stepmother and stepsister and the boys and girls he had known in high school.

Sam Benton, Jr., his face older now than his years, pinched and disgusted, sat alone in the center of the floor, looking steadily at the straw, speaking to no one.

Twice a day, for fifteen minutes, the boxcars halted and the men swarmed down onto the cracked blue stone of the roadbed to relieve themselves, to get water in large, flashing ten-in-one cans or helmets, to wash and shave, to walk up and down, visiting friends in other companies. Then the little referee whistles blew and there was a scattering, a scramble to climb up. "This our car? Look and see if that's our stuff. No, we're in the next one." The splintery, sun-faded maroon boxcars, marked "40 Hommes aux 8 Chevaux," chalked with innumerable American names, dates and towns, rolled on again, beginning to finish their second World War.

Several times on the adjacent track, boxcars filled to over-flowing with former Russian slave laborers and prisoners of war passed us coming from the opposite direction on their way into the Russian zone. Men, women and children waved and smiled. Many of the women were in native costume: long full skirts, blouses, embroidered aprons and babushkas. How, I wondered, had they been able to hold onto them through their years of imprisonment and servitude? Boughs had been lopped from young trees and fastened to the outsides of the boxcars, and flanking the open doors were huge wilting bou-quets of field flowers. From within came the plink and tinkle of a balalaika, or the wheeze of an accordion and voices sing-ing Russian folk songs. In some cars a little fire was laid on bricks and a kettle was simmering. The tops of all these cars were piled high with "acquired" two-wheel bicycles. There might be fifteen or more of such family cars, and then came those filled with Russian soldiers who had been prisoners of war, all dressed now in new green American fatigue suits and GI shoes.

Once our two trains stopped, leaving only a narrow aisle between. Crowds of Russian and American soldiers swung down, milling about and beaming. "Yay, Russky! Tovarish!" our men said. The Russians smiled, but seemingly could not say the equivalent in English. At first American cigarettes and parts of rations were given away, but within a few min-utes bartering and selling sprang up. Halting German was the common language. The Russians wanted American wrist watches and cigarettes. The latter were snapped up for as high as fifty cents a pack in our Invasion money; within five minutes the price had soared beyond that, and I heard one of our men asking a young Russian who had bought a carton of Camels for fourteen dollars, "For Russky camraden?"

"Naw!" came the answer. "Fer Deutschers!" To be resold

in the black market. He was offering a German Lüger for seventy-five dollars.

Not as many Russians as Americans had hopped down. The less enterprising sat on their high bales of hay, smiling down with bright childlike interest. Some looked like overgrown infants; others were astonishingly old to be in uniform. Every racial type seemed represented. There were those who looked like stout Eskimos, others like elongated Chinese, and still others like fat placid Turks. Many, save for the newness of their fatigues and a breadth of face, were indistinguishable from the Americans. The whistles sounded again, and the trains rolled on in opposite directions.

Toward sunset, a train filled with German prisoners came slowly past: car after car of glum blank faces staring at us. There were no outcries from our cars, no jeering. Nothing. The last few cars, special Pullmans, carried German officers and what appeared to be influential civilians. Their cars and ours, separated by only a few feet, came to a stop.

A German woman in her late forties, well preserved, well coifed, evenly powdered, wearing a dark printed silk dress and a string of pearls, stood expressionless at her window directly opposite the door where we were standing. She stared through us coldly and calmly for perhaps half a minute, then gradually her eyes reddened and filled with tears. She turned away, and a gray-haired man in a gray suit tried to console her; he gave her the handkerchief from his breast pocket and patted her shoulder. She pulled herself together, and back came her face as expressionless as before, only now her eyes were covered with black sunglasses. The effort was still too much for her: a cord worked in her throat, her lips trembled. She gave up, and the man led her away from the window.

Almost immediately her place was taken by a German colonel, bony, severe-looking and pale.

"Gut afternoon," he said to me. "Could you tell me, please, if you are coming from Thüringen?"

Thüringen: Thuringia. "No, I couldn't," I said.

"Do you mean that you are not? Or that you are not permitted to say?"

"I'm not saying."

"Oh." It had taken him a moment to understand. "We have heard a report that the Russians are to occupy all of Thüringen. We know—we have read—that the Americans *have* been there. Could you tell me—it means so very much to me—

please could you tell me if that is correct about the change, the Russians?"

"Yes, that's correct. The Russians are occupying all of Thuringia. They're moving in now."

"I see. I thank you very much." He made a stiff bow, and I heard his heels click. He had been pale before, but now he went suddenly paper-white. He turned and sat down as if his legs had been shot from under him. A moment later the trains slid past each other.

The following day we crossed the border and came into France. I imagined almost at once that I could sense a difference. Fences sagged and straggled, underbrush was everywhere, and a wide stream, bordered by Normandy poplars and willows that trailed out into the water, was choked with cattails and lily pads. About the first grim farms an air of spunky individuality, often ugly but welcome to the eye, replaced the German neatness and regimentation.

Now only occasionally—in a twisted, rusting truck or in a tank destroyer left lopsided in a field, in a pitted white wall or the broken windows of a deserted house—was any sign of war apparent. The trees had come out, screening the damage. Fields of pale-yellow wheat were growing up, sprinkled with thousands of tiny scarlet poppies. For hours we passed wheat fields, then iridescent light-purple cabbages, long slow-spinning rays of lettuce, rustling corn, wheat again, and all through it the fine scarlet dots of poppies. Out in their fields with their horses, the French farmers, turning from war and from us, did not bother to wave back. High over all arched a heedless, beautiful blue-and-white summer sky.

We came through the first small provincial towns, past odd little railroad stations with clipped trees standing in narrow beds of gravel, with lace curtains and brass flowerpots hanging up in the windows of the station house, and French posters lining the station walls.

Out into the country again. The late-June afternoon reached its height; an hour after, the long shadows began to fall. Leaving. We were leaving. There was a wrench, a sag of spirits. Why? What were we leaving behind? One's thoughts went back to the apple orchard, to Metz, to the December evening when for the first time we surveyed the border of Germany lying before us, and—what was it—a sadness, nostalgia came over one. Out of the montage of memories, I

521

thought back to a day of sifting, drizzling rain, to a hill just before the Siegfried Line, covered with a drenched plant that looked like heather, and Ted Jameson, leading me up a steep footpath, saying, "There's where Sergeant Janovic was killed. And Sergeant Stancliff. You knew them, didn't you? Their bodies are still there. *Look!*"

1946 December—The Reunion

The telephone rang, and when I picked up the receiver a voice with a German accent said, "Hollo? Iss Lester Atvell there? This is someone who knew him from the Army—from C Company, Two Forty-Third: Anton Brauer!"

We greeted each other with cordial shouts and he went on to explain that Lieutenant MacKenzie was at his apartment, as were two other men of our old platoon, Bill Woods and Julius Weinberg, more frequently known as Julie or Kelly. Lieutenant MacKenzie had just read them a letter I had written him a few days before, asking where one of the men of C Company was buried—his parents had written to ask me—and from my return address Brauer was surprised to see that I lived only seven or eight blocks away from him. Would I like to come down for the evening? I would? Fine!

It was toward the end of Christmas week and there had just been a heavy fall of snow. The night was cold and dark with a stiff wind blowing; lighted Christmas trees glowed at the windows as I walked past.

I rang the bell, and when I heard the click I went into the lobby. Off to one side, seen through an arch, Brauer had come to the door of his ground-floor apartment.

"Come in! Come in! Merry Christmas, Atwell!" We shook hands. "It is good to see you! I have no idea you live so close! How long have you been out of the Army?"

"A little over a year. And you?"

"A year."

He looked the same: of average height, strong, with a neat round head, thinning light hair, finely cut features and a little mustache. I recalled that he had had brothers in the German Army and Navy and that he came from Czechoslovakia. He was a man twenty-eight or nine; as a staff sergeant he had been independent, shrewd, responsible and fair.

In the foyer of the apartment I met his stepson, a good-sized boy of eleven or twelve, and his wife, Marian, a blond woman with a smiling, rosy, attractive face, vital eyes, a black dress with a black sequined collar. She had been preparing food in the kitchen.

"And here is MacKenzie," Brauer said.

More hesitant than I remembered, as if expecting to meet a stranger, Ward MacKenzie was coming out of the living room, his hand extended. His grip was not too strong, but he intended it to be firm and warm. Out of uniform, he looked less assured and he had grown a mustache. Tall, well built, with dark wavy hair, good features and exceptionally white, strong teeth, he was wearing bluish gabardine slacks, a white shirt and gold cuff links.

We went into the living room, where a Christmas tree stood brightly lighted. The two other boys were there in their shirt sleeves, looking younger, healthier and neater than I had ever seen them. Bill Woods's hair, which had been crew cut in the Army, was now grown out; Julie's was sharply, cleanly parted. Their complexions were clear and ruddy. Both were in their very early twenties.

My last memory of Bill Woods had been late at night in the cellar near Olzheim. He had received a long scalp wound; blood was dripping down his glasses and nose and he was holding onto his helmet, which had been ripped up the front by a bullet, saying with a laugh, "I've been having a wild time." And Julie I remembered as a poor, pale, pinched figure, limping past in a drizzle on a wide, curving muddy road, on his way back from the hospital after his wound had healed, to rejoin C Company and go into combat again. At the time he looked about thirty-three years old.

After a few minutes, during which everyone was talking and laughing at once, we sat down. Brauer asked what I'd like to drink. Highball? Vodka? Beer? He made the first drink for me and set down a bowl of pretzels. I discovered that Ward MacKenzie was taking a master's degree in French; he planned on entering the diplomatic service. Bill Woods and Julie were also making use of the GI Bill, one to study engineering, the other accounting. Brauer, I was surprised to learn, was a hairdresser in a large department store. His wife had a beauty salon on Fifty-seventh Street.

The talk—all of C Company and mostly of its second platoon—which my arrival had interrupted, now flowed back again. Remember? they kept asking. "Remember Smathers? Atwell, you were there; remember the party where he cooked the goat? That's where we first went into combat, up on that mountain. Hey, remember Billings? And his pal, Clayton? And who was the other B.A.R. man? You know. Not the one who froze his feet, not Dehn."

"Dave Rossofsky," I said.

"*Your* friend." Bill Woods laughed. "And what a character he was! Remember him with the socks pulled on instead of gloves?"

"Atwell, did you ever hear from Rossofsky again? After he was wounded?"

"No. There was no way of writing at the time, so I never knew if he lived or died; and I don't have his home address."

The names, the faces, the piercing cold, the truck rides and war-smashed, snowy towns rose up in memory.

"That Bulge!" Brauer cried. "My God, that was the worst thing! Never have I known such cold. And snow! And *snow* and snow. And always, I keep thinking, if you live through this, there is the CBI to look forward to."

"Wasn't that day wonderful when you heard the Japs gave up?"

"What timing!" Julie cried. "Just at the end of the furlough. The very end, when I was saying goodbye, getting my uniforms pressed to go back—I guess we'll all remember that day."

MacKenzie was saying a little later, "I don't think I'll ever forget how bad I felt the day I had to go out into the forest and identify McGrath's body."

"God, what a tragedy that was!" Brauer cried. "One of the best men that ever lived, that McGrath. Cheezus, that he should be killed and some of the schmucks that were left to come back—"

"I saw him lyin' there half out of the jeep, upside down, his helmet off an' that red hair just brushin' the snow. Honest to God, it—it hit me the most awful wallop. We had been one team for so long. His eyes were open and I remember his face was light green as if ohll the blood had drained out of him. It was so silent and white out there an' the evenin' was comin' on. I remember thinkin' to myself, 'You're next,' but that wasn't why I felt so bad."

"And then," said Julie, "when they were bringing his body back past us, they came so slow. All the guys in the company lined up. I was—I was choking inside and then all of a sudden I started to cry. I didn't give a damn; I couldn't help it. That swell guy. You know what it was like? That part in Ernie Pyle's book where they brought the captain's body down. And boy, that night in the foxholes, morale went down to zero. Guys standing guard, freezing to death, crying. That was rough."

Everyone sat silent for a few minutes.

"Well come on, boys, drink up!" Brauer urged, and after a while the talk burst out again. "You know," he said, over at the table mixing drinks, turning to survey us with a smile, "this is the best time I have had since I am home. Chust having you guys here, talking about the old times in C Company, the Second Platoon."

There was a feeling of closeness, of heart-warming liking one for the other. At the same time I was aware that our time together was limited, that the night was passing. Cars sped by on the snow, the apartment elevator groaned in its ascent, footsteps could be heard through the ceiling. The world, its problems and its striving was everywhere outside this one brightly lighted room where the past was still alive.

The rain, the mud, the Siegfried Line, those pillboxes where Stancliff was killed, where Colonel Hessig got hit. . . .

"One of the worst days I ever lived through was the day I lost the thirty men at Olzheim, when we had to go down that road an' take the farmhouse there," Ward MacKenzie said. "They piled up there at the fence and ohll the German machine guns had to do was keep firin'."

"And even ven some of us get inside the house," Brauer recalled, "some of us run into one bedroom and some in the other. We are going to knock out the machine guns, but the tank comes up and opens fire on us.

"I shouted for everyone to get down, get down the cellar. We were running out of the room when the tank fired again. We were all knocked down the stairs by the concussion an' when I came to, I was covered with plaster and Ciani was lyin' on top of me with his arm blown off and half his back blown away—an' he was talkin' to me. God! I—we—I remember we got him down the cellar—"

And Brauer, an iron man in such emergencies, then crawled up over the rubble on the stairs to see if any of the men in the second bedroom were alive and he found all of them dead. "One," he said, "with the whole face turned yellow. I never saw such a thing. The color of that cheese right there. Not a mark on him. He died of concussion or shock. The others were blown all over the room. Like rags and blood they were. Just shreds. I came down the cellar and every twenty minutes we release the tourniquet on Ciani's arm, on the stump. I tell him, 'Hang on, Ciani. Help will come at any minute.' We had nothing for him, no bandages, no morphine, nothing. I tore off part of my undershirt, filthy dirty from wearing it. Vot the hell, that's all we had. I knelt beside him, I prayed with him. So did Pop Evvers, though he is not a Catholic. 'Hang on, Ciani, hang on,' I keep saying. Five hours in the dark that voice goes on and on, and then he dies. Cheezus, I will never forget."

"I admit when we got out of there—crawled out that cellar window—I went ohll to pieces. They brought me down to that aid station place in another cellar an' ohll I can remember sayin' is that I didn't want to go to the hospital, I had to get back to the men. Captain Liebert had just been killed an' you had taken command, Brauer."

"Not of the company," Brauer said quickly. It was a sore point.

"No; Jack Ziegler had taken command of the company."

"That was chust his luck that I am stuck down the cellar and Jack Ziegler takes over—chust as it is his luck ven a whole platoon of Germans walk up to him to surrender. For that he gets a battlefield commission. Not that he was not a good man, but there were many good men."

Before I had arrived at Brauer's apartment, they had been discussing Braaf and Louden, two of the men who had deserted from C Company and who had been arrested and court-martialed.

"Braaf got forty years," Bill Woods told me, "and the kid —Louden—he got ten."

I saw Braaf, his face mottled with the cold, shaking hands with me at a time when no one in the company would talk to him; and I remembered Louden, with his adolescent mustache and his limp, saying, "Ah, the hell wit it. They won't help me."

"That Braaf was no good, no goddamn good at all!" Brauer said furiously. "Believe me, if I should see him today, I vould laugh in his face. One of these 'tough' guys. Joining that goddam Tiger Patrol."

And suddenly there was the Tiger Patrol in their rustling, ghostly white capes and the long underwear pulled on over their uniforms, trooping silently into the darkened aid station at the chateau.

"You know when Braaf and Louden ran away," MacKenzie said, "they got as far back as Luxembourg City and they lived there for five days—I guess on the black market. Then Louden was out on the street alone one day. He saw an MP and he walked over suddenly and gave himself up. Told the MP he had another man with him, another deserter, an' to follow him to the house where they were both living and to come in in about five minutes an' pretend it was a routine house-to-house check. The MP did an' he arrested the two of them without Braaf's knowin' to this day that Louden gave away on him. That act of Louden's, of course—plus his extreme youth an' the fact he had been wounded—was accepted at his court-martial as extenuatin' circumstances."

"But that was a rotten thing for him to do. It was all right if he wanted to give himself up."

"Ah, that Braaf—about four times before that he ran way," Brauer said. "Everytime you say, 'All right, boys, come on, let's go,' you look around, Braaf is not with you."

"But Braaf had been wounded too and he might have been at the breaking point."

"So were we all at the breaking point." Bill Woods laughed.

"Well, I know this much," I said after we had argued the thing back and forth, "if either of them had been officers in our battalion, they'd have been patted on the back for sticking it out so long, and sent back in honor to the hospital. It would never have been necessary for them to run away."

MacKenzie, who had left the room, returned in time to hear me, and with a smile admitted the truth of what I said.

"There was one officer, though, who didn't make it," he added, "and that was Lieutenant Millbank. Now there was a really good man who just cracked up and couldn't help himself. After that first day in the Saar he was a goner. It left just McGrath an' myself, an' that night—we didn't sleep at all—we talked it over an' we thought if Millbank could go to the hospital fo' a few days' rest, he might pull out of it all right, so we wrote a message to that effect, gave it to him in the mawnin', an' sent him off with a runner to deliver it to Colonel Hessig."

Pieces of what had been a huge, unfinished jigsaw puzzle kept falling into place.

"What happened was this," he continued. "It was awful. Millbank had no idea what was in the message an' he presents it to Colonel Hessig, thinkin' he was being of some value to us. As I understan' it, the C.P. was full of officers wakin' up, and Hessig reads the message. Well, he turns around in a rage and in front of everyone, calls Millbank a yellow son of a bitch, dirty coward an' everything else he could think of, which, if you'll remember, was plenty. He sent Millbank flyin' back to the company an' he threatened if he ever heard of him leavin' the front lines fo' *any* reason, he'd have him court-martialed fo' cowardice."

Now I could understand why Lieutenant Millbank, while trotting back to the company, kept bursting out with "Terrible! Terrible! My God Almighty!" What memories of the war he must have! What could he ever tell his wife? Or his sons?

In the room with the Christmas tree, our voices began to sound hoarse from talking. The ash trays were emptied and soon were filled up high again. Occasionally someone, still talking, got up and made himself a cheese sandwich at the table.

"Well, y'ohll remember Sergeant Weems in the Heavy Weapons Platoon?" Ward MacKenzie accepted a fresh highball from Brauer. "A couple of days after he shot himself through the foot, two of his best friends came forward an' offered to appear against him in court-martial proceedings. They swoah he told them several times—even the day before —that if things ever looked tough, he wouldn't think anything of puttin' a bullet through his hand or his foot. Ohll those men stood trial, ohll the ones who shot themselves, but every one of 'em got off. You could never prove it wasn't accidental.

"Oh, I don't know," he remarked a little later, "life was so damned cheap. A pack of cigarettes was worth more at the time. I remember when Captain Liebert said to me, 'If I get killed, you can have my leather jacket,' an' I said, 'Okay,' so when someone came up in a jeep to tell me he'd been killed, the first thing I said was 'I'll have to go and get his leather jacket,' and the man said, 'You can't, sir. A tank ran over him.'" I realized that the Captain Liebert they mentioned was the officer I had seen staring fixedly into the candlelight in the farmhouse kitchen at Schonberg when I went up with Phil's litter squad to get the man with the broken arm. "Even now I—I still have nightmares about ohll those things," Ward MacKenzie said. He turned to me. "Have you ever written anything about the war?"

"No, I haven't so far."

"I often thought I'd like to write about the war. I'd like to do a story about McGrath. I've done a few poems, but—"

The others looked at him, startled. Poems!

"No, but there was something about McGrath you boys didn't know. I guess maybe you did, Brauer. The truth is, McGrath was crackin' up. By the time he died he was goin' fast. It wasn't too apparent on the outside, but I could tell. He didn't care about orders or anything else; ohll he was tryin' to do was keep as many men alive as possible.

"Well, I guess you know he was what you'd cohll a very moral kind of guy. An' especially as far as sex goes. I know in England I had this gal, an' once when we were both a little drunk I sneaked her up to my room at Winton Hall. It was about two o'clock in the mawnin. McGrath was asleep there an' he got up out of bed to go across the hall an' sleep somewhere else, an' when she saw him in his shorts, she said he was the one she wanted to sleep with. He just walked out. I mean —no, but as I say, he had started to crack up and then . . . You'll remember that little town where we came to Christmas Eve? Well, he was out, inspectin' where the men were billeted, an' I was upstairs in a bedroom in the house where we were to stay an' there was this girl, or woman, there, dark, quite good-lookin', about twenty-eight, 'bout McGrath's own age. I was talkin' to her in French. She was a widow, her husband had been killed two years befoah an' she seemed—oh,

530

disgusted with war an' with life. She was getting ready to leave, doin' up some things. I was takin' off my shoes an' socks in front of this stove like out in the center of the room, an' as I was talkin' to her—it was getting dark—McGrath comes in. Well, we weren't supposed to be talkin' to civilians —you remember that.

"I stopped an' he threw down his equipment an' he gave her a look. An' she stood lookin' right back at him. It was the longest look I ever saw any two people exchange. He asked me who she was, an' I explained. He never took his eyes off her. Well, I began to feel out of place, sittin' there, so I bent over like to preten' takin' off my shoe, an' when I looked up again they had moved around in back of the stove an' they were locked in this tremendous, passionate embrace. I—I picked up my stuff without makin' a sound, picked up my shoes an' socks an' tiptoed out of there an' closed the door. An' that door stayed closed ohll night long. I didn't see McGrath till the next day. He never said a word about it an' of course I didn't—I couldn't. You couldn't get too close to him that way. But you know, I have an idea if I were to go back there an' find that town, there'd be a little redhead kid of McGrath's there. I like to think he left a son."

He gave his head a slight shake.

Marian Brauer came into the room just then with platters of food, enormous quantities of it: cold cuts, potato salad, pickles, several kinds of bread, deviled eggs, lettuce and tomatoes, hot coffee cake and a steaming Bavarian pot of coffee. "Now, I'm not trying to hurry anyone," she said with a laugh. "Stay as late as you like. I'm glad Anton has someone to talk all this over with. It's so much better than him trying to tell me. I do the best I can; I listen and I remember, but I know it's not the same thing telling an outsider, and it's something, I guess, you just have to get out of your system."

While eating, little silences fell. Our minds, however, went on reviewing the months in Europe. Julie, nervous by nature, in the midst of swallowing, waved one hand impatiently, beat on the arm of the chair and broke into choking laughter. "I know! I'll tell you someone we forgot: Shorty Witherspoon!"

The rest of us burst out laughing, recalling little Shorty at Metz in his brief role as company messenger, unable to understand or remember the night's passwords, crying out whenever he was challenged, "Wait! D-d-don't shoot! For crissake, don't shoot, it's me! It's Shorty!"

531

We put down the coffee cups, smiling. I lit a cigarette, though my throat felt raw from talking and smoking so much. Bill Woods got up to get his coat: he was leaving to catch the last train back to Long Island. Of his wound, he said to me in parting, "I still have the helmet you let me keep as a souvenir. I'll show you when you come out to the house. It's in the game room, right in the middle of the mantel."

He shook hands all around and left. For a few minutes the evening was threatened. We remained on our feet, silent, smiling a little, embarrassed that we had gone back so completely into the past. Then the ranks closed; we sat down again and began to talk at once. The present again faded away.

MacKenzie, with a sudden intake of breath, as if it could no longer be postponed, said, "Well, I suppose I'd better tell you about—'bout what happened to me at Tambach." There was a little stir but no one said anything. I found myself pinching my thumb, wondering if he had felt all along that we had been thinking about it. "I've already told Bill Woods, but I feel the rest of you ought to know, considerin' I was court-martialed and ohll the rest." He took a swallow of his drink and began minutely to recount the events that led up to the shooting of the German prisoners. "It was that damned Lieutenant Morse makin' a big grandstan' play. I remember that when it happened I was standin' there and I felt sick. Oh, God, I was so sick of the war by then. Every part of it. This friend of mine, the Artillery officer who came up to direct the fire, had just been killed by a sniper. As I say, I was sick.

"Well, a few days passed, a week, I guess. We were miles from Tambach—at Plauen. Yes. An' here's where politics enter the picture. General Purvis was always chewin' the ass off the Artillery colonel about the conduct of his men, accusin' them of ohll the stealin' and rape committed by the entire division, an' the colonel used to burn up. This time Purvis was on the phone, chewin' about something, and the colonel finally exploded. He says at least his men weren't cold-blooded murderers—they didn't go around killin' little high-school boys. Purvis demands to know what the hell he meant, and the colonel tells him to look into what happened at Tambach."

Righteous, indignant, General Purvis immediately began a full-scale investigation. When the Inspector General and his party started for C Company, "someone at Battalion," MacKenzie said, "tipped me off by phone that I had about ten

532

minutes to get ready fo' them. There had been a lot of talk, as you'll remember, and Morse an' I agreed, if anything came up, to deny any part of it. I was to cover him—*an'* myself, because my ass would be out if they found him guilty: I was his superior officer an' I'd be held accountable fo' what he did. I cohlled a formation in a hurry out in the woods there an' I told the men that they remembered nothing that happened at Tambach. They saw nothing, they knew nothing. Not a damn thing. Then I dismissed them an' everything was as usual when the I.G. an' his party drove up. They put every man under oath an' ohll the rest of it, but they didn't turn up a thing, naturally." He smiled. "Everyone stuck together."

The investigation, however, did not end there. Dissatisfied, the Inspector General came back and back. MacKenzie and the officers at Battalion Headquarters became increasingly worried about Lieutenant Morse's ability to stand up under the repeated questioning, and as soon as there was a lull the lieutenant was granted a forty-five-day furlough to return to the United States. "Then the I.G. got wind of the fact Morse was takin' off, and they stopped his jeep on the way to the airport an' held him fo' further questioning. The I.G. drove down to where he was an' told him I had just confessed—which, of course I hadn't—and Morse broke down an' spilled the whole thing. He was arrested an' put in the stockade. Then they came hot-footin' it after me an' I denied any *part* of it, but they took me in too an' the trial began.

"Well, ohll the while I was on the stand I kept swearin' up an' down I didn't know anything about it: I repudiated everything Morse said. An' ohll of a sudden I could feel myself gettin' so damned sick! This terrible pain! An' the sweat was pourin' off me. I was doubled up like this in the witness chair. I got so I could hardly answer—I could hardly see!— but the damn I.G. thought I was puttin' on an act an' kept firin' questions at me, tryin' to trap me. I'll never forget that. Finally I collapsed. Fell right out of the chair.

"I was carried out of the room on a stretcher, with armed guards, an' taken over to a field hospital. It was at night an' they rushed me right onto the operating table an' took my appendix out. I guess it was about ready to explode. I just had a local anesthetic an' the two guards had to stan' there. I—I remember the lights, these big blazin' lights in the tent, an' then when I was being carried out I remember sayin' to the guards or the litter bearers, whoever it was, 'Fo' God's sake, watch out you don't trip over the tent ropes,' 'cause it was pitch-black out there after the lights." He laughed. "A year or so befoah, I was just a kid in college—you might say I was just out of saddle shoes—an' then ohll this stuff was thrown at me."

While he was recovering in the field hospital, the two guards took turns watching him, day and night. They were glad of the easy detail and MacKenzie became friends with both of them. They played cards together and talked. "I had a long time to think over my position while I was lyin' there," he said, and there came back to me the memory of him at Metz the night Smathers cooked the goat, telling us he was the last of a family that had distinguished itself in wars as far back as the time of Mary, Queen of Scots. "I kept turnin' it over an' over in my mind an' then one day ohll of a sudden I saw this tiny little loophole, an' I thought, 'If this works, I'm out!' I don't know if any of you remember, but one day —oh, early in the war—a German sniper was brought in to E Company fo' killin' one of our men, a medic. General Purvis happened to be there."

"I remember! The companies were going by on tanks. I was standing at an upper window, a store window, looking down. A black-haired medic was shot—it was at Lissendorf!"

"That was it! Lissendorf! Well, Purvis gave orders that the sniper was to be taken out, made to dig his own grave an' then be shot down into it. An' he said, 'That's the way to treat these sons of bitches.' So I remembered that. An' I remembered the First Sergeant of E Company—a good friend of mine—was standin' there at the time, an' I happened to know he hated Purvis's guts. I—I got word to the First Sergeant." There was the implication that one of the guards had carried the message, "an' I asked him, as a friend, if he'd mind swearin' to what he saw an' heard that day at Lissendorf. He did even more than I asked." MacKenzie burst into laughter. "He made fifteen of his men sign with him; an' once I had that paper in my possession, I rested easy from there on in."

"Good God!" The justice or injustice of killing the German prisoners had dwindled far to the back of the picture.

When the trial was resumed, the statement signed by the men of E Company was handed to General Purvis with the suggestion that his action that day with the sniper at Lissendorf had been taken as an example and had been dutifully copied by the men of the 67th Division. In consternation General Purvis ordered the entire investigation dropped.

"I got off with a transfer to the Forty-first Division," Mac-Kenzie said. "So did Morse and poor Major Campana, a very decent guy who defended us both at the trial. I hated the idea of leavin' my own division, but at that I guess I was lucky."

The Tambach story had taken a long while to tell. The lights on the Christmas tree burned on through a haze of cigarette smoke, but outside the windows were dark, the night had grown silent. It was very late. The memories now reached further and further back, to days in camp, to Sergeant Hill and the long lines outside his supply room, to Ayres holding mail call out on the grass on summer evenings, to Janovic throwing down his stripes, saying, "I don't treat anyone like a dog."

Brauer, a little later, grew bitter at the mention of OCS in Paris. Not knowing what had happened, I said nothing.

"A lot of goddam nonsense," he said. "If they wanted to make me an officer, why didn't they? Why not do it on the spot like they do for Jack Ziegler? Sending me to Paris to learn how to call out orders and command the men when I had taken charge of the platoon ever since we come into combat. Some little greenhorn of an officer who never saw a day of combat, telling me how to make use of the terrain—ach!" He waved the thing away. Then he turned to me and said in a rush that he had passed all his examinations, had been permitted to go up to the last day, that he had had his officer's uniforms bought and fitted, only to be told then that an investigation of his family in Czechoslovakia had shown Nazi affiliations and for that reason he could not be commissioned.

"I was all right, though, to go back and be a sergeant, to break my ass for them. 'Nazy affiliations!' Atwell, you know, my father—a man that old—he has no politics. You say to my father, 'Join this,' and, by God, for *spite* he would not join. He vould never join anything!"

The subject of Brauer's three brothers, however, hung darkly in the air. "Did the other boys in your family get home all right?" I asked.

Matter-of-factly he replied, "Yes. They got home. All three. Only one I saw. The one in the Navy. Ven we were at Plauen I got a pass. It was only sixty miles and right away I got a lift—a fellow and girl, Czechs, going right past my town. They let me off. It was in the evening and, God, what

535

a feeling to walk down that road! My home. There was not a soul in sight—it was after the curfew—and there I am in my uniform, my American uniform, the rifle on my shoulder. I have not been home since 1937 ven I set out to see something of the world. 'Way off I see my house. We have a big farm and the house is old. Some parts, the center, is built in 1609; there is a stone saying that. And then I see my old man sitting on a bench outside the door. God! You know, such feelings come up in me. It is so quiet everywhere. So the old man sees a soldier coming up the path, he knocks out his pipe and gets up to go inside. And my throat—I cannot say anything. I chust get to the door as he is closing it. I push open, he pushes close. Finally I say, 'Pop, Pop, what's the matter, don't you know me any more?' Then he opens the door. I have my helmet off and he sees me. We fall into each other's arms. He cried like a baby."

Of the weekend he spent there, Brauer had little to say. "I was able to give my father some smoking tobacco. That he loved. I went back two weeks later to say goodbye; the Russians were seizing the farm. Now the whole place is gone. Gone! I would never want to go back there again. Terrible!"

There was a silence, then MacKenzie, who had put Phil Schaeffer in for a Silver Star—it had been demoted to bronze in the actual award—asked if I ever heard from him.

"Yes," I said. "We write every once in a while. He's teaching in a rural high school and doesn't like it." In one of his letters Phil had told me that Teddy Jameson, lacking sufficient points for admission to any college, was still in his tiny country town, taking a mail-order business course. Paul Clifford, his friend through combat, had become a rural mail carrier and was married. Don Stoddard, attending college on the GI Bill, was also married but not to the girl with the unchanging smile and the dimples. Jimmy McDonough, his defense job gone, was driving a taxi and often worked till midnight, trying to make both ends meet.

There was no word from the others, who seemingly preferred to forget the war and settle back into obscurity in small towns and crowded cities across the United States. Phil Schaeffer, acting as unofficial secretary, had written to all but had received very few replies.

"Well, Julie," said Brauer with a grin, "you sing the 'Horst Wessel Song' lately?"

This produced a sudden roar of laughter from Julie. "Boy,

that was hot." He turned to me, still laughing. "Brauer taught us how to sing the 'Horst Wessel' in German, had us all coached, and late at night the squad would come creeping up in the snow. Surrounding the Jerry pillboxes. About seven or eight of us. Brauer would rush in and start shouting and yelling at the top of his lungs in German, telling them it's all over, give up, give up, the whole American Army's outside, everyone else has surrendered. The Germans would jump up, wouldn't know what the hell hit them! Here's a guy shouting at them in German. So out they come with their hands up. They're not even half awake yet. They expect to find thousands of Americans and here's just this little bunch of guys covering them. Then Brauer goes like this—gives the music signal—and we start singing the 'Horst Wessel' at them. Jeez, then they're *all* mixed up; they don't know whether we're Germans dressed up as Americans, Americans, or what the hell we are. And the funniest part of all was me, Weinberg, singing the 'Horst Wessel.'"

Brauer raised his hands, waved them in a swift little dipping motion, and he and Julie began to sing the song, collapsing into laughter at the end of a few lines. "Anyway, Julie, lousy as it was, we had some fun, hey?" asked Brauer. He seemed to be pleading for affirmation. "Once in a while? A laugh here and there?"

It struck me, not for the first time, that everyone in the Infantry had fought an entirely different war.

The heat seemed to have gone down in the apartment. One's eyes burned with the cigarette smoke; one's throat was hoarse from talking. For a while everyone sat looking back in silence. I put my glass down. A minute passed.

"Well, much as I hate to break this up . . ." Julie said. "Anyone know what time it's getting to be?"

"I have twenty after five," MacKenzie replied.

"Twenty after *five!*" Julie shot out of his chair. "We've been here all night! I was supposed to be up early!" Worry crept into his voice. "I have an exam! I was supposed to hit the books!"

Wrenched back to the present, the rest of us got to our feet, blinking and smiling like men waking up. MacKenzie had arranged to stay over with the Brauers until his train left for Georgia. The Brauers had to be to work by nine o'clock. Thoughts of daylight, soon to break, and of the separate lives we would assume struck in on us and we began to be strangers to each other. Julie was leaving with me, and as we all shook hands, wishing each other a Happy New Year, Ward MacKenzie said, "Remember, this time next year. I'm going to try my best to come to New York—an' I want to see you men."

We would keep in touch, we would meet again; we assured each other that we would. But going out through the silent, darkened lobby, I had the feeling that we had had the best of it, that the past can be revived only so often, and with each succeeding time its hold on us would grow fainter and fainter.

10 all-time great CRIME CLUB® Selections for only $5

Here's an amazing opportunity for everyone who enjoys good mystery novels. Just mail the special coupon on the last page of this book. You will receive ten of the most exciting mystery novels ever written at remarkable savings on the original hard-cover prices. Each of these fascinating spine-tinglers has been a bona-fide selection of the Doubleday CRIME CLUB®. That's your guarantee of quality. Now, for the first time, Popular Library presents these top mysteries to you in economical paperbacks. All are complete, not a word cut, jam-packed with tense excitement, brilliant detection and characters you'll never forget. By mailing the coupon right away, you will receive:

BULLET PROOF by Amber Dean —It was a deadly triangle, hair-triggered for murder...even before a killer with an itching finger arrived.

THE 7th MOURNER by Dorothy Gardiner—The group at Harriet Orchard's burial was drenched not in sorrow, but greed, not mourning, but murder.

FIND THE WOMAN by Doris Miles Disney—Dr. Chandler's body has been found floating in a Maine lake, and $100,000 in insurance money says Mrs. C. looks guilty ...but unexpected surprises will keep you guessing.

DEATH & CHICANERY by Philip MacDonald—A collection of mystery tales by a distinguished artist of suspense "exploring the more unexpected and astonishing aspects of human behavior"— N.Y. Times.

DARK LADY by Doris Miles Disney—Although a bloody murder had taken place at the cottage years ago, the young scholar tempted fate by seeking out the answers to long-buried mystery.

DEPART THIS LIFE by E. X. Ferrars—Hilda Gaseley searches frantically for clues to her murdered brother's past...a past involving blackmail, vengeance, a woman acquitted for murder... then Hilda becomes the target.

MURDER RIDES THE CAMPAIGN TRAIN by The Gordons—A mysterious murderer stalks the Campaign Special..."unusually fascinating"—N.Y. Times—"Most exciting ride you've ever taken" —Boston Herald.

DEAD OF SUMMER by Josephine Gill—A sweet young thing, a very ugly case of murder, a sudden slambang finish!

IF SHE SHOULD DIE by Forbes Rydell—A pretty young girl trapped in a town where murder waits around every corner. "The mounting suspense of discovery and intrigue are brilliantly realized"—Boston Herald.

THE LAST ESCAPE by E. C. R. Lorac—A clever criminal ingeniously escapes from prison, setting loose a chain of events that lead to shocking murder.

MAIL COUPON ON NEXT PAGE WITHOUT DELAY